India and Pakistan
LAND, PEOPLE AND ECONOMY

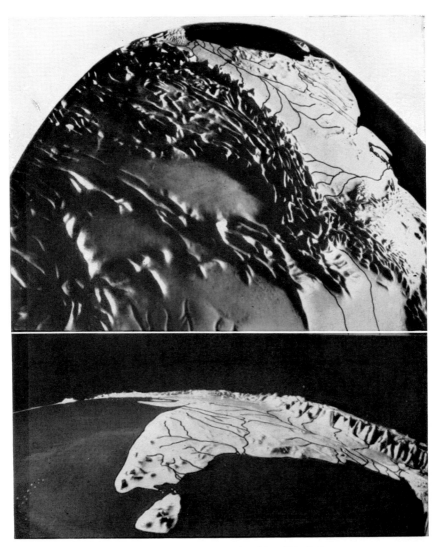

INDIA: APPROACHES BY LAND AND SEA

INDIA
AND PAKISTAN

Land, People and Economy

O. H. K. SPATE & A. T. A. LEARMONTH

With the collaboration of A. M. LEARMONTH

METHUEN & CO LTD
11 NEW FETTER LANE LONDON EC4

India and Pakistan *first published 1954*
Second edition 1957
Reprinted 1960

Third edition revised and completely reset, 1967
SBN 416 42550 X/34H

These sections first published as a University Paperback in 1972
SBN 416 75520 8/49

© *O. H. K. Spate 1954 and*
O. H. K. Spate and A. T. A. Learmonth 1967

Printed and bound in Great Britain by
Richard Clay (The Chaucer Press), Ltd.,
Bungay, Suffolk

Distributed in the USA by
HARPER & ROW, PUBLISHERS INC
BARNES & NOBLE IMPORT DIVISION

To

ARTHUR GEDDES, P. C. MAHALANOBIS,

J. A. STEERS, L. S. SUGGATE

masters and friends

Contents

PART I THE LAND

CONTENTS

CONTENTS

Maps and Diagrams

In the map captions certain abbreviations are used; these refer to the following authors, editors and publishers to whom grateful acknowledgement is made for permission to use various maps. Fuller references are to be found in the map captions or footnotes. Apologies are tendered for any inadvertent omissions.

AAG	Association of American Geographers
AG	Dr Arthur Geddes
Asia	Asia Publishing House, Bombay
B & C	Messrs M. R. Brearey and B. S. Connock
B & D	Drs J. Coggin Brown and K. Dey
BM	Dr Binapani Mukerjee
CDD	Dr C. D. Deshpande
CE	*Chambers' Encyclopaedia* (George Newnes Ltd., London)
COI	Census of India
COP	Census of Pakistan
EA	Dr Enayat Ahmed
EG	*Economic Geography*, Worcester, Mass.
Ek	*Erdkunde*, Bonn
ES	Miss Ethel Simkins
FRI	Forest Research Institute, Dehra Dun
G, GA	*Geography*, The Geographical Association (UK)
GJ	*Geographical Journal*, London
GK	Professor George Kuriyan
GR	*Geographical Review*, New York
GSI	Geological Survey of India, Calcutta
GTT	Professor G. T. Trewartha
GW	Dr G. Whittington
ICAR	Indian Council of Agricultural Research
IGF	*Indian Geographical Journal*, Madras
IJMG	*Indian Journal of Meteorology and Geophysics*
IMD	Indian Meteorological Department, Poona
ISI	Indian Statistical Institute (Regional Survey Unit, New Delhi)
JES	Dr Joseph E. Schwartzberg
K & J	Drs P. P. Karan and W. M. Jenkins
KSA	Dr Kazi S. Ahmad

KR   Dr K. Ramamurthy
LDS   Sir L. Dudley Stamp
LH   Mr L. Hoffmann
Longmans Messrs Longmans, Green, London
LSB   Dr L. S. Bhat
MBP   Professor Maneck B. Pithawala
MR   Dr M. Rahmatullah
NISI   National Institute of Science of India, Calcutta
OUP   Oxford University Press
PS   Dr Paul Siple
RIIA   Royal Institute of International Affairs, London
RT   Dr R. Tirtha
SAM   Dr S. A. Majid
SOC   Survey of Ceylon, Colombo
SOI   Survey of India, Mussoorie
SOP   Survey of Pakistan, Karachi
SP   Shri S. Pandyan
SPC   Professor S. P. Chatterjee
SSB   Dr S. S. Bhatia
TESG   *Tijdschrift voor Economische en Sociale Geografie*, Rotterdam

Tables

(Excluding short tabular statements in the text. All the following Tables are grouped together at the end of Part 3, The Economy.)

From the Preface to the First Edition

Among ruminant animals, writers on Indian affairs form a special class; some refreshing exceptions apart, they chew over and over again the cud of Royal Commissions, Tariff Enquiries, Gazetteers and the like. However rich the original material, nutritional returns soon diminish; hence the writer's vow, made in India, never to add to the mass of Indian literature; of which rash determination this volume is the natural nemesis.

Yet there is some justification, at least for the attempt, in the extraordinary fact that there has been no serious geography of India in English since Holdich's *India* of 1904. Like all Holdich's work, this has many merits: not least a vivid style and an admirable welding of history and geography. But there is surely something odd about a book which purports to be a geography of India and, in its regional sections, actually devotes 48 pages to Afghanistan and 28 to the Indo-Gangetic Plains and the Peninsula put together; a complete failure to subordinate local interest and special knowledge to the demands of a wider architecture. My own all too slight direct acquaintance with India at least shields me from this error. Apart from Krebs' admirable but not very accessible German work, for a really balanced geography of India on an adequate scale we must go back to Elisée Reclus' *Nouvelle Géographie Universelle*, of which the Indian volume was published in 1883. One does not – or at least nowadays one should not – go to *L'Inde* for details other than historical; but for grasp of fundamental relationships, for really masterly presentation of broad essentials, I know of no geographer superior to Reclus. 'That Providence so often unacknowledged', as Febvre calls his book, shall not go unacknowledged here.

. . . . . .

I am aware that a good deal of this book is 'not geography'. One could of course defend this, without undue difficulty, by a discussion of the true content of geography, or could shelter behind the indubitable fact that in Asia, where so much of life is ruled by ancient concepts entirely novel to most Western students, no human geography could be intelligible without much presentation of purely social factors. I prefer a shorter answer: 'I am a man, and think nothing human indifferent to me.'

If anything in this book should give undesigned offence to Indian or Pakistani readers, may I say that I have written in good faith and with good will; and with the conviction that some things which should be said, but which before 1947 might have appeared arrogance or condescension from a member of a ruling caste, can now be said as friendly criticism between equals; and it is in this spirit that I have written. Similarly, it is no disparagement of the devotion of thousands of British 'servants of India' to point out that the results of their actions were at times socially ambivalent.

.　.　.　.　.　.

London, *April 1951*   O. H. K. S.

Preface to the Third Edition

The full-scale revision of *India and Pakistan*, rendered absolutely necessary by the changes of over ten years, would have been incomparably more difficult, if not absolutely impossible, but for the fortunate juxtaposition, within the same city, of Andrew and Nancy Learmonth with the original author; the last-mentioned is very firm on this. The result, naturally, is that though the older structure is preserved, this edition is in many aspects a new book. In particular, Part III – The Economy – has been so completely rewritten that little of the original remains; and the sections on climate and soils, on the whole the weakest parts of the original work, are entirely new, as is the chapter on population.

Generally speaking, the Learmonths are primarily, or indeed almost solely, responsible for Chapter 2 (Climate), the soils section of Chapter 3, Chapter 4 (Population), Chapter 9 (Power and Minerals), and the two 'planning chapters', 11 and 12. The remainder, except of course for Mr Farmer's chapter on Ceylon, can be considered as basically by Spate, but working with the advantage of a rigorous preliminary check by the Learmonths. Every page has been scrutinized, many of them more than twice or thrice, by all parties concerned. The collaboration was less gruelling, with far fewer strains and stresses, than might have been expected. Our thanks are also due to Mr Farmer for his good-natured acceptance of what must have seemed inordinate delays.

An endeavour has been made to get rid of the excessive use of abbreviation in the earlier editions, and to improve the documentation by giving publisher, as well as place of publication, for works likely to be still in print. In accordance with what we hope is a growing trend, metric equivalents of British units have been generally given.

It is most regrettable that Indian official policy imposes obstacles to the use of the 1957 National Atlas of India for purposes of *bona fide* scholarship. Despite early enquiries, it was only at a very late stage that we were made aware of the conditions attached to basing maps on the Atlas, and these were such as to necessitate the scrapping and replacement of several figures, with consequent delay in the appearance of this edition.

The original *India and Pakistan* has had a wonderfully generous reception in the sub-continent and other countries, including Russia; this seems the appropriate place to express gratitude for the award of the Prix Charles Garnier of the Société de Géographie of Paris and the Jawahar Lal Nehru Medal of the National Geographical Society of India, Varanasi. It can fairly be claimed as a work of general utility. It would be extravagant to hope that all imperfections have been removed; but it is reasonable to hope that this new edition, adjusted, to the best of our joint abilities, to the very much changed circumstances of the 1960s, will be received no less generously and prove no less useful.

Canberra, July 1965
O. H. K. S.
A. T. A. L.
A. M. L.

NOTE TO 1972 REPRINT

As this reprint in paperback form goes to press it is both too late for us to integrate an account of the adjustments following the flood disaster in East Pakistan, the civil war that followed, and the India-Pakistan conflict of December 1971, and too early for the consequences to be fully assessed. All we have been able to do in this volume is to add a note to figure 0.1 and p. 10; and in the companion paperback by O. H. K. Spate, A. T. A. Learmonth and B. H. Farmer on *India, Pakistan and Ceylon: the Regions* we have been able to insert a brief outline of these tragic events on p. 599. For continuity's sake we have left the titles unaltered at this stage of production.

O. H. K. S.
L. O. A. L.
A. M. L.

Acknowledgements

For information and for permission to reprint extracts or to reproduce maps my thanks are due to many official agencies in India and Pakistan: the Surveys of both countries; the Geological Survey of India; the Forest Research Institute at Dehra Dun, the Central Board of Irrigation, the Damodar Valley Corporation. Both in England and in Australia the Information Officers attached to the Offices of the High Commissioners for India and Pakistan were most helpful. Information on Goa was supplied by the Agencia Geral des Colonias, Lisbon.

Quotations of generous length were kindly allowed by: Chatto and Windus (Aldous Huxley's *Jesting Pilate*); the Cambridge University Press (G. E. Hutchinson's *The Clear Mirror*); Vora Bros., Bombay (Vakil's *Economic Consequences of Divided India*). Map credits are separately listed. Sections of the book have appeared in *Eastern World*, *The Geographical Review*, *Geography* and *The Indian Geographical Journal*, and thanks are due to their editors for permission to reprint.

My large debt to such writers as Sir Malcolm Darling, Helmut de Terra, Radhakamal Mukerjee and Jathar and Beri is evident, and is I trust amply acknowledged in the appropriate contexts. Mr E. S. Lindley and Sir Robert Bristow kindly gave me first-hand unpublished details on the Punjab canals and the port of Cochin respectively.

From Indian academic colleagues, friends or strangers, I received the most generous assistance. Prof. C. N. Vakil of Bombay and Prof. T. L. Sharma of Agra gave me liberty to base myself solidly on their works. I received also useful information from Prof. M. B. Pithawala of Karachi, Prof. S. P. Chatterjee of Calcutta, and Dr Nafis Ahmad of Dacca. To Prof. George Kuriyan of Madras I owe not only *carte blanche* for material from *The Indian Geographical Journal*, but a detailed check on the Tamilnad and Kerala sections; and a special word is due to the very friendly assistance of Mr C. D. Deshpande of Dharwar. My Indian students at LSE were teachers as well as pupils: E. Ahmad, P. Dayal, P. K. Dutt, M. Guha, S. A. Majid, Binapani Mukerjee. I trust that they will accept this recognition as some apology for my too-frequent impatiences, irascibilities and unpunctualities.

I doubt if this book could have been written had it not been for the facilities of the London School of Economics; not least of which is its proximity to the library of India House, where Miss W. Thorne's kindness and encyclopaedic guidance have been main factors in the achievement of many Indian and other students of the sub-continent. This book owes much also to discussion with many colleagues at LSE especially Prof. L. Dudley Stamp. Prof. R. Ogilvie Buchanan very kindly made the cartographical facilities of the LSE Geography Department available to me even after my departure. Most of the maps were redrawn or scripted by Miss Webb and Miss West, cartographers at LSE, and I also received much help from our technician Mr Judd. Mr W. T. W. Morgan compiled most of the crop distribution maps, and my friend Miss Marjory Fowler drew the vignettes of house types. But my chief debt is due to my colleague Mr D. J. Sinclair who, on my departure for Australia, very generously offered to take over the supervision of the maps from my sketches – some very rough – to the blocks. It will be obvious that this was no light burden, and without his help the task would have been almost insuperable.

For discussions and criticism I should like to thank also Prof. Pierre Gourou of Paris, Prof. S. W. Wooldridge of London and Prof. Raymond Firth, a colleague both in London and in Canberra. My friend Mr B. H. Farmer of St John's College, Cambridge, stepped into the breach when it became clear to me that I could not hope to deal adequately with Ceylon in the time available.

A very special service was rendered me by Sir Douglas Copland, the Vice-Chancellor, Prof. Marcus Oliphant and Prof. W. R. Crocker, all of the ANU – the last in his other capacity of Australian High Commissioner at New Delhi. With them were associated Mr C. Rajagopalachariar, Mr K. P. S. Menon, Prof. S. Bhatnagar and Dr D. N. Wadia: to all of them my gratitude. And to Mr J. N. L. Baker for the inception of the book. I owe the conception of the frontispiece to a verbal hint from Dr Arthur Geddes.

Invaluable secretarial assistance was given by Miss Donne Shirwin at LSE, Miss Joan Binns in Canberra; the latter greatly lightened the labour of indexing.

It would be an impossible, though a most pleasant, task to thank all those who helped me on my later visits to India: but I cannot refrain from expressing my gratitude to Prof. P. C. Mahalanobis, through whom I was enabled to see much of the new India – Bhakra, Chandigarh, the Damodar, Hirakud – and also that jewel of the old, Konarak.

Lastly, I should like to place on record the inspiration I have received from Reclus' *L'Inde* and Preston James's *Latin America*; the latter is the best regional geography in English known to me. Their value has been immense, however far I have fallen short of such exemplars.

O. H. K. S.

Further Acknowledgements for Third Edition

Valuable assistance, in the form either of permission to use material or of direct comment, has been received from the following gentlemen in India and Pakistan: Professors Kazi S. Ahmad, O. P. Bharadwaj, Shyam S. Bhatia, S. P. Chatterjee, V. L. S. Prakasa Rao, M. Shafi; Col. N. Ahmed; Dr Mohammed Anas; Messrs R. D. Dikshit, C. Mukerjee and R. Sinha. Dr L. S. Bhat, Dr M. N. Pal, and

Mr C. Subramanian were especially helpful in gathering information, as was Mr A. A. Chowdury of the Office of the High Commissioner for Pakistan, Canberra. Elsewhere, thanks are due to Professors B. L. C. Johnson and G. T. Trewartha, Drs D. J. E. Schwartzberg and G. Whittington. To all, our gratitude.

A special word is due to our cartographers, Messrs H. Gunther and M. Pancino of the Research School of Pacific Studies and Mr P. Daniell of the School of General Studies, ANU.

By an inadvertence which is much regretted, earlier acknowledgements did not indicate that the source for the frontispiece was the 1:20,000,000 relief globe designed by Professor D. L. Linton, modelled by Mr C. d'O. Pilkington Jackson, and published (if that is the right word) by Messrs George Phillips, 1935.

Canberra, *July 1965*   O. H. K. S.
                                                                   A. T. A. L.

Conventions and Preliminary Data

NOMENCLATURE

1. Now that India and Pakistan have existed as independent countries for twenty years, the distinctions used in earlier editions seem no longer necessary: the context should show when 'India' means the Republic and when it means the sub-continent. The cumbersome term 'Indo-Pakistanian sub-continent' is avoided solely on grounds of simplicity. 'Bharat' is apparently a legally correct style for India (cf. *The Statesman's Year Book*) but is not in fact used to any serious extent either popularly or officially, and is avoided here.

2. The internal territorial divisions of India and Pakistan now seem reasonably stable, and it is no longer necessary to distinguish the old Princely States from the units of the Republic of India, nor can one equate Madhya Pradesh with the (British) Central Provinces. In Pakistan, the merging of the former units in the one entity of West Pakistan leaves Baluchistan, the Punjab and Sind as regional names only.

3. There have been a number of changes in Indian place-names; the more important are listed in the Appendix, p. 828. The new names are normally used in this edition, with cross-reference from the old ones in the Index. It should be noted that the form 'Ganges' is retained in Pakistan for the Ganga, and the older form is used in Pakistani contexts.

ADMINISTRATIVE UNITS

4. Most of the States of India are divided into Divisions, and these into Districts, of which there are 326. The Districts may be taken as roughly equivalent to English Counties; in Uttar Pradesh, for example, they have an average area of 2,105 square miles (5569 km²) and population of 1,365,674. Districts are sub-divided into *taluks* (*taluqs*) or *tahsils* (*tehsils*), normally from 3 to 8 to a District. In Bengal, however, the next unit to the District is the Sub-division, followed by the *thana*, which is much smaller than the average tahsil or taluk.

5. Some areas of India are 'Union Territories' under the direct control of New Delhi. Apart from the federal capital itself, they are all outlying, and some of strategic significance: Himachal Pradesh, the North-East Frontier Agency (NEFA), Nagaland (now being advanced to statehood), Tripura, the Andaman and Nicobar Islands, the Laccadive Islands and Minicoy. The former foreign holdings – French Pondicherry, Portuguese Goa, Diu, Damão (Dadra and Nagar Haveli) – are also under direct control. Sikkim is connected to India by special treaties.

6. The old Provinces of West Pakistan have now been merged in the one unit: the old West Punjab comprised the present Divisions of Rawalpindi, Lahore, Sargodha and Multan; Sind those of Khairpur and Hyderabad with Karachi District (now in Kalat Division); Baluchistan those of Quetta and Kalat; the North-West Frontier Province those of Peshawar and Dera Ismail Khan, in-

cluding various Tribal Agencies. The more local units of Pakistan are similar to those of India.

NUMERATION, ETC.

7.   Indian statistics are increasingly given in metric units, and in this edition metric equivalents are normally given in parentheses after the British units, despite the typographical inconvenience. In one or two cases metric equivalents have been omitted where the typographical result of inserting them would have been too abominably messy; it seems needless to print '3 feet (1 m.)'; and where say a figure of 100 inches is followed closely by one of 25, it seems pedantically offensive to assume that the reader cannot divide by four.

8.   There are a few exceptions to the general rule:

   (a) tons are usually given in long tons, except in the Tables where the Indian sources themselves use metric; the difference between long and metric tons is usually too slight to worry about;

   (b) water flow is given in cusecs: the conversion is 1 cusec = 101·9 cubic metres per hour;

   (c) population densities are given only per square mile, except in one or two special cases; the ratio is a simple one, 1 square mile = 2·59 km², so that the density per square kilometre is roughly two-fifths that per square mile.

9.   The old Indian system of numeration, binary for smaller numbers and essentially decimal in the larger, is being increasingly decimalised: thus the Rupee is divided into 100 *naiye paise* (*pice* in Pakistan) replacing the old 16 annas. The Pakistani Rupee = £0·07½ stg, the Indian since devaluation = £0·04½; 100,000 RI = £4,762, say £4,750 or $12,000; 100,000 RP = £7,471, say £7,500 or $20,000.

10.   Notation of large figures differs from the European style. There are two useful words, *lakh* or *lac* = 100,000 of anything and *crore* = 100 lakhs or 10,000,000, and big numbers are often set out in lakhs and crores: thus 1,581,000 in European notation becomes in Indian 15,81,000 (15·8 lakhs) and the 1941 population of 388,997,955 may be written 38,89,97,955 (38·9 crores, or 38 crores 89·98 lakhs). The words lakh and crore are occasionally used in this book, but not the Indian notation.

OTHER CONVENTIONS

11.   The standard form for periodical references is: Author, title in quotes, name of periodical (or abbreviation), volume in Arabic numerals, date, pages. However, since many Indian periodicals do not maintain continuous pagination through a volume, such references include the part number: *IGJ* 17/3 (1942), 23–36 refers to Volume 17 Part 3 of the *Indian Geographical Journal.*

12.   Publisher as well as place of publication is given for all books published after 1945, though in a few cases the publisher has not been traced. In the case of such firms as the Oxford University Press, place of publication is London or Oxford unless otherwise stated. Most Indian Government publications are issued by the Manager of Publications, Civil Lines, Delhi.

13.   Indian topographical or technical terms of frequent occurrence, such as 'doab', 'terai', 'sal', 'kharif', are italicized at the first mention only; those which

occur more rarely are italicized wherever used. As such terms, if not explained by their context, are fully explained at their first occurrence, the Index serves the purpose of a glossary.

14.   Population figures are for 1961 unless otherwise stated; figures of density of population should be read as including the words 'per square mile'.

15.   Capitalization presents problems. It still seems standard to use an initial capital for 'River' in specific river names; less standard to use 'Range' and 'Hills', but here lower case initials can cause ambiguity: the 'Purbeck Hills' are *not* the same as the 'Purbeck hills', which include all the hills of the Isle of Purbeck. On the other hand 'valley', 'delta', 'plateau' seem better with lower case initials except in what are virtually regional names, e.g. Damodar Valley, Bengal Delta, Shillong Plateau. Some inconsistencies doubtless remain in the text.

Maps. Maps in this volume have been compiled at various periods and many do not show the present international boundaries. Examples are Schokalskaya's classic soil map in Figure 3.4, Champion's vegetation map in Figure 3.2 and mortality maps for the former British India 1921–40 in Figures 4.8 and 4.9. These should be interpreted in relation to the areal distribution pattern which is the primary object of the map, and Figure 0.1 used in relation to international boundaries.

Abbreviations

Standard and self-explanatory abbreviations, such as ac. (acres), fn. (footnote), *Jnl* (Journal) are not given here.

BIBLIOGRAPHICAL:

CGR	*Calcutta Geographical Review*
Gaz.	*Gazetteer*
GJ	*Geographical Journal*
GR	*Geographical Review*
GRI	*Geographical Review of India*
HJ	*Himalayan Journal*
IGJ	*Indian Geographical Journal*
IR	*India Record*
JMGA	*Journal of the Madras Geographical Association*
NAI	*National Atlas of India* (Preliminary Hindi Edition, Calcutta 1957)
n.d.	no date, no data
ND	New Delhi
NGJI	*National Geographical Journal of India*
NY	New York
O(C)UP	Oxford (Cambridge) University Press
OPIA	Oxford Pamphlets on Indian Affairs
PGR	*Pakistan Geographical Review*
RCAI	(Report of) Royal Commission of Agriculture in India
Mem. (Rec.) GSI	*Memoirs (Records) of the Geological Survey of India*
SOI (P)	Survey of India (Pakistan)

OTHER:

BG	Broad Gauge
DT, ST	Double Track, Single Track
EIC	East India Company
NSA	Net Sown Area
TCA, TSA	Total Cropped (Sown) Area

PART I

The Land

FIG O.I INDIA AND PAKISTAN 1967. 1, international boundaries; 2, state boundaries; 3, cease-fire line in Kashmir; 4, national capitals; 5, other towns (those
underlined are former French and Portuguese holdings); 6, state capitals; 7, Union
Territories (also underlined islands). In November 1966 the Indian Punjab State
was divided into a Punjabi-speaking largely Sikh Punjab States, some hill areas
being transferred to Himachal Pradesh and the Hindi-speaking east becoming the
new State of Hariana. As we go to press with the 1972 reprint, Bangladesh has
been recognized by the Indian and various overseas governments as replacing
East Pakistan.

India as a Unit of Geographical Study

The lands which until August 15th, 1947, formed the Indian Empire, and are now divided into the Commonwealth Republics of India and Pakistan, were never one country until welded together by British power. At long intervals, indeed, a single dynasty secured loose but nearly universal sway; nor did the British themselves administer the sub-continent as a whole, large areas and populations remaining under vassal Indian rulers. But the British connection brought to most of India a common system of administration and law, railways, a common language for the intelligentsia, new forms of economic organization, new ideals of polity. To the extent that these transcended the fantastically inter-locking internal divisions, India became one country; in that lay the British achievement.

Persians and Greeks extended the name Sindhu – 'the river' – from the Indus, to which it belonged, to cover such of the land as they knew; and hence the Muslim name Hindustan, properly applied to the area of most firmly based Islamic power in the north. Beyond the Narmada and the Chota Nagpur jungles, which lie across the root of the Peninsula, was the Deccan, the Sanskrit Dakshina-patha or 'Southland'; beyond the Krishna again Tamilnad lived its own life, inheriting the most ancient traditions of Hinduism, perhaps affiliated to the pre-Aryan Indus civilization, itself contemporary with the early empires of Meso-potamia and Egypt. In Hindu literature the sub-continent as a whole is styled Bharata-Varsha, the land of the legendary King Bharata; but it seems safe to say that there was little feeling of identity over the whole country.

Yet for twenty-five centuries at least the entire area, a few margins and enclaves apart, has received the impress of the complex, hardly definable but always easily recognizable culture of Hinduism, which indeed, with Buddhism, once stretched beyond the western borders to the Hindu Kush. Those regions where the cultural landscape displays few or none of the tokens of Hinduism are for the most part mountainous and arid, mountainous and cold, or mountainous and jungle-clad: the Islamic hill country of the western borderlands, the Buddhist high Himalaya in the north, in the east the hills of the Burma border inhabited by a congeries of spirit-worshipping Mongoloid tribes.

Historically, then, it seems pointless to stress the facts that 'India' was rarely (if ever) a single political entity and that its peoples, in common speech at least, had no one name for the whole. For at least two centuries there has been sufficient definiteness about the idea of 'India' to make the area so connoted a feasible unit of study; and despite its partition into two great states, 'India' remains valid as a

3

geographical expression for all the lands between Kanya Kumari (Cape Comorin) and the towering peak K2, respectively in 8° and 36° N.

Isolation and Contact by Land and Sea

Geographically also India is an intelligible isolate. The huge salient of the Peninsula, the keystone of the arch of the Indian Ocean shores, strikes the eye at once; and on the inland borders are the ramparts and fosses of the giant ranges which in large measure wall off the sub-continent from the rest of Asia. These are, however, by no means complete barriers: in that role they are most important as insulating India from the Polar air masses which rule so much of the climate of central Asia, and so ensuring to the sub-continent a practically self-contained monsoon system of its own. But from a human point of view the values of the mountain wall are often determined as much by what lies beyond as by its own topography.

Behind the stupendous bulwarks of the Himalayas lie the vast and all but empty plateaus of wind-swept Tibet, home of a twisted in-bred culture peculiar to itself. Clearly the contacts on this side have been few: a little trade creeping painfully through the high passes – many higher than the loftiest Alpine peaks – and, far more important, seekers of many faiths. To the east the ranges of Assam are much lower, but rain-swept for half the year, and guarded by thick jungle: contact with the Irrawaddy trough is far easier by sea, and it was by sea that the germs of civilization were brought from India to the ancestors of the Burmese, who had gradually filtered down from the marches of Tibet and China.[1] On the west the great arcs of Baluchistan, loop on loop of sharp arid ridges cleft by the narrowest and wildest of gorges, are backed by the burning deserts of Seistan; Makran in the south was once more fertile, and through it the Arabs passed to conquer Sind in the 8th century AD. But the great entry lies farther north, guarded on the Indian side by Peshawar and the Indus crossing at Attock.

Here the belt of mountains narrows to under 250 miles (400 km.) between Turkestan and the Punjab, and the core of the mountain zone, the Hindu Kush, is pierced by numerous passes, blocked by snow in winter but in other seasons practicable without great difficulty. Over this Oxus/Indus watershed lies the major passage through which people after people has pressed into the plains of Hindustan, whether impelled by desiccation in the steppe or by the political pressures of the constantly shifting fortunes of central Asian war. Of all these incursions, those of prime importance are the organized invasions of various Muslim leaders, culminating in the Mogul Babur's conquest of Hindustan in AD 1526; and the distant folk-wandering of the Aryan-speaking people of the steppes, who had entered certainly by 1000 BC and may have been in at the death of the Indus civilization a few centuries earlier. Horsemen, meat-eaters, mighty

---

[1] There was some cultural influence of Mahayana Buddhism through Manipur in Burmese proto-dynastic times (c. 9th–11th centuries AD), but it amounted to little; see G. E. Harvey, *History of Burma* (1924), Ch. I.

drinkers, they contrast strongly with the dark-skinned 'snub-nosed Dasyus', the Dravidian heirs of Indus culture. From the millennial interaction of these two great groups is woven much of the rich tapestry of Hindu myth, and probably also of the darker fabric of caste.

On the whole, then, India is clearly marked off from the rest of Asia by a broad no-man's-land of mountains, whether jungle-covered, ice-bound, or desert; though obviously among the mountain-dwellers themselves no hard and fast line can be drawn dividing those solely or mainly Indian in history and cultural affinity from those solely Burmese, Tibetan, Afghan, or Iranian. The critical area is in the northwestern hills, and here we find in the past great empires slung across the mountains like saddle-bags, with bases of power on the plateau at Kabul or Ghazni or Kandahar, and also in the Punjab plains.

The significance of the mountain barrier, and especially of this great gateway, is clear enough, and more than amply stressed in the British literature, since the Afghan disaster of 1842 almost obsessed with 'the Frontier'. The question of maritime relations is more difficult, and indeed they are often slurred over by easy generalizations about harbourless coasts. But for small craft the west coast is not lacking in harbourage, nor should the delta creeks of the Bay of Bengal be overlooked: Portuguese keels were far from the first to plough the Indian seas. It is true that, until the coming of European seamen, no considerable power was founded *in* India from the sea; but some were founded *from* India.

An active trade linked the Graeco-Roman world with Ceylon and southern India, and to Ceylon also came trading fleets from China. In the west – the significantly 'Arabian' Sea – the active agents were Arabs, who may indeed have been the intermediaries for the trade which indubitably existed between the Indus civilization and Sumeria. From the later Middle Ages onwards not only commercial but also political contacts with southwest Asia, and even northeast Africa, were important: an 'African' party played a prominent role in the politics of the Muslim Deccani Kingdoms, and until 1958 a tiny enclave of Oman territory, the Gwadar Peninsula, survived on the Baluchistan coast.

To the east the initiative came from India. Hindu traders and colonizers took their civilization by sea to the southeast Asian lands, and in the first centuries of the Christian era history in Burma, Indonesia and Indo-China begins with these pioneers. A few years before William the Conqueror impressed Europe with the organizing ability displayed in crossing the English Channel, the fleets of the Chola Kingdom in Madras and the equally Indian Kingdom of Sailendra or Sri Vijaya in Sumatra entered upon a century-long struggle across 1,000 miles of open ocean. So much for isolation by sea!

The actual node of shipping, however, was and is not in India itself but in Ceylon, and the full exploitation of the key position of India waited until the Indian Ocean was as it were subsumed into the World-Ocean by Vasco da Gama; a reminder of the importance of human and technological elements in locational relations. The reasons for the rapid supersession of Portuguese power by the less spectacular but more efficient Dutch and British are a matter of general European rather than Indian history. But it is worthy of note that the Portuguese, consciously pursuing a Crusade against the Moors, concentrated on the west coast, hemmed in by the Ghats and later by the Marathas, so that they had greater impediments to territorial acquisition than their rivals, even had the pattern of dominion laid down by their second and greatest Viceroy, Afonso de Albuquerque, called for landward expansion. Though Surat, seaward terminal of the great route to Hindustan, was bitterly contested by all three powers, the British were more active on the east coast: and when the Mogul Empire collapsed the land lay open before them.

Diversity and unity in the sub-continent

The isolation of India, then, is but relative; yet isolation there is, and within the girdle of mountains and seas has developed the almost incredibly complex culture of Hinduism: not unaffected by outside influences, certainly, but, in so far as we can dimly descry the origins of some of its yet existing cults in the earliest Indus civilization, native to this soil. Hinduism gives, or until very recently has given, a certain common tone to most of the sub-continent, but it contains within itself a vast range of diversities, not to mention the enclaves of primitive tribes and the fossils of ancient faiths, such as the Jains, the Parsees, the Jews of Cochin, the 'Syrian' Nestorian Christians whose traditions go back to St Thomas the Apostle. Confronting it, and ever drawing strength from its bases in arid Asia, is the great rival creed of Islam. For millennia the Peninsula has been virtually a cul-de-sac into which peoples and cultures have infiltrated or been driven, retaining much of their ancient rules of life and yet ceaselessly reacting upon one another, and, for the most part, if not welded together at least held together in the iron clasp of the caste system, a unique solution[2] to the problems of plural society, which are in essence resolved by recognizing, canalizing, and in fact sanctifying the plurality. It is no exaggeration to say that among the peoples of India are groups at all levels of economic development from that of jungle-folk barely out of the Stone Age to that of monopoly capitalism, with more than a tinge of state planning. The difficulties of building no more than two nations out of this heterogeneous human stuff are obvious.

This human heterogeneity is seconded by more purely geographical factors, which give some colour to the generally accepted description of India as a 'sub-continent'. The concept of a sub-continent is far from clear, but the term has its uses, especially now that 'India' as the name of a state is the name of but a part of the old India, and it will often recur in the following pages.[3] So far as it has a meaning distinct from the shorthand usage just mentioned, 'sub-continent'

[2] Unique at least in degree of development.
[3] The use of 'India' as a convenient geographical expression implies no disrespect towards Pakistan; the term 'Indo-Pakistani sub-continent' is rather cumbersome for general use.

conveys an idea of size and numbers, and these it certainly has: India and Pakistan together have an area of 1,628,194 sq. miles (about 4,215,000 km²) and a population, by the 1961 Censuses, of 532,955,695. As a demographic unit the sub-continent, and indeed India alone, ranks second only to China. This great population is of course unequally distributed: the sub-continent contains, in the deserts of Baluchistan and the Thar and in the high desolation of outer Kashmir, tens of thousands of square miles almost devoid of inhabitants, while in Bengal Dacca Division has 6,000,000 more people than Belgium on an area one-third greater, and this with only four towns of any size and with very little industry.

It is only to be expected that so vast an area, bordered by mountains incomparably the most massive of the world, intersected by rivers of the first rank, should contain very considerable physical diversity. In essence the sub-continent falls into only three macro-regions: the Extra-Peninsular Mountain Wall; the Indo-Gangetic Plains; the old Peninsular Block. But these contain a multitude of distinctive *pays* within themselves. Even in the broad alluvial monotony of the Indo-Gangetic Plains factors of climate, soil, aspect and hydrology give rise to clear, if not clearly-marked, regional divisions; and although the transitions, like those in a suite of fossil echinoderms, are almost imperceptibly gradual, the extremes are extreme indeed: from the desert environs of Karachi to the almost unbelievably dense stipple of homesteads between Calcutta and Dacca.

Yet there is a sort of massive architectural simplicity in the pattern of the three great divisions: the old Peninsular platform, wrapped round by the great trough from the Indus to the Ganga Delta, a trough filled with the debris of the mountains which again enfold it on three sides. This is not accidental, since it is the rigid resistance of the old block which has moulded the frozen waves of the mountains, though their onset has in turn warped the root of the Peninsula to form the scarps and ranges from Gujarat to Chota Nagpur. It is aesthetically fitting that the historic heart of India should lie on the divide between Indus and Ganga, which is also the passage between the Aravallis and the Himalayas, perhaps the oldest surviving and the youngest ranges on the globe. This is the great node of Delhi, for over two thousand years, since the far-off legendary battles of the *Mahabharata* epic, the key to power in Hindustan.

Underlying the life of India is one great common factor, expressed it is true in divers modalities and degrees: the rhythm of the monsoonal year. The peoples of India and Pakistan are predominantly agrarian, and even most of the industrialization of today, like the great dynastic achievements of the past, is after all built upon the ancient foundation, the toil of the dwellers in 650,000 villages. The tapestries of their lives are wrought in various colours – the lush green of the deltas, the drab khaki of the deserts – but nearly everywhere the fundamental lineaments of the pattern are similar, and are controlled by the seasonal cycle in which the great bulk of the rainfall comes in the warmer half of the year: this is so whether the annual fall is 450 in. (11,430 mm.) on the Assam Plateau, or under 15 in. (381 mm.) in the Punjab, the only really large exception being the

7

Tamilnad coast in the southeast. There is also – away from mountains – a certain sameness in the régimes of temperature, annual or diurnal; but here, though we commonly think of India as 'tropical', it must be remembered that half of the area and over half of the population are north of the Tropic of Cancer. To a large extent, however, this is offset by the mountain wall forming an insulated compartment; and although in the Punjab night frosts bring the mean January temperatures down to the level of an English May, clear skies and intense insolation raise day temperatures to a tropical level, so that all beneath the Himalayas is essentially tropical, despite latitudes of 25–30°. Outside the Himalayas agriculture is nearly everywhere tropical in type, and it is rain, not temperature, that essentially decides what crops shall be grown.

Problems of Economy

Rain, or at least water: for of all the physical problems of India those of soil and water are supreme, and in many areas life depends on canal, tank or well. Two-thirds of the people live directly from the soil, and the cultivated area is less than one acre to each dweller in the countryside. This simple ratio is the core-problem of India and Pakistan; the extension of agriculture (if that is possible to any large degree) and the security of much existing cultivation depend on a better use of the water which falls directly on to the face of the land and that which is locked in snowfields or sealed within the earth. The improvement of the pitifully low yields from a cultivated area barely adequate to present population depends in part on better water-control, in part on better treatment of the soil itself, in general inadequately manured and exploited for generations without ceasing, so that in many areas it seems to have reached the irreducible minimum of fertility. Here the 'peculiar institution' of cow-sanctity, with consequent bovine over-population, raises issues special to India.

Apart from food the resources of the sub-continent, and especially India, are extensive indeed: a wide range of minerals, of fibres, of vegetable raw materials, of timber products; wealth almost incalculable in iron and manganese. Yet it may be questioned whether, in relation to numbers, even India is really a rich country, and Pakistan on the whole is definitely a poor one, as well as being split into two very ill-balanced sections 1,000 miles apart. Power resources are as yet a weak link in the chain of industrialization: the really good coalfields are concentrated in one corner of the Peninsula, and while the hydro-electric resources are great, many potential sites are ill-placed for development, and exploitation is rendered costly by the great seasonal variation in the flow of the rivers. And in the last resort a prosperous industry must depend on a prosperous countryside: the agrarian problem is central to all the problems of development. On all fronts, progress depends on real co-operation between India and Pakistan, not just the present avoidance of war, and on a refashioning of social relationships, which still too often, in the long run, imperil social order. Some advance, at least, is being made in this respect.

A vast tropical land, mountain-ringed, the immeasurably old plateaus and warped eroded hills of the Peninsula girdled by rain-swept deltas, arid wastes and the long leagues of tillage in the Gangetic Plain; a landscape clad naturally by dense jungle or open thorny scrub, but profoundly changed by the toil of generations of peasants whose prosperity or dearth depends primarily on the secular rhythm of the monsoon; home of a diversity of cultures under the hegemony of Hinduism – one of the greatest, most individual, and most self-contained of human institutions; open on one side to wave after wave of peoples from the steppe, for a thousand years bringing with them a more rigid and more austere creed; subjugated by the alien strength, military and economic, of modern imperialism, and now newly free, though divided, to build if it can of its own strength and for its own purposes, to marry its ancient philosophies to new techniques: such is the skeleton of Indian geography which we shall endeavour to clothe with living flesh.

GENERAL BIBLIOGRAPHICAL NOTE

The amount of specifically geographical writing about India is relatively small, though Indian and Pakistani geographers are rapidly increasing it. But the amount of literature with a geographical bearing is vast. It is inevitable that any book on India will owe much of its background to works not cited nor even, perhaps, consciously remembered.

Specifically geographical works

There seems to be no modern geography in English, other than school texts, devoted solely to the sub-continent. Sir T. H. Holdich's *India* in the Regions of the World Series is very stimulating and admirably written, but its regional sections (apart from those on the northwest and the Himalayas) are rather slight, and it appeared in 1904. N. Krebs, *Vorder Indien und Ceylon* (Stuttgart, 1939) is a good text with interesting maps; but there is a certain lack of systematic treatment, and the Himalayas and Baluchistan are omitted. Recent general works which deal at some length with India and Pakistan include:

G. B. Cressey, *Asia's Lands and Peoples* (McGraw-Hill, NY, 3rd ed. 1963).
N. Ginsburg (ed.), *The Pattern of Asia* (Prentice Hall, Englewood Cliffs; Constable, London, 1958).
P. Gourou, *L'Asie* (Hachette, Paris, 1953).
J. E. Spencer, *Asia East by South* (Wiley, NY; Chapman & Hall, London, 1954).
L. D. Stamp, *Asia* (Methuen, London; Wiley, NY, 12th ed., 1966).

For Pakistan, there is a short but useful text: K. S. Ahmad, *A Geography of Pakistan* (OUP, Karachi, 1964).

Periodicals

The leading geographical periodicals in India and Pakistan, in alphabetical order, are:

> *Bombay Geographical Magazine* (Ruparel College, Mahim, Bombay 16).
> *Deccan Geographer* (Hyderabad).
> *Geographer* (Aligarh).
> *Geographical Review of India* (formerly *Calcutta Geographical Review*; Geog. Soc. of India, Senate House, Calcutta 12).
> *Indian Geographical Journal* (formerly *Journal of the Madras Geographical Association*, Madras).
> *Indian Geographer* (Association Indian Geographers, PO Box 644, New Delhi).
> *National Geographer* (Allahabad).
> *National Geographical Journal of India* (Banaras Hindu University).
> *Oriental Geographer* (Dacca).
> *Pakistan* [formerly *Panjab*] *Geographical Review* (Lahore).

Unless otherwise stated, these are obtainable from the respective University Departments of Geography. All contain articles of value, as the footnotes to this book will show; but there is some unevenness, partly due to the desire of each Department to run *the* national journal.

Non-geographical periodicals of value are too numerous to be noted here; exception may be made for *The Eastern Economist* (New Delhi). There are many official and quasi-official journals, mostly issued from Delhi or Karachi, such as *The Indian Forester, Indian Agriculture, Pakistan Development Review* and so on. The annual handbooks such as *Pakistan Economic Survey* (Ministry of Finance, Rawalpindi) and *India: A Reference Annual* (Ministry of Information and Broadcasting, Delhi 6) are indispensable.

Official Publications

The mass of official literature, especially in India, is intimidating. There are six fundamental sources which must be mentioned. These are:

> (*a*) the Census Reports, both the general and the provincial volumes;
> (*b*) the *Records* and *Memoirs* of the Geological Survey of India (Calcutta);
> (*c*) the *Report of the Royal Commission on Agriculture in India* (1928);
> (*d*) the *Gazetteers*;
> (*e*) the *Settlement Reports*;
> (*f*) the numerous drafts, outlines, and interim surveys of the progress of the Five Year Plans, issued for the Indian Planning Commission by the Ministry of Information or the Manager of Publications.

The *Gazetteers* are issued in three series: (i) the *Imperial Gazetteer of India* (Oxford, 1908) – four introductory volumes covering geography, history, ethnography, economics, etc. – containing much information of permanent value –

followed by 20 volumes with alphabetical entries, and an atlas volume; (ii) the *Provincial Gazetteers* (1908–9), one or two volumes to each major political unit (including states and Agencies); (iii) the *District Gazetteers* (various dates). Despite their age the *Gazetteers* are still of much use, though the District volumes, on which the others are based, are very unequal indeed, excellent or the reverse according to the conscience, enthusiasm, and ability of the local District Commissioners. They have been at once a blessing and a curse to Indian geographers; no comparable area of the world has anything like this survey of all aspects of life, county by county as it were, on a standard pattern which facilitates reference – a Domesday and much more; but they have to some extent fostered a gazetteer habit of mind – enumerating rather than selective – and the repetition of stereotyped statements long out of date; and since 'It's all in the *Gazetteer*' they have to some extent inhibited the essential geographical attitude of going to see for one's self. We have used the four general volumes and the Provincial series extensively, but not as a rule the District volumes, which are on a scale more appropriate to regional monograph work.

This remark applies also to the *Settlement Reports*, which are minute surveys of agricultural possibilities and development, made for the assessment of Land Revenue.

Maps

The most useful general series is the Survey of India, 'India and Adjacent Countries', 1/1,000,000, published in various styles at various dates. Larger-scale SOI maps are on 1/253,440, 1/126,720, and 1/63,360: the modern full-coloured sheets are beautiful and astonishingly accurate productions giving an immense amount of information on vegetation, land use, and the cultural landscape; most major regions of the sub-continent have at least fair coverage in this style; for some areas there are only ¼-in. uncoloured hachured maps. 'Guide Maps' to the major cities and hill stations are scale 1/21,120 or larger. Topographic maps are being revised on metric scale and some 1/50,000 are available. Purchase of large-scale Indian maps may be restricted.

The Geological Survey has a general map (rather out-of-date) on the 1/2,000,000 scale; ¼-in. maps will be found in the *Records* and *Memoirs* on selected areas.

Some special atlases and maps are referred to in the appropriate chapters. By far the most important is the *National Atlas of India* edited by Professor S. P. Chatterjee and published by the Ministry of Education. This is a splendid and most valuable production, though its usefulness is diminished by the fact that the legends and information are entirely in Hindi; an English version is given but, in the absence of an administrative overlay with English key, it is difficult to follow. A revised and entirely English edition of the *Atlas* is now in preparation. The following maps have already been published on the 1/1,000,000 scale: population maps of Delhi, Rajkot, Jaipur, Lucknow, Nagpur, Calcutta, Bombay,

Hyderabad, Madras, Trivandrum; physical maps of Bhopal, Nagpur, Calcutta, Bombay and Trivandrum; transport and tourism maps of Bhopal and Bombay. Also, on the 1/6,000,000 scale, India-Physiographic Regions and Parliamentary Constituencies. We do recommend to the reader to keep closely in touch with the publication programme. The best one-sheet map is Bartholomew's 'India and Pakistan' (1/4,000,000); there appear to be some inaccuracies in the contours, but on this scale they are not very serious. Many official maps are rather poor, but higher standards are now being set, for example in Census reports. The SOI issues several general maps on the scale 1/4,500,000 (71 miles to the inch), including a political map which is a very useful outline.

Background

Almost any book on India adds something to the general picture, though it may not be drawn on for any specific detail. Of travel books, Aldous Huxley's *Jesting Pilate* (1924) remains one of the most perceptive, and there is some good writing in R. Cameron, *Time of the Mango Flowers* (Heinemann, London, 1958); not perhaps a travel book in the ordinary sense, but invaluable as an overall picture of the rural scene, is Kusum Nair, *Blossoms in the Dust* (Praeger, NY, 1962) – the title, justified in the text, yet disguises a treatment both vivid and intensely serious.

Perhaps the most useful single volume on India before Partition and Independence was L. S. S. O'Malley (ed.), *Modern India and the West* (London, 1941). G. T. Garratt (ed.), *The Legacy of India* (Oxford, 1937) and H. G. Rawlinson, *India: A Short Cultural History* (London, 1943) remain perhaps the best introductions to the vast intellectual and aesthetic history of the undivided sub-continent. For those who wish to go further, there are such works as H. Zimmer, *Philosophies of India* (Meridian Books, NY, 1956) and his magnificent *The Art of Indian Asia* (Pantheon (Bollinger Series), NY, 1955). A. L. Basham, *The Wonder that was India* (Sidgwick & Jackson, London, 1962) may be mentioned here.

It is virtually impossible to select from the plethora of socio-political commentary, but the autobiographies of Gandhi and Nehru are essential for the Westerner wishing to understand the modern Indian scene; it is unfortunate that there is no Pakistani counterpart. Mention may be made of S. S. Harrison's thought-provoking book *India: The Most Dangerous Decades* (Princeton Univ. Press, 1960), H. Tinker, *India and Pakistan: A Short Political Guide* (Pall Mall Press, London, 1962), and I. Stephens' sympathetic study *Pakistan: Old Country, New Nation* (Pelicans, Harmondsworth, 1964).

The judicious student will not neglect more creative writers: *Kim* (despite its romantic view of the British Raj) and *A Passage to India* retain their classic value as interpretations. More recent novelists of insight are Philip Woodruff, Christine Weston, Rumer Godden; much of Mulk Raj Anand's writing suffers from being that of a political expatriate, but at his best he is very moving; Ahmed Ali's

Twilight in Delhi is an exceedingly subtle study of a society in decay; and for the Dravidian South, the incomparable novels and tales of R. K. Narayan give the very feel of small-town life with delicate and wistful artistry.

There is no good anthology of Indian verse, or indeed of Indian writing in general, either translated into or originally written in English; a wonderful volume could be compiled. It must suffice to mention two poets, one of them indubitably among the great: this is Mohammed Iqbal, whose *Secrets of the Self* is great philosophical verse with a biting edge; many of his poems have been translated by V. G. Kiernan in *Selections from Iqbal*, in Murray's Wisdom of the East series. Opposed to Iqbal's austerity is the Miltonic grandeur and all-embracing sweep of Sri Aurobindo's metaphysical epic *Savitri*. Finally, there is the other side of India – the rustic ethos, realist, salty, earthy, of the *Panchatantra* stories, still and deservedly a best-seller after a circulation of a millenium or two.

Postscript. To the list of general works on p. 9 should be added J. Durand-Dastes, *L'Inde* (Presses Universitaires Françaises, Paris, 1965); not seen but well reviewed; to the list of periodicals, *Indian Journal of Geography*, Jodhpur. Finally, Volume I of a new *Gazetteer of India* appeared in 1965, too late to be used in this work; it is an excellent volume, auguring well for the new post-Independence series. There is an admirable bibliographic survey by P. P. Karan, 'Recent Contributions to the Geography of South Asia', *Cahiers de Géographie de Quebec*, Sept. 1966, 317–32.

CHAPTER I

Structure and Relief

The Triple Tectonic Division

The familiar division of India into three major geomorphological components – the ancient block of Peninsular India, the Himalayas and their associated young fold-mountains east and west, and between these two the Indo-Gangetic Plains – is generally valid. The physiographic contrasts between these macro-regions are most striking; broadly speaking the Peninsula is dominated by an open senile topography, witness to vast periods of geological quiescence, while the Himalayas display the most youthful and highly differentiated relief on the face of the earth, and the Indo-Gangetic Plains present a monotonous aggradational surface of great extent.

Nevertheless the Peninsula has its youthful, or rather rejuvenated, landforms and the Himalayas their worn-down erosion surfaces, and structurally also the division is not absolutely clear-cut. The Peninsula has not been entirely immune from the impact of the great Tertiary orogeny, while conversely concealed extensions of the old block have exerted an important influence on the folding, on both local and regional scales, in the northwest and northeast Himalaya. Again, despite the sharpness (on the map) of the northern edge of the Indo-Gangetic Plains, the outermost Himalayan foothills – the Siwaliks – represent a late buckling of the erosion products of the mountains themselves, deposits not essentially different from some of those now forming. The three grand divisions are therefore related in a rather more intimate way than is implied by the bald statement that the Himalayan folding is the resultant of the relative moving together of the old blocks of Gondwanaland, of which Peninsular India is a part, and Angaraland or Laurasia.

I. THE PENINSULA

Geology (Figs. 1.1, 1.2)

The northern boundary of the Peninsular block may be taken as an irregular line running from Kutch along the western flank of the Aravalli Range to near Delhi, and thence roughly parallel to the Yamuna (Jumna) and the Ganga as far as the Rajmahal Hills and the Ganga Delta. Embayments of the Indo-Gangetic alluvium naturally penetrate south of this line, which in the west has a ragged contour in sharp contrast to the long smooth Himalayan front; and the ancient

14

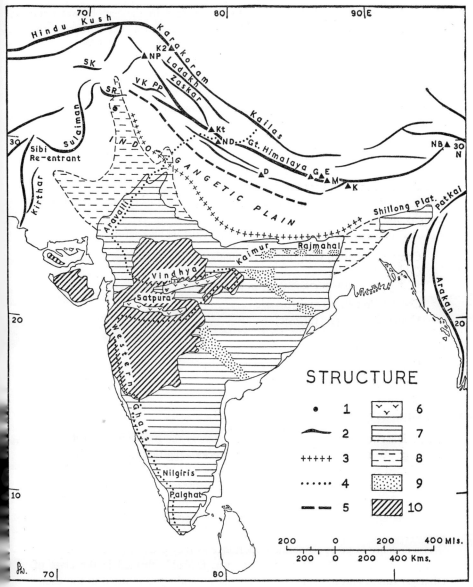

FIG 1.1 STRUCTURAL OUTLINES. 1, northernmost Aravalli outcrops; 2, trend of main Tertiary fold ranges; 3, boundary of Indo-Gangetic trough (Wadia); 4, Bay of Bengal/Arabian Sea watershed; 5, Siwalik Hills; 6, Narmada and Tapti troughs; 7, Peninsular Block; 8, concealed extensions of 7; 9, Gondwana troughs; 10, Deccan Lavas. SK, Safed Koh; SR, Salt Range; PP, Pir Panjal; VK, Vale of Kashmir. Peaks not on Fig. 1.5: G, Gaurisankar; Kt, Kamet; M. Makalu.

Peninsular rocks are relatively close to the surface in the gap between the Rajmahal Hills and the Shillong Plateau (which is indeed an outlier of the Peninsular block) and again in a northerly wedge indicated by the Kirana Hills of the Punjab (Figs. 1.1, 1.5).

The Peninsula is formed essentially by a great complex of very ancient gneisses and granites, which form the surface over more than half its area. The relations of this complex with the oldest metamorphosed sedimentaries are not clear; the old view that the gneisses formed a floor on which the younger rocks were deposited has been considerably modified, as it is now known that much of the gneiss is intrusive into the Dharwar rocks; there were at least three phases of granitic intrusion before the Cambrian. But at all events the Peninsula has been a great landmass from very early times and, except for the Deccan Lavas, rocks younger than pre-Cambrian have a restricted extension in synclinal and faulted troughs and basins.

The Peninsular formations, with their approximate ages, are:

> Coastal Alluvium, with that of Narmada and Tapti basins
> Coastal Tertiaries
> Deccan Lavas (late Cretaceous to ? early Tertiary)
> Coastal Cretaceous and Jurassic
> Upper Gondwana (Jurassic)
> Middle Gondwana (Triassic)
> Lower Gondwana (Permian to Carboniferous)
> Vindhyan (Cambrian, ? some Ordovician)
> Cuddapah and Delhi (Algonkian)
> Dharwar and Aravalli (Huronian)
> Gneisses and Granites (at least in part Lewisian).

The Dharwar and Aravalli formations 'possess the most diverse lithological characters, being a complex of all kinds of rocks – plastic sediments, chemically precipitated rocks, volcanic and plutonic rocks – all of which generally show an intense degree of metamorphism.'[1] The chief occurrences are in a series of narrow belts, the troughs of tight-packed synclines, in the Mysore–Dharwar–Bellary area; flanking the Chota Nagpur Plateau on the north and south, and in patches westwards as far as Nagpur city; and in the Aravallis. Those of the Bihar–Orissa area are of great economic importance as they contain the most valuable iron ores of India. The Aravalli Range was probably formed in the close of Dharwar times, and has since been peneplaned and again uplifted in the Cambrian, and possibly again before the Permo-Carboniferous glaciation; it may perhaps claim to be the oldest mountain system, still recognizable as such by its relief, on the earth's surface.

The earth-movements responsible for the folding of the Aravallis and other Dharwarian areas were succeeded by a prolonged period of erosion and sub-

---

[1] D. N. Wadia, *Geology of India* (Macmillan, London, 3rd ed. revised, 1961), 95.

sidence, though two diastrophic cycles may have intervened before the Delhi or Cuddapah orogeny. A great unconformity separates the Dharwarian from the 20,000 ft. (6,100 m.) of slates, quartzites, and limestones which form the marine *Cuddapah* system, deposited presumably in great synclinal basins. The Cuddapah

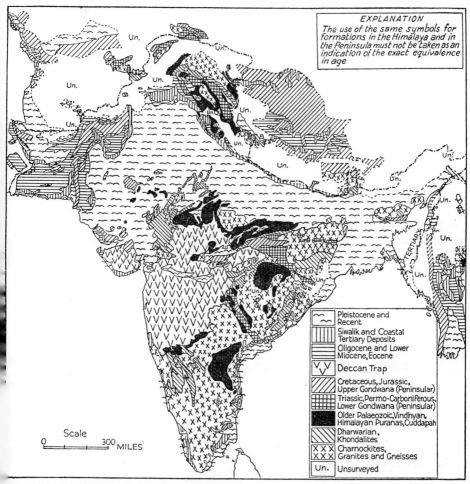

EXPLANATION
The use of the same symbols for formations in the Himalaya and in the Peninsula must not be taken as an indication of the exact equivalence in age

~~	Pleistocene and Recent
‖‖‖	Siwalik and Coastal Tertiary Deposits
≡	Oligocene and Lower Miocene, Eocene
V V	Deccan Trap
///	Cretaceous, Jurassic, Upper Gondwana (Peninsular)
⊞	Triassic, Permo-Carboniferous, Lower Gondwana (Peninsular)
■	Older Palaeozoic,Vindhyan, Himalayan Puranas, Cuddapah
⧄	Dharwarian, Khondalites
X X X X X X	Charnockites, Granites and Gneisses
Un.	Unsurveyed

Scale
0   300 MILES

FIG 1.2 GEOLOGICAL OUTLINES. After D. N. Wadia. *Courtesy* Chambers' Encyclopaedia.

rocks are preserved mainly in a big belt on the east of the Deccan, between the Krishna (Kistna) and Penner Rivers, and in the valley of the upper Mahanadi; except in the long border-ridges of the Nallamalai and Velikonda Hills they are little disturbed. The Delhi quartzites occur in narrow tightly-packed belts in the centre of the great Aravalli synclinorium; they form the rocky echelonned ridges, low but persistent, which terminate in the famous Ridge at Delhi.

Vindhyan rocks overlie the Cuddapahs in the lowest part of the Krishna-Penner trough, but their main occurrence is in a belt along the northern flank of the Peninsula from the Chambal to the Son, broken by the expanse of ancient Bundelkhand Gneiss around Jhansi; west of the Aravallis patches of lavas of Lower Vindhyan age are found around Jodhpur. In the lower part of the system marine shales, limestones and sandstones are found, but above these are great thicknesses of nearly horizontal fluviatile and estuarine sandstones, including the famous red sandstone used for many of the best Mogul buildings. In general the Vindhyans are little disturbed or metamorphosed, except in the patches west of the Aravallis. The most striking feature formed by the Vindhyan rocks is the scarp which marks the northern flank of the Narmada and Son valleys; in the west this is largely formed of Deccan Lavas, but Vindhyan rocks occur between Bhopal and Itarsi, and dominate farther east in the remarkably even and continuous Kaimur scarp overlooking the Son.[2] Much farther south, Vindhyan rocks are found in the Bhima valley between Sholapur and Raichur, and probably underlie much of the Deccan Lava country.

The *Gondwanas* consist of great thicknesses of sandstones with some shales and clays; they are of continental origin, fluviatile and lacustrine deposits laid down in geosynclinal troughs on the ancient plateau surface; these were formerly thought to be rifts produced by tensional faulting, but F. Ahmad has argued convincingly against this view. They show a striking parallelism to sequences of similar age in South Africa, Australia and South America, notably in the presence of glacial basal conglomerates and the famous *Glossopteris* flora; this parallelism is of fundamental importance in discussions of continental drift and cognate subjects. The isolated occurrence of marine limestone at Umaria (Madhya Pradesh) is now paralleled by a similar outcrop 100 miles to the southeast, and this 'solitary record of an evanescent transgression of the sea-waters into the heart of the Peninsula' is now less inexplicable.[3] More immediately important, perhaps, is the fact that nearly all India's coal comes from Gondwana formations, the bulk of it from the Damodar Valley on the flanks of the Chota Nagpur Plateau. More or less continuous belts of Gondwana rocks are found along the lower Penganga and Godavari Rivers, and between the Mahanadi and the Brahmani from Talchir on the latter river to the headstreams of the Narmada and the Son, while the Damodar is marked by a string of outcrops. This disposition suggests strongly that these rivers, in contrast to Narmada and Tapti, occupy *ancient* structural troughs.

[2] The geographical and geological usages of the word Vindhyan must be distinguished. The Vindhyan *Hills* are taken as extending roughly from 75 to 78° E and are mostly formed of Deccan Lavas; eastwards the same general line is continued by the Bhanrer and Kaimur Hills, which are formed of Vindhyan *rocks*.

[3] For Gondwana deposition, see Wadia, *op. cit.* 172–80, and F. Ahmad, 'Palaeo-geography of the Gondwana Period in Gondwanaland . . .', *Mem. GSI* 90 (1961), 64–68; for Umaria relationships, Wadia 231–2 and Ahmad 25–26, 71, 81–83. Ahmad's paper is a most important contribution to Peninsular problems.

The *Deccan Lavas* (styled Deccan Traps in the older literature) are generally from 2,000 to 5,000 ft. (610–1,525 m.) thick and reach a maximum of 10,000 ft.; they cover some 200,000 sq. miles (518,000 km²) with their mesa-like terrain. These practically horizontal and in the main remarkably homogeneous basalts were probably extruded from fissures towards the end of the Cretaceous, though a flora which seems to be of early Eocene age was found between some of the flows. The lavas were poured on to a land surface which had already attained an advanced stage of maturity, and form a most striking feature in the geomorphology of the Peninsula, with an obvious family likeness to the great basaltic flows of the Columbia Plateau and of southern Brazil.

Finally, in Kutch and Kathiawad and along the southeastern coast, patches of marine Jurassic, Cretaceous and Tertiary rocks bear witness to marginal transgressions of the sea; oil search may reveal seaward extensions.

Structural history

After the deposition of the older Peninsular sedimentaries the first clearly recognizable event seems to be the folding of the Aravallis in the earlier Vindhyan period. The Upper Vindhyan sandstones were probably formed of debris from these mountains, then at their highest elevation. It would seem also that the more disturbed portions of the Eastern Hills (Nallamalais and Velikondas) were elevated at the same time. The Aravallis then suffered planation, and presumably a later rejuvenation in early Gondwana times.

It does not seem necessary to posit a great 'Vindhyan Range' as the source of the Gondwana tillites, which were more probably deposited by ice-sheets than by valley glaciers. However, such orogeny as took place seems to have been Palaeozoic rather than pre-Cambrian, and the concept of the Peninsula as an almost completely stable block is dubious. The proto-Vindhyan ranges might be associated with the probably middle Palaeozoic Salt Range orogeny, and there was further uplift in post-Gondwana times, perhaps even in the initiatory phases of the Himalayan orogeny.[4] At all events, planation has more than once been followed by rejuvenation. Thus Wadia regards the highlands of Ceylon, and the Palani and Nilgiri Hills, not as merely 'the residual stumps of an eroded plateau' but as great horsts uplifted in post-Jurassic and early Tertiary times, and his conclusions are in general supported by Dupuis.[5] These periods are significantly close to those of intense mountain-building activity in the Himalayas, the extrusion of the Deccan Lavas, and possibly the subsidence of the Arabian Sea to form the Western Ghats.

These are the most striking events in the later history of the Peninsula. The date of origin of the Ghats is a major problem; there is palaeontological evidence

[4] Ahmad, *op. cit.* 69–71.

[5] D. N. Wadia, 'The three superposed peneplains of Ceylon', *Rec. Dept of Mineralogy, Ceylon*, Profl Paper No. 1 (1943), 25–32; J. Dupuis, *Les Ghat Orientaux et la Plaine du Coromandel, Travaux de la Section Scientifique* (Institut Français, Pondichéry, Tome II, 1959), *passim*.

for the existence until late Jurassic times of a Gondwana landmass separating the area north of the present Arabian Sea from a sea which connected South Africa and Madagascar with the east coast of India. The long straight edge of the Ghats, developed on practically horizontal Deccan Lavas and on ancient gneisses, itself strongly suggests faulting and subsidence on a very large scale; Krishnan speaks of downfaulting, probably Miocene, of the order of 6,000–7,000 ft. (1,830–2,135 m.). The view that the Ghats owe their origin to the subsidence of a landmass to the west seems supported by the absence of evidence for a simple eastwards tilting of the whole block: the main lines of the well-developed river-pattern are apparently of great age and carry no suggestion (such as gaps through an old more or less central watershed) of the reversal or diversion of an original west-flowing drainage. The Palghat Gap hardly throws any light on the problem; it has been regarded as the ancient valley of a river flowing either from the east or, before the assumed Arabian Sea subsidence, from the west. Questions of isostasy and continental drift are obviously involved; it is difficult to see how, on the generally accepted view of isostasy, foundering on this scale could take place in a relatively immobile sector of the earth's crust; and on the other hand an appeal to splitting and drift must face the youthfulness of the phenomena.

This youthfulness is indicated by the absence of river-capture on any significant scale, except in the valleys of the Kalinadi, Gangavati–Bedti and Sharavati; these are developed on the gneisses. The wide and almost senile valleys of the east-flowing rivers are on the whole graded almost to their heads, nearly in sight of the Arabian Sea, and contrast very strikingly with the youthful gorge-like courses of the west-flowing streams. These latter have only 50 miles (80 km.) in which to fall 2,000 ft. (610 m.) or more to base-level; the straight-line distance from the watershed to the Bay of Bengal is 300–600 miles (c. 480–965 km.); and the western slopes of the Ghats have a rainfall three or four times as great as that in their lee. Yet, on the Deccan Lavas at least, there has not apparently been time for large-scale capture, and the deep canyons suggest that the streams are still eroding vertically faster than they cut back the valley-sides. It seems likely, therefore, that the origin of the Arabian Sea coast must be very late, perhaps as late as the Pliocene.

On the east coast the lithology and stratigraphy of the marine deposits seem to indicate that since the latter part of the Palaeozoic the general run of the coastline has been sub-parallel to its present position, with alternating epeirogenetic transgressions and retreats of the sea.[6]

The anomalous direction of the west-flowing Narmada and Tapti Rivers is another problem. The most favoured explanation is that they occupy two rifts formed by sag-faulting at the time of stress implied by the Himalayan folding: the long Vindhya/Kaimur and Satpura/Mahadeo scarps, and the trend of the south coast of Kathiawad, might be taken as supporting this view.

These troughs, however they originated, are now floored with considerable

[6] See the folding map in Dupuis, *op. cit.*

20

deposits of alluvium; in the Narmada trough, they are 500 ft. (150 m.) or more thick and occupy a definite rock-basin, another indication of faulting. The straightness and relative steepness of the Narmada from Handia to the sea indicates a recent origin for this section: below Handia the fall is 900 ft. in 300 miles (1 in 1,756 m.), the 300 miles upstream has just half as much. Possibly the Narmada once flowed out through the Burhanpur–Khandwa gap into the present Tapti; warping on a line Handia–Paithan (Fig. 1.3) would probably account for interruptions of profile producing this aggradation; this in turn might be con-

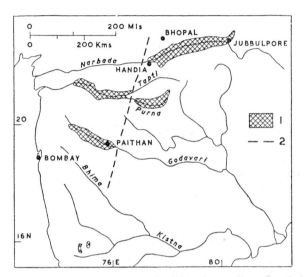

FIG 1.3 DECCAN ALLUVIUM. 1, alluvial basins; 2, line of probable warp. After E. Vredenburg. *Courtesy* GSI.

nected with the presumed faulting of the Western Ghats. The irregularities are slight, but in view of the degree of grading shown by the major Peninsular rivers they are significant, even though the warping is hardly strong enough to be readily detectable in the massive layers of the Deccan Lavas. 'All these changes agree in showing that a very extensive, though moderate, disturbance has affected the Peninsula at a late period previous to modern times.' The Marble Rocks Falls on the upper Narmada, near Jabalpur (Jubbulpore), may also be due to recent movement, or alternatively to superimposition.[7]

As has been mentioned, the major Peninsular rivers are as a rule remarkably graded; there are, however, marked interruptions to profile where they cut through the Eastern Hills in relatively constricted valleys. On the southern flanks of the Mysore plateaus there are numerous falls and gorges, and these again connect with the uplift of the southern horsts.

[7] See E. Vredenburg, 'Pleistocene movement as indicated by irregularities of gradient of the Narbada', *Rec. GSI* 33 (1906), 33–45.

Summing up, the main elements of Peninsular geomorphology are the great plateau of granite and gneiss (with higher bosses such as the Nilgiris) occupying nearly all the south and east; the mesa-like country of the Deccan Lavas in the west centre; the old shallow troughs of the Krishna, Godavari and Mahanadi systems; the much-worn Aravalli Range; and the Vindhyan scarplands of the north, with the Narmada–Son and Tapti troughs or rifts. Even this brief and incomplete generalization suggests that Peninsular India has much more geomorphological variety than is generally credited to it. The general aspect, however, is certainly one of old age, except along the escarpment of the Western Ghats and in a few hillier areas; but there are erosion surfaces of more than one cycle, and evidences of important and relatively recent changes of level, mostly negative.[8] On the whole, it may fairly be said that the general lineaments of the Peninsula seem to be much more in accord with Lester King's concepts of pediplanation than with classical Davisian peneplanation.

Present relief

The Peninsula thus consists of a great tabular block with a general slope to the east; its bold outlines are less simple on the north, owing to the very ancient but oft-rejuvenated Aravalli folding and the strain on the block of the tangential forces which produced the Himalayas; while in the south it is accidented by a number of relatively youthful horsts.

The Aravallis themselves are now no more than the stumps of a once lofty range; they reach their highest point at Mount Abu (5,650 ft., 1,722 m.) in the southwest, sink to low hills in the Jodhpur–Jaipur saddle, and rise again to the northeast before petering out in little echelonned ridges, half buried in the Indo–Gangetic alluvium, and reaching as far as the Delhi Ridge. Western Rajasthan is a debateable land, pene- or more likely pediplaned and largely smothered by the dunes of the Thar Desert, but with little hills of Vindhyan lavas and marine Jurassic and Tertiary beds. East of the Aravallis, the lower Chambal may be regarded as occupying a strike valley in the Vindhyan scarplands, but above Kota (Kotah) it is probably superimposed, cutting across the strike, and its upper reaches are more nearly consequent on the Deccan Lavas of Malwa. The Chambal and Betwa valleys are of great human and historical importance, providing a broad belt of relatively favourable country (Malwa) between the gnarled and arid Aravallis and scarp-rimmed Bundelkhand Gneiss terrain around Jhansi; the Malwa scarps face south and east at heights of 1,500–1,800 ft. (455–550 m.). The Vindhya (Deccan Lava) and Kaimur (Vindhyan sandstone) Hills form a great scarp overlooking the Narmada valley and that of the subsequent Son; their drainage is practically all northwards to Yamuna and Ganga, neither Narmada nor Son having any important north-bank tributaries. There is definite evidence in the Son valley of a drainage pattern superimposed from a

[8] Mostly, but not entirely, as is shown, e.g. by the presence of a submerged forest at Bombay, and of lignite 240 ft. (73 m.) below ground at Pondicherry.

higher plateau valley, the main outlines of which, however, were not dissimilar from those of the present.[9] This Vindhya–Kaimur scarp exceeds 2,000 ft. (610 m.) in only a few places, but is remarkably regular and free from gaps.

Beyond the Son, the gneissic plateaus of Chota Nagpur reach 3,500 ft. (1,070 m.) in the Hazaribagh Range, but the most extensive level, that of the Ranchi Plateau, is at rather more than 2,000 ft. with a few monadnocks. The Peninsula itself may be said to terminate in the Rajmahal Hills (largely basalts of Gondwana age), but a sill of old rock relatively near the surface of the Gangetic alluvium connects it with the outlying Shillong Plateau. South of the Rajmahals lie the economically very important coal-bearing Gondwana basins of the Damodar Valley, with sandstone ridges striking east–west in a synclinal trough; and south of the Ranchi Plateau a corridor at just over 1,000 ft. (305 m.) leads from the Ganga Delta to the Brahmani and Mahanadi basins, between the plateau and the broken forested hills of Orissa – the most northerly section of the Eastern Hills – at 3,000–3,800 ft. (915–1,160 m.).

Between Narmada and Tapti lie the Satpura/Mahadeo Hills; there are some suggestions of folding and upheaval, so that they may represent an ancient tectonic range, but their present aspect is of scarped blocks (on the whole steeper towards the Tapti) largely covered with Deccan Lavas but with some gneissic inliers. From their eastern continuation in the Amarkantak plateau (Maikal Hills), a mixed Deccan Lava and gneissic upland, radiate the headwaters of the Narmada, Son and Mahanadi, as well as those of the Wainganga, an important tributary of the Godavari. The Burhanpur–Khandwa gap, possibly once occupied by the Narmada, and the saddle used by the railway between Nagpur and Jabalpur should be noted.

All this northern sector of the Peninsula (except for the northeast/southwest trends of the Aravalli-lower Chambal area) is dominated by strong east–west lineaments, probably influenced by buckling and sagging of the northern flanks of the old block under the stress of the Himalayan orogeny; there are of course local deviations, such as northeast/southwest strikes in the Maikal and Hazaribagh Hills.

To the west, Kathiawad is mainly Deccan Lava, with a fringe of marine Jurassic and Tertiary rocks, which predominate in Kutch: a country of small folds, dissected plateaus, and scarplands, all on a minor scale, linked to the Peninsula by the great alluvial plain of Gujarat. The subsidence which has formed the salt-marshes and bare mud-flats of the Rann of Kutch is of recent date and perhaps still continuing; much of the flooding was produced by the earthquake of 1819.

South of the Tapti the Western Ghats begin; they are sometimes referred to as the Sahyadri Range, but this is an unhappy term as it attaches the idea of a mountain range to the crest of a scarp, and the name Sahyadriparvat is also

[9] R. D. Oldham, 'Notes on the geology of the Son Valley', *Mem. GSI* 31 (1901), 1–178; an amazingly 'modern' geomorphological study for its date.

applied to the Ajanta Hills. The Ghats almost at once reach a height of 3,000–
4,000 ft. (915–1,220 m.) and maintain this, with many interruptions, but few of
significance, for some 250–300 miles (400–480 km.), with some culminations up
to 5,000 ft. (1,525 m.). There is a very steep and wildly dissected fall to the
undulating and narrow coastal lowland of the Konkan, but once over the crest
the broad practically senile valleys of the plateau begin almost immediately. The
Deccan Lavas form the Ghats to a little north of Goa, and here the seaward face
is like a great wall, but dissected by deep canyon-like valleys into spectacular
mesas, buttes and pinnacles. South of Goa the old gneisses and granites come in,
and here more rounded forms prevail; for about 200 miles (322 km.) the crest
sinks below 3,000 ft. (and here are the only significant river-captures), but then
rises again to the great gneissic boss of the Nilgiris, reaching in Dodabetta
8,760 ft. (2,670 m.). This culmination is essentially a much-worn massif,
elevated and re-dissected, so that it forms bold, swelling hills and downlands,
with very steep drops on all sides. Southwards, across the Palghat Gap, the
wilder and more forested Anaimalais and the Cardamom and Palani Hills are
similar in origin; Anaimudi in the Anaimalais is the highest point in the Peninsula,
8,840 ft. or 2,694 m. The falls on the rejuvenated rivers of these southern horsts
are among the most important sources of hydro-electric power in India.

The Palghat Gap is apparently of tectonic origin; its summit is a broad table-
land not much over 1,000 ft. Except for the little Shencottah gap right in the
south (where the width of the Peninsula is too restricted for sea-to-sea communication to be of much importance) this is the only really easy passage across the
Ghats from the Tapti to Kanya Kumari, a distance of some 880 miles (1,610
km.). The Kerala coastal lowland west of Palghat widens out and has more
definitely the aspect of an emerged sea-floor than has the Konkan; it is fringed
by a long series of lagoons and bars.

The 'Eastern Ghats' are something of a misnomer, and are much less strongly
marked than the Western; indeed, between the Godavari and the Krishna they
almost disappear. There is no structural continuity: dissected massifs of older
Peninsular rocks in the north; relics of ancient mountains such as the Nallamalai, Velikonda and Palkonda in the centre, south of the Krishna; gneissic
horsts, the Shevaroy, Pachamalai and so on in the south. In view of this heterogeneity the term 'Eastern Ghats' is avoided in this book, being replaced by
'Eastern Hills' for the northern, 'Cuddapah Ranges' for the central and 'Tamilnad Hills' for the southern groups; if less handy than the old name, this is also
less misleading.[10] Except in the wild forested country of the Orissa hinterland

[10] The term 'Ghat . . . really implies a place of access. The Western Ghats were the
places at which roads from the westward led up to the plateau . . . the "Eastern Ghats"
are a figment of the imagination, the name . . . having been loosely applied to sundry
groups of hills that have no connection' (W. T. Blanford in *GJ* 3 (1894), 193). The
primary idea seems to be that of a step or terrace – as in burning ghats and other riverside
platforms – and is thus appropriate to the mesa-like stepped topography of the Deccan
Lavas of the Western Ghats. The comment by Dupuis (*op. cit.* 18) misses the point.

and Bastar, the most jungly part of India, these groups seldom exceed 3,000 ft. (915 m.), but are often very difficult dissected country.

In Andhra Desa and Coromandel the coastal plains, much wider than on the west coasts, have a complex origin. Here and there are small inland-facing cuestas of marine sediments, Tertiary or Jurassic; lines of gneissic inselbergen were once literally off-shore island-hills; inland, at the foot of the hills and plateaus, vast pediments formed by sheet-floods from the Pliocene onwards merge insensibly seawards into a Miocene marine abrasion surface. At the mouths of the greater rivers these features are masked by extensive deltaic deposits, and the coast is often fringed by lagoons.[11]

Within the frame formed by the Satpura/Maikal/Hazaribagh Hills, the Western Ghats, the Eastern Hills and the Cuddapah Ranges, lies the true Deccan. In Lester King's view, the plateau basically represents an early Cainozoic planation (his 'Indian' landscape cycle), with older Gondwana and post-Gondwana surfaces surviving in the southern horsts and Ceylon, and (as it were in fossil form) in the Lameta series beneath the Deccan Lavas: 'Quite clearly these basal formations represent the ancient calcreted Gondwana or post-Gondwana surface.'[12]

In the north the Bombay–Calcutta railway, once it has climbed over the Ghats into the Tapti basin, meets no serious obstacles; the watersheds between the Tapti, Godavari and Mahanadi drainages are often mere swells, with perhaps small serrated relict hills crowning the pediments which really completely dwarf the slopes from which they have been formed. In the northwest, the most typical Deccan Lava country, such 'ranges' as the Ajanta and Balaghat Hills are no more than maturely dissected flat-topped ridges, often enough, it is true, with steep flanks or even narrow hogsbacks caused by the juxtaposition of retreating scarps. But so geometrical are the lines of the lava flows that the landscape looks like nothing so much as an over-simplified block diagram. On much of the vast gneissic expanses in the east and south the aspect is even more monotonous: great, often sub-arid, plains separated by thin worn-down ridges, the disjointed vertebrae of watersheds. In places bosses or dykes of harder granite, gneiss or quartzite give a more rugged relief, low but very steep and fantastically cragged tors and serrated ridges; in Mysore and on its border with Maharashtra, the Dharwar quartzites, preserved in narrow synclines, crop out in belts of steep-sided little hills. But in comparison with the vast monotonous plains, these more accidented areas are but small.

The Peninsular rivers find their way from these broad uplands to the sea by relatively narrow corridors; the correspondence of the gap shared by the Brahmani and Mahanadi, and that of the lower Godavari, with belts of Gondwana rocks has been taken to suggest a tectonic trough origin; the Krishna and the

---

[11] For a full description, Dupuis, *op. cit.*, *passim*; there is an English summary.
[12] L. C. King, *The Morphology of the Earth* (Oliver & Boyd, Edinburgh and London, 1962), 325; the pages devoted to India are perceptive and stimulating.

Penner appear to be superimposed across the Cuddapah Ranges. The passage is generally marked by rapids. It is noteworthy that none of these rivers is directly

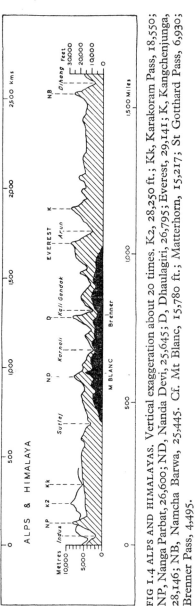

FIG 1.4 ALPS AND HIMALAYAS. Vertical exaggeration about 20 times. K2, 28,250 ft.; Kk, Karakoram Pass, 18,550; NP, Nanga Parbat, 26,600; ND, Nanda Devi, 25,645; D, Dhaulagiri, 26,795; Everest, 29,141; K, Kangchenjunga, 28,146; NB, Namcha Barwa, 25,445. Cf. Mt Blanc, 15,780 ft.; Matterhorn, 15,217; St Gotthard Pass, 6,930; Brenner Pass, 4,495.

followed by an important route to gain access to the plateau; thus the main Madras–Bombay railway crosses the Cuddapah Ranges diagonally, by a strike corridor between the Velikondas and the Palkondas, reaching the Penner above the point where it begins to break through the ranges.

II. THE HIMALAYAN OROGENY (Figs. 1.4–1.6)

Introductory

The vast scale of the ramparts which form the continental borders of India may be appreciated from Fig. 1.4, from which it will be seen that the main Himalaya alone, which stretches over 22° of longitude (some 1,500 miles, 2,415 km.) between the Indus and the Brahmaputra, could be wrapped round the Alps. Of the 94 Asian peaks which exceed 24,000 ft. (7,315 m.), all but two are in the Himalaya and the Karakoram; and no other continent has peaks of this height.

The unravelling of Himalayan structure is very far from complete, but already great nappes, perhaps less complicated than those of the Alps but much thicker and deeper-rooted, have been traced. Much of the area is still very imperfectly known geologically, and many phases of the history are still very controversial. There has of course been intense metamorphism and in many cases no reliable dating of the rocks is as yet possible: 'a large number of apparently independent rock groups has been established, each under a purely local name, thus giving rise to a confusing variety of sub-divisions, no two of which can be definitely correlated.' In some parts uplift has been considerable since the mid-Pleistocene, in others are great stretches of subdued topography at high altitudes, the relics of old planation; elsewhere the deepest gorges on earth alternate with the terraces of old lakes and the undulating hills of intermont basins. It is impossible in the space available to give a really comprehensive account of the geological and geomorphological complexities; but this may be the less serious in that the spectacular attractions of the Himalaya continue to draw expeditions and a consequent rich documentation.

During Mesozoic times the Himalayan area was occupied by the great geosynclinal Tethys Sea; there is a marked contrast in facies between the sediments of the Tibetan plateaus, laid down in this sea, and the rocks of the Himalayan area proper, which include both ancient and relatively recent crystalline intrusives and sedimentaries allied to those of the Peninsula. The orogenic activity which transformed the Tethys geosyncline appears to have taken place in three main phases:

(i) the elevation of the central axis of ancient crystallines and sedimentaries in Oligocene times; during this phase the important Nummulitic limestones were deposited in a series of basins, especially in Ladakh;

(ii) a Miocene movement, which folded the Murree sediments of the Potwar basin;

(iii) a post-Pliocene phase, which affected the Mio-Pliocene Siwalik sediments and which, apparently, has not yet entirely ceased.

Initial disturbances probably preceded the first of these, and the Karakoram, which has no marine Tertiary, may have been uplifted in the Cretaceous. There is naturally a great variety of structures and of tectonic relationships.

Geographically the Himalayas have been divided into five longitudinal zones:

(i) the outer zone of the Siwalik Hills and the *Duns* or longitudinal valleys behind them;

(ii) the Lesser Himalaya, including a great number of minor ranges at 6,000–10,000 ft. (1,830–3,050 m.);

(iii) the zone of spurs from the main ranges, presenting the general aspect of a very deeply dissected planation surface at about 15,000 ft. (4,570 m.);

(iv) the Great Himalaya itself, with many peaks over 20,000 ft. (6,095 m.);

(v) the Indus–Tsangpo furrow at about 12,000–14,000 ft. (3,660–4,270 m.); this is succeeded by the old worn-down mountains of the edge of the Tibetan Plateau, up to 19,000 ft. (5,790 m.) high.

To the north again are the Karakoram–Muztagh Ranges, which connect the Himalaya via the great Pamir knot with the Kun Lun and other ranges to the north of the Tibetan median mass.

The geological and tectonic zoning does not quite correspond to this purely topographical division. There are of course great local variations, but in general the old Gondwana foreland (masked by the Tertiary Murree and Siwalik sediments) is succeeded by an autochthonous zone – 'recumbent folds of the Eocene with cores of Carboniferous–Trias rocks'; this again by a nappe zone which includes the pre-Cambrian slates of Hazara and the Kashmir basin; then the axial crystallines, 'a geanticline within a geosyncline', consisting of very ancient gneisses with many later gneiss and granite intrusions; and finally by fossiliferous Tethys or Tibetan sediments ranging from Cambrian to Tertiary in age. The axial crystallines, roughly along the Tsangpo furrow, really mark the tectonic boundary between India and High Asia; as King puts it, 'the fold-girdles of Gondwana and Laurasia here lie "back to back" '.[13]

The Himalayas: layout

The following account of the main components of the mountain system is intended not as a detailed regional description but simply as a framework for reference.

From the great Pamir complex the ranges splay out east and west in two vast virgations: the Tien Shan–Kun Lun–Karakoram and the Alai–Hindu Kush respectively. The Alai and Hindu Kush are succeeded on the south by the lower ranges of Afghanistan and Baluchistan, which in turn are looped around the Sibi re-entrant. North of this the Sulaiman presents a steep face to the Indus Plains, while to the south the hills fan out again, the Kalat country between the north–south Kirthar Range (on the Sind–Baluchistan border) and the east–west Chagai hills (in northwest Baluchistan) being a mass of echelonned ridges sinking to the Seistan depression and swinging round east–west, parallel to the coast, in Makran: 'each arc is in reality a series of concentric arcs connected at their extremities, leaving between them arid depressions.' These mountains are of simple anticlinal structure and developed for the most part in relatively soft Cretaceous and Tertiary sandstones, with a flysch facies in the north. The parallelism between the Sibi re-entrant and the greater re-entrant north of the Punjab is striking (Fig. 1.1); it is no accident that just as the northwestern syntaxial area culminates in the giant peaks of the Karakoram and Nanga Parbat, the highest points between the Safed Koh (34°N) and the sea are in the angle around Quetta. It seems likely that, as in the northwestern syntaxis, a concealed projection of the Gondwana block is responsible.

The structure of this northwestern syntaxis has been elegantly educed by Wadia: put briefly, the Tertiary folding has wrapped itself round a projection of Gondwanaland, indicated for example by the outcrop of old rock in the Kirana Hills (Fig. 1.5). Fronting the Punjab plains is the great (and much overthrust) monoclinal scarp of the Salt Range; behind this, between Indus and Jhelum, is the Potwar Plateau or basin, formed on folded Murree and Siwalik beds which are largely masked by a loess-like silt.

From Bunji to Hazara the Indus flows in a great gorge at about 3,000–4,500 ft.

[13] *Op. cit.* 470.

(915–1,370 m.) with sides up to 15,000 ft. (Fig. 14.1); west of it are the wild ranges of Chitral and Kohistan. Northeast from the great bend at Bunji the country rises to the Karakoram, which in K2 (28,250 ft., 8,610 m.) has the second highest peak in the world; altogether there are 33 peaks over 24,000 ft. (7,315 m.) in an area comparable to that of the Swiss Alps (cf. Fig. 14.5). The ranges here are certainly older than those to the south, initially perhaps even Hercynian, but they have been much affected by rejuvenation and faulting. The Karakoram and Muztagh merge eastwards into the Kailas Range, which is simply the high edge of the Tibetan Plateau overlooking the Indus–Tsangpo furrow; the relationships and nomenclature of the ranges here are still a matter of some dispute.[14] Mention should be made of the Ladakh Range lying along and cut through by the Indus; in the east it separates that river from its important tributary the Shyok, which leads up to the Karakoram Pass (18,270 ft., 5,568 m.).

The Great Himalaya begins at the culmination of Nanga Parbat (26,629 ft., 8,127 m.) in the angle of the Indus. To the north it is flanked by the Zaskar Range, overlooking the Indus, and by the high dissected plains of Rupshu and Deosai; to the south by the series of more or less continuous or echelonned ranges known collectively as the Lesser Himalaya. The famous Vale of Kashmir lies between the Great Himalaya and the most westerly range of the Lesser Himalaya, the Pir Panjal; uplift here has been very considerable since the mid-Pleistocene. The Pir Panjal crest is merely a residual ridge on a broad plateau-like surface, and its accidented relief is due mainly to glaciation. The origin of the Vale itself is obscure: Wadia speaks of it as 'an exaggerated instance of a dun' or longitudinal valley, and his section shows it as occupying a synclinal on the back of the great Kashmir Nappe; while de Terra holds that it is a recently depressed intermont basin, pointing to marked evidence of faulting on the Himalayan flank. The floor of the Vale is formed mainly by the terraces of the Karewas beds, deposits of a Pleistocene lake. The longitudinal depression of the upper Jhelum in Kashmir is continued by the upper Chenab, and it seems likely that the upper Jhelum may have flowed out to the southeast before being captured by the present master-stream: the directions taken by its tributaries suggest this rather than the converse evolution, with the Chenab as captor, put forward by Pascoe. The longitudinal section of the upper Sutlej and its tributary the Spiti is not a continuation of this Jhelum–Chenab trough but lies north of the Great Himalaya, the Sutlej having a spectacular transverse course right across both Great and Lesser Himalaya.

On the southern flank of the mountains the Tertiaries of Potwar narrow out eastwards (Fig. 1.5) into the Siwalik Hills, which extend as far east as the Kosi River (87° E) and less continuously beyond that: the gaps in the Siwalik deposits

[14] It is almost as dangerous for the uninitiate to venture into Karakoram and Himalayan nomenclature as it would be to penetrate the mountains themselves. See the numerous papers in the *GJ* for 1936–38, ending with the report on 'Karakoram nomenclature', *GJ* 91 (1938), 125–52. For the relations of the Indus and the Ladakh Range see below, 443, and indeed all this section should be read in connection with Chapters 14 and 15.

around the Tista River have been attributed to the greater force of monsoon erosion opposite the passageway formed by the Ganga Delta, but the work of Heim and Gansser suggests that they may have been overridden by Himalayan nappes. The Siwaliks are formed of great thicknesses (15,000–20,000 ft., 4,570–6,100 m.) of Mio-Pleistocene sands, gravels and conglomerates, obviously erosion products of the Himalayas themselves, and although rarely exceeding 3,000 ft., they bear striking witness to the extreme youth of the mountain-building. The Siwaliks are backed by a discontinuous series of longitudinal vales – the *duns* – behind which are a number of southwards thrusts, the Boundary Faults once thought to represent successive boundaries between sedimentation and mountain-building but now recognized as the soles of great nappes. The Siwalik front to the plains is remarkably even and regular, and here again faulting may play a part – between Beas and Sutlej there is evidence for sub-recent thrusting of Upper Siwalik deposits over the older alluvium.

The Great Himalaya itself extends in a vast arc, convex to the south, from the Indus to the Brahmaputra; most of the peaks over 25,000 ft. (7,620 m.), though not Everest, are formed of granites and gneisses, but much of the area is made of old metamorphics which have some definite Peninsular affinities. After the great extent and height of the range, the most striking feature is the contrast between the relatively gentle and rounded forms of the slope to the Indus–Tsangpo furrow and the wildly fretted southern face. Apart from the great gorges of the Indus, Sutlej and Dihang (the transverse section of Tsangpo–Brahmaputra), the range is deeply cut into by the headwaters of the Ganga (Bhagirathi and Alak-nanda Rivers), Sarda (Kali), Ghaghra (Seti, Karnali, and Bheri), Gandak and Arun; the last-named has a considerable plateau section behind Everest. On the whole the rivers tend to cut through the range in its culminating massifs; while the detailed work of Wager on the Arun strongly supports antecedence,[15] many features seem due to capture. Everywhere the descent is far steeper to the south than to the north, and some north-flowing streams seem to have lost much of their catchments and their valleys to be choked with their own debris. Thus in the Zoji La, north of Kashmir, the track up the south-flowing stream ends in a deep gorge and a 2,000-ft. (610 m.) ascent, beyond which is a well-graded valley opening to the north: very much the Maloja Pass type.[16] The assymmetrical development of the two slopes is, however, much more pronounced east of Sutlej, where the excess of precipitation on the southern face is much greater than in the west. Looking to the fact that elevation clearly took place in stages, a compromise view may be possible, that 'capture has created and antecedence maintained' the transverse gorges.

---

[15] L. R. Wager, 'The Arun river drainage pattern and the rise of the Himalayas', *GJ* 89 (1937), 139–50.

[16] R. D. Oldham, 'The making of Indian geography', *GJ* 3 (1894), at 187–90; despite its age this remains a most stimulating paper. Cf. L. M. Davies, 'Note on three Himalayan rivers', *Geological Mag.* 77 (1940), 410–12.

Corresponding to Nanga Parbat in the west, the eastern culmination of the Great Himalaya is the 25,000-ft. peak of Namcha Barwa, overlooking the Dihang gorges. The continuation of the axis farther east is very uncertain; Mason and Wadia incline to think that it swings round to a north–south alignment under the influence of the Shillong Plateau and the old Yunnan block; but Kingdon Ward adduces arguments (largely based on a floristic divide) to suggest that the real continuation is still eastwards and is cut across by the great antecedent trenches of the upper Salween, Mekong and Yangtse; the Himalaya may override the weaker folding of the Naga–Patkai arcs.[17]

This eastern area is much less known than the western and central Himalaya, but there seems to be at least a suggestive parallelism with the northwestern syntaxis; while the Shillong Plateau itself is relatively undisturbed, the Tertiaries to either side, in the Himalayan foothills and the Patkai–Naga ranges, show a good deal of thrusting and overturning, although further away from this peg or fulcrum the mountains of the Burma border are formed of simple open folds. On this view, the Brahmaputra valley in Assam is a ramp-valley forced down between the Shillong Plateau and the Himalayan thrusting. At any rate the Assam–Burma ranges seem to correspond in a general way with those of Baluchistan, and their north–south trends are doubtless associated with the northeastern wedge of the Peninsular Block and the resistance of the Yunnan Block. They are developed in relatively soft Cretaceous and Tertiary sandstones and shales, and have a markedly Jura-type structure of quite simple anticlines and synclines, with some shallow thrusting.

The northwestern syntaxis (Fig. 1.5)

The great syntaxis of the Himalayan arcs in the northwest, already briefly noted, is of much more than local significance: it forms a great knee-bend some 300 miles (480 km.) deep and affects the strike of the ranges probably as far as the foot of the Pamirs; a very striking expression of it is the wedge of Murree and Siwalik deposits at the sharp angle of the Jhelum near Domel.[18]

The extension of the old Gondwana block beneath the Punjab alluvium is evidenced by the Kirana outcrop, an outlier of the Aravallis only 60–70 miles (97–113 km.) from the Salt Range. The Salt Range itself, with its steep front to the plains, its long dip-slope northwards under the Potwar deposits, its thrusts showing a horizontal movement of some 20 miles, and its curiously twisted alignment, is very largely controlled by this concealed Peninsular salient. The stability and competence of the basement rocks of the old foreland, underlying the Tertiaries of Potwar, is shown by the fact that the mantle of Murrees and Siwaliks is merely wrinkled up on the basement, not metamorphosed or even much indurated; they are in fact only *plis de couverture* of no great depth. Again,

---

[17] F. K. Ward, 'The Himalaya east of the Tsangpo', *GJ* 84 (1934), 369–97.

[18] See Wadia's important paper, 'The syntaxis of the north-western Himalaya', *Rec, GSI* 65 (1931), 189–220.

the Murree sediments are strikingly different petrologically from those of the Siwalik Hills, being probably derived from iron-bearing Peninsular rocks rather than from the rising Himalaya.

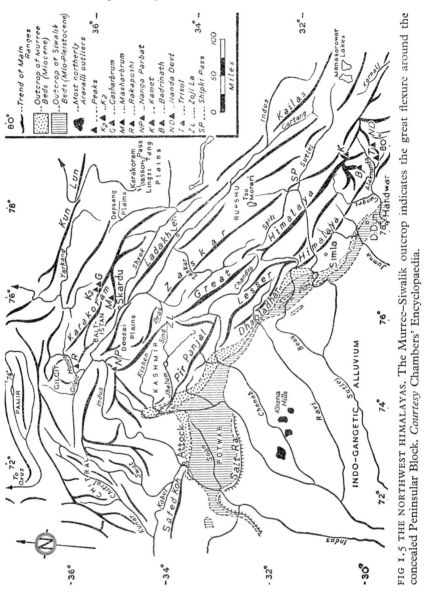

FIG I.5 THE NORTHWEST HIMALAYAS. The Murree–Siwalik outcrop indicates the great flexure around the concealed Peninsular Block. *Courtesy* Chambers' Encyclopaedia.

The influence of Gondwanaland on the alignment of the Himalayas has thus been profound: round the great salient the ranges are wrapped in loops, the strike of the rock systems paralleled by that of the planes of thrusting on to the foreland. The Great Himalaya represents the original axis of uplift of the Tethys geosyncline, bending sharply southwards at each end (into the Baluchistan and Assam ranges) where the northwards pressure of the Peninsular block ceases. The Himalayan compression, on this view, would not be merely the expression of an outward creep from central Asia, but largely due to underthrusting from the ocean floors and northwards drive of the old block, and this seems in reasonable accordance with modern views of isostasy and orogenesis.

Himalayan thrusts and uplifts (Fig. 1.6)

Current views on the rise of the Himalayas place great emphasis on tangential processes analogous to nappe formation in the Alps; in fact it may be said that the detailed work of Auden in Garhwal, Heim and Gansser in Kumaon and Hagen and others in Nepal have established the Himalayas as essentially formed by the mightiest thrusting on the globe.

Heim and Gansser look on the border zone north of the Siwaliks as 'an old surface of erosion, over which the older Himalayan formations were thrust, and through the gaps of which they advanced in huge arch-shaped waves', as on the northern border of the Alps. The deposition of the great thicknesses of the Siwalik beds is regarded as made possible by tectonic downwarp; conditions were similar to those of the present-day Gangetic alluviation but the foredeep lay farther north, to be later pushed southwards by tectonic advances involving successive detrital accumulations.

The general concept is perhaps best shown by Heim and Gansser's scheme, which harmonizes very well with that of Auden in Garhwal:[19]

(i) imbricated marginal thrusts, Simla–Kumaon;

(ii) interior secondary thrust-sheets;

(iii) the Main Central Thrust Mass, with deep-rooted injected crystallines, 10–20 km. thick covered with 10–15 km. of Algonkian–Mesozoic sediments; this is a *pli de fond*, produced by thrusting at depth succeeded by vertical uplift;

(iv) Palaeozoic and Mesozoic sediments thrust and recumbently folded on to the back of the main root;

(v) the 'exotic' Tibetan thrust (the Kiogar *Klippen*), one of the most baffling problems of Himalayan geology;

(vi) Flysch zone south of the Trans-Himalaya, with a possible weak counter-thrust northwards.

The major thrust marks the contrast between the unfossiliferous undated rocks of the Lesser Himalaya, and the pre-Cambrian to Cretaceous fossiliferous sequence of the 'Tethys Himalaya'. Everest itself is formed of outliers of these sedimentaries perched on top of the truncated Khumbu nappe.

[19] A. Heim and A. Gansser, 'Central Himalaya: geological observations of the Swiss Expedition, 1936' (*Mem. Soc. Helvétique des Sciences Naturelles*, 73, Zurich, 1939); see also the magnificent illustrations in their more popular book, *The Throne of the Gods* (London, 1939). Gansser's important *Geology of the Himalayas* (Wiley, 1964), unfortunately arrived too late for use in this edition.

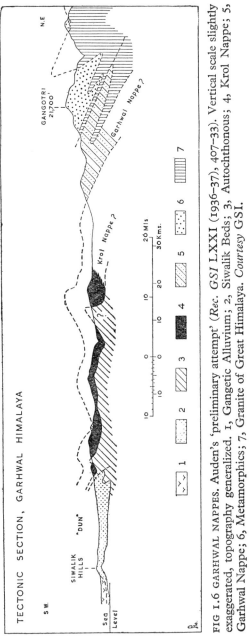

FIG 1.6 GARHWAL NAPPES. Auden's 'preliminary attempt' (*Rec. GSI LXXI* (1936–37), 407–33). Vertical scale slightly exaggerated, topography generalized. 1, Gangetic Alluvium; 2, Siwalik Beds; 3, Autochthonous; 4, Krol Nappe; 5, Garhwal Nappe; 6, Metamorphics; 7, Granite of Great Himalaya. *Courtesy* GSI.

The general nappe concept is reasonably straightforward, but the relations of the central crystalline core are very obscure, and thrusting is not the only mechanism involved; some allowance must be made for vertical movements, if only because such vast transfers of load as are implied by the Siwalik and Gangetic deposition, and the thrust movements themselves, obviously must have isostatic implications. According to de Terra, there has been uplift of some 6,000 ft. (1,830 m.) in the Pir Panjal since the middle of the Pleistocene, and 'young uplifts must have affected the entire Himalayan and Karakoram ranges'. Garwood suggested that there was isostatic uplift consequent on the relief from load afforded by the shrinking of Himalayan glaciers; Wager, more plausibly, stresses that due to the removal of vast quantities of erosion products by the extremely active south-flowing rivers. He envisages horizontal compressive forces forming a Tibetan plateau in approximate isostatic equilibrium, but extending farther south than it does now; this phase was followed by a rise of the southern margins of the plateau to maintain this balance as the rivers carried away much of its substance, and this in turn would maintain or increase their erosive power.[20]

These conclusions may be to some extent supported by Heim and Gansser, who suggest that the position of the highest peaks opposite the greatest foredeep of the Gangetic Plain may be 'the expression of a balance movement' in areas of greatest exchange of load. But on the whole Wager's view seems to minimize unduly the role of persisting tangential movements – such as those mentioned by Heim and Gansser as overriding Siwalik features, which could only be possible at a late date. Hagen postulates Mesozoic compression of the Tethys between the Gondwana and Laurasian blocks, and later the formation of the 'old original Himalayas' by large-scale thrusts affecting the basal rocks from the northern edge of the Peninsular foreland, overturning them and producing southwards thrusting of the order of 100 km. To the north, the raised edge of the Tibetan plateau caused an 'unsymmetrical transformation' of the drainage pattern, the south-flowing streams having a greater gradient and more precipitation and cutting deep transverse valleys. Then 'once again . . . the nappe-roots were squeezed, like toothpaste out of a tube, at least 3,000 metres upwards'; this took place only about 600,000 years ago. There was then sinking in the main Himalayan area, presumably isostatic, and this forced up the Mahabharat mountains of Nepal, damming the southwards drainage and forming the longitudinal duns and lake basins.[21] On the whole a compromise seems called for, and is indeed implicit in recent work: thrusting may still be going on in the border regions and vertical uplift both there (e.g. in the Pir Panjal and the Kathmandu valley) and in the inner (Tethys) Himalaya.

[20] Wager, loc. cit.; cf. H. de Terra and T. T. Paterson, Studies on the Ice Age in India (Carnegie Inst. Pubtn No. 493, Washington, 1939).

[21] T. Hagen, Nepal: The Kingdom in the Himalayas (Kümmerley & Frey, Berne, 1961), 49–53. This a popular (and most beautifully illustrated) account; the detailed evidence is in papers by Hagen (and also P. Bordet and A. Lombard) which have not been seen but are cited in the bibliography to P. P. Karan, Nepal: A Cultural and Physical Geography (Univ. of Kentucky, Lexington, 1960), 98.

The Tibetan Plateaus

There is a marked difference in facies between the deposits of the Tibetan Plateaus and those of the folded Himalaya. Marine Eocene sediments are found only south of the Ladakh and north of the Kun Lun, and during Upper Cretaceous times there seems to have been a major massif in the Karakoram–Kun Lun area, at a time when the ranges farther south either did not exist or were still in the early stages of uplift. Erosion was then more active in these areas, before the rising Himalaya shut off precipitation from the south, and de Terra has worked out several erosion-levels; his work tends to stress vertical uplift, at least in the later stages. An interesting approach is provided by the ecological work of G. E. Hutchinson: the fauna of Panggong and other west Tibetan lakes has an older appearance than that of Kashmir and Ladakh and points to central Asian rather than Indian associations.[22]

Relics of the old levels occur in the form of high rolling plains such as the Aksai Chin, Depsang and Lingzi Tang north of the Muztagh range, and these appear to be on the site of the oldest (late Cretaceous) uplift and to have extended southwards into the Karakoram region, where the spurs have high accordant levels and have been truncated by the former extension of the Karakoram glaciers. There are at least three old erosion surfaces in the Karakoram–Muztagh area: the high Muztagh peaks (24,000 ft., 7,315 m.) and planation surfaces at about 20,000 and 15,000–16,000 ft. (6,095 and 4,570–4,880 m.). Another level is represented by the Deosai plains east of Nanga Parbat and by the high spurs of the Kashmiri and Ladakhi mountains. According to Hayden the heights of the transverse ranges of the Lesser Himalaya are so uniform that it is impossible to resist the impression that they form parts of a dissected erosion surface, and this is confirmed by Heim and Gansser.

De Terra's general conclusion is that the wide extension of mature or old forms points to an uplift not earlier than the late Tertiary. The first level represents an early Tertiary very old relief, with a few monadnocks, which was uplifted and dissected to form a second series of mature or old forms. This phase was succeeded by the first Pleistocene glaciation and the formation of the third level during an interglacial. After the maximum glaciation the fourth level was established in the Riss–Würm interglacial, at which time much of the plateau was occupied by large freshwater lakes. The final retreat of the Würm ice was succeeded by 'recent uplift and post-Pleistocene rejuvenation, particularly effective along the Indus drainage', with local tilting of terrace and lake deposits in Rupshu, between the Indus and the Zaskar Range. The linking of such features in the west and in the heart of the orogeny with the more mobile

[22] 'Limnological studies at high altitudes in Ladakh', *Nature* (New Series), 77 (1933), 497–500; cf. his very curious and fascinating book, *The Clear Mirror: A Pattern of Life in Goa and Indian Tibet* (CUP, 1936).

phenomena of the southern border zones would be an interesting, if arduous, task.[23]

Himalayan glaciation, Recent and Pleistocene

The glaciers of the Himalayas and the Tibetan ranges, although much shrunken, nevertheless include in the Karakoram area the largest in the world outside sub-Polar regions: the Fedchenko (in the Pamir) and the Siachen are 48 and 45 miles (77 and 72 km.) long respectively, and the Biafo, Báltoro, Batura and Hispar all exceed 36 miles (58 km.). Elsewhere the glaciers are not so spectacular, but in Kumaon and Sikkim those of the Badrinath and Kangchenjunga massifs reach a length of 16 miles. The western glaciers are not only larger than those of the centre and east, but they descend to lower levels – in Kashmir as low as 7,000–8,000 ft. (2,135–2,440 m.) against 13,000 ft. (3,960 m.) on Kangchenjunga. This is attributable partly to higher latitudes (36° in the Karakoram to 28° for Kangchenjunga) and partly to the more direct exposure of the east to the monsoon: total precipitation is much greater in the east, but the air masses are warmer, while in the west a much higher proportion falls as snow. The snow-line on the southern face varies from about 14,000 ft. in the eastern to 19,000 in the western Himalayas (4,270–5,790 m.); on the drier Tibetan side it is some 3,000 ft. (910 m.) higher, except in the more northerly areas where precipitation conditions are more uniform; in Ladakh it is about 18,000 ft. (5,485 m.).

Mention may be made of the small glaciers of the Pir Panjal, which are exceptional (for the southern ranges) in being better developed on the north face: the Pir Panjal is a much less decisive climatic divide than the Himalaya proper, since we are here within the influence of the winter westerly depressions. The firns are largely fed by winter precipitation, so that aspect can have its usual value instead of being largely counterbalanced by greater precipitation on the southern slopes.

A distinction must be made between the longitudinal and the transverse glaciers of the Karakoram. The latter are naturally shorter and more fluctuant, variations depending largely on local topography, and have a much steeper grade. The Yengutsa glacier is believed to have advanced 3 miles in 8 days in 1903, 'coming out of its side valley and covering up the fields of Hispar village. . . . Such abnormally rapid movements may be due to earthquake shocks or to the sudden release of masses of ice that have accumulated to such a size and shape that they are no longer stable on the floor upon which they rest. Possibly accumulations of wind-swept snow would also cause instability.'[24]

The longitudinal movements are very complex; at times they are more rapid than those of the Alps – up to 5 ft. 10 in. (1.78 m.) on the Báltoro in 1909, while the Biafo snout has retreated by ablation as much as 400 yards (366 m.) in one

[23] De Terra and Paterson, *op. cit.*; de Terra, 'A scientific exploration of the eastern Karakoram and Zanskar-Himalaya', *Himalayan Jnl* 5 (1933), 33–45, and 'Physiographic results of a recent survey in Little Tibet', *GR* 24 (1934), 12–41.
[24] J. B. Auden, 'Glaciers', *CGR* 1/2 (1937), 46–52.

August. But in general they are 'either stationary or in very slight secular retreat owing to excess of ablation'. Thus the *net* movement of the Báltoro is practically nil as the contributions and deductions of its 50 transverse branches cancel out. The permutations due to aspect, shape, surrounding topography, gradient, climatic and seismic influences are endless, and variations in snout movement 'may be due to causes which are in distinct cases secular, periodic, seasonal, or accidental'. Even in the transverse glaciers there seems to be little evidence of any cyclical periodicity. Particular interest has been excited by the oscillations of the Chong Kumdan (Fig. 14.5) which intermittently advances across the upper Shyok, causing serious floods as far away as the Punjab when the ponded waters eventually break out. The great 1841 flood, which swept away a Sikh army on the dry bed of the Indus at Attock, was however probably caused by the release of water dammed by a landslide from the Hattu Pir cliff on the slopes of Nanga Parbat.[25]

An important general factor bearing on glacier movement is stressed by de Terra, who points out that 'the crustal mobility of the Kashmir basin locally determined the extension of glaciers' in the Pleistocene, and thinks that similar processes may be responsible for the rapid glacier movements of the Nubra/Shyok watershed. These western glaciers frequently appear almost smothered under morainic debris, especially in summer, when excessive ablation leads to a great development of fantastic ice-pinnacles.

Obviously the Pleistocene ice was far more extensive than that of today, but the amount of extension is a matter of dispute and the evidence is complicated by recent uplift. The maximalist view is that of Trinkler: 'it is highly probable that during the Ice Age the whole mountainous region, from the Kun Lun mountains in the north to the Himalaya in the south, was buried under ice.'[26] This view is not generally accepted. Dainelli worked out a sequence of four main glaciations corresponding to the Alpine Mindel, Riss, Würm, and post-Würm I; de Terra agrees with the sequence but would put it rather earlier.

Many of the Lesser Himalayan ranges which do not carry permanent snow have clear traces of glacial erosion and moraines; terminal moraines are found at about 8,000 ft. (2,440 m.) below Laching in Sikkim. Coulson, who thinks that in Kangra glaciers came down to 3,000 ft. (915 m.), emphasises the elevation of the Pir Panjal since the Pleistocene and argues that 'the general statement that there is no evidence of glaciation in the Himalaya and sub-Himalaya below 5,000 ft. (1,525 m.) must be discounted in view of the fact that elevation of these ranges has occurred after the main glaciation'.[27] This extreme view must be regarded

[25] K. Mason: 'Indus floods and Shyok glaciers', *Himalayan Jnl* I (1929), 10–29; 'Upper Shyok glaciers, 1939', *ibid*. 12 (1940), 52–65; 'The glaciers of the Karakoram and neighbourhood', *Rec. GSI* 63 (1930), 214–78; 'The study of threatening glaciers', *GJ* 85 (1935), 28–41.

[26] E. Trinkler, 'Notes on the westernmost plateaux of Tibet', *Himalayan Jnl* 3 (1931), 42–50.

[27] A. L. Coulson, 'Pleistocene glaciation in north-western India', *Rec. GSI* 72 (1938), 422–39.

as not proven, as is the case with the attribution of certain boulder beds in Siwalik rocks to the melting of ice-tongues from the Waziristan highlands. A minor problem is the existence on the Potwar Plateau, between Attock and Campbellpur, of erratic blocks, some of which apparently derive from the high central Himalaya; these may have been transported by floods consequent on the breaking of ice-dams, or by icebergs floating down a lake along the line of the present Indus.

Some Himalayan river problems

At an early stage in the exploration of the Himalayas the remarkable layout of its rivers attracted attention; in particular the longitudinal courses of the Indus, Sutlej and Tsangpo on the Tibetan Plateau, and the great gorges of these and other rivers cutting right across the Great Himalaya in the vicinity of its highest peaks, challenged explanation; on the southern flanks there is also a considerable development of longitudinal vales and such peculiar features as a series of sharp Vs pointing to the northwest in many of the rivers at or near their crossing of the Siwalik/alluvium boundary. The lithology of the Siwaliks, and especially their boulder and shingle beds, also calls for explanation, and there are such oddities as the similarity of Indus and Ganga dolphins to be accounted for.

In 1919 E. H. Pascoe and G. E. Pilgrim independently presented an elaborate and comprehensive hypothesis, the basis of which is essentially that Siwalik deposition took place along a great longitudinal river – Pascoe's 'Indobrahm', Pilgrim's 'Siwalik River' – which flowed to the northwest, the direction in which the Siwalik deposits coarsen and widen, between the still rising Himalayas and the northern flanks of a Peninsular block then continuous into Assam. This great master-stream was later disrupted in the west by headward erosion of left-bank tributaries of its own lower course (equivalent to the lower Indus of today), and in the west by similar action on the part of a proto-Ganga and a proto-Brahmaputra. Pascoe also envisaged a great 'Tibetan River' flowing northwestwards along the Tsangpo–Manasarowar Lakes–Sutlej–Gartang–Indus line, a trough which certainly seems to have some structural continuity; this river might have flowed out into the Oxus, or might have debouched on to the plains by one of a number of transverse gaps such as the Photu Pass, whose summit is only 250 ft. (75 m.) higher than the Tsangpo valley floor. This river also was disrupted by headward erosion on the part of the Irrawaddy–Chindwin, the Meghna–Brahmaputra, the Sutlej, and the Indus.[28]

The phenomena which these hypotheses sought to explain are extremely complicated: setting aside a mass of detail, some of the largest rivers in the world flowing in mature longitudinal courses, and then cutting across the loftiest mountains in the world, present a problem not paralleled in scale elsewhere. A

[28] E. H. Pascoe, 'Early history of the Indus, Brahmaputra, and Ganges', *Qtly Jnl Geol. Soc.* 75 (1919), 138–59; G. E. Pilgrim, ' . . . History of the drainage of Northern India . . .', *Jnl Royal Asiatic Soc. of Bengal*, New Series 15 (1919), 81–99. More detail was given in earlier editions of the present book, 28–33.

vast mass of evidence was adduced in support of these complicated orgies of river piracy and capture, and it is almost with regret that one admits that theories so ingenious and so elegantly worked out are now generally regarded as untenable. So far as concerns Pascoe's Tibetan River, de Terra in 1933–34 literally re-orientated the problem by drawing attention to the longitudinal valleys of the Karakoram–Panggong area, by contrast to 'the transverse drainage of the Central Himalaya. The ancient character of this pattern becomes clearer as we try to eliminate its secondary attributes such as transverse cutting or capture by the Indus.' He agrees that the longitudinal valleys antedate the transverse sections – as seems obvious – but holds that in pre-glacial times the drainage of the Karakoram–Ladakh area flowed southeast and east along the Tsangpo furrow and possibly into eastern Tibet and Szechwan; the southeasterly courses of the Shigar, Nubra and upper Shyok support this, whereas for his west-flowing river Pascoe had ignored these and relied on the westerly trend of a number of Tsangpo tributaries. The concept of two mighty longitudinal streams on either side of the rising Himalayas is indeed startling, but if the Indobrahm or Siwalik is accepted, the balance of evidence is in favour of its westwards course, and conversely for the 'Tibetan River'. The opposition is direct and unreconcilable.

On the main question of the Indobrahm, de Terra is decidedly hostile. He holds that the Siwalik deposits are 'local precipitates of an antecedent slope drainage', 'successive fan and basin sediments . . . their origin differs in no way from that of other foredeep fillings (Alps, Rocky Mountains)'. His arguments are not completely conclusive, but the hypothesis has also been cogently criticized, mainly on stratigraphic grounds, by Krishnan and Aiyengar. They stress (an old point) the maturity of the gap between the Rajmahal Hills and the Shillong Plateau, completely incompatible with the recency demanded by the Pascoe–Pilgrim hypothesis, and make a most telling criticism by bringing forward the width, thickness and lithology of the Tipam sandstones of Assam, corresponding to the Siwaliks and indicating (on Pascoe–Pilgrim principles) estuarine conditions near the *source* of the supposed river. The negative arguments seem strong enough to discredit the Indobrahm, even though the solution proposed – foredeep deposition on a littoral of almost continuous lagoons, with recently rejuvenated transverse streams forming the boulder beds – may not be final. But it seems probable that the solution will be somewhat along these lines, and this seems supported by Geddes's review of the problem. There remain a few doubts: those nasty little Vs at the Siwalik/alluvium boundary are ignored or glossed over by the critics; but on the whole it seems likely that the simpler answers are the more correct, and the Indobrahm is now a vanished river in more than one sense.[29]

[29] H. de Terra, *op. cit.*, 1934; cf. *Studies on the Ice Age in India*, 300–1; M. S. Krishnan and N. K. N. Aiyengar, 'Did the Indobrahm or Siwalik River exist?', *Rec. GSI* 75 (Profl Paper No. 6, 1940); A. Geddes, 'The alluvial morphology of the Indo-Gangetic Plain', *Trans Inst. British Geogrs.* 28 (1960), 253–76.

The Sutlej provides a problem of its own. Its source is apparently fed by underground water from the Manasarowar Lakes and in its longitudinal section it flows in a deep canyon cut in the soft fluviatile beds of Nari Khorsum; this upper course is distinctly arid and the river itself appears to be a misfit. This might be explicable if it were an old outlet for the 'Tibetan River', and Pascoe thinks that the Sutlej captured part of the Tibetan River and then lost again to the rejuvenated Tsangpo after the Dihang had cut back into the furrow; but this is not very clear. Burrard points out that the Sutlej has a much deeper trough than its neighbours the Giri (a headstream of the Yamuna) and the Beas, and has no large cis-Himalayan tributaries, which suggests that it is younger than the others: 'the question as to how the Giri and the Beas have confined their giant neighbour into a trough less than 20 miles wide remains worthy of consideration'; more worthy if it is put conversely, how the Sutlej has been inset between the two. On this, Davies thinks that the Sutlej is the youngest of the great Himalayan rivers and has developed owing to the collapse of the main Himalayan axis along the line of an old Gondwana fault-trough; in support he cites the deep Shipki gorge and a break in the Ladakh Range northwest of Gurla Mandhata.[30]

III. THE INDO-GANGETIC PLAINS

Structure and surface

The great crescent of alluvium from the delta of the Indus to that of the Ganga represents the infilling of a foredeep warped down between the Gondwana block and the advancing Himalayas. Its relations with the mountains are obscure and involve the interpretation of difficult geodetic data: the older view that the sediments are some 15,000 ft. (4,570 m.) deep, deposited in a great rift or trough sinking beneath the weight of alluvium, has been challenged by Glennie on the basis of gravity anomaly readings which indicate a maximum of around 6,500 ft. (1,980 m.).[31] The Himalayas themselves appear to be largely if not entirely compensated at some distance within the mountains, but on the plains deflections are to the south and suggest an upwarp of denser sub-crustal material from Orissa to Baluchistan.[32]

Be this as it may, it is clear that the filling is of very unequal depth and the Indo-Gangetic Trough does not correspond to the full extent of the Indo-Gangetic Plains; its approximate limits are shown on Fig. 1.1. Occasional outcrops of older rock indicate that the alluvial cover is thinner in the Indus than in the Ganga valley. There is evidence also for concealed ridges or swells of the

[30] L. M. Davies, 'Geographical changes in North-west India', *Proc. 6th Pacific Science Congress* (Univ. of California Press, Berkeley, 1940), 483–501.

[31] E. A. Glennie, 'Gravity anomalies and the earth's crust' (Survey of India Profl Paper No. 27, Dehra Dun, 1940); cf. C. A. Longwell, 'A challenge to isostasy', *GR* 23 (1933), 682–3.

[32] See King, *op. cit.* 16–17; M. S. Krishnan, 'The structural and tectonic history of India', *Mem. GSI* 81 (1953), at 80–84.

basement prolonging the Aravalli axis between Delhi and Hardwar, and also northwest from Delhi towards the Salt Range. There is also the very important and relatively shallow sill between the Rajmahal Hills and the Shillong Plateau; south of this the floor of the Ganga Delta seems to be still sinking.

The plains are remarkably homogeneous topographically: for hundreds of miles the only relief perceptible to the eye is formed by floodplain bluffs, the minor natural levées and hollows grouped by Geddes as 'spill patterns', and the belts of ravines and badlands formed by gully erosion along some of the larger streams, e.g. the lower Chambal (Fig. 18.5); the slopes of the broad interfluves or doabs (do=two, ab=water) are barely if at all perceptible. On this vast aggradational surface the only marked topographical changes are those associated with the numerous shifts and diversions of the rivers. These, however, are of the greatest importance: as Geddes points out, the plain on the Himalayan side is built up of great alluvial cones, with interlocking 'inter-cones'; and on the Peninsular flank, the Son likewise has built up a great cone or fan. On these cones the rivers swing from side to side; at present this is most notable on the Kosi (below, 565), but the past behaviour of the Yamuna, discharging now on the Indus and now on the Ganga side, has mixed their fauna and so meets one of the points raised in support of the Indobrahm.[33]

There are other important surface differences. Along the outer slopes of the Siwaliks there is commonly a fairly steep talus gravel slope, the bhabar, in which all but the larger streams lose themselves, seeping out lower down in the marshy, jungly and naturally intensely malarial terai strip. The older (Pleistocene) alluvium is known as bhangar and as a rule occupies higher ground than the Recent khadar, which occupies the floodplains and grades into the most recent deltaic silts. The bhangar in the Bengal Delta forms low and sometimes lateritic uplands such as the Barind and the Madhupur Jungle. Generally the alluvium is a fairly stiff clay, with more or less sand according as it is near to or far from the hills; in the bhangar there are irregular limey concretions (kankar) and in places there may be as much as 30% of calcareous matter in the alluvium. In the drier areas of Uttar Pradesh and West Pakistan there are stretches of barren saline efflorescence known as reh or kallar; this has spread with the spread of irrigation and, especially in West Pakistan, is a most serious and costly problem (below, 508 and Fig. 17.5).

Contrasts: Himalayan and Peninsular, Indus and Ganga

A factor of the greatest importance in the human geography of India is the strong contrast between the rivers of the Peninsula and those of the Himalayas. It is easy to overlook or underrate the very large proportions of the basins of the Indus, the Brahmaputra, and even the Sutlej, which are included within the mountain zone. The Himalayan section of the Indus drainage alone (excluding the Kabul River) is over 100,000 sq. miles (259,000 km^2), larger than the entire

[33] B. Prashad, 'The Indobrahm or the Siwalik River', Rec. GSI 74 (1939), 555–61.

basins of most European rivers; its Sutlej tributary itself drains 20,000 sq. miles, 51,800 km². Even those rivers which do not penetrate behind the wall of the Great Himalaya have not inconsiderable mountain courses. Erosion is extremely active and vast quantities of detritus are brought down: the Ganga and the Indus have been estimated to carry some 900,000 and 1,000,000 tons of suspended matter daily, and the Brahmaputra more than either. Still more important, the rivers from the Himalayas are not solely dependent on the monsoon months for their water-supply, but have also a supply from the melting of the Himalayan snows. This is the more useful as it comes at the height of the hot weather – February to April – when the Peninsular rivers are lowest. Even in the north the régimes are indeed very variable; the Indus above the Panjnad confluence can vary from 10,000 to 1,000,000 cusecs. But there is usually some water available for irrigation, and the northern rivers are also locally useful for small craft, though except in the deltas inland water transport is of very little account in India.

By contrast, the Peninsular rivers flow in broad shallow valleys, graded almost to their heads and with only slight interruptions of profile, already noted, at the passages through the Eastern Hills. They are entirely dependent on a rainfall concentrated in five or six months of the year, flowing over or through a thin soil cover; they are therefore almost dry in the hot weather. A river like the Krishna, with a bed up to a mile wide and running a banker in the rains, may have a trickle of water only two or three yards wide in March. The Peninsular rivers are therefore less useful for irrigation than those of the north; and where irrigation is possible it needs a proportionately much greater expenditure on barrages and reservoirs; whereas in the north the best options were taken up long ago, under the British, India of the Plains has to face larger and economically less remunerative works in a time of rising costs.

Within the Indo-Gangetic Plains, Geddes draws attention to a significant difference between the Indus and the Ganga system. The Five Rivers of the Punjab combine to form one united stream which flows through a practical desert, receiving no other tributary; 'the Yamuna–Ganga system is enriched by one confluent river after another' and flows in the direction of increasing rainfall. Thus 'the Plain of the Ganga forms part of its water "catchment"; in contrast, the Plain of the Indus could truly be described as an area not of water catchment but of "losement" '. The Indus rivers, losing water, tend to drop their detritus early; those of the Ganga, continually reinforced by the many large tributaries, carry their load much further. Thus the Indus soils are generally coarser, there is a much larger area of fine silt in the Ganga basin, and the 100-fathom line is much farther out to sea off Ganga than off Indus.[34]

[34] Geddes, *op. cit.* in fn. 29; this is much the most authoritative recent study of the Plains.

IV. THE COASTS

The coasts of India are very little indented by large inlets, the only significant ones being the Gulf of Cambay and the Rann of Kutch, to which may be added the wide inlet of the Padma–Meghna mouth in East Pakistan; but the west coast has many small inlets, the east its delta creeks.

Beginning in the northwest, the Baluchistan coast west of Somniani Bay is markedly 'Pacific' in type, the Makran ranges trending parallel to the coast; Sewell's researches indicate that this is definitely a fault coast.[35] It is succeeded by the Indus Delta, off which a great trough reaches a depth of some 3,700 ft. (1,130 m.) at its mouth; this is thought to represent a former extension of the Indus during the glacial fall of sea-level. Kutch and Kathiawad have generally low alluvial coasts; the Rann embayment is, as we have seen, in part of extremely recent date, and the south coast of Kathiawad may be controlled by east–west faulting associated with the Vindhya–Narmada line. The alluvial east coast of the Gulf of Cambay is actively prograding, but from Damão down to Goa the coast is a succession of little inlets and rocky points with, however, a remarkably straight general alignment undoubtedly due to late (perhaps Plio-Pleistocene) faulting.[36] In detail the coast is complicated in both plan and elevation, and here, at Bombay and Goa and a few smaller inlets, are almost the only good natural harbours of India – maritime activity has always been relatively great here – associated with slight submergence.

From Karwar south to Kanya Kumari the coastal lowland widens out and in Kerala is faced by a great extension of long bars and lagoons; emergence is dominant, and the contrast with the northern part of the west coast suggests that there may have been a slight tilt, depression in the north under the weight of the Deccan Lavas and the pressure of the Himalayan folding, upheaval in the south: the pivot would be about Goa.

On the eastern side of the Peninsula the steepness of the submarine contours (sharper than on the west) is puzzling unless it indicates subsidence of the Bay of Bengal; but the most recent movements of any consequence have been elevatory. There are of course considerable stretches of prograding deltas, and off that of the Ganga is a submarine trough, the 'swatch of no ground' corresponding to that of the Indus. The east coast of the Bay of Bengal is again strongly longitudinal; changes of level have probably been complex, as raised beaches are found on some of the Burmese off-shore islands, while the general pattern suggests some subsidence complicated by the formation of deltas, mangrove swamps and large mud volcanoes.

[35] R. B. S. Sewell, 'Geographic and oceanographic researches in Indian waters', *Mem. Royal Asiatic Soc. of Bengal*, 9, summarized in *GJ* 73 (1934), 135–9, and 74 (1934), 154–6.
[36] See notes by S. K. Guha and M. S. Krishnan in *International Oceanographic Congress Preprints* (Amer. Asstn for Advancement of Science, Washington, 1959), 26, 34–36.

BIBLIOGRAPHICAL NOTE

D. N. Wadia's *Geology of India* (Macmillans, London, 3rd ed. revised, 1961) is the standard work; M. S. Krishnan's *The Geology of India and Burma* (Higginbothams, Madras, 4th ed., 1960) is rather lighter in weight than Wadia but deals with tectonic and geomorphological matters more consecutively. K. P. Rode, *Geo-Kinetic Evolution of Greater India* (Mem. Rajputana Univ. Dept of Geology, No. 4, Udaipur, 1954) has a very speculative approach somewhat akin to S. W. Carey's hypotheses; it is effectively criticized in F. Ahmad's 1961 paper cited in fn. 3 above.

On the Himalayas, the standard work of a sort is S. G. Burrard, H. H. Hayden, and A. M. Heron, *A Sketch of the Geology and Geography of the Himalaya Mountains and Tibet* (Govt of India, Delhi, 2nd ed., ?1933) – an indispensable mine of factual detail but exceedingly badly arranged and in places much less than scientific; such criticism might seem presumptuous from a critic who has never penetrated beyond Simla, but the curious reader is referred to K. Mason's review in *The Himalayan Journal*, 7 (1935), 113–24, a critique equally authoritative and amusing. This journal contains a wealth of papers on Himalayan topics; other Himalayan papers not directly cited in the text include:

K. Mason, 'The Himalayas as a Barrier to Modern Communications', *GJ* 84 (1934), 1–16.

J. B. Auden, 'The Structure of the Himalayas in Garhwal', *Rec. GSI* 71 (1936–37), 407–33.

A. Heim, 'The Himalayan Border Compared with the Alps', *Rec. GSI* 72 (1938), 413–21.

A thoughtful paper on the Plains is W. A. Wood, 'Rivers and Man in the Indus-Ganges Alluvial Plains', *Scottish Geog. Mag.* 40 (1924), 1–15. There is a comprehensive review of the Peninsula in E. Ahmad, 'Geomorphic Regions of Peninsular India', *Jnl of Ranchi University*, 1/1 (1962), 1–29; in his conclusion Ahmad, without committing himself, seems to lean towards King's pediplains rather than the classic peneplain concept.

CHAPTER 2

Climate

INTRODUCTION

Almost every aspect of life in the Indian sub-continent is affected or even dominated by the monsoon. This is a truism, but how far is it true? In this popular sense the monsoon climate implies a climate with a cool dry season of northerly winds – the 'Northeast Monsoon' in December to February giving way to a hot dry season from March to early June, a hot wet season of south-westerly winds, the 'Southwest Monsoon' – *the* monsoon of the opening sentence – and a retreat to the dry cool season around the winter solstice. The picture is useful, but the sub-continent has several climates rather than a single climate. The popular image of the monsoon climate best fits the tract lying north and west of a line joining Goa to Patna, and even within this area is upset by the presence of the small but significant depression rains of the cooler months in Punjab and the northwest. With this qualification the popular usage will be accepted for the moment, without any implication as to the causation of the seasonal reversals of wind and weather.[1] Discussion of the causes of the monsoon has long been dominated by the classic hypotheses of workers of the late 19th century, notably Blanford and Eliot, based on interpretation of the data then available concerning pressures and winds, temperatures and rainfall, at that time based on surface recording stations only.[2] Knowledge of the influence of upper air conditions upon the climate of India has greatly increased in the last forty years, and though much more knowledge is still required it is now possible to weave together a description of the seasons and their variations from year to year with something of modern theory on the causal factors at work.

The following account of the seasons takes count especially of modern views

---

[1] For a most interesting discussion of the different meanings attached to the word monsoon, see P. Pédélaborde, *Les Moussons* (Paris, 1958), trans. M. J. Clegg (Methuen, London, 1963), Chapter 1. Future references to this work will give page references from the English translation.

[2] For a modern appreciation and critique, M. J. Webb, 'Some aspects of the early work of H. F. Blanford and Sir John Eliot on pressure disturbances over the Indian land areas 1867–1893', *IGJ* 35/1 (1960), 1–9. The original works include: H. F. Blanford, *The Climates and Weather of India, Ceylon and Burmah* (1889); Sir J. Eliot (ed.), *Climatological Atlas of India* (1906); [Sir J. Eliot], 'Meteorology' (Chapter III, 104–56 in *Imperial Gazetteer of India*, Vol. I, Oxford, 1909. W. G. Kendrew, *Climates of the Continents* (OUP 5th ed., 1961), 155–92, gives a splendid account blending modern and classic views.

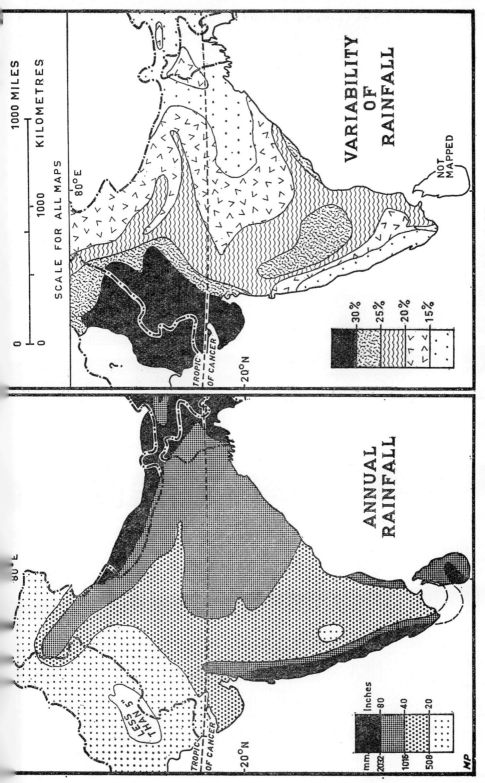

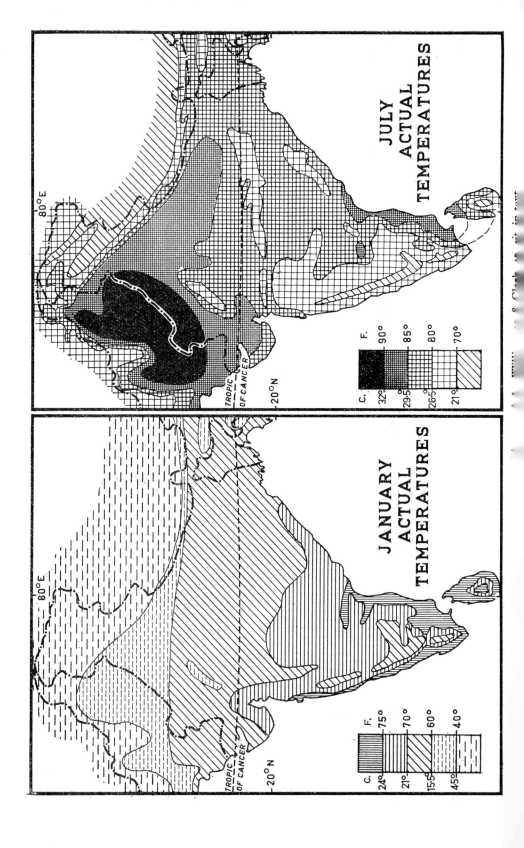

JULY ACTUAL TEMPERATURES

C.	F.
32°	90°
29.5°	85°
26.5°	80°
21°	70°

JANUARY ACTUAL TEMPERATURES

C.	F.
24°	75°
21°	70°
15.5°	60°
4.5°	40°

80° E

20° N

TROPIC OF CANCER

that storms yielding precipitation are commonly associated with surface convergence of air containing some moisture, and also with upper troposphere divergence of air currents which permits the upward movement of the moist air to altitudes sufficient for condensation and precipitation to take place; and that

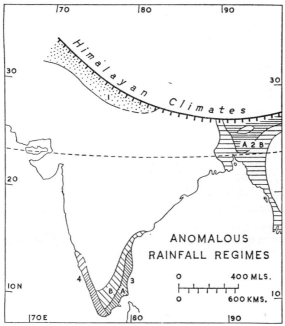

FIG 2.2 ANOMALOUS RAINFALL REGIMES. I, 1–5 in. in cold weather (January–February); 2A, over 20 in., 2B, 10–20 in., in hot weather (March–May) from Nor'-Westers; 3A, over 10 in., 3B, 5–10 in., in retreating monsoon (November–December); 4, dry season only 3 or 4 months. (10 in.=254 mm.)

jet-streams in the lower stratosphere – narrow corridors of high winds in a cloudless sky and a means of equilibrium in the global circulation whose importance has only been realized in the last twenty years or so – also have a marked bearing on rainfall at the surface, for precipitation tends to occur especially around its right entrance and left exit sectors.[3] A synthesis concerning this modern viewpoint will follow the seasonal accounts, on pp. 56–63.

The cool season

In January the cool and mainly dry season is at its height. The northern two-thirds of the sub-continent have mean temperatures below 70°F. (21°C.),

[3] The reader new to the jet-stream might start with G. T. Trewartha, 'Climate as related to the Jet Stream in the Orient', *Erdkunde*, 12 (1958), 205–14, an authoritative account up to that date and relevant to the Indian sub-continent. The *Proceedings* of the Delhi Symposium on the Monsoons of the World in February 1958 (New Delhi, 1960) takes many of our points much further, with stimulating discussion by meteorologists well versed in modern data and theory.

commonly with afternoon temperatures of 80°F. (27°C.), with night temperatures quite often at or below freezing point and sometimes a morning fog. This
is a pleasant season for the well-clad, well-fed and well-housed, but also a season
of ill-health from bronchitis and pneumonia, for many and especially poorer
people. The nights are broken by the sound of coughing resounding through
flimsy buildings. The rainy western disturbances bring rainfall, important for the
growing of wheat and barley though small in total (Peshawar 8 in. (203 mm.) in
November to April, Lahore 4 in. (102 mm.), Delhi 3·1 in. (79 mm.), Benares
2·3 in. (58 mm.)), and in the rear of a depression there is often a wave of cold
weather extremely cold by local standards. Meantime the northern mountains
and especially the Himalayas receive considerable amounts of precipitation,
largely in the form of snow.

The southern third of the sub-continent has rather warmer, fine conditions in
the west, with frosts occasionally in plateau areas and commonly in valley sites
in the highest tracts (Nanjanad in the Nilgiris has an average of 12 nights of
frost in January).[4] The southeast by this time has had its main rainy season, but
there are appreciable amounts in a few hill-stations (Kodaikanal) and in Ceylon,
especially the northeast (Trincomalee). Here rice is still green, when in the
north wheat is almost ready for harvest.

The cool season weather and climate are dominated by locally subsident air:
the Himalayan barrier protects the sub-continent from the true winter monsoon
current blowing from Siberia across China, and it may be considered as part of
the seasonally quasi-permanent or recurrent sub-tropical high pressure cell
(centred over Turkestan not Siberia), giving the light, cool, dry winds from
north to northeast – a land trade-wind if you will. At about 40,000 ft. (12 km.)
and just south of the Himalaya is the quasi-permanent winter position of a
westerly jet-stream. (See Fig. 2.5.)[5] In contrast, the Himalayan region is within
the westerlies; this westerly stream reaches the surface, or almost so, in the
extreme north of the Indo-Gangetic plains and southwards from there it continues as an upper westerly stream over the north to northeast subsident air,
above an inclined plane of discontinuity in the atmosphere, higher to the south
and reaching heights of 10 km. (32,800 ft.) or more over Ceylon (see Fig. 2.6).
Also this westerly air-stream bears the westerly disturbances already noted,
bringing small but agriculturally significant cool season rains to the north of the

---

[4] C. Balasubramanian and C. M. Bakthavathsalu, 'A preliminary study of frost formation
at Nanjanad (Nilgiris District)', *Indian Jnl Met. & Geophys.* 7 (1956), 404–5.
[5] K. M. Ramamurthi, 'A jet stream over northern India revealed by a Comet de-briefing
report', *Indian Jnl Met. & Geophys.* 6 (1955), 277–8 is interesting for its source – an early
case of the captain of a jet airliner in the lower stratosphere asking for permission to depart
from his agreed route because of encountering an adverse jet-stream. Various observations
have been put together to give the generalized picture shown in Fig. 2.5, and there has
been much controversy in the meteorological literature as to whether this quasi-stationary
cool-weather position of the jet-stream is orographically controlled by the Himalaya, as a
sort of standing wave, just as a submerged boulder may cause a curved standing wave
reaching downstream in a fast-flowing river.

sub-continent, and important even beyond that for their influence on other weather phenomena such as the nor'westers of Bengal (see p. 575). These western disturbances have long been regarded as continuations of Mediterranean depressions, and recent work confirms that many are of this origin. Some, on the other hand, arise as secondary depressions over Iran, connected with primary depressions farther north, over southeastern Europe and southern Russia – occasionally the secondary being much more significant than the primary

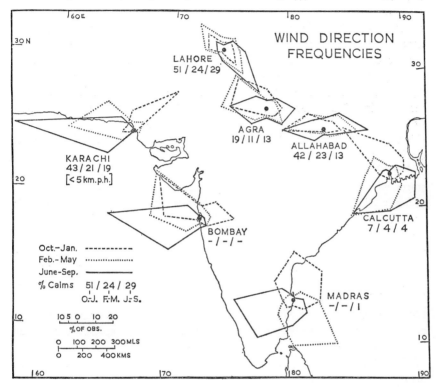

FIG 2.3 WIND DIRECTION FREQUENCIES, 1939. Angles of polygons at distances from station proportionate to number of observations of winds from each quarter. It should be noted that: (i) the southeast winds at Madras come mainly in January–April; (ii) the Arabian Sea current was relatively weak in 1939. *Source:* Indian Meteorological Dept., *Scientific Notes*, VII, No. 80.

depression. Some of the western disturbances of the northern part of the sub-continent, in contrast, arise locally, possibly from waves in westerlies in the upper troposphere or much lower and reaching or almost reaching the surface in the north of the Indo-Gangetic plains. The disturbances from the Mediterranean reach the Punjab more or less occluded, with little frontal structure at the surface. Their frequent deepening and activity is related to upper air divergence, either ahead of a trough in the upper troposphere westerlies, or in relation to the jet-stream, which, it must be remembered, fluctuates and moves from its mean position like a streamer in the wind.[6]

The hot weather

By March the days and nights are getting hot in many northern and inland areas, and heat continues to increase through April and May, causing tension in families and communities, until the 'bursting of the monsoon' (i.e. the southwest monsoon) in early or mid-June. The heat equator has migrated to the northwest of the sub-continent, in latitudes of 25–30°N. In the middle Ganga plains, day shade temperatures are commonly 100–110°F. (38–43°C.) and night temperatures reach 60–65°F. (16–18·5°C.), but as yet with relatively low humidities (c. 40–50% and 20–30% respectively at 8 a.m. and 4 p.m.). Hard work and concentration, even in sedentary occupations, become more difficult, and rest more evasive. Bed-clothes are hot to the touch and rooms stifling, so that many people carry their beds out of doors to flat roofs, gardens, waste ground or roadside spaces. In the afternoon there is often a hot dusty wind, and turbulence carries dust into the air to give the peculiar brassy sky of mid-summer. Vultures and kite-hawks soar on upward wind-flurries, and there may be a whirling duststorm, when a little rain may reach the ground. Diseases of dust increase. In areas of heavy soils, deep cracks give a place of aestivation for insects and for a whole ecological complex including small snakes and rodents, only revealed in the search for the mode of transmission of relapsing fever. After the wheat harvest and early ploughing there is little work in the fields until the rains come. In May temperatures are higher and humid air may add to the discomforts and stresses (morning relative humidity 30–40% at 80–85°F. (28–30°C.) and 20–30% at 105–110°F. (41–43·5°C.) in mid-afternoon). In the south and east early though variable rains may come with the violent squalls of the nor'westers or the even greater violence of a tropical cyclone. Rainy days are interspersed with trying humid days; wherever monthly rainfall is over an inch or so ploughing and the sowing of paddy in nursery beds begins. The southwest of Ceylon has one of its main peaks of rainfall.

During the hot dry weather, conditions are at first mainly anticyclonic both at the surface and aloft. Westerly disturbances continue, yielding less rainfall in the hot dry conditions at first, though later involved in the formation of the nor'-westers of Bengal. Towards midsummer the heat low develops over the northwest of the sub-continent and the unpleasantly humid equatorial air is drawn in, but the north and west do not enjoy widespread rains. In the upper troposphere the air-stream remains westerly, but now dry and relatively warm, so that the

[6] P. R. Pisharoty and B. N. Desai, '"Western disturbances" and Indian weather', *Indian Jnl Met. & Geophys.* 7 (1956), 333–8; M. S. Singh, 'Upper circulation associated with a western disturbance', *ibid.* 14 (1963), 156–72; N. C. Rai Sircar *et al.*, 'A preliminary study of 5-day mean flow patterns in relation to 5-day precipitation in North India during winter season', *ibid.* 11 (1960), 238–57.

temperature inversion along with the lack of upper air divergence prevent widespread precipitation. The jet-stream remains, or better fluctuates in force and position, around its winter station. Meantime the upper troposphere easterlies occur over only Ceylon and Kanya Kumari. Local indraught of sea-breeze type, perhaps along with some upper air divergence over Kerala, permits the development of considerable precipitation, giving high yields over the central highlands of Ceylon and the Cardamoms and the Western Ghats, but also widespread falls over the interior plateaus of South India.

The early rains of northeast India and East Pakistan, mainly due to the nor'westers, are much better studied at present. They are line squalls bringing thunder and lightning and intense precipitation often in the form of hail, the line sometimes regenerating several times, the downdraught from the first line promoting enough turbulence, especially downwind, to provoke the second and so on. They are commonly associated with divergence related to the westerly jet-streams, or to westerly disturbances in the upper troposphere, sometimes intensified by 'inphase superposition' of a wave in the upper troposphere easterlies,[7] and develop, given an association of favourable conditions: (1) low level convergence, (2) upper air divergence, (3) sufficient inflow of moist air at low levels, and (4) unstable lapse rates – often provided through cold air advection aloft. The almost tornado-like dust-storms of Punjab, *andhis* of Uttar Pradesh, and the *kal baisakhis* of Bengal are closely related phenomena, involving very strong convectional movements, in which the tops of the cumulonimbus clouds quite commonly reach 50,000 ft (15·25 km.). There is a very rich literature on these storms, on account of their danger for aircraft and their occurrence within range of a well-equipped weather radar station at Calcutta.[8] Other thunder-storms are associated with random convection within the same air mass, or with cold fronts, often with advection of cold air aloft.

In the early hot weather, too, there is the season of cyclonic storms and tropical cyclones (the hurricanes or typhoons of other sub-tropical regions) in the Bay of Bengal and less frequently in the Arabian Sea. These bring consider-able amounts of rainfall, though very variable from place to place and time to time, and often cause terrible havoc in the densely peopled Bay of Bengal deltas, particularly if gravity, normal tide and wind action conspire to cause a storm

[7] 'In-phase superposition' involves, in this case, the merging of an upper (upper tropo-sphere) wave with a lower wave nearer the ground, with which it has come to be 'in phase' or coincident.

[8] Examples from the *Indian Jnl Met. & Geophys.* include: S. Mull, H. Mitra, S. M. Kulshreshtra, 14 (1963), 23–36 ('Tropical thunderstorms and radar echoes'); A. C. De, *ibid.* 37–45 ('Movement of pre-monsoon squall lines over Gangetic West Bengal as observed by radar at Dum Dum airport'); A. C. De, *et al.*, 8 (1957), 72–80 ('Regenerative drift of a thunderstorm squall of the S.W. Monsoon season'); N. S. Rai Sircar, *ibid.* 21–32 ('On the forecasting of Nor'westers in Gangetic West Bengal'); P. Koteswaram and V. Srinivasan, 9 (1958), 301–12 ('Thunderstorms over Gangetic West Bengal in the pre-monsoon season and the synoptic factors favourable for their formation'); see also C. Ramaswamy, 'On the sub-tropical Jet Stream and its role in the development of large-scale convection', *Tellus,* 8 (Stockholm, 1956), 26–60.

surge (cf. p. 575 below). Tropical cyclones will be discussed more fully in dealing with the months of the retreating monsoon when they are most active.

The rains

In the weeks before the bursting of the southwest monsoon over much of the continent, the ebb and flow of the various participating forces in the lower troposphere, the upper troposphere and the lower stratosphere (i.e. the jetstream) impart great variability to these early, locally vital rains – a topic which will be discussed later in relation to the year as a whole.

Over all the north and west of the sub-continent the 'bursting' of the monsoon, commonly in a great thunderstorm, is something of an emotional experience, a relief after the mounting tensions of the last humid weeks of hot weather. Roughly south and east of a line from Goa to Patna the rains have already started, though in many parts there also the coming of the monsoon proper is eagerly awaited. Yet after the initial relief the season is trying enough. Mean temperatures for July of 80–90°F. (27–32°C.) over much of the sub-continent, and over 90°F. (32°C.) in the northwest, imply high afternoon temperatures uncomfortable in the humid air, and nights are often hot and sticky (relative humidity 60–70% at 4 p.m. and 70–80% at 8 a.m.). Work in the fields includes bursts of really strenuous activity, ploughing, transplanting rice, and so on, and even since the widespread control of malaria an older man may have a malarial rigor, or anybody an attack of dengue; the return of conditions more congenial for houseflies spreads dysentery from carrier to fresh host, and periodically cholera also from its endemic homes in the deltas fronting the Bay of Bengal. After the burst of the monsoon the sub-continent mostly settles down – or so everyone hopes – to an alternation of sudden, intense, and quite local thunderstorms with more widespread, long but less intensive rainfall of depression type. But the onset of the monsoon may be late, or it may withdraw for considerable periods – 'breaks in the monsoon' over nearly the whole sub-continent, though often accompanied by very heavy downpours over the Himalayas with consequent flooding in riverine parts of the Indo-Gangetic or Brahmaputra plains. Or the monsoon may withdraw early. It is vital to complement maps of averages with maps of variability, or of probability of receiving some figure of rainfall crucial in some particular context (Figs. 2.4 and 2.8). Even beyond that one should bear in the mind's eye a yet more kaleidoscopic picture of local variations which may be literally a matter of life and death for this or that group of rural communities.[9]

The warm humid air of the monsoonal indraught towards the heat 'low' of the northwest of the sub-continent, invoked in the classical interpretation of the Indian monsoons, is clearly a factor of significance today as in 1686 when Halley

[9] The *Indian Jnl Met. & Geophys.* contains topical reports on the seasons, and also from time to time articles on local rainfall for Community Development Blocks; the States also issue Season and Crop Reports, and while these can not be used for quantitative assessment of out-turn of crops, they do broadly reflect the vagaries of the weather.

wrote, or as in the late 19th and early 20th centuries when Eliot and Blanford made their fine syntheses.[10] So too the air-mass school have made their contri-

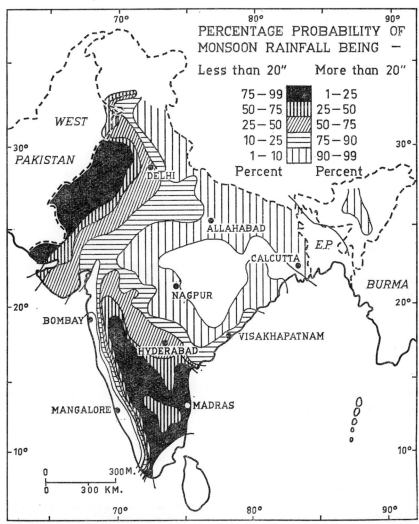

FIG 2.4 PERCENTAGE PROBABILITY OF MONSOON RAINFALL: comparison with the variability map in Fig 2.1 suggests the more precise tools now available. After B. N. Sreenivasaiah and S. Yegnarayan in *Proc. Symposium on . . . Floods and Droughts in India, 1958* (Indian Met. Dept, Poona, 1959). The strip near the Western Ghats should be shaded as for 1–10% probability of less than 20 in.

[10] M. J. Webb, *op. cit.*; E. Halley, 'An historical account of trade-winds and monsoons with an attempt to assign the physical cause of the said winds', *Phil. Trans. Roy. Soc.* (London, 1686); P. R. Crowe, 'The trade wind circulation of the world', *Trans. Inst. British Geog.* 15 (1959), 39–56; Y. P. Rao, 'Some characteristics of the S.W. monsoon circulation', *Indian Jnl Met. & Geophys.* 12 (1961), 413–18.

bution to thought about this most discussed of monsoon climates: contrasts between tropical continental air and equatorial maritime air, for instance, are significant, causing some storms, though contrasts within Em air, for instance between the Bay of Bengal and the Arabian Sea branches of the Indian monsoon, do not seem to be sufficient by themselves to generate the easterly depressions which bring widespread monsoon rains to the Ganga plains and the north of the sub-continent generally.[11] The recently prevailing school of thought in tropical meteorology, which may be called the 'upper air and perturbation school', began by making some positive contributions at points where the previous theories were weakest – notably in offering a fresh approach, if not as yet a complete explanation, concerning the later and sudden 'burst' of the monsoon over the north and west of the sub-continent as compared with the south and east and Burma. More recently still, papers mainly from the Indian Meteorological Department promise that we may soon have an explanation for the 'burst' of the monsoon, its 'breaks' or lulls, and its regional vagaries from year to year, integrating for the first time the dynamics of air moving in the lower troposphere, the upper troposphere and the lower stratosphere.

The 'burst' of the southwest monsoon, according to most modern authorities, is connected with a sudden change of the upper troposphere air-stream over the sub-continent from westerlies to easterlies, and in particular with the sudden withdrawal of the quasi-permanent winter and hot-weather station of the westerly jet-stream from south of – and rather higher than – the Himalayas, to a position north of the Tien Shan (Figs. 2.5 and 2.6). An east to west jet-stream does appear in the lower stratosphere above the upper troposphere easterlies; this jet is not as yet well studied, but is commonly at about $15°N$, and believed to be related to a modification in the 'normal' global heat exchange mechanism necessitated by 'over-heating' of air above the Tibetan plateau, an enormously hot area in summer for its latitude and altitude.[12] A quasi-permanent upper-air trough moves from a position over the Bay of Bengal between Ceylon and the Kra Isthmus to a summer station over the northwest of the sub-continent, and with this change there is now upper-air divergence over the lower troposphere convergence of the long-studied heat low at and near the surface. Cumulus formation in unstable equatorial maritime air is now able to tower up to heights of 30,000–50,000 ft. (9·1–15·25 km.) or even more, and in a normal year widespread storms, often thundery, sweep across the hitherto parched north and west of the sub-continent over the course of a week or ten days.

In many years the extreme northwest, the Thar desert and the lower Indus

[11] M. A. Garbell, *Tropical and Equatorial Meteorology* (Pitman, London, 1947), for an immediately post-war synthesis; but cf. H. Riehl, *Tropical Meteorology* (McGraw-Hill, New York, 1954).

[12] P. Koteswaram and C. A. George, 'On the formation of monsoon depressions in the Bay of Bengal', *Indian Jnl Met. & Geophys.* 9 (1958), 9–22; V. Srinivasan, 'Southwest monsoon rainfall in Gangetic West Bengal and its association with upper air flow patterns', *Indian Jnl Met. & Geophys.* 11 (1960), 5–18.

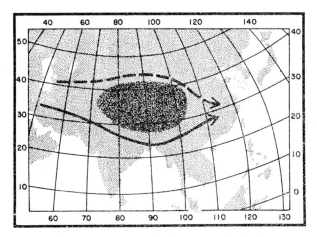

FIG 2.5 SHIFT IN THE JET STREAM: the jet stream in the lower stratosphere is thought to occupy a quasi-stationary winter position south of the Himalaya, moving about early June to a position north of the Tien Shan; this move, with the consequent adjustment of upper air flows, is believed to be an important factor in the 'burst' of the monsoon over India. From G. T. Trewartha in *Erdkunde*, 12 (1958), 205–14, after M. T. Yin in *Jnl Meteorology* (1949).

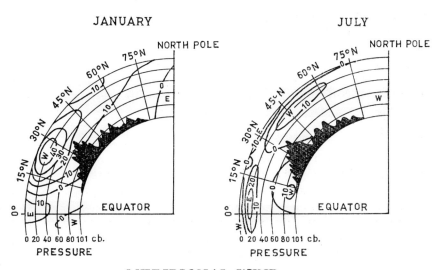

MERIDIONAL WIND
SECTIONS, 100° E

FIG 2.6 MERIDIONAL WIND SECTIONS, illustrating the shift in the upper troposphere westerlies ('W'); cf. Fig 2.5. After Y. Mintz, cited by K. R. Ramanathan in *Symposium on Monsoons of the World*, 1958 (Indian Met. Dept, Poona, 1960).

area, remain rainless or almost rainless. The relatively thin lower troposphere layer of equatorial maritime air is prevented from rising by a marked temperature inversion, the upper air having been influenced by a trajectory above the plateaus of southern Iran and West Pakistan, and the warm upper air has been portrayed as projecting above the lower Indus in a kind of snout, which may extend to spread drought, or contract to permit the occasional rainy year in the desert lands.[13] The semi-arid and famine tract inland from the Western Ghats is often regarded as a rain-shadow area, dry because of adiabatic tendencies in descending air. Poona does receive katabatic winds[14]; but modern workers query whether the descent is of sufficient order to account for the phenomenon and suggest an anticyclonic curve in the trajectory of the air.[15] The 'dry zone' of Ceylon is regarded as receiving föhn-like winds during the southwest monsoon.[16] Thunderstorms have a predilection for some particular sites, as along the Western Ghats where orographic rising occurs along the scarp facing the southwest monsoon or somewhat to its leeward in a standing wave, notably during the spectacular burst of the monsoon behind Bombay. Or, as already noted, it may be associated with random convection, or with cold air advection aloft, often connected with some form of trough or wave or depression.[17] West of the Western Ghats much rainfall is generated by small-scale vortices, about 50–100 miles (80–160 km.) in diameter, larger than those with a cumulo-nimbus cell but smaller than a tropical cyclone; the whirling movement is probably started by the deflection of the monsoon current by the Ghats, and their discovery helps to explain the very heavy rainfalls experienced away from the Ghats edge (Mangalore 117 in. (2,971 mm.)).[18] Tropical cyclones may form; fewer storms start in the Arabian Sea than in the Bay of Bengal, but at this season the Bay storms are generally milder, cyclonic storms or even depressions rather than the severe type classed as tropical cyclones.[19] The broad easterly depressions of great

[13] J. S. Sawyer, 'The structure of the inter-tropical front over N.W. India during the S.W. Monsoon', *Quart. Jnl Roy. Met. Soc.* 67 (1947), 346–69; later authorities have had doubts about the hypothesis put forward – e.g. P. Koteswaram, "The easterly Jet Stream in the tropics', *Tellus*, 10 (1958), 46.

[14] S. Atmanathan, 'The katabatic winds of Poona', *Indian Met. Dept. Sci. Notes*, 4 (1931), 101–15.

[15] G. T. Trewartha, *The Earth's Problem Climates* (Univ. of Wisconsin, Madison; Methuen, London, 1961), 168.

[16] G. Thambyahpillay, 'The kachchan-föhn wind in Ceylon', *Weather* (London, 1958), 107–14.

[17] E.g. K. L. Sinha, 'Influence of distant monsoon lows on weather around Jodhpur', *Indian Jnl Met. & Geophys.* 9 (1958), 251–4; on the other hand local influences may at least complement an upper-air/lower-air relationship, see B. N. Desai and C. Ramaswamy in correspondence discussing a paper by the latter on the jet-stream, *Tellus*, 9 (1957), 135–6.

[18] P. A. George, 'Effects of off-shore vortices on rainfall along the west coast of India', *Indian Jnl Met. & Geophys.* 7 (1956), 225–40; K. Raghavan, 'On the strong monsoon winds at Nagercoil', *ibid.* 6 (1955), 274–6.

[19] S. N. Raychoudhuri, Y. N. Subramanyan and R. Chellappa, 'A climatological study of storms and depressions in the Arabian Sea', *Indian Jnl Met. & Geophys.* 10 (1959), 283–90.

climatological significance moving up the Ganga from Bengal, and also depressions, cyclonic storms and tropical cyclones in the northern part of the Bay of Bengal, are now known to be related to waves or troughs in the upper troposphere easterlies, passing westwards at the rate of about 10 per month at this season, and occasionally to the passages of troughs in the easterly jet stream or in jet-fingers related to it.[20] As already noted, the recurrent station of this jet-stream seems to be farther south, at about 15°N, and further advances in understanding the main synoptic types yielding regional rains and lulls may be expected when further upper-air soundings become available from radiosonde and rawin balloon ascents (recording pressure, temperature, etc., and wind respectively).

Even now, however, some explanation is available for several of the five main synoptic types classified by Rahmatullah (1952) – for which no clear link with the upper air perturbations was clear even to a leading authority like Riehl writing in 1954 (see Fig. 2.7).[21] Waves in the upper troposphere easterlies are noted above as explaining weather activity over the classic position of the intertropical convergence of earlier workers (here between the Bay of Bengal and Arabian Sea branches of the south-west monsoon) over the Ganga plains. (The modern view might be that occasionally the Arabian Sea and Bay of Bengal branches of the monsoon may be sufficiently different in temperature to generate frontal activity on Bjerknes lines, but that this is seldom the primary cause of 'weather'.) Similarly, periods of heavy rain over South India may well become more intense and widespread when a synoptic situation similar to Rahmatullah's type *e* is reinforced by acceleration in the jet-stream at about 15°N up to its trajectory over South India (thereafter it decelerates), with upper vorticity advection, therefore vertical ascent, expected around its right entrance and left exit sectors.[22] And the 'break' in the monsoon over all the plains and peninsula of the subcontinent is related to the passages of several *westerly* disturbances in close succession over the Himalaya (where westerlies still hold sway even during the southwest monsoon); these are believed to pull the monsoon trough north into the Himalaya, causing heavy rains which may flood riverine tracts in the plains but cause the cessation of actual rains over the whole area south of the submontane tract.[23]

[20] V. Srinivasan, 1960, *op. cit.*; D. N. Moghe, 'Periodicity of the Indian S.W. monsoon current', *Proceedings* of the Delhi symposium on the Monsoons of the World in February 1958, Delhi, 1960, 229–34; but cf. S. Jayaram, 'Test of the randomness of the series of occurrences of depressions/cyclones in the Bay of Bengal', *Indian Jnl Met. & Geophys.* 12 (1961), 529–30.

[21] V. Rahmatullah, 'Synoptic aspects of the monsoon circulation and rainfall over Indo-Pakistan', *Jnl of Meteorology* 9 (1952), 176–9, cited in Riehl, *op. cit.*

[22] P. Koteswaram and C. A. George, 'On the formation of Monsoon depressions in the Bay of Bengal', *Indian Jnl Met. & Geophys.* 9 (1958), 9–22.

[23] D. A. Mooley, 'The role of western disturbances in the production of weather over N.E. India during different seasons', *Indian Jnl Met. & Geophys.* 8 (1957), 253–72; P. R. Pisharoty and B. N. Desai (1956), *op. cit.*

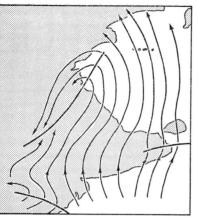
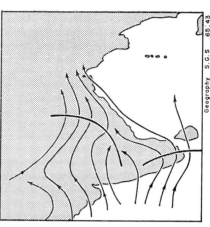
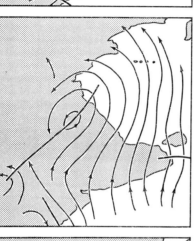
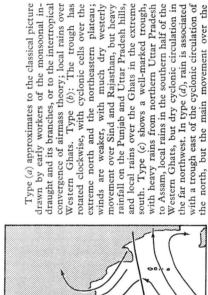
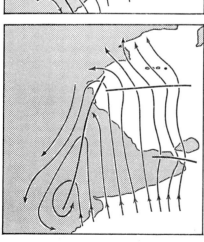

Type (a) approximates to the classical picture drawn by early workers of the monsoonal in-draught and its branches, or to the intertropical convergence of airmass theory; local rains over Western Ghats. Type (b): The trough has rotated clockwise, with cyclonic cells over the extreme north and the northeastern plateau; winds are weaker, with much dry westerly movement over Sind and Rajasthan, but heavy rainfall on the Punjab and Uttar Pradesh hills, and local rains over the Ghats in the extreme south. Type (c) shows a well-marked trough, with heavy rains from northern Uttar Pradesh to Assam, local rains in the southern half of the Western Ghats, but dry cyclonic circulation in the far northwest. In type (d), rain is associated with a trough east of the cyclonic circulation of the north, but the main movement over the northern half of the sub-continent is towards the

far northeast, with heavy rain there but lower air divergence and anticyclonic conditions from eastern Uttar Pradesh to southern Maharasthra and south to the Gulf of Manaar. Type (e) shows a great cyclonic circulation centred on the Mysore Plateau; in the north, a trough in the easterlies has moved to the extreme west, leaving a great swathe of anticyclonic conditions behind it so that all the north is dry; local rains over the Western Ghats in the south and possibly some widespread rain over Mysore. Read (a)–(e) clockwise from top left.

SUMMER CLIMATE: representative types at 5,000 ft. (1·5 km., i.e. lower air) windfield, August 1949.

These lines of thought are beginning – if only beginning – to throw some light on possible causes of fluctuation in date of onset of the southwest monsoon. High temperatures in March over north India seem to relate to good monsoon rains in the south (and high March temperatures over the south itself with poor monsoon rains),[24] while late heating over the Himalayas and the Tibet plateau is related to late retreat of the westerlies from over the sub-continent and therefore late onset of the monsoon (and *vice versa*).[25] Variability of this, the main source of rain for most of the sub-continent, is clearly of vital moment to the people, farmers and townsfolk alike; and it is not just a problem of variability of total amount but also of variability within the rainy period in relation to crop needs. This is discussed elsewhere, but meantime the complex strands involved should be noted.[26]

The retreating monsoon

The southwest monsoon retreats gradually across the north and west of the sub-continent, in contrast with its sudden burst, sometimes with recrudescences. Over much of the north September is a fairly dry month, but sticky and hot – there is a distinct rise in temperatures in many stations. Then there is a gradual cooling, and at last a day when the first cool northerly breeze arrives, welcome and stimulating or foreboding of chilly nights to come, according to circumstances. The main rice harvest is gathered and the threshing is done in pleasant conditions; fields to be sown with wheat or barley are ploughed. The Hindu festival of light (Dewali) often takes place on a beautiful, still, starlit autumn night. Meantime the retreating monsoon brings the second and main peak for the ragi and rice lands of the Mysore plateau and the main rains of the year to eastern Madras and northeast Ceylon, and paddy fields are ploughed and planted, millet and groundnuts sown. The general pattern is towards the re-establishment in the north of the cool season pattern already seen for the early weeks of the year, towards the return of the westerlies and the westerly jet south of the Himalayas, interacting with subsident air at the surface. By October storms may be related to troughs in the upper troposphere westerlies or in the westerly jet stream – sometimes interacting violently with a trough in the retreating upper troposphere easterlies as in a violent storm over the lower Yamuna plains.[27] Farther south the rains of southeastern India may also occur in violent thunderstorms, but are commonly in wider disturbances in which an

[24] P. Jaganathan, 'Predisposition of the upper air structure in March and May to the subsequent rainfall of the Peninsula', *Indian Jnl Met. & Geophys.* 13 (1962), 305–16.

[25] N. C. Rai Sircar and C. D. Patil, 'Horizontal distribution of temperature over India in May in years of early, normal and late S.W. monsoons', *Indian Jnl Met. & Geophys.* 12 (1961), 377–80, and also their 'Study of high level wind tendency during pre-monsoon months in relation to time of onset of S.W. monsoon in India', *ibid.* 13 (1962), 468–71.

[26] B. N. Sreenivasaiah *et al.*, 'Reliability of rainfall during the monsoons in India and a study of the rainfall excesses and deficiencies', *Proceedings* of the 1958 New Delhi Symposium on the Meteorology and Hydrology of Floods in India (Delhi, 1959), 39–48.

[27] D. R. Swaminathan, 'On a destructive hailstorm in the Gormi area of Bhind district on 30 Oct., 1961', *Indian Jnl Met. & Geophys.* 13 (1962), 481–4.

easterly depression from the Bay of Bengal moves across the peninsula – sometimes resulting in very hot weather in the western coastal plains, in the lee of the Western Ghats where katabatic effects are accentuated in a zone of subsident air.[28]

The late summer and autumn months have the most frequent occurrence of tropical cyclones, in the Arabian Sea and especially and more disastrously in the Bay of Bengal, where the recurved maritime course commonly causes terrible havoc in densely peopled deltaic lands, both by winds and often also by flooding following the building up of a storm surge in the Bay. Recent work has again shown that heavy rains from these easterly disturbances are associated with upper air divergence, and that this may come from upper air *westerly* waves, and it has been shown how varying positions of the renascent sub-tropical high pressure area (or zone of recurring cells of high pressure), and varying altitude of southerly and northerly winds contribute to a drought year like 1949 and a wet year like 1946 or 1960.[29]

The violent tropical cyclones seem to arise in a basically similar fashion, but have very marked pressure gradients, destructive surface winds almost parallel to the isobars around the calm of the 'eye of the storm'. Very strong convergence vorticity is associated with very heavy rainfall, and the whole mechanism is sustained by strong upper air divergence while moving for two or three days – rarely for five or six even on recurved tracks – along a path often starting as easterly then curving round to become westerly, and probably reflecting the influence of both a lower air easterly and an upper air westerly trough.[30] These cyclones are similar to the hurricanes and typhoons of other sub-tropical areas. They are nowhere of greater human significance, because of the vast populations affected by this phenomenon primarily of maritime weather in the semi-aquatic rice-growing environment of the low-lying deltas. Fortunately, means of forecasting are improving, partly through greater understanding as knowledge grows concerning the dynamics of the upper atmosphere, and also through new means such as microseismic recording instruments, permitting early detection of storms at sea where weather records are scarce or by the chance of passing ships.

In opening the discussion of the Indian monsoons, we elected to use at that stage a mainly popular usage – though one deep rooted in the people of the subcontinent – for the concept of the climate of alternating monsoons and for *the* monsoon, the rains, the southwest monsoon. More technically, the most widespread usage, at least as yet, probably involves a marked reversal of winds as between cool dry land-winds in winter and warm rain-bearing sea winds in

[28] I. V. Doraiswamy, 'High maximum temperatures on the North Konkan coast', *Indian Jnl Met. & Geophys.* 9 (1958), 259–66.

[29] K. V. Rao, 'A study of the Indian north-east monsoon', *Indian Jnl Met. & Geophys.* 14 (1963), 143–55; P. R. Pisharoty and B. N. Desai, 1956, *op. cit.*

[30] P. Koteswaram and S. Gaspar, 'The surface structure of tropical cyclones in the Indian area', *Indian Jnl Met. & Geophys.* 7 (1956), 339–52; N. C. Rai Sircar, 'Note on vertical structure of a few disturbances over the Bay of Bengal', *ibid.* 7 (1956), 37–42.

summer, preferably through 180°, on the lines of a gigantic land and sea breeze mechanism, annual instead of diurnal in pulsation. So far as monsoon Asia as a whole is concerned, this concept remains useful, granting that dynamic as well as purely thermal factors, pulsations, waves and perturbations have to be taken into account rather than simple monsoonal indraught and outblowing – 'In fact, Asia breathes out during the winter and in during the summer, as the first authors thought'.[31] The Indian sub-continent shares in this, 'probably the largest local perturbation on the general circulation of the atmosphere'.[32] Yet in the Indian monsoon there are many singularities, due largely to relief so far as can be seen at present. The shape of the Peninsular block, the Indo-Gangetic plains and the great Himalayan arcs together with the lesser mountain arcs of the northeast and northwest, interact to place the sub-continent under the influence in winter of a poleward displacement of recurrent cells of sub-tropical high pressure, over Turkestan and over the Bay of Bengal, the northern plains and the peninsula being protected by the Himalayas from the intense cold of the Siberian high pressure system. In the summer monsoon, again, the junction zone between the Bay of Bengal and the Arabian Sea branches of the southwest monsoon recurrently becomes the site of a marked poleward displacement of the inter-tropical convergence zone. We have seen how upper air conditions interact, including poleward movement of these in turn; these compare with a more complete reversal in an 'upper air monsoon' over the rest of Monsoon Asia,[33] so that the Indian sub-continent has an end-product milder, less violent in contrast – if also less widespread in the diffusion of ample rains – compared with the rest of Monsoon Asia. Much of the detailed mechanism has long been known to be in common with other tropical climates, and as knowledge of tropical perturbations grows, and of their relations with waves in the easterlies – over the Pacific as over the Gangetic plain – and with troughs in the upper troposphere and the jet-streams, more is seen to be in common. At present, however, the easterly jet at about 15°N, continuing over the Sahara, seems to be distinctive, and perhaps related in an area to the summer heating noted over Tibet. Analogues from other tropical climates, too, can be described, and with considerable profit in comparative regional geography. There remain the many singularities in assemblage, in interplay of local topography and climate with the currents and waves at various atmospheric levels up to the stratosphere – in fact a rich and by no means fully studied regional climatology – and if the distinctiveness in meteorological and climatological principle is perhaps less than might have been claimed a few years ago, it is sufficiently stimulating in itself and especially so now that we can view it more clearly and more in a global perspective.

Climate and human activities

In the account of the march of the seasons, the briefest remarks have been made

[31] P. Pédélaborde, *op. cit.* 173.   [32] Y. P. Rao, 1961, *op. cit.*
[33] P. Pédélaborde, *op. cit.* 172–3.

concerning the feel of the Indian monsoons to people living there, and also about selected climatic relations with particular diseases. Looking back over the whole field, no aspect of climate is of greater human import than the incidence of flood and drought. These have been mapped in a general way for India only (Figs. 2.4 and 2.8); this kind of mapping is useful in general appreciation of the problem, particularly when complemented by knowledge of the local patterns of

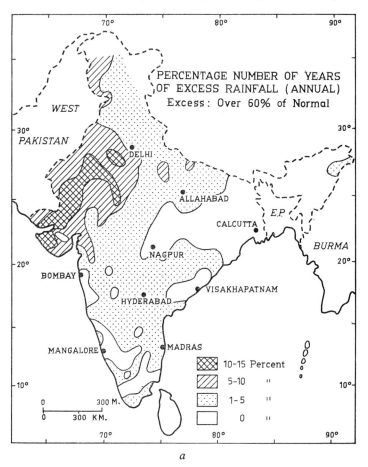

PERCENTAGE NUMBER OF YEARS OF EXCESS RAINFALL (ANNUAL)
Excess: Over 60% of Normal

10-15 Percent
5-10 "
1-5 "
0 "

a

settlement, cropping, etc. Beyond this, a great deal of meteorological work goes on in the hope of being able to make better forecasts of these climatic accidents, at short, medium and long range, and on various areal scales also. An important geographical contribution, a generation ago, was in the mapping of variability of rainfall for the sub-continent, for the year as a whole.[34] This pioneer map may now be complemented by a more recent map using a more refined formula than

[34] A. V. Williamson and K. G. T. Clark, 'The variability of the annual rainfall of India', *Quart. Jnl Roy. Met. Soc.* 57 (1931), 43–56.

was available to the pioneer workers (see Fig. 2.8).[35] Such work is of great value in making our regional thinking more quantitative. In specific fields it is less valuable than probability maps dealing with the chances of a certain severity

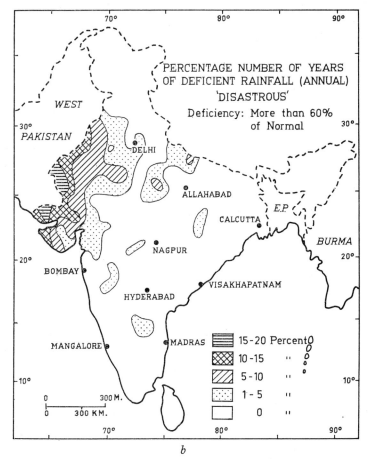

PERCENTAGE NUMBER OF YEARS
OF DEFICIENT RAINFALL (ANNUAL)
'DISASTROUS'
Deficiency: More than 60%
of Normal

WEST PAKISTAN

DELHI

ALLAHABAD

CALCUTTA

E.P.

NAGPUR

BOMBAY

BURMA

VISAKHAPATNAM

HYDERABAD

MANGALORE

MADRAS

15-20 Percent
10-15   "
5-10   "
1-5   "
0   "

0   300 M.
0   300 KM.

b

FIG 2.8 EXCESSIVE AND DEFICIENT RAINFALL. Like Fig 2.4, and from the same source, these maps illustrate the probability approach to climatology.

[35] B. N. Sreenivasan and S. Yegnarayan, 'Reliability of rainfall during the monsoon in India and a study of the rainfall excesses and deficiencies', *Proceedings* of the 1958 New Delhi Symposium on Meteorological and Hydrological Aspects of Floods and Droughts in India (Delhi, 1958), 39–48. Other mapping of interest includes: M. N. Pal's combined mean monthly rainfall and variability maps in A. T. A. Learmonth and L. S. Bhat (eds) *Mysore State Vol. I An Atlas of Resources* (Asia Publishing House, Bombay, 1960); H. A. Mathews, 'A new view of some familiar Indian rainfalls', *Scottish Geog. Mag.* 52 (1936), 84–97 (using quartile diagrams in the way suggested by P. R. Crowe), along with similar work included in the long series of articles by S. B. Chatterjee, included in his *Indian Climatology* (Commercial Printers, 63a Hari Ghose St., Calcutta, 1955); see also *GRI* 12–15, 1950–53).

of flooding or drought, or a certain degree of crop failure. Climatic relations with crop yields are clearly important in a society still largely peasant and partly though decreasingly dependent on subsistence cropping and local self-sufficiency. At a teaching or exploratory level, simple cartographic correlations like Stamp's maps of particular crops and selected isohyets are useful, though not always able to stand up to statistical testing because of exceptions on both sides of a climatic line. There is a major technical difficulty in going farther. The moisture requirements of a particular crop may be generalized – though in work designed for practical use it is better to deal with an individual variety – but there remains the complex task of relating the detailed seasonal incidence and intensity of precipitation to the changing needs of the growing crop. Progress is being made, notably at the Agricultural Meteorology Division of the Indian Meteorological Department, situated at Poona, with which is associated since 1945 the standardized recording of crop-weather data (with reference to locally important varieties of particular crops) at 40 stations throughout India. When sufficient data have accumulated it may be possible to correlate crop moisture requirements with regional climates, but the time for geographical synthesis is scarcely ripe.[36]

Classification of the climates

The classification of the climates discussed earlier in this chapter should serve to pull together the preceding discussion and give a basis for cross-reference with other chapters in the book, both regional and systematic. It is an extremely interesting exercise to compare different classifications, whether designed specifically for the study of the regional climatology of the sub-continent or as world classifications. In this edition of the present work the author of this chapter has sought rather to select only one or two classifications likely to be most useful to the reader of this book as such.

The Kendrew–Stamp classification of the climates of the sub-continent is given, along with some comment and additional information, in Fig. 2.9. This classification is empirical, arbitrary and subjective, but uses quantitative limits to the regions in easily understood units like temperature and rainfall. It does reflect some of the main climatic regions as they appeal to the people or the traveller, and it is simple enough to carry in the mind's eye. Stamp's addition of a line dividing continental from tropical India – roughly across the root of the peninsula – is useful at least as a reminder of a significant division. It is based on the 70°F. (21°C.) isotherm for mean monthly temperature for January, reduced to sea-level; it might have been better, though more complex cartographically, to use actual temperatures. It indicates something of the areas where temperate crops like wheat and barley are important as cool season crops, a feature of profound significance to diet and health and many aspects of the human

[36] Editorial: 'Agricultural meteorology in the Indian Meteorological Department 1932–57 – a review', *Indian Jnl Met. & Geophys.* 8 (1957), 1–28, and indeed the whole of this Agricultural Meteorology Silver Jubilee Number.

geography. (Actually wheat growing as an important food crop extends a good deal farther south in the uplands of the western Deccan.)

Of the world classifications, Thornthwaite's second (1948) classification is, like most others, oriented largely to plant requirements.[37] But it does manage to

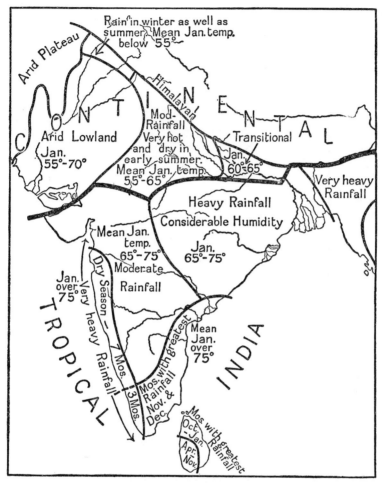

FIG 2.9 THE CLIMATES OF INDIA. This simple empirical and descriptive map may be compared with Köppen's (Fig 2.10); it brings out forcibly the distinction between the more 'continental' North and the Peninsula.

[37] C. W. Thornthwaite, 'An approach towards a rational classification of climate', *GR* 38 (1948), 55–94. See also, however, a major critique from an experienced Indian worker, and an alternative proposal of criteria for the sub-continent, in G. Y. Shanbag, 'The climates of India and its vicinity according to a new method of classification', *IGJ* 31 (1956), 1–25. Shanbag holds that Thornthwaite's concept is too little rooted in observations in growing plants, and proposes a formula related to actual plant growth at different temperatures, related in turn – by purely empirical formula it appears – to mean monthly

break away from the nexus to particular plant associations as means of defining climatic limits, and depends on limits which, though arbitrary, are objective. Thornthwaite seeks to classify the climates in degrees of aridity or humidity according to regularly spaced values of an index, a ratio, based on (1) annual water need or potential evapotranspiration, (2) annual water surplus, when actual precipitation received exceeds potential evapotranspiration, and (3) annual water deficit, when potential evapotranspiration exceeds actual precipitation received. Seasonal variations in aridity or humidity are to be similarly classified.

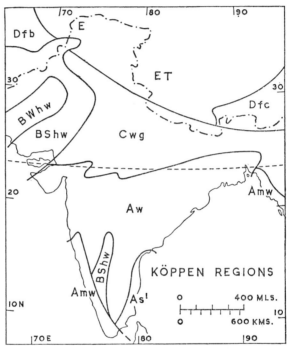

FIG 2.10 KOPPEN CLIMATIC REGIONS. Aw, tropical savannah (at least 1 month under 2·4 in.); Amw, monsoon with short dry season (rain-forest); As¹, dry season in high sun period. BShw, semi-arid steppe, hot, winter drought (wettest month 10 times rainfall of driest); BWhw, hot desert. CWg, dry winter (wettest month 10 times rainfall of driest, 'Gangetic' temperature régime (hottest month before solstice and rains). Dfb, cold humid winters, cool summers; Dfc, as Dfb with shorter summer (over 4 months below 50° F.). E, 'Polar' – warmest month under 50° F.; ET, 'Tundra', warmest month between 32 and 50°F. (0 to 10°C.).

precipitation for each month of the year. An approximation is used to minimize computation. The maps resulting are extremely attractive, on the whole, to the geographer with a good knowledge of Indian plant and crop distributions. One great difficulty, admitted by Shanbag, is that his basic formula relating temperature to plant growth is founded on one rather old set of experiments dealing with maize. Pending further work, it seems best to prefer Thornthwaite's, with disadvantages widely known to workers all over the world, for the main discussion.

Similarly temperature classes – microthermal, mesothermal and megathermal – are to be classified according to regularly chosen intervals in potential evapotranspiration, as a measure of temperature efficiency, the classification again to be subdivided according to seasonal variations in temperature efficiency. A fourfold basis of classification results (humidity or precipitation effectiveness and its seasonal variations, temperature efficiency and its seasonal variations). When more measurements of potential evapotranspiration become available, some such method as Thornthwaite's will certainly offer a considerable advance in climatic classifications oriented towards vegetation. Meantime, he has offered a method of estimating potential evapotranspiration based on two variables only, recorded temperatures and latitude, testing it from a large number of irrigated areas in North America. The formula has yielded reasonable results from other parts of the world, and a map of moisture régime drawn by V. P. Subrahmanyan for the Indian sub-continent is reproduced in Fig. 2.11.

The map of moisture régime is particularly sensitive and useful, and though empirical – and the connection with local experimental data remote – its objectivity alone makes it worthy of serious study. Granting the need for much more observational work, a correlation of a crop or vegetation pattern with this map can be taken seriously, and not as evidence of circular reasoning in which apparent cartographic correlation 'proves' a relationship, which is in fact an assumption on which a certain map was based!

Thornthwaite's version of the temperature régime is disappointing, in that almost all the sub-continent is classed as megathermal – for simplicity in mapping the author disregarded subclasses in temperature efficiency and in seasonal incidence therein.[38] Unfortunately the table of values published with his paper is for 30 representative stations only, not for the 250 stations for which estimates were made, and so interpolations cannot be made to see whether one of the boundaries corresponds to Stamp's divide between continental and tropical India. It would be worthwhile to investigate this, and also to apply the new Thornthwaite formula to a succession of years, so that the core area of a particular climate might be distinguished from the area of fluctuating climates.[39]

Finally, the classification of climates from the point of view of human comfort and efficiency has still many formidable obstacles to overcome. Meantime Fig. 2.12 is offered as a very tentative and interim solution to this problem.[40]

[38] For this reason the map is not reproduced. Instead the Köppen map, Fig. 2.10, is used to represent a map based on a widely used and understood formula which does distinguish North from South India in respect of temperature régime.

[39] R. J. Russell, 'Climatic years', *GR* 24 (1934), 92–103. An Indian worker, not traced at present, has applied this concept to the Thornthwaite 1933 formula, since superseded.

[40] D. H. K. Lee, 'Clothing for global man', *GR* 39 (1949), 181–213, and personal communication from P. Siple, American Embassy, Canberra, November, 1964.

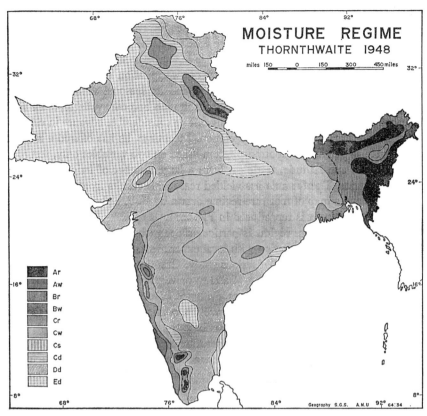

FIG 2.11 MOISTURE RÉGIME, on Thornthwaite's 1948 formula, i.e. moisture index $(Im) = \dfrac{100s - 60d}{n}$, where s = annual water surplus, d = annual water deficiency, and n = annual water need (or potential evapotranspiration), all expressed in the same units. From V. P. Subramanyam in *Indian Jnl Met. and Geophysics*, 7/3 (1956), 253–64.

KEY

Moisture index	Climatic type	Sub-types
100 and above	A Perhumid	r = little or no water deficit
		s = moderate summer water deficit
20 to 100	B Humid	w = moderate winter water deficit
		s_2 = large summer water deficit
0 to 20	C_2 Subhumid	w_2 = large winter water deficit
0 to −20	C_1 Dry subhumid	d = little or no water surplus
−20 to −40	D Semiarid	s = moderate winter water surplus
		w = moderate summer water surplus
−40 to −60	E Arid	s_2 = large winter water surplus
		w_2 = large summer water surplus

On this map, types C_1 and C_2 have been merged, types s and s_2, and types w and w_2.

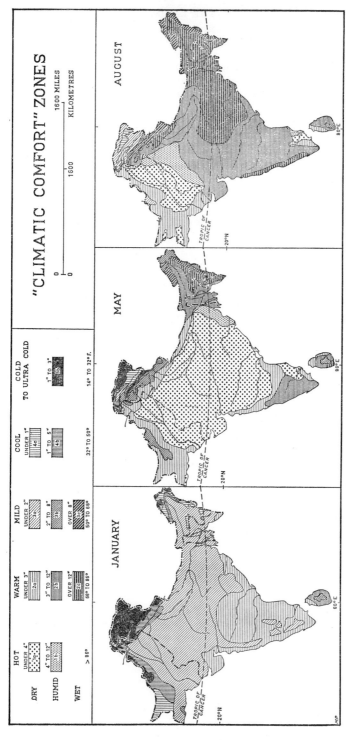

FIG 2.12 'CLIMATIC COMFORT' ZONES. *Source:* P. Siple, American Embassy, Canberra, and US Quartermaster-General's Department.

BIBLIOGRAPHICAL NOTE

In this edition the main sources, including classics in the field, are indicated in the text and footnotes. For up-to-date work, the reader is referred to the oft-cited *Indian Journal of Meteorology and Geophysics*, the various geographical journals published in the sub-continent – for instance the valuable series of articles on climate in the *Pakistan Geog. Rev.*, and S. S. Bhatia, 'Bibliography of Indian Climatology', *Indian Geographer*, I, 1956, 55–64.

CHAPTER 3

Vegetation and Soils

I. VEGETATION

Original forest dominance

The natural vegetation of the Indian sub-continent, except on the higher mountains and in the more arid parts of Baluchistan and the Thar, is essentially arboreal. It has, however, been cleared, exploited and degraded to such an extent that this statement has little practical significance today. Something like a fifth of India is officially regarded as forest, against a notional optimum of a third; but of this area of 277,000 sq. miles (717,000 km²), nearly 100,000 sq. miles are 'unclassed' and most of this is forest only by courtesy, and this also applies to a good deal of the nominally 'Protected' forest. 'Reserved' forests are under half of the total forest area, and many of these, especially in the drier areas, are more subject than they should be to grazing and even illicit exploitation under cover of vague rights to minor forest produce. In any case, many of the best and least degenerated forests are in largely inaccessible Himalayan areas, there is very little forest of any sort in the Indo-Gangetic Plains, and much of the forest area of the Peninsula is really only scrub-jungle, very open or stunted. Pakistan is in even worse case, with only 13,500 sq. miles (35,000 km², 3·7% of area) under forest. Yet there is good historical evidence for large forests even in the central Punjab in Alexander the Great's day, on the Yamuna in the time of Mahmud of Ghazni (11th century); and the Gangetic Plain was probably originally covered with vast forests, mainly of sal. Today, as Legris points out, it is only very rarely that one can travel as much as 186 miles (300 km.) through even secondary forest that looks like forest, and then only by avoiding main routes, even on the Madhya Pradesh/Orissa borderland.[1]

Three millenia of clearing for cultivation and of unregulated grazing, both often promoted by burning the jungle, have thus stripped the forest from nearly all of the plains and much of the lower hills and plateaus, or turned it into scrub (Figs. 3.1, 3.2). In the Indo-Gangetic Plains as a whole woodland is practically confined to the terai, riverine strips, and village groves of mangoes and tamarinds, while over vast areas of the Deccan men and animals have produced the *aspect* of a short-grass savannah with scattered trees. 'Thin grass cover and scattered acacias . . . rough pasture, scattered acacias . . . thin cover of acacias, euphorbias'

[1] P. Legris, *La Végétation de l'Inde* (full reference in Bibliographical Note), 336–8, 343–8.

– such phrases occur time and again in field-notes of Peninsular journeys. But 'it is doubtful if there are any examples of tropical climax grassland [except in a few small scattered instances], though grassland is common enough as a secondary seral stage and it may be a very stable preclimax under the influence of fire and grazing. The typical savannah type of other countries is also apparently absent as a true climatic climax, closed deciduous forest grading into thorn forest without any open grassy park-like stage, in the absence of biotic influences.'[2] Legris goes further: 'Savannah results essentially from the regular passage of fire, but it presupposes a feeble density of human and cattle population. . . . It has practically disappeared in all the highly populated regions of the Deccan, where it remains theoretically possible but has been replaced by a bio-edaphic pseudosteppe.'[3] In effect, the biotic factor in the production of the 'savannah' areas of India is even more predominant than in other countries, and hence it is not possible to equate them in India with particular climate–soil complexes with any degree of confidence.[4] The forest classification must be taken as the basis of any vegetation study; but recent work has made it possible to indicate, at least provisionally, the ecological niche of the main grassland types.

The lack of gregariousness in tropical forests is well known; on the whole the floral landscape is rarely marked by an absolute preponderance of one species or even an assemblage of species. The nearest approaches to this condition are the Himalayan rhododendron belts, the semi-desert vegetation of the northwest, and bamboos locally in the south and the northwest, usually on old clearing. Palms, and especially acacia and sal, 'give a mark to the vegetation over considerable areas, but they are far from taking the place of assemblages. They are at best conspicuous features of the landscape.' The floristic affinities of India are in the main with the Malaysian realm, but, in the northwest, Mediterranean and south-west Asian elements have entered on a broad front, and Legris indicates some penetration from tropical Africa down the east of the Western Ghats. In the Himalayan temperate belt, Chinese forms are not few, with some European ones in the north and west; and other European, and even American, elements are represented, presumably by unrecorded importations of the last four centuries. An example is the cashew nut, so important in Goa and Kerala, brought from Brazil by the Portuguese.[5]

Climate is the major determinant of forest types, and on a broad view rainfall is more important than temperature, except in the Himalayas, since its range of

[2] H. G. Champion, *Forest Types* (full reference in Bibliographical Note), 14. Much of the terai is a tall-grass savannah. Important grasses are *sabai*, used for paper-making, and *khaskhas*, for the mats which, kept constantly wet, are a useful hot-weather cooling device.
[3] Legris, *op. cit.* 361.
[4] As is done for example by C. A. Cotton, 'The theory of savanna planation', *Geography*, 46 (1961), 89–101, and M. M. Cole, 'Vegetation and geomorphology in Northern Rhodesia', *GJ* 129 (1963), 290–310.
[5] C. G. Calder, 'An outline of the vegetation of India', in S. L. Hora (ed.), *An Outline of the Field Sciences of India* (India Sci. Congress, Calcutta, 1937), 71–90; Legris, *op. cit.*, Carte 20.

variation is so much the greater. Soil factors are generally of secondary significance, though of course they play a decisive role in controlling the distribution
of species and associations within the major types, mainly through variations in

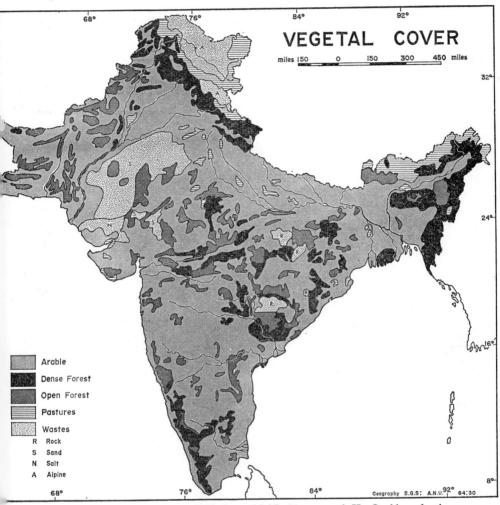

FIG 3.1 VEGETAL COVER: compiled from *NAI* Pl. 11 and K. S. Ahmad, *A
Geography of Pakistan* (1946).

ground moisture leading to the occurrence of wet types well outside their normal
rainfall limits, and *vice versa*. Topography in the narrow sense is responsible for
certain minor types, e.g. alpine flora, tidal forest, some savannahs on sub-
Himalayan terraces; these are limited in extent but of interest as specialized
adaptations to environment or as being of special economic importance. Excluding these, four grand vegetation divisions may be recognized on a rainfall basis:

75

over 80 in. (2,032 mm.): evergreen (rain) forest;

40–80 in.: deciduous (monsoon) forest;

20–40 in.: drier deciduous forest grading into open thorny scrub;

under 20 in.: thorny scrub and low open bush merging into semi-desert.

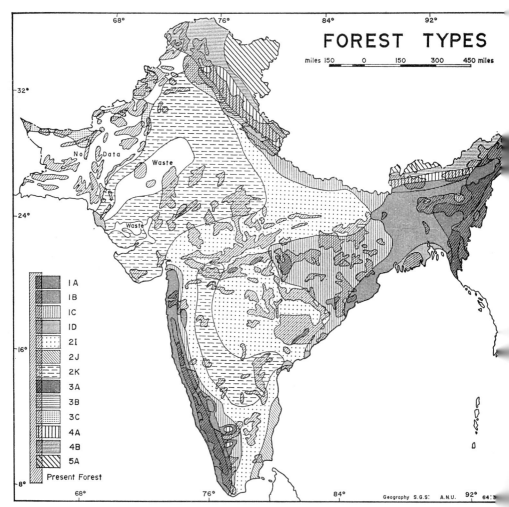

FIG 3.2 FOREST TYPES. *Sources:* As for Fig 3.1, with addition of H. G. Champion, *op. cit.* (1936) in text. Key to symbols is given on pp. 77–79.

Legris takes a rather more physiognomic approach, distinguishing humid, dense dry, thorny, and Himalayan formations.

It must be emphasized that these limits are approximations only, that transitions are usually gradual, and that there are numerous anomalies of detail: 'the familiar 80 inches rainfall limit for rain forest . . . is open to the exceptions of the occurrence of the type with only 50 inches [1,270 mm.] under very favourable conditions, and its absence with even 200 inches unsuitably distributed when it is associated with either a very porous or an impervious soil.' Again, while the broad lines are clear enough, there is considerable confusion of nomenclature; Legris cites one Himalayan type which has been given 17 names by various authors, and classified as high-altitude tropical, temperate, montane temperate, cool temperate, and subalpine.[6]

Vegetation classification

The classic forest classification is that of H. G. Champion, who distinguished altogether 116 types, some of them subdivided. But many of these are local, and they fall into 15 main types, or 13 if we group Alpine forests and scrubs together. Legris considers that, even after Schweinfurth's elaborate work, Champion's classification is still the most useful for the Himalayas. However, since Champion's book was published in 1936, a good deal of critical work has been devoted to the problem, largely on lines he himself anticipated, and in particular his work has been complemented, though not as yet superseded, by that of G. S. Puri. The biotic modification of the forest cover is emphasized by Puri, who is reasonably confident that three of Champion's main types – dry deciduous, thorn, and dry evergreen forest – are biotic seral stages to moist deciduous forest; or, to put it conversely (as does Legris) are essentially degraded from more humid formations.[7] Puri also considers that the Nilgiri grasslands are biotically controlled, and in this he is at one with Legris, who cites peat borings showing little if any sign of climatic change but definite carbonaceous layers indicating extensive burning.[8]

The following tabular statement therefore follows Champion in general, with some modification and rearrangement along Puri's lines. Prefixed numbers (1A, 1B . . .) refer to the keys of Figs. 3.2 and 3.3; grassland types are enclosed in square brackets; asterisks indicate types thought by Puri to be definitely biotically induced.[9]

1. *Moist Tropical Types*
    1A. Tropical wet evergreen
    1B. Tropical moist semi-evergreen

[6] Legris, *op. cit.* 285.
[7] *Ibid.* 204–8, 236, 248–9.
[8] *Ibid.* 219–23; Puri, *Indian Forest Ecology* (Oxford Book Co., New Delhi, 1960), 249.
[9] A more detailed treatment may be found in A. T. A. Learmonth, *The Vegetation of the Indian Sub-Continent* (Dept of Geography, School of General Studies, Australian National University, Canberra; Occasional Paper No. 1, 1964); this includes floristic data, especially on the grasslands, difficult to fit into the scale of this book, and types not mappable on the scale of the map used for figs. 3.2 and 3.3 (hence the gaps in the system of code-letters used below).

IC. Tropical moist deciduous
ID. Tidal (edaphic)
[IP. Savannah grassland of moist plains*]
[IR. *Dichanthium-Cenchrus* grasslands on sandy soils*]

2. *Dry Tropical Types*
   21. Tropical dry deciduous*
   2J. Tropical dry evergreen*
   2K. Tropical thorn
   [2L. *Dichanthium-Cenchrus**]

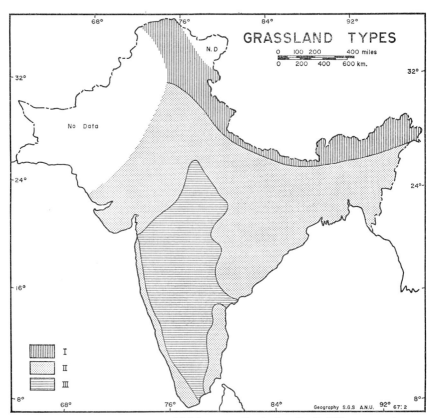

FIG 3.3 GRASSLAND TYPES, highly generalized after R. O. Whyte, *op. cit.*
(1957) in Bibliographical Note. For symbols 3E, 4L, etc., see pp. 77–79. I,
Northern mountain and hill grasslands (3E, 4L, 5F); II, Grasslands on
sandy soils, alluvial deserts and crystalline plateaus (mainly IR and 2L,
with IP along the northern hillfoot and 3E on Aravallis and Assamese hills);
III, Deccan Grasslands (typically 2M, with 2N in rare paddy tracts, some
2L and 3D and some 3E on ridges, dissected hills and scarps).

2. *Dry Tropical Types*
 [2M. *Sehima-Dichanthium*★]
 [2N. *Bothriochloa* in paddy tracts★]

3. *Montane Subtropical Types*
 3A. Wet hill
 3B. Subtropical pine
 3C. Subtropical dry evergreen
 [3D. Hill savannah, *Cymbopogon*★]
 [3E. Hill savannah, *Arundinella*★]

4. *Montane Temperate Types*
 4A. Wet temperate and Himalayan moist temperate
 4B. Himalayan dry temperate
 [4L. Temperate grassland★]

5. *Alpine Types*
 5A. Alpine
 [5F. Alpine and Subalpine grasslands★].

Moist Tropical types

IA *and* IB. *Tropical wet evergreen and semi-evergreen.* These are typical rain-forests. The true evergreen is found in a strip along the Western Ghats at 1,500–4,500 ft. (455–1,370 m.), south of Bombay, and up to 3,500 ft. (1,070 m.) in Assam; much of Bengal and the Orissa littoral may once have been covered by semi-evergreen forest. The best evergreen forest is naturally found in the areas with really high rainfall, over 120 in. (3,048 mm.), and a relatively short dry season; on the drier side it is bordered by the semi-evergreen, which in turn merges with IC, tropical moist deciduous. The rain-forest is very dense and lofty, the upper storey reaching 120–150 ft. (37–46 m.) with individuals of 200 ft.; some of the largest are dipterocarps. Owing to the deep shade the floor is relatively bare, but along the edges of breaks in the cover (such as stream-margins) undergrowth of palms and bamboos may be extremely dense. Buttressed trunks are common and epiphytes highly developed. The number of species is very large indeed, especially on the Ghats; the Assam forests and still more the semi-evergreen tend to be rather more gregarious, representing a transition to moist deciduous.

 The forests are exploited under State forestry departments to favour the more economic species. So far elephant rather than tractor power is used, and seasonal saw-pits are common; but more advanced methods for pulp and paper mills, such as those of Bhadravati in Mysore and Karnaphuli in East Pakistan, are increasing. Veneer and plywoods are produced; rattan-canes have been over-exploited.

1C *and* 21. *Tropical deciduous.* These may conveniently be treated together; 21, tropical dry deciduous, is regarded as a biotically-induced variant of the moister 1C, theoretically seral to it but more practically regarded as degenerative from it: it is most unlikely that the process of degradation is reversible, under Indian conditions, on more than a very limited scale.

These, the monsoon forests *par excellence*, form the natural cover over nearly all of India between the Himalayas, the Thar and the Western Ghats; areas with a moderate (40–80 in., 1,016–2,032 mm.) rainfall. But they are, of course, less resistant to fire and other man-induced interference; vast areas have been completely destroyed, and the biotically controlled drier facies has replaced the moister over very much of its original area. The moist forest forms a long strip on the east of the Western Ghats, and the economically very important sal type covers the northeast of the Peninsula – Chota Nagpur, Orissa, eastern Madhya Pradesh; and there is a long strip along the Siwaliks, the bhabar, and the terai from 77 to 88° E. The rest of the area is of the drier type, shading off into thorn forest.

Although most trees lose their leaves for some 6 to 8 weeks in the hot weather, the actual leaf-fall periods vary from species to species, so that the forest is rarely absolutely leafless, and undergrowth in moister areas is often evergreen. Nevertheless the general aspect is decidedly burnt-up and bare in April–May. The moist forest is higher (80–120 ft. against 50–75) than the dry, which indeed breaks down into thorn or scrub in climatically or edaphically arid areas. Undergrowth is usually denser than in the rain-forest; climbers and bamboos are very common, especially perhaps in the moister types.

Economically these are the most important forests of India; the number of commercially important species is greater than in the evergreen, and they are also on the whole more gregarious. This is so more particularly of sal (*Shorea robusta*), which 'is very generally more aggressive than any of its associates and competitors in natural gregarious habit, coppicing power, resistance to burning, regeneration under burning and grazing, adaptability to soil and site conditions; though it suffers from frost, it survives where few other species could'.[10] These traits have been fostered by selective forest management. Sal often forms pure stands (perhaps biotically induced rather than the climatic climax) of close and high forest (80–120 ft., 24–36 m.), with a shrubby undergrowth replaced by grass in areas liable to burning. Edaphically it avoids purer sands and clays, too dry or too wet. The hard durable timber is in great demand, especially for railway sleepers and constructional work; 50 miles of railway construction is said to have demanded 20,000 tons of sal or teak. Teak (*Tectona grandis*) is characteristic of the monsoon forest in the west; its distribution is to some extent complementary to that of sal in the Peninsula, sal dominating the northeastern quadrant. While teak is a calcicole, sal is probably a calcifuge. Like sal, it is reasonably resistant to burning, which indeed may assist regeneration, by splitting the pericarps, if it

[10] Champion, *op. cit.* 76.

takes place before the seedling stage; but it is a poorer colonizer, and except where artificially aided not nearly so gregarious as sal.[11] Indian teak production, mostly from Mysore, is much less than that of Burma (in normal times), and despite its greater fame the timber is on the whole less important in India than is sal, though valuable for its termite-resistant qualities.

The evergreen sandalwood (*Santalum album*) is a valuable resource in Mysore; a very hard and close-grained yellow wood with a fragrant scent, it is used for carved boxes and ornaments and for incense, and more or less sandalwood may be included in more or less expensive funeral pyres. Other important trees are sissoo or shisham (*Dalbergia sissoo*), very common along the eastern sub-Himalayan zone, producing a hard timber used for building, furniture, cart-frames and wheels; hurra (*Terminalia chebula*), less significant for its timber (which is nevertheless hard and suitable for furniture, carts and turnery) than for its fruits, the myrobalans which provide a valuable tan-stuff and are also used for dyes and mordants; mahua (*Bassia latifolia*), the flowers of which are eaten as a sweetmeat and are a potential source of alcohol; and khair (*Acacia catechu*), common on the more arid margins of the dry deciduous type. Minor forest products range from honey to bats' dung for manure.[12]

1D. *Tidal forests*.[13] The tidal forests are the most widely known of the specialized tropical types, but confusion has been caused by the indiscriminate use of the word 'mangrove' and by even more indiscriminate descriptions by travellers of the most luxuriant parts of mangrove forests as if they were the standard. While the *Rhizophora* mangroves which border tidal channels do form dark high forests, much mangrove is low and light olive in colour, most disappointing to those who have been led to expect giant knee-roots and crocodiles behind every tree.[14] The common feature of the numerous species of mangroves, and of other trees of the tidal marshes, is the existence of pneumatophores or breathing-roots, sticking out of the mud like a field of tent-pegs driven in upside-down. In the early stages of colonization of the mud-banks the plants are scattered, and in conditions of poor silt-supply (e.g. on parts of the west coast) the mangrove 'forest' remains very open and the trees low, at high tide looking like olives growing out of the water. Just as the reputation of rain-forest as impenetrable is based largely on its luxuriance along the streams, where the

[11] These statements may need some qualification. Sal is more dependent on soil moisture than is teak, which is more sensitive to chemical properties of the soil, and the former is thus more affected by lowering of the water-table owing to biotic interference; this encourages fungal attacks on the shallow root system. In places sal seems to be degenerating and even retreating before teak. See K. N. Chaudhuri, 'Regenerating of the dry peninsular sal forests of West Bengal', *Indian Forester* 84/1 (1958), 4–18; D. H. Kulkarni, 'Geography of sal and teak', *Proc. IX Silviculture Conference 1956* (Dehra Dun, 1960), 108–16; and cf. Puri, *op. cit.* 183.

[12] M. N. Ramaswamy, *Minor Forest Products in Mysore: A Survey* (Govt Press, Bangalore, 1945).

[13] There is a good discussion in Legris, *op. cit.* 320–5; for the economic side, see 'Symposium on mangrove vegetation', *Science and Culture* (Calcutta), 23/7 (1958), 329–36.

[14] Personal experience!

whole side of the forest is accessible to light, so the popular conception of mangrove swamp is based on the gallery of high dense growth along the tidal channels, trapping the silt at every tide. Behind this rapidly accreting zone is usually an infilling of smaller species; both the ground surface and that of the vegetation canopy are saucer-like in section.

Mangroves fringe the seafaces of most of the Indian deltas. In the Bengal Delta they are backed by the great tidal Sundarbans, named from the sundri tree (*Heritiera fomes*). This pneumatophore forms a closed forest which is over 100 ft. high in the higher areas where the water is fresh or brackish in the rains. At still higher levels, in Bengal and elsewhere, are tangled brakes of screwpines (*Pandanus* spp.), canes, and palms such as *Phoenix paludosa*. The creeks are often lined by *Nipa fruticans*, a palm with dense masses of fronds springing directly from a low stump. These forests have a considerable economic value. The mangroves themselves are an important source of fuel, sometimes under management as such; sundri is a hard durable timber much used for construction and boat-building; gewa (*Exeocaria agallocha*) is used for newsprint; the fronds of *Nipa* are a common thatching material, its sap can be made into gur or toddy, the leaf-stalks are used as fishing-floats and to give buoyancy to sundri logs.

[1P. *Savannah grassland of moist plains.*] This is found in a long strip eastwards from about 77°E; it is a hygrophilous to mesophilous vegetation of coarse grasses including *Phragmites karka*, *Saccharum* spp., and *Imperata cylindrica*. Itself biotic in origin, it is even more sensitive than the forests to heavy grazing and burning, and the drier soil climate which ensues leads to the formation of a distinctly xerophytic vegetation or even to bare ground not even invaded by prostrate forms such as *Eleusine* and *Paspalum*. Nevertheless there are still very considerable stretches of tall grassland along the terai.

[1R. *Dichanthium-Cenchrus grassland.*] This very wide-spread grassland is also a dry formation (1R is grouped with 2L on Fig. 3.3); it is seral to very varied forest types. The distinction between 1R and 2L is that the former is found on sandier soils in climatically more humid areas. As in all the Indian grasslands, burning and overgrazing have led to very severe deterioration, and there are very many degraded sub-types. These include poor grasslands dominated by non-palatable annuals such as *Aristida* spp. and a low scrub of *Cassia auriculata* over bare eroded soil, and in extreme cases great swathes of badland erosion as along the Chambal.

Other Edaphic Types. These include beach vegetation (not of course confined to the moist tropical habitat), tropical freshwater swamps, riverain forests, khair-sissoo on sandy floodplains, bamboo brakes, various scrubs on lateritic soils, and alluvial savannahs. Owing to limitations of data and still more of scale, they have not been included on Figs. 3.2 and 3.3.

On beaches and dunes fringes of casuarina are common; along the eastern littoral it is often planted on sandy soils as a quick-growing source of firewood, and it also helps to stabilize coastal dunes.

Freshwater swamp forests are found in badly drained and aerated clayey depressions in areas with over 50 in. (1,270 mm.) of rain: they form pure stands of medium-sized trees, largely evergreens, which may or may not have an evergreen undergrowth according to the amount of biotic interference. The riverain and freshwater swamp forests vary greatly with local climatic and edaphic factors, and with interference by men and animals; they range from dense jungle and cane-brakes through thin strips of more or less open woodland into swampy savannah. A notable riverain type is the khair-sissoo association on new sandy alluvium in northern India. In areas where the progression would be towards semi-evergreen forest, as in alluvial tracts of Assam, canes trailing horizontally as much as 200 ft. (61 m.) form dense brakes, an impenetrable thorny thicket with a few tall trees, including palms. Some of these subsidiary edaphic types, for example bamboo brakes and secondary dipterocarp forest, are of course also strongly influenced by biotic factors, and one of Puri's types – moist alluvial savannah – is firmly biotic: grazing and burning on useful floodplains and terraces keep the vegetation, naturally seral to a riverain woodland and eventually to tropical moist deciduous forest, at the savannah stage.

Dry Tropical types

21. *Tropical dry deciduous.* This has been discussed with the moist deciduous type, from which it is by and large a biotically controlled regression. Occupying a vast area in central and Peninsular India and also along the Siwaliks and terai from central Nepal to Himachal Pradesh it is, as Legris points out, in contact with practically all types, and transitional facies are important. The common climatic characteristic of its domain is a long and intense dry season, with a moderate rainfall concentrated into a few months. On the drier side, it degenerates into thorn forest, 2K.

2J. *Tropical dry evergreen.* This is a very peculiar formation with a very limited range, almost confined to the Madras littoral between Point Calimere and Madras itself. Legris, who thinks its general significance has been exaggerated, casts doubts on its affinities to the dry forest of northern Ceylon. It is found with a rainfall of about 40 in. (1,016 mm.), received mostly in October through December, and with generally high humidity. The forest, where it still exists, has a closed but low (30–40 ft.) canopy with shrubby, often spiny, undergrowth. Bamboos are rare, but lower grasses may be present. The existence of an evergreen forest with such low rainfall is botanically interesting, but most of it has been cleared for agriculture or casuarina plantations. The residuals are now regarded as a biotically controlled forest, degraded from evergreen high forest.[15]

2K. *Tropical thorn forest.* In areas with under 30 in. (762 mm.) annual rainfall, such as the northwest and the Peninsular interior to the lee of the Western Ghats, the dominant vegetation is open stunted forest breaking down into

[15] Only small patches are shown on the Cape Comorin sheet of the Pondicherry 1/1,000,000 vegetation map (see Bibliographical Note). See also Puri, *op. cit.* 246, and Legris, *op. cit.* 227–33. He prefers the term semi-deciduous.

xerophytic bush, and in the northwest grading into practically complete desert. Biotic factors over the centuries are regarded as more important than climate and soil in producing and maintaining these forests, degraded from the tropical dry deciduous type, itself largely biotic. As Legris puts it:

> 'This vegetation taken as a whole continues to degrade, or at most seems stabilized in a peneclimactic stage in equilibrium with the biotic factors. Can one in such a case speak of a progressive vegetational series? . . . One finds in each region a whole series of stages of floristic and physiognomic degradation deriving from each other. One can, then, consider each of these ensembles as constituting a phylum, a progressive vegetation series ending at the most evolved type existing in present ecological conditions, which is the plesioclimax. This plesioclimax is definitely not the most evolved physiognomic type possible, and *a fortiori* it differs from the floristic climax. It is only an evolved stage of the series, useful for determining the direction of the progression.'[16]

In this type, trees are low (20–30 ft., 6–9 m. maximum) and may be widely scattered; acacias are very prominent, widely and pretty evenly spaced in consequence of the wide radius of the roots, which ensures each tree its own little territory. Euphorbias are also conspicuous, sometimes locally dominant and attaining the size of small trees. The Indian wild date, *Phoenix sylvestris*, is common, especially in damper depressions; its fruit is far inferior to that of the true date-palm (*P. dactylifera*) and is rarely used directly as food, though a thick molasses-like gur can be got by tapping the tree from an incision into a pot (still used to ferment for *todi* in some states).

There are patches of taller and fairly close woodland in locally favoured areas, but the general effect is depressing, and well depicted by Aldous Huxley:

> 'Once in every ten or twenty yards, some grey-green plant, deep-rooted, and too thorny for even camels to eat, tenaciously and with a kind of desperate vegetable ferocity struggles for life. And at longer intervals, draining the moisture of a rood of land, there rise, here and there, the little stunted trees of the desert. From close at hand the sparseness of their distantly scattered growth is manifest. But seen in depth down the long perspective of receding distance, they seem – like the in fact remotely scattered stars of the Milky Way – numerous and densely packed. Close at hand the desert is only rarely flecked by shade; but the further distances seem closed with a dense dark growth of trees. The foreground is always desert, but on every horizon there is the semblance of shadowy forests. The train rolls on, and the forests remain for ever on the horizon; around one is always and only the desert.'[17]

This admirable passage was written of Rajasthan, but it applies to much of the Indus Plains (and of Australia), and, with larger trees and a less dead foreground, to vast areas of those of the Ganga and the Peninsula.

---

[16] Legris, *op. cit.* 258–84, gives a most interesting account of some of the detailed variants; the quotation is at 258–9.

[17] *Jesting Pilate* (1927 ed.) 71–72; quoted by courtesy of Messrs Chatto & Windus.

In many areas deterioration continues through grazing by cattle and browsing by goats, and this type is more important as a source of fuel and fodder than of timber. Khair (*Acacia catechu*), however, which sometimes forms fairly dense closed stands over considerable areas, is used for carts, tool handles and so on, and also, more importantly, for tan-stuffs and *cutch*, a brown or yellow-orange dye for sails, cordage and nets, canvas bags, and in Burma for the robes of the Buddhist monks. Another product of this tree is *kath*, mixed with lime, betel-vine leaves, and areca nuts to form the red *pan* chewed all over India. Babul (*A. arabica*) is perhaps more common than khair in the northwestern lowlands, and has similar uses.

[2L. *Dichanthium-Cenchrus grassland*.] As noted above, this grassland is found also over large areas with more humid climate and has not been distinguished from 1R on Fig. 3.3. Most of the species are erect grasses 3–5 ft. high; it covers a very wide range of climates and soils.

[2M. *Sehima-Dichanthium grassland*.] This is the most typical grassland of the Deccan, at its best on well-drained *regur* or black soil sites. It is seral to the tropical dry deciduous forest; many of its grasses are excellent as fodder, but it is easily degraded into poorer associations with *Aristida* and *Cymbopogon* spp.

[2N. *Bothriochloa grassland*.] This is a very localized type, found in irrigated paddy lands east of Poona, on immature black soils. The dominant grass is the sweet-scented purple-headed kanker (*Bothriochloa odorata*), which is unpalatable to cattle but used for thatching.

Other Edaphic Types. As in the moist tropical zone, there is a great variety of minor types, both strictly edaphic and what Puri terms subsidiary edaphic, that is edaphic variations within a climax type. These include riverain woodlands or gallery forest, a great variety of more or less open and often thorny scrub forests, dune and saline vegetation.

In the north, the khair-sissoo riverain association extends into these drier areas and may be seral to the tamarisk–poplar association which occupies similar soils. Inundation babul (*Acacia arabica*) occupies floodplains in central India and the northern Deccan; where flooding lasts for six weeks or so, babul may form pure stands up to 40–50 ft. (12–15 m.) high, with some *Populus euphratica*. The dry stiff alluvial clays of the Gonda–Bahraich area in Uttar Pradesh are dominated by *Aegle marmelos*, a tree used as it were mainly for by-products rather than timber – the pulpy rind-fruit for beverages and drugs, the seeds for pill-boxes and necklaces.[18] In the upper Gangetic plains, recent clayey alluvium with high salinity is occupied by scrub of coarse halophytic grasses and scattered acacias and wild dates. Dry bamboo brake, dominated by *Dendrocalamus strictus*, occurs on the dry hillsides and sandy or gravelly alluvium of the Siwaliks.

Puri's somewhat arid floristic lists may be supplemented from Legris, who traces the very interesting transition from fairly dense but low *Anogeissus*

[18] There is a wealth of such detail, impossible to give consistently here, in *The Wealth of India* (Council of Scientific and Industrial Research, New Delhi, 1948—).

pendula forest on the Aravallis, through the very open *Prosopis spicigera* belt east of the Aravallis from Kutch to the Punjab, to the desert of the Thar. The area of the Thar and middle Indus was certainly more wooded in protohistoric and early historic times (this may have a bearing on the Indus Civilization), but it has been and still is ravaged both by overgrazing, especially of goats, and a desperate search for fuel. Now shrubs and trees are absent; plants have a bushy or tussocky habit, scattered tussocks ensuring a more complete distribution of the scanty soil moisture, and are marked by such xerophytic adaptations as pilosity and the disappearance of leaves; in some places edible herbs and grasses can only survive under the protection of spiny bushes. There are tracts of pseudosteppe where grasses may reach 6 ft. high and serve to stabilize the sand; but in some cases even the tussocks of *Calligonum* are uprooted for fuel by the village women, and here fixed dunes may become mobile once more. In the *Prosopis* belt there is an interesting type of 'forest farming': individual trees are carefully conserved and pruned and may reach 50 ft. (15 m.); millets, mustard, and where possible irrigated wheat are grown in their shade. *Prosopis juliflora*, however, introduced to reclaim the dunes, invades such cultivable land as there is.[19]

Montane subtropical and temperate types: (a) Southern

The tropical formations cover almost all extra-Himalayan India where forests exist; the subtropical and temperate types, however, occur in two widely separated areas: the Nilgiris and Anaimalai–Palani Hills in the extreme south, and the Himalayan and Assamese mountains in the north. Although the Nilgiri flora shows marked affinities, as yet unexplained, with that of Assam and Manipur,[20] it seems simpler to depart from the Champion–Puri sequence and to treat the two areas separately.

3A. *Wet hill forest (southern)*. Owing to the restricted area of the southern hills, the subtropical zone is difficult to distinguish from the clearly differentiated tropical rain-forest below and the temperate forest above. It occurs at 3,500–5,000 ft. (1,070–1,525 m.) on the Nilgiris and Palanis, and is described as essentially a 'stunted rain-forest', not so luxuriant as the true tropical evergreen. Sub-types occur on the higher parts of the Western Ghats and the summits of the Satpura and Maikal Hills, and perhaps as far away as Mount Abu in the Aravallis; but in these localities the forests have been so much reduced and changed that it is difficult to trace connections.

[3D. *Subtropical hill savannah, Cymbopogon type*.] This type has a very wide range, from the Aravallis to the Nilgiris, with local variations both seral to wet hill forest in regressional sub-types. The dominant is usually *Cymbopogon martini*, which is of poor grazing value, but there are scattered stands of the more useful *Themeda* spp. In some places very degraded grasslands are dominated by

[19] Legris, *op. cit.* 270–9.
[20] Calder, *op. cit.* 87; *Imperial Gaz.*, I, 188.

xerophytic *Aristida* spp., and this is especially marked in the more northerly extensions on the hills of central India.

4A. *Wet temperate forest (southern)*. This occurs above 5,000 ft. on the Nilgiris, Anaimalais and Palanis, with rainfall of 60–250 in. (1,524–6,350 mm.) or more and monthly mean minima of about 45–55°F., maxima of 60–75° (7–13 and 16–24°C.). The forests (*sholas*) are found as a rule in the lower or sheltered aspects of bold open downland, often on the steep sides of V-shaped valleys incised into the hillsides and plateaus; the effect is often that of a rich rolling savannah or parkland with occasional peat-bogs. The forest is climatic but its boundary with grassland is biotic; once the smoother areas have been cleared wind, with fire, is a powerful inhibiting factor. It is dense but rather low (50–60 ft., 15–18 m.) with much undergrowth and many epiphytes, mosses, and ferns; both tropical and temperate elements are found: magnolias, laurels, rhododendrons, planes, elms and *Prunus*. Exotics include cinchona, wattle and eucalypts.

Montane types: (b) Himalayan

In the north the great altitude range of the Himalayas and the higher latitudes (up to 36°N) introduce new climatic and topographic features; the topography is far more fragmented; temperature and aspect, and hence insolation, become of great importance. There is a general distinction between the wetter east and the drier west, the change occurring at about 86–88°E; an outline of the zoning is shown in the tabular statement on page 88.

3A. *Wet hill forest (Himalayan)*. This is a fairly high (70–100 ft., 21–30 m.) and dense forest at 3,000–6,000 ft. on the Himalayan ranges east of 88° E, reaching rather higher levels in Assam. Evergreen oaks and chestnuts predominate, with some ash and beech. Sal may be found in suitable sites at lower levels, probably owing to biotic interference; climbers and epiphytes are common.

3B. *Subtropical pine forest*. This occupies a long belt from 73 to 88° E on the Himalayan slopes, mostly at 3,000–6,000 ft.: patches occur on the higher Khasi and Assam–Burma Hills. The dominant tree is chir or chil (*Pinus roxburghii = longifolia*), forming large pure stands; there is often a grassy floor with bulbous plants and little undergrowth, except for stunted evergreen oaks in wetter areas. Chir is a useful timber for furniture, boxes, building and railway sleepers; resin tapping is important, and there is a potential paper industry from offcuts. In the Khasi Hills and the Assam–Burma border area, the dominant species is *Pinus khasya*, at 4,000–5,000 ft.

3C. *Subtropical dry evergreen forest*. Like the tropical dry evergreen, this occurs in a restricted area, but at the opposite corner of the sub-continent. It is found at 1,500–5,000 ft. on the Himalayan foothills and the Salt Range in Kashmir and West Pakistan, with patches in Baluchistan: rainfall is 20–40 in. (508–1,016 mm.) and about a quarter of this falls in December through March; summers are very hot, and winters cold enough for frosts to be fairly common.

Wild olives (*Olea cuspidata*) are thought to represent climax forests; *Acacia modesta* is also common and seems to be a pioneer species establishing itself on

TABULAR STATEMENT OF HIMALAYAN FOREST ZONATION

W   40–80 in. ⟵————————————86–88° E——————————⟶ 80–100 in. + E
(1,016–2,032 mm.)   (2,032–2,540 mm.)

		Altitude		
		16,000 ft. (4,880 m.)		
			Rhododendrons	
		15,000 (4,570)	plentiful Junipers	
ALPINE	Birch	14,000 (4,270)		ALPINE
	Junipers	13,000 (3,960)		
	Silver Fir			
	Shrubby rhodo-dendrons	12,000 (3,660)		
		11,000 (3,355)	CHIEFLY CONIFERS	
	CONIFERS *Abies pindrowi* 7,500–11,000	10,000 (3,050)	Junipers Rhododendrons, willows	UPPER TEMPERATE
TEMPERATE	*Pinus excelsa* 6,000–10,000 *Cedrus deodara* 6,000–8,500	9,000 (2,745)	Bamboo (*Arundinaria racemosa*)	
	Pinus longifolia 3,000–7,000 Yew, cypress BROAD-LEAVED Oaks spp. 4,000–12,000	8,000 (2,440) 7,000 (2,135)	BROAD-LEAVED Oaks, chestnuts, maples, magnolias, laurels, alders, birches	LOWER TEMPERATE
	Walnuts, elms,	6,000 (1,830)		
	poplars, maples, ... horse-chestnut	5,000 (1,525)		
SUB-TROPICAL AND TROPICAL	*Rhodo. arboreum*	4,000 (1,220) 3,000 (915)	Mixed forests, often evergreen, with moist bamboo	SUB-TROPICAL AND TROPICAL
	Mixed deciduous, sal, dry bamboo (Siwaliks) Riverain, savannah (terai) Dry thorn and scrub (extreme W)	2,000 (610) 1,000 (305)	Sal, mixed deciduous, tropical evergreen, riverain, moist savannah (terai)	

Adapted from Troup's Figs. 46 and 47 in Tansley and Chipp,
'Aims and Methods in the Study of Vegetation'.

open, exposed and skeletal soils. The forest is low and scrubby and has a general resemblance to Mediterranean maquis; though it is a climatic type, grazing and fire are certainly biotic controls over its limits and variations. Considerable tracts are covered by the dwarf creeping palm *Nannorhops*.

[3E. *Subtropical hill savannah, Arundinella type*.] Above 4,500 ft., from the western Himalaya to the Burmese border, grasslands are dominated by various species *Arundinella* and *Themeda*. The Shillong Plateau has considerable stretches of almost treeless grassland, biotically induced, with various species of *Saccharum*, *Themeda* and wild sorghum, as well as the tall *Imperata cylindrica*. Most of the grasses flower at the end of the rains or in the cold weather, and are subject to great fires in the hot weather.

4A. *Moist temperate forest*. This is the most widespread Himalayan type, extending over the whole length of the range in the 40–100-in. rainfall zone. There is a *wet temperate forest* at 6,000–9,500 ft. east of 88° E, a closed forest mainly of evergreen oaks, laurels and chestnuts, with undergrowth often dwarf bamboo, confined to the wetter areas. The moist temperate type ranges from 5,000 to 11,000 ft.; in the more humid east it occupies the outer ranges, and here broad-leaved evergreens are mixed with the dominant conifers, becoming fewer to the west. Aspect is of great importance: 'the conifers tend to avoid hot southern exposures, being there replaced by oak forests.'[21] Pines, cedars, silver firs, spruce are the most important trees, forming high but fairly open forest with shrubby undergrowth including oaks, rhododendrons, laurels and some bamboos. The forests have suffered greatly from fires and from lopping to clear land for grazing. West of 80° E deodar (*Cedrus deodara*) forms large pure stands in the intermediate ranges of moderate rainfall (45–70 in., 1,143–1,778 mm.); its fine, durable wood is much used for construction timber and railway sleepers.

4B. *Dry temperate forest*. In the inner Himalayan ranges, as in Kashmir and northern Sikkim, areas with under 40 in. precipitation (much of it as snow) carry a somewhat open and xerophytic forest. Conifers, including deodars and junipers, predominate, with scattered oak and ash; in places there is a *Quercus-Ilex* community with a shrub layer of plants such as *Daphne*, and a ground layer of various grasses and oak seedlings.

[4L. *Montane temperate grassland*.] At about 6,500 ft. decreasing temperatures bring in a grassland association in which representatives of subtropical genera such as *Arundinella*, *Pennisetum*, *Chryosopogon* and *Dichanthium* are mixed with more temperate forms such as species of *Deyeuxia*, *Stipa*, *Agrostis*, *Danthonia* and *Poa*. Like the alpine grassland higher up, these are used for transhumant herds and flocks; they may owe their preservation from overgrazing and erosion to the simple fact that weather conditions make all the year round grazing impossible; such uninterrupted grazing takes place in all other grasslands, though the proper period would be only three or four months.

Edaphic and Biotic Types. Cypress occurs on dry sites overlying limestone and on steep slopes protected from fire; the undergrowth is xerophytic. Deep moist recent soils may carry a temperate deciduous forest with mixed plane, birch,

---

[21] Champion, *op. cit.* 225.

elm and so on; riverain types include alder forest on new shingle deposits, and *Hippophae* scrub on stream gravels at 7,000–10,000 ft., forming thickets with some poplars and willows. Biotic types include various pine forests and oak scrubs, and *Thach* parkland which is formed by grazing, lopping and burning in oak forests until the undergrowth is replaced by a close sward with scattered trees. Most of these types are widely distributed in suitable sites, and the vegetation mosaic in the topographical conditions of the Himalayas is naturally often very complex; it is impossible in a general review to do justice to its permutations.

5A. *Alpine forest.* The vegetation of the Himalayas from about 9,500 to 11,500–12,000 ft. is largely a dense shrubby forest of silver firs, junipers, pines, birches and rhododendrons, the last growing to over 30 ft. high. Most of the trees are crooked and tend to branch low down on the bole.

[5F. *Alpine grasslands.*] Above 7,000–8,000 ft., the temperate grassland (4L) gradually gives way to pastures dominated by temperate forms such as those mentioned above and species of *Poa*, *Glyceria* and *Festuca*, among other genera. Drier areas, such as parts of Kulu and Kangra, have xerophytic variants which include genera (such as *Themeda*, *Dichanthium*, *Cenchrus*) and even species common in the subtropical and even the dry tropical grasslands. All the alpine grasslands are used for extensive transhumant grazing.

Alpine Edaphic and Biotic Types. Deodar forests seem to be peculiarly and quite permanently adapted to Himalayan floodplains at any altitude between 4,000 and 11,000 ft., while blue pines seem equally at home on the lacustrine Karewas terraces of the Vale of Kashmir. High level blue pine forests occur on moraine and similar loose detrital material, especially where the progression has been set back by new snow or earth slides; they are rather ephemeral forests quickly dispersed by fire. The Alpine forest grades into a low evergreen scrub, and this again, on the drier Tibetan side with under 15 in. (264 mm.) precipitation, into very open xerophytic bush, with willows along the streams. Edaphic factors, including soil moisture from glaciers and periglacial phenomena, may be responsible for tracts of birch–rhododendron and *Pinus excelsa* seral to silver fir–birch, especially on moraines; the climax may be dominated by oaks. Where the forests give way to transhumant pastures, their limits are biotic, and biotic factors are also important in the scrubs.

Bamboos and palms

Two groups of plants are of such peculiar importance in the life of India as to deserve a special note; these are the bamboos and the palms.

The bamboos are of course really grasses; they are found throughout India except in the extra-Peninsular mountains west of the Sutlej. The commonest and most gregarious of the hundred and more species is *Dendrocalamus strictus*, with stems 30–50 ft. high and 1–3 in. diameter. This is an 'all purpose' bamboo: huts and scaffolding, basketry and mats, sticks, furniture, household and agricultural implements; the leaves are used for fodder and the stems and rhizomes are burnt. In wetter Bengal and Assam it is replaced by *D. hamiltonii*, a larger plant used among other things for timber-rafting. Also in Assam is *Melocanna bambusoides*, forming immense thickets like giant hay-fields on abandoned areas of shifting cultivation: this secondary growth is practically impenetrable and vast areas of good forest on the hills of Chittagong and Arakan have been replaced by *Melocanna*. In accessible areas, however, it is exploited as a raw material for paper-making, and is the basis of the East Pakistan paper industry at Karna-phuli. In southern India the thorny *Bambusa arundinacea* is common, often cultivated in magnificent clumps up to 100 ft. (30 m.) high.

In the Shan States and many other parts of southeast Asia, including southern China, bamboo enters into almost everything in daily life, including the soup, and one might almost speak of an essentially bamboo-based culture. Probably no part of India, except the Assamese hills, has such a well-developed 'pure' bamboo culture, but the wide usefulness of the plant is attested by the ubiquity with which it is cultivated in village groves. Its quick regrowth provides an immense resource for the expanding Indian paper industry; a resource, however, which is not inexhaustible and needs proper conservation. A possible future use is as a source of industrial cellulose. The output of bamboos from Indian groves and forests must be reckoned in hundreds of millions of stems yearly.[22]

Of the palms, there are eight wild species of the date (*Phoenix*), as well as the cultivated date which is grown especially in the Punjab and Sind but has nothing like the importance it possesses in southwest Asia. The common wild date (*P. sylvestris*) 'is one of the most conspicuous trees in India. . . . In some regions it is almost the only tree visible . . . on salt lands and about springs in the Deccan, forming a gregarious forest growth.'[23] The stems of the wild date are often tapped for the juice, which is turned into gur or a kind of toddy (cf. above 84).

The coconut (*Cocos nucifera*) is found all round the coasts, but is especially important in Kerala, its greatest concentration, the Cauvery and Godavari deltas, and East Pakistan; and inland, it is widely grown in central Mysore. Its scores of uses are far too many to enumerate, but we may note here that the densest rural populations are found where paddy and coconut are the leading crops, so that not even the village site is unproductive (cf. below, 679). The toddy or Palmyra palm (*Borassus flabellifer*) occurs both wild and planted in most plains regions, especially perhaps in the drier southeastern coastlands, though it is also important in Bihar. On the sandy *teri* tracts of Tirunelveli in the extreme south it forms forests which, while primarily important for tapping, can be managed for timber. Palmyra sap is the chief source of toddy, the only spirituous drink of the rural masses, and with tens of millions of trees scattered over the countryside, liquor control is likely to be difficult. Probably, however,

---

[22] There is a comprehensive view of bamboo and its uses in J. Oliver, 'Bamboo as an economic resource in southern Asia', *Geography*, 41 (1956), 49–56.
[23] J. S. Gamble, *A Manual of Indian Timbers* (2nd ed., 1902), 731.

more is used in the making of gur. An important cultivated palm is the areca (*Areca catechu*), grown in such hot and humid regions as Kerala, Bengal and Assam. The nuts, which hang down in long strings and bunches, are used for necklaces and other ornaments; cut and polished their reticulate convolutions are very handsome. But its most important use is for chewing with lime wrapped in the leaves of the betel vine; this is the *pan* responsible for the great gouts of red saliva which disfigure so many streets and buildings.[24] *Nannorhops*, branched and with a half-creeping habit, covers large areas in the Salt Range, the Kurram valley, and Baluchistan with its matted thickets; the leaf-buds and fruits are edible, the seeds used for rosaries which used to be exported (through the one-time Omani port of Gwadar) to Mecca. In the jungles are many climbing palms (*Calamus* spp.), often thorny, supplying canes and rattans. The estuarine *Nipa fruticans* has already been mentioned.

Nearly all the palms are valuable sources of matting and thatch; many can be used for light constructions, house-posts, water-troughs, and so on; and while coir, from the coconut, is the best-known palm fibre, it is far from being the only one. The sheaths of the leaves, like those of bamboo stems, are used as a wrapping material. In earlier cultures palm leaves were used as a writing surface, especially those of areca and palmyra. Most important for this purpose was the Talipot (*Corypha umbraculifera*), the largest of Indian palms, sometimes over 100 ft. high. It is common in Kerala and Kanara, planted in Bengal. The leaves, often 10 ft. in diameter, are used as mats, fans and umbrellas. This is indeed one of the most magnificent of tropical trees.

Importance of the forest cover; climate and erosion

Much has been written in India of the direct climatic influence of forests, and they are of vital importance in increasing the effectiveness of precipitation by checking run-off, maintaining the water-table, and increasing humidity by transpiration. The problem of rehabilitating India's forests, which in most of the more accessible areas have been virtually ruined, is extremely serious.[25] In the early 19th century the increasing demands of the towns, and later of the railways and of the growing population for arable land, led to a very rapid deforestation: the Company's governments seemed simply unaware that a problem existed – there was obviously a great deal of jungle. . . . The first (ineffectual) step towards conservation was made in 1855, and in 1878 a Forest Act set out the general policy of reservation and protection. This was to assure the timber supply

---

[24] 'Betel-nut' is a misnomer. *Pan* has astringent qualities and its chewing, in moderation, is probably mildly beneficial. It is not unpalatable, tasting rather like tooth-paste, but very salivatory, and thus may be a source of acute embarrassment to the polite Westerner, whether the disposal problem be his own or another's. Only when chewed with tobacco, as in some areas, is it clearly a carcinogen.

[25] Sir H. Glover, *Erosion in the Punjab* (Govt of Punjab, Lahore, 1946); R. M. Gorrie, 'Countering desiccation in the Punjab', *GR* 38 (1948), 30–40; A. P. F. Hamilton, 'Siwalik erosion', *Himalayan Jnl* 7 (1935), 87–102.

– still very low per capita – as well as for catchment protection. Despite the efforts of the Indian Forest Service, however, deterioration can scarcely be said to have been kept within bounds, in face of the continuous population increase.

Erosion is severe in almost all States, and it has been conservatively estimated that some 150,000,000 acres (60,700,000 ha.) are affected more or less seriously. In the Punjab Siwaliks, indiscriminate lumbering and charcoal burning, over-grazing (especially by goats), and annual fires produced conditions in which often torrential rains gouged out ravines hundreds of feet deep, and large areas in the plains were ruined by sandy outwash, changes in stream-courses, and a falling water-table as seepage from the hills diminished (Fig. 18.1). Progress has now been made both in checking erosion and in reclamation; farther east the Siwalik forests in Uttar Pradesh are less damaged, and, despite recent inroads, the forests of Nepal are likely to remain a protection for some considerable time.

In the wetter and less-populated eastern Himalaya and the Assam–Burma Hills erosion is not so spectacular, but a new factor is introduced by *jhuming*, the shifting agriculture of the hillmen, also widespread in the hillier parts of central and Peninsular India. The more valuable deciduous monsoon forests are more affected than the rain-forests, and as it is generally easier to clear new forest (which is more fertile and produces more ash) than to return to old ground, large areas become covered with secondary growth, usually dense and useless even for grazing: bracken, the tangled bush *Eupatorium odoratum*, dense thorny thickets of *Lantana*, bamboo brakes. While it is now recognized that *jhuming* is not so black as it was once painted, it does require careful regulation, difficult to enforce, if it is not to lead to serious erosion and forest deterioration. With increasing population and official encouragement, the tribes may change to settled agricul-ture, but for this they must have land and this means a demand for opening forest reserves.

Throughout central and southern India forest control is rendered extremely difficult by shifting cultivation, the complex intermingling of forest, often poor and open, with village lands, and immemorial rights of grazing, lopping and collecting all sorts of minor products. Hence much land once decently wooded has now become a mere scrubby waste, water-tables have been lowered, sheet-erosion is very prevalent. Spectacular gully-erosion has formed badland belts along the Yamuna, the Chambal and the edges of the Punjab doabs. Contour-bunding, afforestation, excluding of grazing (leading to dense grass cover which can be *cut* for fodder), the introduction of the *kudzu* bush as a soil-binder and for fodder, have produced some effect; but much remains to be done.

The importance of the close linkage of grazing, fuel and manure problems cannot be overemphasized. There is a vicious circle: lack of firewood in the all but treeless plains enforces the use of cattle-dung as fuel instead of manure; grazing areas are extremely limited and the pressure of the cattle population on scraps of village waste inhibits forest growth. To replace cow-dung by wood fuel would call for nearly 25,000,000 acres (10,000,000 ha.) of quick-growing plantations on a 10-year rotation: a theoretical solution virtually impossible to realize.[26] The use of cow-dung to produce domestic gas, retaining the sludge as manure, may in time provide a way out (cf. below, 265, 291).

Ecology of the plains

As a coda to this discussion we may take the plains of Uttar Pradesh as a sample of the present ecology of a densely-settled area.[27] It was originally densely forested: in the 16th–17th centuries, wild elephants, buffaloes, bison, rhinoceros, lions and tigers were hunted in the Ganga–Yamuna doab. Some of these animals have disappeared, such as the bison, the rhinoceros (surviving under protection, in Assam), and the lion, whose last Indian home is the Gir sanctuary in Kathiawad. The rest have been enormously reduced in numbers, but with fewer predators and food-competitors wild pigs, small deer, rodents, and monkeys (these with a certain religious sanction) have improved at least their relative position; and all are highly destructive to crops.

Away from the terai and the riverain strips of khair, sissoo, and tamarind, very little woodland survives. There are patches, partly planted, of useful trees, dhak (*Butea frondosa*), mahua, and nim (*Melia indica*); the first is more durable in water than out of it, and is used for well-piling, water-coops, and so on; nim is a sacred tree, used for images as well as ordinary furniture and tools, with a variety of pharmacological uses. But the commonest tree, at least in the west, is babul. This acacia is not palatable to cattle, but its seeds are spread by sheep and goats, and it is more likely to expand than to contract as a result of grazing. Another plant highly resistant to cattle is *Zizyphus* spp., which forms dense masses of thorn-bush. Along with deforestation there go lessened soil-humidity and, owing to loss of transpiration, micro-climatological desiccation. Such secondary wild or waste vegetation as can exist is thus markedly xerophytic, such as the 'dry meadow' of western Uttar Pradesh, which with overgrazing breaks down to coarse tussocks, useless annual grasses, and a few rosette-plants.

A different type of ecological change is the provision of a free field for indigenous or introduced pest plants. The coarse *kans* grass, particularly prolific on the borders of Uttar and Madhya Pradesh, seizes upon fallow and may be so densely matted as to inhibit ploughing, though after a cycle of 10 to 15 years it dies away and the land can be reclaimed. In Bengal the water-hyacinth, introduced as an ornamental pond-plant, has completely blocked scores or even hundreds of miles of minor streams, dislocating the drainage, and it may even overrun flooded paddy fields; and its possible economic uses are a poor return for the difficulty of holding it within bounds.

Mukerjee sums up:

[26] For the interesting calculation, see Legris, *op. cit.* 337.
[27] Based on R. K. Mukerjee, *The Regional Balance of Man* (Madras, 1938), Chs VI and VII. There are many thumb-nail sketches in the Gazetteers.

'. . . the vegetation is now rather delicately balanced against man at about the dry grass-land or the thorn-scrub stage. The soil over most of the Indo-Gangetic plain seems to be supporting about all the human and bovine life that is possible under existing methods of exploitation. . . . Relaxation of pressure immediately results in a movement of vegetation towards the climax. But no relaxation is possible under present conditions. Dry grass-land and thorn-scrub formations remain practically stationary.'

And if, as he thought, the plains were demographically saturated when he wrote, they are super-saturated now. The picture is depressing.

II. SOILS

Introduction

In a general view of the soils geography of a large region such as the Indian sub-continent, it is wholly proper to consider first and even mainly the broad pattern of soil orders and sub-orders largely related by pedologists to macro-regional and regional complexes of climate and vegetation, slope and regolith. Some more detailed pedological surveys will be discussed in this chapter, for their value in critical appraisal of the broader classifications discussed, but as in the earlier editions of this book the regional chapters will be the main recipients for some of the myriad local names for soils and the shrewd empirical accounts of their differential productivity described in the District Gazetteers and in the Settlement Reports assessing the land revenue for a certain period for each District. In many places there is nothing to replace these fascinating accounts for intimate local detail, based in close observation through centuries of intensive farming.[28]

Up to the 1930s – and not uncommonly since – the traditional classification of the soils was in four main categories: alluvium, regur (black cotton soils), red soils and laterite. Alluvium was distinguished according to the main rivers depositing it, along with coastal alluvium, while there was a useful recognition of calcareous soils, soils including a concretionary layer a few inches deep and saline soils.

In 1932 came Z. J. Schokalskaya's gallant but premature effort to synthesize existing knowledge in the framework of Russian pedological principles. The key to Fig. 3.4 is sufficient indication of her lines of thought. While there were inevitably grave flaws in her interpretation, such as the wide area of 'tropical and sub-tropical dry steppe on older alluvium and on hard rocks' from the Bastar highlands to the Maikal hills, it was a remarkable achievement for a

---

[28] V. L. S. P. Rao, 'A note on soil classification', *Bombay Geog. Mag.* 4/1 (1956), 21–25 contains an interesting table comparing Revenue classification ('local classification') with laboratory classifications based on mechanical analysis of top-soils.

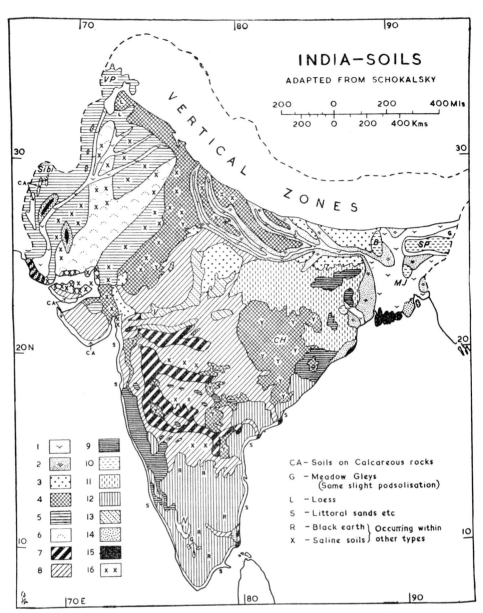

INDIA–SOILS

ADAPTED FROM SCHOKALSKY

FIG 3.4 SOIL TYPES. Adapted from Schokalskaya. 1, alluvial, traces of bog process, on newer alluvium; 2, meadow type on older alluvium; 3, prairie type; 4, tropical and sub-trop. dry steppe on older alluvium and hard rocks (Y = yellow soils); 5, serozems, often saline, some loess; 6, sandy semi-desert serozems; 7, deep regur; 8, medium-light black soils (incl. re-deposited regur in valleys); 9, laterite (high and low) and some higher lateritics; 10, lateritic; 11, sub-trop. red, less leached; 12, trop. red; 13, brown under deciduous forest, slightly or not leached; 14, swamp, peat-bog, and muck; 15, solonchaks; 16, solonetz. B, Barind; CH, Chhattisgarh; MJ, Madhupur Jungle; N, Nilgiris; SP, Shillong Plateau; V. Vindhyan Hills; VP, Vale of Peshawar.

scholar working abroad, and still stimulating today, despite the changes in pedological science in the generation since she wrote.

The Soil Survey of India was set up in 1956, and it has done a great deal of useful work. The large contiguous tracts for which soil surveys have been completed are some of the main river valley project areas such as the Damodar basin and the Hirakud command area. Other areas have been surveyed, but they tend to be in small scattered plots, apparently selected haphazard – but not at random in the statistical sense – or for convenience in access. Many of the studies also suffer from the drawback that they are excessively purist in approach, selecting mainly, or even exclusively, soil borings for profile study which are 'natural' or as little as possible affected by human activity, and avoiding say borings from paddy fields. In recent years, however, there are moves towards a less selective and purist approach, in which the mapping of soil erosion, for instance, is regarded as an integral part of general soil survey, and not something that belongs to a separate department, though soil conservation is in fact handled by a separate government organization.

It is significant that the soil map in the 1957 Preliminary Hindi Edition of the National Atlas of India is simpler and less ambitious than is Schokalskaya's map, though if the time had been ripe for an advance on her techniques this would surely have been attempted; however, it adds indications of soil texture (in over-printed colour screens) and maps the wide areas subject to accelerated soil erosion of varying severity, notably in problem areas now subject to soil conservation measures such as the Chambal valley and the Siwalik Hills. Here we have generalized from these and other sources on a rough working map, Fig. 3.5, to assist the following discussion; soil texture is treated in an expanded caption opposite, and in the text. While it would have been simpler and far safer to accompany these maps with an empirical description of the soil distribution patterns, an attempt will be made in the following pages to interpret the areal patterns of the National Atlas soils map in the light of modern soil classifications, notably the United States Department of Agriculture (USDA) 7th Approximation of 1960, and the attempt in 1962 to establish an internationally acceptable classification of the soils of southeast Asia by Moormann and Dudal of FAO. The writer has found that, working from all available material, Indian soils agree broadly with these.

The sources just cited are studies in pedological taxonomy, whereas soils geography is properly a correlative study of the areal distribution patterns of soils. While it would be as premature to attempt a soils geography of the sub-continent today as was Schokalskaya's pioneer pedological study in 1932, some skeletal geographical analysis will be offered. In particular an attempt will be made to complement the National Atlas soils map – interpreted thus at hazard in the light of modern sources – by some local studies illustrating the gain in understanding if one can gain detailed knowledge of repetitive soil patterns within soil macro-regions (corresponding to soil orders and sub-orders). These

studies will be approached from the point of view of Milne's catenary concept.[29]
By implication, the catenary concept offers an opportunity for reassessment of
major soil regions by building up inductively from numerous catenary cross-
sections. This is at least an alternative or complementary method pending the
detailed soil mapping of the whole land surface.

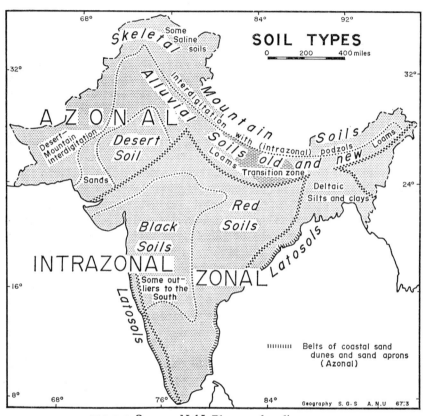

FIG 3.5 *Sources: NAI*, Pl. 10 and earlier maps.

[29] A. G. Milne, *A Provisional Soil Map of East Africa with Explanatory Memoir*, Amani
Memoirs, East Africa Agricultural Research Station, 1936. See *GR* 26 (1936), 522–3.
Milne pointed out from East Africa repetitive patterns which may be studied for instance
by following the sequence of soils from the break of slope between say a plateau of red
tropical soil (to use a neutral and empirical term meantime) and the steep slope of a valley,
often crowned by a laterite cornice, which then becomes less steep after the fashion of a
hanging chain or rope. The only example found in the literature for India and Pakistan
so far has been a comparative study of a long forested tract with a cultivated alluvial tract
west of Kanpur: A. N. Pathak, Harishanker and P. K. Mukherjee, *Jnl of Soil & Water
Conservation in India*, Hazaribagh, 10/1–2 (1962), 7–65 (hereafter cited as *Jnl Soil & Water
Cons.*).

FIG 3.5 SOIL TYPES AND TEXTURE. These Soil Type zones of course include intricate inter-digitation of soil type and also of soil texture. Some examples are given on pp. 108–13. Meantime some regional generalizations about soil texture may be useful, bearing in mind, however, that in detail complex inter-digitation must again be expected.

Mountain (Skeletal) Soils naturally vary greatly with the local rocks, and from the stony sandy hillfoot fans and slope colluvium of the Northwestern Hills or the Aravallis to a more clayey product of mass-movement in the humid south and east of the Himalayas and in Assam.

The Alluvium-based Soils of the Indus–Ganga–Brahmaputra plains, the East Coast deltas and the smaller stretches of floodplain, terrace and deltaic and lagoon alluvium of the rest of Peninsular India vary greatly, in depth and on the present surface, with the alternation of deposition conditions between coarser and finer alluvium and as between older and very recent alluvium. But there is much sandy soil, coarser or finer, in the Lower Indus plains, and rather more loams and clay loams in Punjab and the western Ganga plains; the loams increase and the sands decrease in the central Ganga plains. West of the Transition Zone shown, there is much calcareous *kankar* pan, while irrigation in recent generations has brought waterlogging and saline encrustation to many of the heavier soils in relatively low-lying areas, subject to seepage from canals and lacking in adequate drainage ditches and canals. Farther east in the Ganga–Brahmaputra plains, in more humid atmospheric and soil climates, textural sequences are finer throughout, from loams to very fine silty clays, with some lateritization; and throughout the vast alluvial plains, 'coarse' alluvium has quite a local connotation, much coarser where a major river emerges from the mountain arcs or from the Deccan plateau, finer out into the plain, and more so in the Bengal (and East Coast) deltas. Old alluvium in the Bengal delta and in humid coastal tracts has much lateritic clay.

The Black Soils have the predominantly clay character associated with the soil cracking and 'self-ploughing' of the hot dry weather and the viscous to glutinous stickiness of the west monsoon period. They are less viscous in hillfoot areas with an admixture of slope collumium, and in the redeposited alluvial black soils of river terraces and floodplains.

The Red Soils have mainly a sandy to loamy texture, with rather gravelly sands on upper slopes, then sandy soils, then deeper loamy soils on lower slopes, and loams or sometimes rather clayey soils on the valley bottoms. River terraces and floodplains, and deltas large and small, bring inter-digitation with the alluvium-based soils noted above, and sensitively mapped by Simkins (*op. cit.* p. 693). Within the great Red Soil zone of mainly Peninsular India, there are also the clays of the true laterites – the high laterites of the summit planes of the Western Ghats and of some plateau areas like that near Bidar in northeastern Mysore, and low laterites like those originally described by Buchanan in Kerala or on the low lava ridges running parallel to the coast south of Bombay. There are also a number of indeterminate red, yellowish and whitish clay soils, particularly in the perhumid region of Southwest India discussed in the text in relation to possible identification of the soil type as a latosol.

99

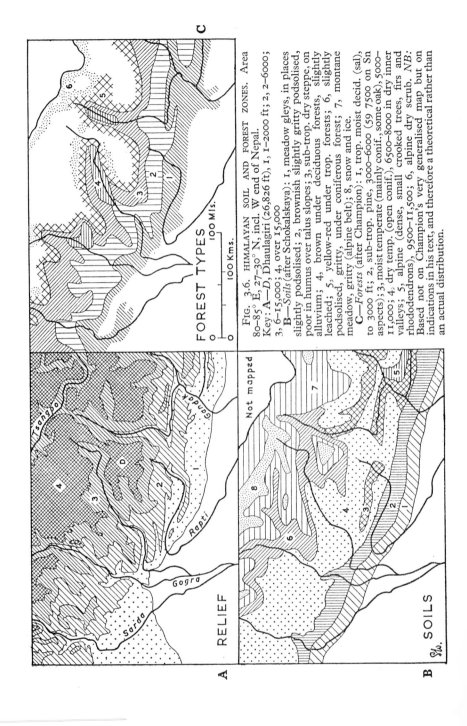

FIG. 3.6. HIMALAYAN SOIL AND FOREST ZONES. Area 80–85° E, 27–30° N, incl. W end of Nepal. Key: A–D, Dhaulagiri (26,826 ft), 1, 1–2000 ft; 2, 2–6000; 3, 6–15,000; 4, over 15,000

B—*Soils* (after Schokalskaya): 1, meadow gleys, in places slightly podsolised; 2, brownish slightly gritty podsolised, poor in humus over talus slopes; 3, sub-trop. dry steppe, on alluvium; 4, brown under deciduous forests, slightly leached; 5, yellow-red under trop. forests; 6, slightly podsolised, gritty, under coniferous forest; 7, montane meadow, gritty (alpine belt); 8, snow and ice.

C—*Forests* (after Champion): 1, trop. moist decid. (sal), to 3000 ft; 2, sub-trop. pine, 3000–6000 (59 7500 on Sn aspects) 3, moist temperate (mainly conif., some oak), 5000–11,000; 4, dry temp. (open conif.), 6500–8000 in dry inner valleys; 5, alpine (dense, small crooked trees, firs and rhododendrons), 9500–11,500; 6, alpine dry scrub. *NB*: Based not on Champion's very generalised map but on indications in his text, and therefore a theoretical rather than an actual distribution.

The soils map in the National Atlas, a critique and synthesis

Here we shall review the National Atlas map of soils in the light of the older pedological work of Schokalskaya as well as the more recent work of Moormann and Dudal and the United States Department of Agriculture.

The National Atlas has two zonal soils I, laterite soil and II, red soil. The laterite soil appears to be Buchanan's laterite[30] rather than a true soil profile – i.e. an often rather porous clay, dominantly hydroxides of iron and aluminium, hardening to brick-like consistency on exposure to the weather. The distribution is mainly in the Western Ghats and Cardamoms; apparently high-lying in the northern half of the Eastern Ghats and on the eastern margins of the Chota Nagpur plateau, which also has a patch of laterite farther west in the Hazaribagh Range; in Assam; in a few patches round Kathiawad; and in two areas in the centre of the Peninsula, north of Bangalore and west of Hyderabad. These occurrences differ widely in their present climate–vegetation complexes; many lack a complete soil profile, the laterite being found (often quarried) near the surface. The Schokalskaya–Spate map specifically includes high and low laterites, and the areal distribution is somewhat different, but similar arguments seem to apply. It seems almost inevitable that the 'laterite soils' as mapped should be regarded as the laterite horizons of truncated soil profiles, partly denuded by erosion on uplift, and fossils or relics of a past climate–vegetation-soil complex including deep soil profiles with a laterite horizon. In places, however, they appear to be alluvial or redeposited. If protected from erosion these soils are far from worthless, but the humus content is confined to a shallow top layer, as the forest trees are shallow rooted: their removal endangers the humus content and regeneration is difficult.[31]

The Red Soils of the National Atlas map are as much of an omnibus category as ever, comparable with the hedging bet of the 'lateritic soils' classification of some years ago. The Schokalskaya–Spate map does attempt to break up this very large area into tropical red soils, sub-tropical red – less leached – soils, sub-tropical and tropical dry steppe soils on hard rocks, with much yellow soil, and once again, 'lateritic soil'. In the earlier editions of this book attention was drawn to the improbability of the large tract of sub-tropical steppe soils in the northeast of the Peninsula, and it is significant that the editor of the National Atlas has judged that there was insufficient detailed knowledge to justify any subdivision. Do the more modern classifications, approaching through soil profile analysis, offer any help? It seems likely that between the Western Ghats and the sea there may lie a coastal belt of humid climates, natural vegetation

[30] F. Buchanan, *A Journey from Madras through the Countries of Mysore Canara and Malabar*, 1807; cf. C. G. Stephens, 'Laterite at the type locality, Angadipuram, Kerala, India', *Jnl Soil Sci.* 12 (1963), 214–17.

[31] G. Aubert, 'Soil with ferruginous or ferralitic crusts of tropical regions', *Soil Science*, 95 (1963), 235–42; M. N. Ramasawamy and D. R. Gouda, 'The humus content of lateritic soils in the tropical evergreen forests of Mysore', *Indian Forester*, Dehra Dun, 82/8 (1956) 395–8.

approaching rain-forest, and of dark red and reddish brown latosols or locally of red-yellow latosols in the classification of Moormann and Dudal. This was of course evolved for southeast Asia, and one can only argue from climatic and biogeographic analogues. Many of the soil profiles one sees in the field, in recent roadside cuttings and the like, seem to correspond well with their description of deeply weathered and leached soils, with a low content of primary minerals and the clay fraction dominated by kaolinite and sesquioxides, the profile generally deep and uniform with little horizon differentiation. The surface layers are of low organic content and the soils are fairly acid (about 4·5–6·5). It is notable, and confusing, that Buchanan's laterite is not regarded as a marked feature of these soils. It is true that in the hot humid zones of south and southeast Asia, occurrences of Buchanan's laterite, indeed of any well-marked C horizon, are surprisingly rare in the field if one approaches field exposures without any preconceived ideas on pedogenesis. But the attachment of the name latosol to soils in which laterite proper seldom occurs is unfortunate; the only justification seems to be that within the same general area there do occur many of the known occurrences of laterite proper, including that originally observed by Buchanan. But presumably their origin lies either with a different climate–vegetation complex or with a different parent material in solid rock or regolith (maybe with a different *soil* climate).

In the USDA 7th Approximation these soils would be classed as oxisols (soils dominated by oxides), of the sub-order udox (an oxide soil in a humid climate); bizarre as the vocabulary is at first, one can see by comparison with Moormann and Dudal the advantages of a fresh approach, empirical and descriptive rather than prematurely genetic in concept.[32] If Buchanan's laterite does not occur in the latosols or oxisols, where does it belong? In the scheme of Moormann and Dudal laterite proper, and the deep white or whitish-grey B horizon often streaked horizontally or reticulated horizontally and vertically by red iron-rich bands, belong to the red-yellow podsolic soils or the grey podsolic soils. In the USDA classification, these correspond to the ultisol order (ultimate soils), mainly in the sub-order ochrult (pale or light-coloured ultisols), but some with some characteristics of oxisols (see above) and some of alfisols (soils dominated by iron and aluminium derivatives). These soils have a humiferous A_1 horizon, a somewhat paler and more leached A_2 horizon, and normally 1–2 m. of pale, blocky Bt horizon with clay coatings on the peds, and low SiO_2/R_2O_3 or SiO_2/Al_2O_3 ratios (i.e. a very heavily leached horizon under conditions of very effective chemical weathering resulting in the leaching out of silicates and rutiles). There are often one or more C horizons of red Buchanan's laterite, rich in iron and aluminium oxides (Fe_2O_3 or Al_2O_3).

[32] Soil Conservation Service, U.S. Department of Agriculture, *Soil Classification: a Comprehensive System*, 7th Approximation, Washington, 1960. See Addendum for a note of the derivations of the mainly classically-based technical vocabulary suggested: this is an interesting nomenclature even if some of the names come strangely to the eye and tongue.

These soils occur over a very wide range of climate from about 40 in. (1,016 mm.) mean annual rainfall (about 60 in. (1,524 mm.) in equatorial and sub-equatorial latitudes) upwards to very wet climates indeed. They seem to form especially on acid to medium-basic parent material, whether bedrock or regolith, and this may account for their inter-digitation with the latosols or oxisols, and they may in fact paradoxically contribute the true laterite to the latosol zone. In wetter climates they are deeper and more acid than in the less humid areas. Schokalskaya found only limited evidence of podzolization, in meadow gleys, mainly round the Assam hills, and in the Nilgiris and other high areas in the south. It is possible that considerable parts of peninsular India, mapped as in the Red soil zone, have or originally had what Moormann and Dudal class as Non-calcic Brown Soils – rather shallow kaolin-rich clays under open forest in climates with a severe dry season and under 60 in. mean annual rainfall (perhaps a little less in northern India?). This soil-type is described as usually uncultivated in southeast Asia; in peninsular India it may have been cultivated for millennia and over-cultivated for centuries, and so difficult to identify – but degenerate profiles may be important. Erosion is widespread and remedial measures, while understood, are difficult to put into practice; they may involve treatment of entire catchment areas, closing of grazing lands or expensive works.[33]

The National Atlas map distinguishes two intra-Zonal Soil types – III, Black Soil and IIIA, Podzol Soil. The latter appears to be confined to the lower parts of the Himalayas, neither alluvial like the Vale of Kashmir, saline like some of the intermont basins of northern Kashmir, nor mountain soils like most of the mountain chains. Podzolization is not here regarded as an important pedogenetic process in the plains or in peninsular India, in contrast to the views of Moormann and Dudal.

The Black Soils are mapped as intra-zonal within the Red Soil zone, and noted in the text of the Atlas as mainly on the Deccan traps but also found on gneisses and schists in the Krishna–Tungabhadra basin and south of the Vaigai basin in Madras. By far the largest part of the Black Soils are mapped as clays, but relatively small areas are distinguished as clay loams, loams and sandy loams. The clay loams are mainly in an area marginal to the Black Soils around the upper Narmada and the upper Tapti, while the loams and sandy loams are apparently related to alluvial tracts, though not all actual occurrences of these are mapped. The Schokalskaya–Spate map distinguishes deep *regur* (the indigenous name for black cotton soil) in the western Deccan and in a series of belts about WNW–ESE across the west-central part of the Peninsula. The rest is classed as medium-

---

[33] For illustration of the complexity of the problem see (1) C. S. Pichamathu, *Soil Erosion and its Prevention* (Mysore Govt Dept Bangalore, 1951), a first rate analysis of types, causes and remedies; (2) B. C. Acharya, 'Nature and extent of soil erosion in parts of Kalahandi Dt, Orissa', *GRI* 20 (1958), 93–96, a specific case of soil erosion linked with shifting cultivation; (3) K. Venkoba Rao, 'Need for pasture development in Bellary Dt', *Jnl Soil & Water Cons.* 7/4–5 (1959), 91–98 indicates the effects of closing an area on the regeneration and soil patterns.

light black soils (including re-deposited *regur* in valleys); the occurrences in the southern part of the Peninsula are not mapped. Much of the Vindhya and nearby hills and of the Mahadeo Ranges are mapped as 'brown soils, under deciduous forest, slightly or not leached'; this differentiation seems of value, and might be linked with Moormann and Dudal's (Acid) Brown Forest Soils (in the USDA classification in the order of Inceptisols, i.e. soils in the stage of inception, sub-order ochrept, i.e. pale inceptisols, with some in the order of mollisols, i.e. soft soils).[34] The soils are normally up to 31·5 in. (800 mm.) deep, with a lighter and brighter brown B horizon under a darker A or A_p horizon, and pH values usually over 5 and often over 6 on parent material intermediate between acid and basic rocks. They occur in rainfalls of wide range, from some 24 to 120 in. (610–2,748 mm.), and it may well be that it is soil of this type that one has seen on forested slopes in western Mysore; in fact there may be important occurrences of these forest soils within the Red Soil zone wherever the forest cover is considerable.

Moormann and Dudal term the black soils grumosol (viscous soil); in the USDA classification they fall within the order vertisols (soils which are inverted, in the well-known 'self-ploughing' process of exchange of top-soil and sub-soil through cracking in the dry season, with soil fragments falling from near the surface down the cracks to a depth of one or two metres); the sub-order is normally aquert (vertisols associated with wetting) on flat land, with ustert or dry vertisols on undulating terrain. These soils are the widely known clays, dark brown to black (darker on flat or relatively low-lying areas), usually rather poor in organic matter, often strongly granular, and with an A horizon usually 2–4 in. (5–10 mm.) deep giving way to an AC then a C horizon, the sub-surface horizons often with prismatic pod-like blocks. Clays are generally of the montmorillonite group, strongly swelling and shrinking with changes in moisture content; hence the very marked cracking and fissuring of the dry season already noted. There seems to be a general correlation with rainfall conditions ranging around semi-aridity; grumosol pedogenesis may occur more readily on basic parent rock like the Tertiary basalts of the Deccan, which underlie much the greater part of these soils; considerable tracts are on acid igneous rocks like gneisses, and there the clay minerals differ in detail, while the soils are on the more acid side of the range encountered in general – about 6·0–7·5 on the surface, 7·8–8·5 in depth, but under 7·0 over acid rocks. Naturally a very wide range of conditions is seen in the field, from the special type of alluvium of redeposited *regur* noted in Schokalskaya (and earlier by Simkins, for instance), to the stony *regurs* near the foot of a basalt scarp which are presumably a special case of entisol (recent soil) or inceptisols (soils near the stage of inception) – or mixed soils (category VI in terms of the National Atlas map).

[34] Within these the next smaller category, the great (soil) groups include the eutrochrepts ('fertile' pale inceptisols, i.e. with high base exchange capacity), dystrochrepts ('infertile' pale inceptisols, i.e. with low base exchange capacity) and some ustochrepts ('burnt' pale inceptisols, i.e. in climates with dry hot summers).

The azonal soil types of the National Atlas map are: IV, alluvial soil (new); V, alluvial soil (old); VI, colluvial and skeletal (mixed) soil; VII, coastal soil; VII, saline soil; IX, desert soil and X, mountain soil. As noted earlier, the Atlas maps broad patterns of textural differences; these are very important, here as elsewhere, to the man on the land, and some are noted in our Fig. 3.5 and its caption, and to some extent in the ensuing discussion of inter-digitation of soil types (p. 108). Meantime types IV to X are treated in a different order.

Category VI, the colluvial and skeletal (mixed) soils are clearly very important. Their origin implies a close relation to parent material, in which sense they are azonal, though there may be an intra-zonal element by admixture with the prevailing zonal soil type. The main area of this soil type shown in the National Atlas is in the Wainganga basin in central India, quite conformably with its irregular and undulating topography (see p. 707); but these colluvial soils are of much wider significance, even though they can not be mapped as yet for the whole country. To appreciate their importance one should compare the broad areas of the zonal and intra-zonal types with a relief map say of part of peninsular India, on as large a scale as possible, not smaller than 1:1,000,000, and consider that a belt of colluvial and mixed soil lies along each scarp-foot. Some of these belts may have or have had profiles similar to Moormann and Dudal's (Acid) Brown Forest Soils, discussed earlier. Most of these soils, however, would lie within the Regosols of Moormann and Dudal, in their sub-category of variously textured slope colluvium, mostly sandy loams, clay loams or sandy clay loams, but extending to sandy and gravelly soils, and even stony 'lithosolic regosols'. All these would be entisols (recent soils) in the USDA classification. The discussion of these soils will be taken up again later in the chapter, in relation to the inter-digitation of the several soil types, and the catenary concept.

Category V alluvial (old) soil of the National Atlas is also an important type. It is shown mainly along the northern and southern hillfoot zones of the Ganga and Brahmaputra plains, and along the western margin of the Bengal delta (the eastern margin is in East Pakistan). Comparison with climatic and vegetation maps suggests that there must be major differences in present pedogenetic processes over such a large and diverse area – apart from differences in the parent material provided by the alluvium, like the lime-rich deposits of the Gandak in Uttar Pradesh.[35] In the west, these soils are not shown farther west than the middle of the Ganga–Yamuna doab and the lower Chambal basin, whereas there must be, indeed there are, comparable types even though gradually changing under drier climates, in the Punjab. There are also small but locally important

[35] An area of heavy incidence of goitre is associated with lime-rich alluvium and drinking water, unusually severe for the plains and comparable with isolated populations in limestone mountains. See a series of papers beginning with H. Stott, 'Distribution and causes of endemic goitre in the U.P., Part I', *Indian Jnl Med. Res.* 18 (1930–31), 1059–85. For a study of the effects of irrigation on these soils see R. D. Baksi *et al.*, 'Investigation of the soils of North Bihar and their role in irrigation projects', *Jnl of Soil & Water Cons.* 4/4 (1956), 152–8.

areas of old alluvium on the margins of the east coast deltas, and probably in a few other areas. The Schokalskaya–Spate map is interesting here, for easterly tracts in the Ganga–Brahmaputra plains are shown as meadow type on older alluvium; in Bihar the map shows prairie type soils on these areas though without specific reference to old alluvium, while in Uttar Pradesh and Punjab it shows sub-tropical steppe on older alluvium with saline patches, while the comparable tracts in lower Punjab and Sind are mapped as serozems, often saline with some loess.

Moormann and Dudal note the varying development of horizons, on alluvium from little even of the A_1 or A_p horizons in very well-drained soils, to well-marked A_1 or A_p or even peaty surface horizons where the water table is high. Some old alluvium would come within their category of wind-blown sands, within the regosols, the A horizon being weakly developed or absent (e.g. in shifting dunes) and little or no B horizon, yet there may have been a long period of weathering with the development of strong colouring, marked leaching of carbonates, and even the disappearance of weatherable minerals. This process would presumably vary, being related to the red-yellow podzol soils process in the humid areas, to semi-desert processes, with calcareous concretions (kankar) at some inches' depth, in the drier north and west. It seems likely that some of the older river terraces have developed some Low Humic Gley Soils of Moormann and Dudal (by analogy with their territory). A little-disturbed soil of this type is a grey or greyish-brown hydromorphic soil, the A_1 or A_p horizon not very thick and giving way to a much lighter and distinctly leached A_2 horizon and then to a textural B horizon, alluvial and with a much higher clay content. The B horizon is conspicuously mottled, with a light brownish-grey to light olive grey matrix and weak to moderate subangular blocky structure not necessarily with conspicuous clay coatings round the peds. Some of the mottling may tend towards concretionary laterite on drying, and there may be a C horizon of groundwater laterite, commonly at 3–6 ft. (1–2 m.). It seems likely that much paddy land on river terraces is of this type, altered by cultivation over the centuries. In the USDA classification these are of the order of ultisols (ultimate soils), of the aquult sub-order (hydromorphic ultisols) and great group ochraquult (pale or leached aquults).

Type IV of the National Atlas, alluvial soil (new), corresponds with two types in the Schokalskaya–Spate map – alluvial soils, with traces of bog processes on newer alluvium, and in places swamp, peat-bog and muck soils. Moormann and Dudal note the variation from little or no horizon development to well-marked, even peaty, A horizons, as already noted in relation to older alluvia; they note the well-marked variations in soil texture from sandy to loamy to clayey, which Geddes has shown so evocatively to relate to present and former water-channels wandering across alluvial fan or cone, flood-plain or delta and not only at the surface but also in depth. He notes the variations according to the catchment of the river – dark, relatively heavy clay from calcareous or basaltic hinterlands, whereas if red-yellow or grey podsolic soils predominate in the catchments there may be a much poorer alluvium, often lighter in colour, and with a dominance of 1 : 1 lattice clay.[36] The east coast deltas have often been cited as examples of poorer alluvial soils derived from mainly red-soil hinterlands, though this applies to the Mahanadi and the Cauvery rather than the Godavari and Krishna.

Some of these new alluvial soils are very acid, with pH values sometimes under 2 and commonly 3–4·5 and sometimes with free aluminium and sometimes iron also. Acid soils, at about 4·5–6 are typical, but in contrast some give very basic reactions, as in the areas already noted. In the USDA classification these are all entisols, and they probably cover the gamut of sub-orders, aquents (wet recent soils), psamment (sandy recent soils), ustent (burnt, i.e. dry-climate and especially hot–dry summer recent soils), and udents (humid-climate recent soils).

The Coastal Soils, type VII of the National Atlas, are the littoral sands, etc., of the Schokalskaya–Spate map, Moormann and Dudal's regosols of the wind-blown sand variety, and in the USDA classification are of the order of entisols, mainly of the psamment sub-order. Horizon development may be entirely lacking, or there may be a slight organic-rich A horizon development, possibly at several depths, especially in drier areas; correspondingly in wetter areas older and especially relatively fixed dunes may show some progress towards podzolization, and there is probably similar development, less easily observed, on coastal sand-aprons.

The Saline Soils (National Atlas type VIII) correspond well with the solonchaks of the Schokalskaya–Spate map, except that the latter does not show the saline tracts of northern Kashmir; Schokalskaya's solonetz, however, interestingly if fairly diagrammatically portray the high and growing incidence of saline-crust on heavy-soiled interfluvial hollows associated largely with seepage from irrigation canals and consequent water-logging. The National Atlas category IX, Desert Soils, corresponds in a general way with two types in the Schokalskaya–Spate map, serozems, often saline, with some loess, and sandy semi-desert serozems. The sandy semi-desert serozems envelop the Aravalli ranges, extending to the Rann of Kutch, towards Delhi and north almost to the Salt Range, whereas the National Atlas treats the Aravallis as in the Red Soil zone, southern Punjab as simply alluvium differentiated by texture, and the rest as desert. Here we have lost the analogic guidance of Moormann and Dudal, for there are no deserts in southeast Asia and therefore none in their classification. All these soils, and probably Schokalskaya's solonchaks and solonetz as well, are in the USDA order of aridosols, which name does explain itself; it is too early to try to discuss even generally the sub-orders of orthid (true arid) and argid (arid, with illuvial argillic white clay) and their interesting sub-divisions into great groups according to exchange of horizons, hardness, saltness, etc.

[36] A. Geddes, 'The alluvial morphology of the Indo-Gangetic plain, its mapping and geographical significance', *Trans. Inst. British Geog.* 28 (1960), 253–76; H. Stott, *op. cit.*

Category X of the National Atlas is confined to the Himalaya, where it is broken by small areas of podzols, of alluvium (only in the Vale of Kashmir) and of saline soils in patches in the north of Kashmir. The Schokalskaya–Spate map notes the presence of strong vertical zoning; Moormann and Dudal would treat these as regosols of their second category, variously textured slope colluvium, and some of their skilful generalization about a very varied group has already been noted. Here the vertical zoning from tropical to Alpine and glacial climates would add to the variety. Again these recent soils would be entisols in the USDA classification; one can see the relevance of the sub-order (already noted) and of the great groups distinguished according to relations with cold climate, sand, water, minimal horizon development, agriculture, sod development and the like, but so much work would be needed to apply them to this enormous and complex region that it seems unlikely that we shall ever see this except by example or type study.

The inter-digitation of zonal, intra-zonal and azonal soil types; human interference and soils geography

Even in the preceding discussion it has been explicit or implicit at several points that there is inter-digitation of soil types; obviously some of this is on such an intimate scale that it can best be discussed in a regional context; sometimes, however, it is on such a large scale that it could be shown on a map of India, even on the small scale used in this book, but for the lack of data of comparable nature from all over the sub-continent. Some examples may make the point, and at the same time illustrate some of the biotic influences on soils geography.

The southwest of India, with its long wet season, is perhaps in the latosol zone, but if so acid parent material seems to encourage also deep red-yellow podzols, as on the low plateaus of Kerala and western Mysore. From the high laterite of the Cardamom Hills and the southern part of the Western Ghats westwards down the steep face, lie acid brown forest soils, still partly under rainforest, partly under plantations for tea at high levels, coffee a little lower, and rubber on the lower slopes. Shade trees are left in the coffee and tea gardens, and though clear-felling precedes rubber planting, precautions against soil erosion are taken – terracing fits in with easy tapping – and cover crops under the rubber trees are now common.[37] The low plateaus of Kerala have a good deal of laterite, exposed on the cornices above the valleys, elsewhere with a relatively thin and vulnerable cover of residual podzolic clay, with scrub or grassland, locally forest, and some clearing for tapioca gardens. A valley section or catena in this area shows an increasing depth of slope colluvium below the laterite cornice, with

[37] Farther north, the forests east of the Ghats edge in Satara District have so far proved to protect soils against excessive erosion even in the presence of *kumri* or shifting cultivation; but in the interests of the longevity of the reservoir for the Koyna project (see p. 656), mixed farming with grazing of cattle may be encouraged. M. M. Kibe and N. B. Puranik, 'Note on soil conservation survey for land use planning in Koyna project, Satara, Bombay State', *Jnl Soil & Water Cons.* 6/4 (1958), 176–83.

scrubby grazing and perhaps some tapioca patches – rather liable to soil erosion – and some paddy terraces on the lower, gentler slopes. The river terraces and flood plains have sandy to silty alluvium, and rice terracing and bunding have led to widespread, mainly biotic development of grey paddy soils, with some signs of wetness and mottling. Rather similar development has taken place in the intrinsically rather infertile lagoon alluvia in belts parallel to the coast and the multiple sandbars. The sandbars and sand-dunes show early development of dark A horizons, probably partly biotic, under the coconuts and other orchard trees, and in older dunes some progress towards podzolization, with hard-pan formation. Sand-aprons show very pure sand, perhaps in a field of pineapples, but there may be some groundwater laterite at a foot or two down.

The Red Soil zone as a whole has important but narrow belts of slope colluvium on the lower slopes and on the pediment at the foot of many hundreds of miles of steep scarps in the Western and Eastern Ghats, the Hazaribagh ranges and the scarps bordering the Chota Nagpur plateau and the Damodar rift valley, the Aravallis, and many others. These soils may bear recent additions through accelerated soil erosion higher up, notably associated with overgrazing, though the National Atlas map classifies most of this as moderate rather than severe. There are of course ribbons of alluvium following most major rivers for most of their courses – gorges are the most notable exceptions – and in places with older alluvium on terraces.[38] In places these alluvia include redeposited *regurs*, as in parts at least of the black soils reaching far east near the Godavari and Krishna rivers. The major rivers have considerable alluvial deltas – note the Cauvery, Godavari–Krishna, and Mahanadi, but the last is mapped as dominated by coastal alluvia in the south and by saline swamps in the north; all these deltaic soils have been much altered by paddy cultivation, tending to equate them in a sort of biotic gley soil. Between the major deltas, coastal alluvia including dunes and sand-aprons are important, some altered by casuarina plantations, irrigated for the first few years by shallow *kuchcha* (unlined) wells tapping the water-table in the dunes. The largest single area of moderately severe erosion on these soils is in the Chota Nagpur plateau, partly through the activities of tribal people practising shifting agriculture, partly through overgrazing from settled Hindu villages with rice and millet fields; part of this area has had considerable experience of both problems and successes in soil conservation measures under the Damodar Valley project, including terracing and exclusion of grazing from vulnerable slopes, usually measures involving land consolidation or close co-operation between farmers.

The Black Soils area similarly includes important areas of slope colluvium, bordering the Vindhya–Bhanrer ranges, the Satpura–Mahadeo hills, the

[38] These are well-mapped for Peninsular India in E. Simkins, 'The agricultural geography of the Deccan plateau of India', Supplement to *The Geography Teacher*, n.d., ?1926. See also B. N. Murthy and N. S. Iyengar, 'Estimate of life of reservoirs in first phase of development of Damodar Valley Corporation', *Jnl Soil & Water Cons.* 5/1 (1956), 17–20, and other papers in this journal.

Chandor–Ajanta or Sahyadriparvat ranges (and much of the gently sloping plains fringing the structural valleys of the Narmada and Tapti), as well as the fingers of high plateau extending east along the interfluves from the laterite-capped platforms crowning the northern part of the Western Ghats. These belts are important, for their mixed and immature nature makes them more versatile and in particular more easily irrigable than are the mature grumosols of great flat stretches across the Deccan plateaus. In some places man imitates nature by bringing newly weathered black sand from basalt crags to mix with the silts of small flood-plains, and small dams are also made to trap more silt. The alluvial ribbons of river terraces and flood-plains, again, of redeposited *regur*, are important in varying the picture. Again they are better aquifers than the grumosols proper over solid basalt, they are more irrigable and wells can be dug or bored. The region as a whole has a very high proportion under cultivation, particularly on the black cotton soils proper; accelerated soil erosion is heavy, despite the generally flat character of the land, for the viscous soils of the wet season almost flow, and field runnels are heavily overloaded with eroding soils and roadside ditches contain new miniature deltas after a storm. The table

Sholapur Dt (total rainfall) 23·9 in. (607 mm.) – ground condition	Mean annual runoff as % total rainfall	Mean annual storm rain of 13·7 in. (348 mm.) in 10·6 storm runoffs causing erosion	
		Soil loss	No. of years to erode 7 in. (178 mm.) topsoil
Natural vegetation	4·77	0·53	1,852
Natural vegetation removed	19·75	17·69	57
Shallow cultivation	22·50	24·82	
Rabi cultivation	18·67	34·54	27
Kharif plot with scoop irrigation	9·92	14·75	68
Bajri-tur (kharif)	16·5	23·8	42
Ploughed and harrowed (fallow)	17·12	32·7	40
Ploughed and harrowed (double-length fallow)	17·5	27·4	

Source: M. M. Kibe, 'The role of vegetal cover in Soil Conservation', *Jnl Soil & Water Cons.*, 6/4, July 1958, 160–6.

shows the influence of different vegetation covers. The grumosols have poor engineering qualities, so that soil erosion bunds must have a masonry base, and it is difficult to give them an effective and useful plant cover though some progress has been made; bushes like *Cassia auriculata* (yielding tanning bark) seem to succeed rather than grasses;[39] and even the closing of an area to grazing may bring a cover of scrub, no doubt seral to higher forms.[40]

[39] C. P. Raju et al., 'Bunding in deep black soils of Andhra State', *Jnl Soil & Water Cons.* 4/6 (1956), 143–8, and N. K. Ghumare, 'Studies in the behaviour of contour bunds', ibid., 10/1–2, (1962), 44–64.

[40] G. S. Puri, 'The study of dry scrub vegetation under forest management at Dhond, Poona', *Proc. Nat. Inst. Sci. India*, New Delhi, 24, Part B/3 (1958), 145–9.

The desert and semi-desert soils have their own problems. Much land fringing the heart of the Thar Desert is in fact cultivated for wheat, barley, linseed, etc., at an extensive scale; there seems to be some tendency to over-cultivation and for dunes long fixed to start moving. Severe gullying is developing, extending outward from the steep sides of desert and semi-desert wadis, and associated no doubt with overgrazing. Work in the area has shown how effective even the exclusion of grazing stock can be in rehabilitating the vegetation of a developing badland tract, restoring its water-table and gradually building up its soil status again. Check-dams in major gullies, brush-wood cover to help planted trees to begin growing, and a whole range of conservation measures can be deployed in the worst or most urgent cases.[41] Following treatment, rotational grazing may be possible.

The well-known belt of badlands lying several miles deep on both banks of the lower Chambal, in slightly more humid conditions, can in time be controlled by similar measures, planting fuel wood and grass; but the economics are such that the more urgent task is to protect soils still agriculturally viable on the Malwa plateau.

Even the great alluvial plain of the Indus–Ganga–Brahmaputra contains a surprising element of inter-digitation within it. The old alluvium a few feet higher than the fringes of the Bengal Delta, and in 'islands' within it, is relatively lightly populated and relatively well-wooded, with a relatively infertile residual red-yellow podsolic clay over laterite, which is exposed on the margins as a cornice.[42] The delta contains slight variations in texture, from sandy soils to sandy loams, to loams, to silty clays, and with them variations in soil acidity to some very saline soils – those fringing the seaward edge of the delta uncultivable as yet.[43] Everywhere along the hillfoot, from Assam to the exit of the Ganga from the mountains, hillfoot slope colluvium gives way to coarse hillfoot gravels and major alluvial fans or cones. Farther west, accelerated soil erosion following late 19th-century deforestation of the ill-consolidated sediments of the Siwalik ranges has added a veneer of sandy and gravelly fans spreading even across valuable well-irrigated hillfoot fields. (See also p. 535.) In the great alluvial plains are the alternations of texture according to their recent patterns of

[41] The large literature includes: O. N. Kaul, 'Management of the Chambal ravines in Rajasthan', *Indian Forester*, 88/10 (1962), 725–30; V. Srinivasan, W. C. Bonde and K. G. Tejwani, 'Studies on grasses and their suitability to stabilize and maintain bunds in ravine lands of Gujarat', *Jnl Soil & Water Cons.* 10/1–2 (1962), 72–77, and many other papers in these useful journals.

[42] See S. J. Bhunan, M. Zacharia and F. Rahman, 'Soils of the Khiyar Tract, East Pakistan', *Soil Sci.* 91/5 (1961), 369–74: A. Karim and A. Qasem, 'Study of the soils of Barind Tract, East Pakistan', *Soil Sci.* 91/6 (1961), 406–12; S. Bhattacharya, 'Soil erosion in Santhal Parganas', *GRI* 18/2 (1956), 1–4; Forest Directorate Govt of Bengal: *An Afforestation Scheme for the Laterite Zone of West Bengal* (Calcutta, 1956).

[43] For West Bengal we owe a long series of detailed papers to Professor S. P. Chatterjee and his colleagues; an early example is: S. P. Chatterjee, R. Lahiri, S. Venkatraman and S. Mukherjee, 'Pedogenesis in West Bengal', *GRI* 18/3 (1956), 1–10; the series may be followed in successive volumes of the *Review*.

alluviation,[44] sometimes varying markedly according to the parent material in the river catchment in the Himalaya or the Plateau – e.g. the easily shifted mica-rich deposits of the Kosi, the lime-rich alluvia of the Gandak, and the sandy spread of the Son. The lower Chambal deposits are subject to the five to ten-mile wide belt of notorious badland erosion, now being controlled in a multi-purpose project mainly aimed at soil conservation. In the western half of the Ganga plains and in the Indus plains old alluvium tends first to contain *kankar* (a calcareous concretionary deposit) a few inches down, and farther west to be saline. Seepage from irrigation canals has greatly increased the incidence of waterlogged soils and of saline-encrusted soils, especially in heavy-soiled hollows in the alluvium, and major campaigns to combat the salt are in progress, particularly in West Pakistan, including the use of tube-wells to lower the water-table, to irrigate and to drain and flush saline tracts.[45]

The difficulties of generalizing about the Himalayas have already been noted. Acid brown forest soils must be important locally, and slope colluvium very widely, deeper on lower slopes; while the National Atlas map shows belts of podzols on the highest slopes there can be only the most skeletal Alpine soils, developing on glacial and peri-glacial material, even on rock wastes in the north of Kashmir and the far northwest of West Pakistan. In places the forest has been stripped, sometimes succeeded by gullying, sometimes by terraces for paddy, as in parts of Nepal, sometimes by terracing for tea plantations as in the Darjeeling area. Naturally there is particular concern over grossly accelerated soil erosion and landslides in the Kosi catchment (mainly in Nepal), where a multi-purpose project partly to control floods from violently fluctuating river is under way.[46] Farther west the deforestation and consequent soil erosion in the Siwaliks has been noted; parts of this area have now been subject to soil conservation measures for well over 20 years, and it has been shown how vegetal cover, soil and the water-table may be restored, so that the way may be open for limited and rotational use of the slopes for pasturing or cutting fodder.[47] Many of the hill arcs of West Pakistan are almost devoid of vegetation or soil on the many steep slopes. If there ever was a thin desert scrub, it has yielded to the attack of over-grazing. The process of accelerated soil erosion may have added to the slope colluvium of the lower slopes and the hillfoot fans giving the basis for a little

[44] A. Geddes, *op. cit.*
[45] An example is given from each of the main journals, many articles from which are here subsumed: *Jnl Soil & Water Cons.* 6/4 (1958), 169–76 (B. V. Mehta and R. S. Desai); *Indian Jnl Agric. Science* 33 (1963), 28–33 (S. P. Raychaudhuri *et al.*); *IGJ* 35/1–2 (1960), 10–18 (M. M. Menon); *Proceedings* 8th Silvicultural Confce, 1951, Pt. 2 (Dehra Dun, 1956), 78–82 (K. C. Malhotra); *Indian Forester* 82/4 (1956), 206; *Pak. Jnl Forestry* 11/4 (1961), editorial note.
[46] As in fn. 45, examples are: *Jnl Soil & Water Cons.* 3/3 (1955), 106–15 (P. R. Ahuja); *Indian Forester* 87/4 (1962), 210–19 (O. N. Kaul).
[47] As in fn. 45, examples are: *Pak. Jnl Forestry* 11/4 (1961), 367–74 (N. A. Ali); *Indian Forester* 82/8 (1956), 411 (A. P. Bhattacharya); *Jnl Soil & Water Cons.* 7/4–5 (1959), 3–7 (P. D. Stracey).

irrigation including the use of *karez* (see p. 486). After a scrutiny of the Himalaya and the other northern mountain ranges from this point of view, it is easy to appreciate the great, almost emotional significance attached to the exception – the broad alluvial terraces and plains of the Vale of Kashmir.

Soil conservation

Soil conservation has been mentioned in its context in relation to the main soil regions in the preceding pages. Many problems of research and application surely remain, but for the main regional environments sufficient basic methods have been worked out for one to generalize, as in relation to many other developmental matters, that the remaining and most intransigent problems are social rather than technical. In particular it seems clear from the soil conservation literature, admittedly biased in favour of the measures recommended but weighing the evidence quantitatively, that soil conservation is a good investment even in the short to medium term.[48] Within a few years the increased crop yields pay for the capital costs, and the results are even more impressive if one looks to the saving as against the often irreparable loss of the soil for posterity. For instance the costs of terracing the steep and difficult slopes of the Nilgiris for potato cultivation, which at present causes such devastating soil erosion, are repaid within a few years.[49] The problem of persuading farmers to adopt the measures appropriate to their region and soils is particularly severe; for soil conservation, though it can be done piecemeal on a village by village scale, does need co-operation within the village if it is to succeed, and this may be difficult to secure in an atmosphere of extreme land hunger and where the land is held in scattered plots and strips. Consolidation may have to precede conservation. Perhaps the most significant and hopeful pointer from a small but inspiring experiment in the Upper Damodar is that there followed requests from many other villages for help in framing similar programmes once the news of the increased yields became disseminated.

Soil types, soil fertility, soil productivity

The map of the main climatic-vegetation soil types has been qualified by a discussion of the inter-digitation of differing soils because of geological factors like differential mineral composition of decomposed rock, geomorphological factors like slope or alluviation old and new, and biotic influence both destructive and conservative. There are numerous studies relating to inherent fertility in relation to ecologically suited crops or varieties, but these are often not comparable, based on the experimental farm, plot, or even pot, rather than on peasant

[48] General references include: C. A. R. Bhadran, 'Conservation measures in catchment areas and flood control', *Indian Forester*, 84/12 (1958), 710–17; A. D. Khan, 'Measurement of increase in productivity by adopting soil conservation practices, I & II', *Jnl Soil & Water Cons.* 7/4–5 (1959), 45–50; 50–55; and other papers in these journals.

[49] B. M. Lakshmipathy and S. Narayanswamy, 'Bench terracing in the Nilgiris', *Jnl Soil & Water Cons.* 4/4 (1956), 161–8, and several other papers in these journals.

farmers' fields, and in any case not sufficiently numerous or evenly spaced to allow of mapping on the sub-continental scale treated in this chapter. Some examples may, however, illustrate their potentialities:

An experiment in cultivators' fields in Bihar showed that optimal levels of nitrogenous fertilizers were:

	Fertilizer	Previous Yield	Additional Yield
Clays	40	18	6
Loams	10	17	4
Sandy Loams	15	22	4

The clays, initially more fertile, need more fertilizer for a given response than the medium or low fertility soils.[50]

Such studies multiplied form at once a spectrum and a kaleidoscope, unmappable at present though this may be possible some day. Meantime one admittedly gross and indirectly derived measure is a soil rating index, made up by awarding points to the particular soil for certain characteristics including the predominant crops grown. Mukerjee illustrates the technique in relation to part of the Bengal delta in Howrah district[51]; most of the area rates as of moderate fertility, grade 2, needing more manure than the small area of grade 1 soils yielding some 1,600–2,400 lb. of paddy per acre; even parts of the grade 2 soils are slightly saline, while the grade 3 soils are heavy clays tending to salinity in the swamp of a deltaic hollow. Fig. 3.7 is based on such an index unfortunately calculated by administrative Districts rather than for soil tracts or even for 'spot heights' from which an isopleth map might have been drawn;[52] meantime it may serve *faute de mieux* as a synthesis of this section, at least for India, on the side of application and utilization, as against the bio-ecological aspects with which we began.

[50] P. Sinha and K. P. D. Gupta, 'Crop responses to added fertilizers in cultivators' fields', *Jnl Soil & Water Cons.* 4/3 (1956), 24–30; and many other papers in the soil science journals.

[51] S. N. Mukerjee, 'Productivity rating of the paddy soils of Howrah, Bengal', *GRI* 25/3 (1963), 35–43.

[52] K. B. Shome, 'Rating of soils in India', *Proc. of National Institute of Sciences India,* Silver Jubilee No., (1960), Part A Vol. 26, Physical Sciences Supplement, 260–89.

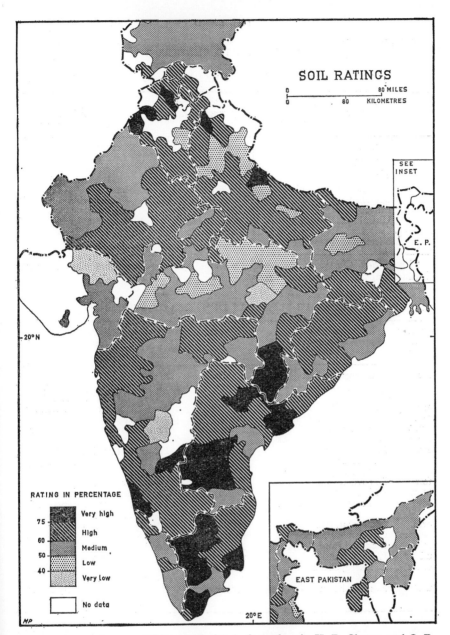

SOIL RATINGS

RATING IN PERCENTAGE

- Very high
- High
- Medium
- Low
- Very low
- No data

75 —
60 —
50 —
40 —

EAST PAKISTAN

FIG 3.7 SOIL RATINGS. This map is drawn from data in K. B. Shome and S. P. Raychauhuri in *Proc. Natl Inst. of Science of India*, 126/A (1960), 260–9. Ratings, unfortunately given on a District basis, were arrived at by multiplying factors of profile, permeability, degree of weathering, texture, structure, stoniness, salinity, natural fertility, and others; pending more refined work interesting regional groupings emerge: the very high ratings of the middle and upper Gangetic Plains and the south and east of the Peninsular plateau, and the low values in a belt flanking the North of the Peninsula.

ADDENDUM TO CHAPTER 3

FORMATIVE ELEMENTS IN NAMES OF SOIL ORDERS *

Name of order	Formative element in name of order	Derivation of formative element	Mnemonicon and pronunciation of formative elements
Entisol	ent	Nonsense syllable	recent
Vertisol	ert	L. *verto*, turn	invert
Inceptisol	ept	L. *inceptum*, beginning	inception
Aridisol	id	L. *aridus*, dry	arid
Mollisol	oll	L. *mollis*, soft	mollify
Spodosol	od	Gk. *spodos*, wood ash	Podzol; odd
Alfisol	alf	Nonsense syllable	Pedalfer
Ultisol	ult	L. *ultimus*, last	ultimate
Oxisol	ox	F. *oxide*, oxide	oxide
Histosol	ist	G. histos, tissue	histology

* From *Soil Classification: A Comprehensive System* (USA Dept of Agriculture, Washington, 7th Approximation, 1960).

FORMATIVE ELEMENTS IN NAMES OF SUBORDERS

Formative element	Derivation of formative element	Mnemonicon	Connotation of formative element
acr	Gk. *akros*, highest	acrobat	Most strongly weathered
alb	L. *albus*, white	albino	Presence of albic horizon (a bleached eluvial horizon)
alt	L. *altus*, high	altitude	Cool, high altitudes or latitudes
and	Modified from *Ando*	Ando	Ando-like
aqu	L. *aqua*, water	aquarium	Characteristics associated with wetness
arg	Modified from argillic horizon; L. *argilla*, white clay	argillite	Presence of argillic horizon (a horizon with illuvial clay)
ferr	L. *ferrum*, iron	ferruginous	Presence of iron
hum	L. *humus*, earth	humus	Presence of organic matter
ochr	Gk. base of *ochros*, pale	ocher	Presence of ochric epipedon (a light-coloured surface)
orth	Gk. *orthos*, true	orthophonic	The common ones
psamm	Gk. *psammos*, sand	psammite	Sand textures
rend	Modified from Rendzina	Rendzina	Rendzina-like
ud	L. *udus*, humid	udometer	Of humid climates
umbr	L. *umbra*, shade	umbrella	Presence of umbric epipedon (a dark-coloured surface)
ust	L. *ustus*, burnt	combustion	Of dry climates, usually hot in summer

BIBLIOGRAPHICAL NOTE

Vegetation

The classic work is H. G. Champion, *A Preliminary Survey of Forest Types of India and Burma* (Indian Forest Records, New Series, Silviculture, Vol. I, Delhi, 1936); a good deal of this chapter is based on it by courtesy of the Director,

Forest Research Institute, Dehra Dun. It is now supplemented by G. S. Puri, *Indian Forest Ecology* (Oxford Book Company, New Delhi, 2 vols 1960), which goes into great floristic detail. Earlier works which are still useful are E. P. Stebbing, *The Forests of India* (London, 1922), for forest administration; R. S. Troup, *The Silviculture of Indian Trees* (London, 1921), which is helpful for the reader outside India who wishes to attach a definite image to a Latin name; and, for its general views, Sir J. D. Hooker, 'Botany' in *Imperial Gazetteer*, Vol. I (1909), the last contribution of a worker whose career began with *Himalayan Journals* in 1847–51!

Recent ecological studies in India owe much to the Section Scientifique et Technique of the Institut Français at Pondicherry. Especially useful is P. Legris, *La Végétation de l'Inde: Ecologie et Flore*, Tome VI of the *Travaux* of the section (Pondichéry, 1963); Tome VII is V. M. Meher-Homji, *Les Bioclimats du Sub-Continent Indien* (1963). The Institute has also begun an extremely detailed vegetation map on the scale of 1/1,000,000, with handbooks; the following sheets have appeared: Cape Comorin, Madras, Godavari, Jagannath, covering the entire littoral from Cannanore round to Lake Chilka and a good deal of the interior. At the other end of the sub-continent, there is a detailed study by U. Schweinfurth, *Die horizontale und vertikale Verbreitung der Vegetation im Himalaya* (F. Dümmler, Bonn, 1957). An important contribution is R. O. Whyte, *The Grassland and Fodder Resources of India* (Indian Council of Agric. Research, Scientific Monograph No. 22, Delhi, 1957).

Soils

Many readers would still wish to progress historically, in relation to thinking about soils at various relatively recent dates. For the traditional classification see *Royal Commission on Agriculture*, 1928, 70–79. An essential and stimulating complement is Z. J. Schokalskaya, 'The natural conditions of soil formation in India', in B. Polynov (ed.), *Contributions to the Knowledge of the Soils of Asia*, No. 2 (Leningrad, Dokuchaiev Institute, 1932), 53–155 – available from the library of the Rothamsted Experimental Station.

A broad and authoritative survey is available, dating from about the beginning of the work of the Soil Survey of India and by its former head, in S. P. Raychaudhuri, Presidential Address on Survey and Classification of Indian Soils, 43rd Indian Science Congress, Agra, 1956, Section of Agricultural Sciences (Indian Science Congress Association, Calcutta – 1), 1–16. The various journals cited in the chapter contain many valuable articles on soil profiles and fertility, erosion and conservation. Much more material of high quality remains meantime in the files of the Indian Soil Survey and analogous bodies in Pakistan and Ceylon. For India, it may be that the time is approaching when we may expect a provisional synthesis of the valuable soil survey documents now available for widespread if patchily distributed parts of the country.

Meantime the foregoing chapter is based very largely on the approach and classification of F. R. Moormann and R. Dudal, 'Major Soils of South-east Asia', Regional Congress of the International Geographical Union (Kuala Lumpur, 1962, mimeographed, 1–52+iv). The author of this section acknowledges deep indebtedness to Moormann and Dudal; error or over-extension of their classification to a part of South Asia almost entirely outside the area they studied, however, must be ascribed solely to the present author. The author, then, found the work of Moormann and Dudal invaluable: the reader may wish to follow, at least until there is available a first-hand modern soil map, pedological study or soils geography of the Indian sub-continent.

PART II

The People

CHAPTER 4

Population and its Problems

————➤ ◁————

INTRODUCTION

The population of the Indian sub-continent in 1961 was about 533,000,000. The recorded rate of increase (1951–61) was about 2·2% per annum in both countries.[1] These rates have often been approached by Western countries during phases of rapid population increase; the absolute numbers involved, however, are very large; at least two-thirds of these very large populations are dependent on agriculture; and while industrialization has made a start and is now being expanded, the position is very different from that of say Britain during the phase of rapid population increase accompanying the Industrial Revolution, the period when the country was becoming 'the workshop of the world'. This is by common consent a sub-continent of over-population, but the degree of over-population in relation to the population capacity at some widely acceptable standard of living is extremely difficult to gauge. Clearly knowledge of population dynamics is as important as five year plans for economic development to employ the extra hands, feed the extra mouths, and in time attain standards of living which we may expect to be associated with lower rates of population increase.

POPULATION DISTRIBUTION

'The density of population is as it were the synthesis of all the geographical phenomena: it expresses eloquently the manner in which man has taken

---

[1] Demographic critiques of the censuses of the two countries suggest that in India the 1951 Census included under-enumeration of perhaps 6–7% (largely of children under 5 and perhaps females also), while the 1961 Census may also include some under-enumeration; the 1951 Census in Pakistan included substantial under-reporting of children, and also of women so that the male predominance at all ages is probably overstated, and the 1961 Census may include under-reporting of over 5%. For Pakistan, the under-reporting in 1951 may have been sufficient to make the calculated population increase of 2·2% per annum 1951–61 also an over-statement. See respectively, for instance, A. J. Coale and E. M. Hoover, *Population Growth and Economic Development in Low-Income Countries: A Case Study of India's Prospects* (OUP, 1959), 354, and K. J. Krotki's valuable series of articles in Vol. I of the *Pakistan Development Review*. India's Registrar-General points out that in the 1961 Census there were almost 1,000,000 *enumerators* (A. Mitra, 'Population on the land in the 1961 Census', *Indian Jnl Agric. Statistics* 15 (1963), 13–82). Since there were almost 200,000 in the 1961 Census of Pakistan, one can appreciate the problems of training and supervision, and the chances of error.

advantage of the land he occupies.' (J. Robert, 'La densité de population des Alpes françaises d'après le dénombrement de 1911', *Rev. de Géographie Alpine* 8 (1920), 124.)

The analysis of a population distribution map which seemed so satisfying in the early 1920s, at least within an area of a relatively homogeneous culture and standards of living, remains a useful exercise for students, though one raising more questions than it solves and inviting further analysis, often impossible for lack of data. The population density map now appears as a beginning rather than an end-product, to be complemented by mapping and analysis of *per capita* income or consumer expenditure, nutritional standards and (in advanced societies) measures of consumer goods and the like to produce estimates of the standard of material living. We shall start with discussion of rural population density and urban population distribution, even if few of the desirable complementary analyses can be more than hinted at for the present. Since Robert wrote, moreover, visual cartographic correlation of the population density map can now be complemented by statistical correlation, even where the base of recording the distribution differs, e.g. as between population and rainfall distributions over areas. Probing attacks using this type of approach for Indian data show that simple statistical analysis breaks down because the relationships involved are too complex and intertwined. Meantime, therefore, we shall use broad generalizations based on visual and subjective analysis.[2]

The excellent map of rural population density in the National Atlas of India (Preliminary Hindi Edition, 1957), on an isopleth basis and in fifteen colours, is based on the 1951 Census and hence is seriously out of date; it is also too complex for easy comprehension. It can, however, provide the starting-point for the compilation of a new and more generalized map of the rural population of the sub-continent, allowing for an over-all intercensal increase of 20% in 1951–61, ignoring as a matter of expediency regional variations: the general pattern is not likely to be significantly altered. For Pakistan the 1961 Census can be directly used; this involves chloropleths based on the smallest administrative units, *tehsils* for West and the smaller *thanas* for East Pakistan. There is therefore an unconformity within the map at the national boundary: in Pakistan the densest shadings are understated, and patches of low populations cutting across administrative boundaries are not well mapped. To avoid irksome repetition of figures in the following discussion, we have given the term 'medium' to densities at around the average for the sub-continent, i.e. about 345 per sq. mile (134 per km^2), and as the key to the map indicates we have given similar descriptive terms to densities ranging from 'extremely high' with over 1,800 per sq. mile (720 per km^2) to 'very low' for densities of under 12 per sq. mile (5 per km^2).

[2] Valuable analyses in the literature include: S. P. Chatterjee, 'Regional patterns of the density and distribution of population in India', *GRI* 24/2 (1962), 1–28; M. K. Elahi, 'Food supply and population growth in Pakistan', *PGR* 21/1 (1957), 1–38.

Densities from medium to extremely high, about or above the average density for the sub-continent, cover nearly all the mainly humid coastal lowlands fringing the Peninsular Block; in the Indo-Gangetic Plains they extend westward into semi-arid country and south into the northern edge of the Peninsular Block, while in the northeast of the sub-continent they cover nearly all of East Pakistan and extend into the Assam valley and west into the Damodar valley and parts of the Chota Nagpur plateau. Clearly these areas include much of the most productive land, especially in respect of food crops, and notably much of the rice land of the sub-continent. Within this great stretch of country, variations, reflecting many and diverse factors, include:

1. A belt of high density stretches north from the rice and market gardening lands north of Bombay, through the Baroda area, and after a gap includes a tract of the cotton-growing country tributary to Ahmedabad.

2. High medium densities south of Bombay, in the terrain of low dissected laterite plateaus and drowned valleys, between the Ghats edge and the sea and reaching south beyond Goa.

3. After a narrowing where the forested high plateaus almost meet the sea near Karwar, this belt broadens and includes considerable belts of very high and extremely high densities almost to Kanya Kumari; the coastal rice lands of Kerala comprise one of the largest stretches of extremely high rural populations in the sub-continent, declining inland in the low coastal plateaus and the spice garden and plantation country of Kerala and Mysore and then falling very rapidly as the country rises in the almost precipitous Ghats edge, to very low densities.

4. Near Kanya Kumari the narrow coastal lowlands show a sharp change to medium and high medium densities associated with the contrast between perhumid Kerala and semi-arid Tamilnad (and between dispersed-linear settlement pattern in Kerala and nucleated settlements based on tank irrigation); there are patches of high density in the main river plains, rising to very high in the lower Cauvery flood-plain and in the rice lands of the delta and in the peri-urban tract round Madras; it is remarkable that the millet and groundnut unirrigated country includes so much medium to high medium density, but one must allow for the effects not only of tank irrigation of part of the land, but also for narrow belts of well-irrigation along the hillfoot zone flanking the low medium to low density hill tracts of the Pachamalais and Shevaroys, and the southeastern raised rim of the Mysore plateau; the high densities of the lower Cauvery extend towards the cotton-millet country round Coimbatore and almost link up with those of coastal Kerala.

5. The coastal belt of above-medium densities narrows north of Pulicat lake, then broadens in the Godavari–Krishna delta which is mostly high with very high densities in the Godavari delta; a salient of high densities reaches northwest along the railway line to the coal-mining area of Singareni and Warangal.

6. The inselberg-studded coastal plains of Northern Circars, with rice and sugar-cane alternating with millet and groundnuts, have high densities, almost linking with those of the Orissa (Mahanadi) deltaic rice lands, which in turn links up with the next feature.

7. The great stretch of populations of high to extremely high densities (over 600 per sq. mile or 240 per km²) in the rice lands of the Bengal delta: West Bengal is generally high, rising to very high and locally to extremely high in a belt following the Hooghly and especially around the Hooghlyside conurbation, and falling to medium in the lateritic Barind tract near the Ganga's turn southeastwards (and extending into East Pakistan); East Pakistan on the other hand is mainly very high, with considerable areas of extremely high densities in the rice and jute tract flanking the lower Padma and Meghna. Islands of lateritic old alluvium, like the Barind or the Madhupur jungle, are mainly of high medium density but might be lower with more sensitive mapping (see introductory paragraph).

8. Most of the Assam valley has high densities, rising to very high in the Nowgong–Tezpur area.

9. The rice lands of the lower Ganga flood-plain tract, including the lower Gandak and Ghaghra, and north to the *terai* on the Nepal border, form a stretch of some 80,000 sq. miles (200,000 km²) of very high densities, the biggest continuous belt in the sub-continent though the densities are a little lower than those of East Pakistan; densities fall to high medium and locally medium on the cone of the still wandering Kosi.

10. Leaving the main rice lands for the wheat-growing northwest, the upper Ganga and Yamuna plains contain a further very large tract, as much again, of high densities with a tract of very high following the East Yamuna canal tract between Delhi and Meerut; and an aureole of high medium to medium densities surrounds these high densities of the Ganga plains, extending into the northern slopes of the Peninsular block in places, or extending in salients like that of the lower Son valley, and also stretching across the Indo-Gangetic divide.

11. In East Punjab (India) and West Punjab (West Pakistan) and through to the Vale of Peshawar, the long densely settled and intensively cultivated hillfoot tracts of well-irrigation have high densities, but most of the canal tracts high medium – though more sensitive mapping of West Pakistan data might raise this a little.

12. Nearly all of this continuous stretch of above-medium density covering over half the sub-continent has been in the coastal plains or the Indo-Gangetic plain, and much the greater part has been in rice lands: there remain the more densely peopled parts of the Peninsula, mainly of medium density – the Mysore plateau, rising to high rural densities between Bangalore and Mysore, the long transitional and contact zone east of the forests of the crest zone of the Western Ghats, in Mysore and Maharashtra, rising to high densities in the

tobacco growing tract southeast of Kolhapur, much of the tank-irrigation country of Andhra, the upper Godavari valley, the middle Tapti basin and after an interruption a belt stretching east through Nagpur and the Wardha and Wainganga basins to the middle Mahanadi rice-bowl, and the interruption to harsh semi-arid conditions where the Aravallis give a little more rainfall and opportunities for tank building.

The tracts with rural population densities *below* medium (below 240 per sq. mile, 96 per km^2), may be considered more briefly:

1. There are considerable tracts of low and very low densities in the forested hills of the northeast, the forested to glaciated and harsh arid plateaus of the far north, and the great tract of semi-arid to arid conditions from the Thar desert to Baluchistan – this last interrupted by low medium to medium densities of the lower Indus plains (locally probably somewhat higher on more sensitive mapping).

2. Low medium densities stretch from the far north of West Pakistan, and after the higher densities of the Punjab along the wetter eastern part of Rajasthan to inland Gujarat and much of Kathiawad and southern Kutch; thence stretching across about half of the Peninsular Block including much semi-arid country of variable rainfall and harvests, but also some humid country of rather poor and easily eroded soils in the northeast of the Plateau; within this great swathe of country are several large tracts of very low densities, largely tribal country – parts of the Satpuras, Vindhyas and Bundelkhand, the Kaimur Range, the Maikal Hills and across the higher parts of Chota Nagpur, the Cuddapah ranges of Andhra, the Bastar highlands north of the Godavari delta, linked to the northeast with the 'Eastern Ghats' of Orissa.

We cannot at the moment complement analysis of rural population density with a geography of standards of living in the countryside, though some hints are available. The falling cultivated area per head has often been pointed out, implying an additional strain on efforts to improve rural living standards;[3] rural unemployment in India is about 7% in young adult groups, and some 15% of those with employment regard themselves as underemployed, and while unemployment in Pakistan is reported as much lower, 3·5% in East Pakistan and 2·8% in West Pakistan, underemployment is high in East Pakistan (some 17%) though under 5% in West Pakistan.[4] The National Sample Survey has revealed the broad picture of consumer expenditure in India (i.e. a rupee value for all items consumed whether bought or home produced): values grade downward

[3] Kingsley Davis, *The Population of India and Pakistan* (Princeton Univ. Press, 1951); P. Dayal, 'Population growth and migration in India', *NGJI* 5/4 (1959), 179–85.
[4] 'Unemployment and Underemployment in India, Indonesia, Pakistan and the Philippines', *International Labour Rev.* 86 (1962), 369–87, drawing largely on the National Sample Survey for Indian data.

from Punjab to Kerala and Madras, and from Punjab to Bengal and the north-east, though here values do not fall as low as in the far south.[5] South India certainly appears as the most underprivileged area, even despite the awful prob-lems of West Bengal including the absorption of refugees, and this picture is

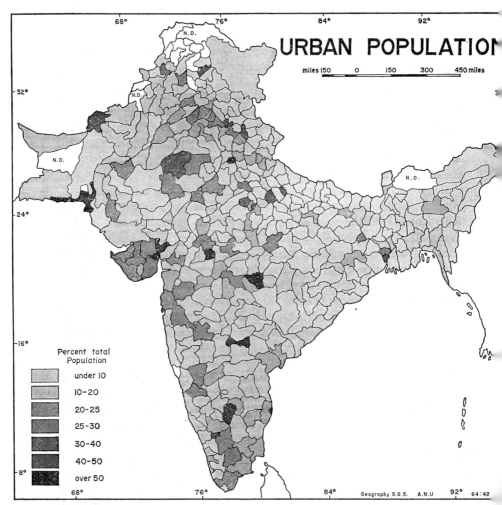

FIG 4.2 URBAN POPULATION. *Sources: 1961 Census of Pakistan* and *1961 Census of India*, Map 9 in Paper No. 1 of 1962 – actually a map of rural population, of which urban is the complementary percentage.

consistent with higher proportions of agricultural labourers in the east and south, and also with the long history of the south as a source of emigrants whether to

[5] For an indication of some stimulating potentialities of material from the 1961 Census, from the Registrar-General himself, see A. Mitra, *op. cit.*

Ceylon or Malaya, Madras city or Bangalore.[6] But there is one slight ameliorating factor, difficult to quantify – in the north, including the northeast, better housing and more clothing and food are needed to cope with the cool weather than generally in the south.

Urban population

The urban geography is discussed as such in Chapter 7, to which frequent cross-reference will be necessary, but both the extent of existing urbanism and of rates of growth in urbanization are essential to understanding of the population distribution map. In India the proportion of population classed as urban was 17·4% in 1951, 17·8% in 1961 (61,800,000 and 79,200,000 respectively);[7] in Pakistan the proportions were 10·4% in 1951 and 13·1% in 1961 (7,900,000 and 12,300,000).

Fig. 4.2 is a map of urban population distribution. There are relatively few under-urbanized areas (i.e. at or under the national averages quoted above): (1) all the northern mountain tracts except the Vale of Kashmir, the Kulu valley and the Darjeeling area; all Assam and the northeastern extremity of India except for the upper part of the Assam plain round Dibrugarh, the Shillong part of the Khasi plateau and the Tripura–Silchar area, in all of which the mapping may be swayed by relatively slender urban resources in relation to quite sparse population; (2) on the Gangetic plains the eastern terai, still partly in marshy forest, is the only large under-urbanized tract, along with the eastern part of the Yamuna–Ganga doab, two small areas southwest of Agra, and the northern fringe of the Ganga delta. In the Peninsula, apart from two small areas north of Bombay, there are two large and significant under-urbanized areas – along the Eastern Ghats from the Godavari gorge northeast to the Orissa hills, and the fringes of the Mahanadi delta.

Large tracts which are relatively highly urbanized include Hooghlyside, parts of the plains of Punjab and western Uttar Pradesh, Rajasthan especially along the fringes of the Aravalli, the Ahmedabad cotton area and Kathiawad with its array of former princely capitals, southern Malwa for similar reasons. The tract from Bombay to Baroda is well urbanized and several parts of the black cotton soil tracts – from Nasik and East Khandesh to Nagpur, from Poona to Sholapur, and away south to Dharwar and Hubli and even past the spice towns of the Ghats crest to the seaport towns from Karwar to Bhatkal.

The core of the former princely state of Mysore is well urbanized between

[6] J. E. Schwartzberg, 'Agricultural labour in India: a regional analysis with particular reference to population growth', *Econ. Devpt & Cultl Change*, 11 (1963), 337–52.

[7] In 1951 a town normally had a population of 5,000 or more, but larger places without urban characteristics might be excluded, smaller places with them included; State Government or Census Superintendents had some discretion. In 1961 there was a more rigorous definition, without discretion to States; all places with municipal or other recognized administration were classed as urban, plus other places meeting three tests: (*a*) population not less than 5,000, (*b*) population density not less than 1,000 per square mile, and (*c*) at least three-fourths of adult male population engaged in pursuits other than agriculture.

Bangalore and Mysore, and so are the core of the Krishna delta area, the Coimbatore and Madurai areas and the relatively sparsely peopled tract north of Kanya Kumari, as well as the much more densely peopled tract of southern Kerala. Several other areas have considerable urban networks, but are not classed as highly urbanized in relation to the dense populations – the Madras area, the Cauvery and Godavari deltas, and much of the lower Ganga riverine belt. The vast majority of the 2,448 towns classed as such in the 1961 census are small market, service and handicraft centres, with a few other urban functions or amenities. Most are growing at about the national rate of increase. The total urban population increased from 62,603,291 in 1951 to 78,835,939 in 1961, an increase of about 21% comparable with the national growth rate of 22%. A typical rate of increase for a small market town over the decade is again about 20%. Some towns are stagnant or even actually declining. These are usually in very poor or backward areas (Sholapur in Gulbarga District, Mysore – not the large textile centre – population 18,352 in 1951 and 17,689 in 1961; Freelandganj in Panchmahals District, Gujarat, 16,696 in 1951 and 14,951 in 1961). A typical older commercial, administrative or industrial centre has increased at about 25% during the decade, and one with new and rapidly expanding industrial elements at about 30% – even a very large unit like Bangalore (1951, 786,343; 1961, 1,206,961).

The data for Pakistan have been mapped using the same class-boundaries for the shadings, and interestingly enough there is relatively little reflection of a pattern of urbanization. The line of hillfoot towns in East Punjab continues into West Punjab in Pakistan, but with this exception West Pakistan shows only individual Districts of high urbanization dominated by particular towns or cities – Karachi, Quetta, Hyderabad, Khairpur and the like. And East Pakistan shows low urbanization: in relation to the very dense population even Dacca, with over half a million people, does not bring its District into the denser shadings. At the same time Pakistan like India has its considerable autochthonous urban tradition, more than many underdeveloped countries, as well as its outward-looking seaports like Karachi and administrative centres like Dacca.

Apart from the great flow of studies in urban geography, especially in classification and land use, referred to in Chapter 7, a great deal of study has been applied to urbanization in relation to population growth as a whole, and in relation to industrialization and programmes to improve standards of living. Much of the literature was written under the influence of the great increases in urban populations in the decade 1941–51, culminating perhaps in the remarkable international seminar on urbanization in India at Berkeley, California, in 1960.[8] The estimates in the table seemed not only reasonable, but also to many inevitable, assuming that they would be attained through industrialization and accompanied by improvements in living standards (cf. p. 130).

[8] R. Turner (ed.), *India's Urban Future* (Univ. of California Press, Berkeley, 1962), especially Kingsley Davis, 'Urbanization in India: past and future', 3–26.

An attempt to programme rapid industrial-urban expansion in consonance with quite conceivable perspective planning was made by one of India's leading workers in this field within the Planning Commission.[9] There were some supporters of at least moderate decentralization, but perhaps the main current of thought was to accept the likelihood of massive centralized development, and

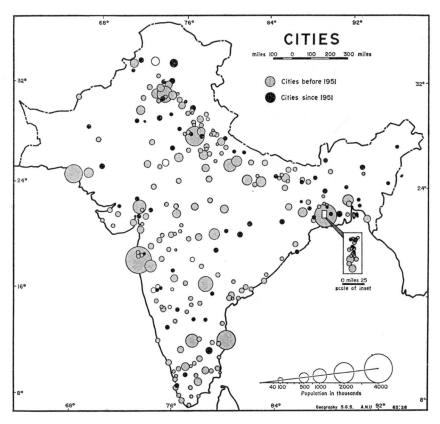

FIG 4.3 CITIES 1951–61. *Sources:* L. S. Bhat in *Geography*, 48 (1963), 315–17; *1961 Census of Pakistan*, Vol. 2.

to work towards improved efficiency in the process of urbanization, to avoid the horrible slums and shanty-town developments described elsewhere in this book.

The period 1941–51 included Partition and the massive population movements of some 7,000,000 moving from India to Pakistan and about as many

[9] P. Pant, 'Urbanization and the long-range strategy of economic development', *ibid.*, 182–91.

THE PEOPLE

ESTIMATED SIZE OF THE TEN MAJOR CITIES IN INDIA
IN 1970 AND 2000
(*In millions of inhabitants*)

| Metropolis* | Estimated proportion in cities: | | | |
| | low | | high† | |
	1970	2000	1970	2000
Calcutta	12·0	35·6	16·0	66·0
Delhi	6·0	17·8	8·0	33·0
Bombay	4·0	11·9	5·3	22·0
Madras	3·0	8·9	4·0	16·5
Bangalore	2·4	7·1	3·2	13·2
Ahmedabad	2·0	5·9	2·7	11·0
Hyderabad	1·7	5·1	2·3	9·4
Kanpur	1·5	4·5	2·0	8·3
Poona	1·3	4·0	1·8	7·3
Nagpur	1·2	3·6	1·6	6·6

* Ranked according to their relative position in the year 2000.
† These estimates were based on a *medium* projection of the population as a whole, from which estimates were worked out, as tabulated, for low and high projections of the proportion of urban to total population. In the cited source a different answer was obtained using (*a*) 20,000 and (*b*) 100,000 as the lower limit of city size, but the difference was slight enough to warrant averaging the two to yield the figures as presented in this table.
Source: *India's Urban Future*, p. 25.

from Pakistan to India;[10] it now appears that this great upheaval was associated with particularly rapid urbanization, and there was some falling off in 1951–61 in rate of increase, though with absolute numbers not very different from the previous decade (urban population in India in 1941, 43,810,000); in 1951 61,870,000 (increase 41·2%); in 1961 79,240,000 (increase 28·1%).[11] On

[10] M. L. Qureshi (ed.), *Population Growth and Economic Development with Special Reference to Pakistan*, Institute of Development Economics, Karachi, 1960; especially W. P. Mauldin and S. S. Hashmi, 'Illustrative projections of the population of Pakistan, 1951 to 1991', 61–84. The total movements amounted to some 7,400,000 from Pakistan to India, 7,200,000 from India to Pakistan; there was a net outflow from East Pakistan mainly to West Bengal of 1,900,000, and of 1,800,000 from northern India to West Pakistan according to this source. There are useful maps in K. S. Ahmad, 'Urban population in Pakistan', *PGR* 10/1 (1955), 1–16. It may be added that casualties during communal riots and massacres were severe, perhaps amounting to 750,000 deaths, mainly in the Punjab.
[11] A. Bose, 'Population growth and the industrialization–urbanization process in India', *Man in India*, 41/4 (1961), 255–75; for a stimulating critique in this field, combining elements from the thinking of Gandhi and Patrick Geddes, see N. K. Bose, 'Some problems of urbanization', *ibid.*, 42/4 (1962), 255–62. In Pakistan for the period 1901–51 there was a fall in the proportion employed in industry, and even in absolute numbers of industrial workers, though changes in classification may be involved. See K. U. Kureishy, 'An analysis of civilian labour force in its bearing on growth of urban population in West Pakistan 1901–51', *PGR* 13/2 (1958), 89–99.

the whole there has been some disappointment that the rate of really successful urbanization and industrialization has not been higher, so as to relieve population pressure in the rural areas. Rapid urban-industrial increase is probably inevitable, at least if the five year plans are to succeed in their objectives. Meantime this slackening in rates of increase still represents very large urban increments in absolute numbers – some 17,000,000 of additional urban dwellers in India alone from 1951 to 1961 – and conditions are by no means good, nor even rapidly improving, for poorer urban groups. Urban unemployment and underemployment remain high – in India 17% unemployed and 16% underemployed, in large towns in East Pakistan over 10% unemployed but only 6% in West Pakistan.[12] There is crowding into the towns from pushing out of poor rural tracts and social groups, rather than urban pull to vacant jobs. The male preponderance in sex-ratio, general throughout the sub-continent, is accentuated in towns, particularly in north India and Pakistan, less so in south India where rural-urban migrants tend more to move in family groups and even to maintain some social cohesion in urban slums.[13] The underprivileged urban groups are above all the casual day-labourers, the coolies or *mazdoor*; there is a strong and positive urban pull when jobs in factories are known to be available, opening the door to what is much more a sort of middle-class life with good regular wages and supervised labour conditions.[14]

To sum up, there is an existing urban tradition and framework sufficient to cope with increasing urbanization and industrialization either in a few large centres or by considerable dispersion and evolution throughout hundreds or even thousands of towns. The prestige and efficiency of municipal authorities is seldom strong in large or small towns, though there are honourable exceptions. Many of the influx into large cities are housed in poor shanty-town slums and many small towns have as yet few urban amenities and services (see Fig. 4.11). But there is little doubt that India is a more fruitful and hopeful field for urban and industrial expansions than are many underdeveloped countries. Census data show that manufacturing industry at larger than household scale employs more than 10% of the population chiefly in a handful of places – Hooghlyside, Bombay, the Ahmedabad area, the Poona area and round Delhi, Agra, Kanpur, Madras, Coimbatore (just under 10%) and in one or two local and isolated areas. Of course, the detailed picture also shows individual small towns with over 10% of the population depending on household industry including weaving, and the 1951 Census (or the National Atlas) shows that several large areas have over

---

[12] ILO., *op. cit.*

[13] J. C. Sen, 'The sex composition of India's towns from 20,000 to 50,000, according to the 1961 census', *IGJ* 37/3 (1963), 90–100; note also the references to G. M. Woodruff's doctoral thesis to Radcliffe College in R. Turner, *op. cit.* and A. Lall, 'Age and sex structures of cities of India', *GRI* 24/1 (1962), 7–29. See also K. S. Ahmad, 'Urban population in Pakistan', *PGR* 10/1 (1955), 1–16, and H. Hussain, 'Some aspects of the rural-urban composition of population in East Pakistan', *ibid.*, 13/1 (1958), 24–28.

[14] Something of this emerges in various social surveys, e.g. R. D. Lambert, 'Factory workers and non-factory population in Poona', *Jnl of Asian Studies*, 18 (1958), 21–42.

10% of the population in village and small scale industries while about half the country has over 5%.[15] Since industrial population is commonly only about one-third of the population engaged in commerce, transport and services, it is clear that India's urbanization and industrialization have not so far progressed fast enough in relation to her problems of population growth and low standards of living, but that there is a very substantial foundation compared with many underdeveloped countries.

Internal migration

Gosal, who has carried out much of the recent geographical analysis of this important topic, has remarked that though the absolute numbers of migrants are large, they are relatively very small in relation to total population, and this remains true following later analysis based on the 1961 Census.[16] Refugee movements apart, migrants move from densely peopled or drought-ridden agricultural tracts to areas newly won for agriculture or where irrigation offers fresh possibilities, or of course to the towns and cities; movements are generally over relatively short distances, and economic motivations predominate.

Notoriously, this is a field where findings vary according to the administrative units for which data are available, but Gosal's work using district data has the advantage of relatively uniform criteria in relation to the size and population convenient for centralized administration. He accounts for the relatively low migration rates by lack of opportunity, ignorance, linguistic problems, and caste and joint family ties. He recognizes regions of low mobility, with under 8% not born in the district: (a) 'saturated' areas in the lower Gangetic plain and delta, and the coastal plains, and (b) sparsely peopled hill areas, lacking in opportunities. Urbanization and industry are little developed, but there is local migration to market, administrative and craft industry centres, which swells to considerable proportions in Andhra and Madras where quite rapid urban-industrial growth has been fed from quite local catchment areas of intense population pressure. High mobility areas (with over 16% not born in the district) include: (a) Assam, a unique case, with almost 20% of immigrants, many long-range, and up to 25% in the upper valley; most came before Partition including many Muslims, about a third since, and while the Bengalis have come mainly as farmers to new rice lands, many migrants from Bihar, Orissa and Madhya Pradesh were wage-labourers on tea plantations, though some have since settled as cultivators: (b) the Hooghlyside conurbation and the Damodar coalfield, with 33%, about equally from local

[15] There is good evidence that at least locally the figures for industrial employment in local areas are distorted because census enumerators have counted traditional caste occupation, not actual employment, while these are in fact often at variance (conversation with Dr J. Schwartzberg, July 1964, and see Bibliographical Note at the end of the chapter).

[16] G. S. Gosal, 'Internal migration in India – a regional analysis', *IGJ* 36/3 (1961) 106–21 and later papers; see also A. Lall, 'Patterns of in-migration in India's cities', *GRI*, 23/3 (1961), 16–23, and detailed studies such as U. Singh on Allahabad (*NGJI*, 4/4 (1958), 163–88, and E. Ahmad on Bihar (*Bombay Geog. Mag.*, 8–9 (1961), 61–68.

districts and from Uttar Pradesh, Orissa and parts of Bihar: (c) northwestern India, where 60% of urban immigrants were refugees, largely for whom a number of 'model towns' (usually in fact suburbs of existing towns) were built, with industrial estates, while Ganganagar is the focus of a new irrigation area attracting a steady stream of immigrants from Punjab: (d) south and southwest Mysore, with 20–40%, attracts coffee plantation labourers, while Bangalore is a rapidly expanding State capital and industrial town, and Kolar Gold Fields have a constant turnover of labour (but a decline in total population 1951–61); (e) in western India Greater Bombay has 73% of migrants, half from the coastal Districts of Ratnagiri and Kolaba, Ahmedabad (32%) draws in people from Saurashtra and Kutch, and Poona (18%) from nearby districts; (f) isolated urban foci of immigration – Madras, Hyderabad, Gwalior, Nagpur, Jabalpur, Indore, Ujjain, Kanpur, Lucknow and Dehra Dun.

The regions of medium mobility include for instance the Upper Gangetic plain, with short- to medium-range movement to new agricultural lands, notably in the terai, movements to areas of expanding well-irrigation in Rajasthan and local movements to towns in Madhya Pradesh.

Linguistic and cultural differences remain sufficiently great to present a real problem to individuals and particularly to families migrating over long distances. It is quite common, for example, to find clusters of south Indian middle-class families in Calcutta or Delhi, exercised to provide schooling for their children in south Indian languages, particularly if their stay is likely to be for a few years only. The progress of Hindi as a national language is of some help, but since long-range migration may be essential in the coming decades, these problems essentially of social geography probably deserve further study.

Demographic structure and trends
Rates of population increase already referred to are quite high but by no means unprecedented, and are exceeded by several countries, notably by much of Latin America today. Rates of increase have, however, been accelerating for the last 60 years, and the demographic situation is clearly a very dynamic one. The expectation of life of a baby born in 1901 was 24 years, in 1921 20 years, in 1941 32 years, and in 1960 45 years. It has been a cliché that in India and else-where death control has been achieved before birth control. While this was also true of Britain during the past phases of demographic expansion already referred to, there is an additional factor – one of India's main causes of death, now largely removed, was malaria. Malaria control or eradication has actually caused an increase in births, previously heavily reduced not only by missed conceptions but notably by increased abortions associated with disease.

Within this broad picture there have been marked regional variations mapped for the period 1881–1941 in Fig. 4.4.[17] Geddes believes that the regionally

[17] A. Geddes, 'The population of India: variability of change as a regional demographic index', *GR* 32 (1942), 562–73.

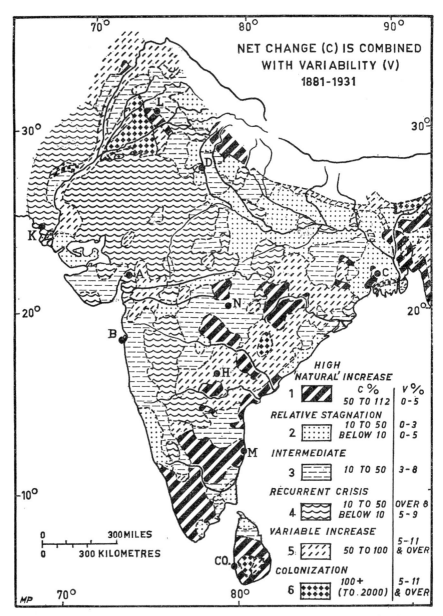

		c %	v %
HIGH 'NATURAL' INCREASE			
1		50 TO 112	0-5
RELATIVE STAGNATION			
2		10 TO 50 / BELOW 10	0-3 / 0-5
INTERMEDIATE			
3		10 TO 50	3-8
RECURRENT CRISIS			
4		10 TO 50 / BELOW 10	OVER 8 / 5-9
VARIABLE INCREASE			
5		50 TO 100	5-11 & OVER
COLONIZATION			
6		100+ (TO 2000)	5-11 & OVER

0 ____ 300 MILES
0 ____ 300 KILOMETRES

MP

FIG 4.4 DEMOGRAPHIC REGIONS, from A. Geddes' pioneering contribution in *GR* 32 (1942), 562–73. Of the four most distinctive demographic types, stagnation was closely related to endemic malaria, recurrent crisis to periodic famine and epidemics, high natural increase to agricultural opportunities, usually in fertile soils or prolific climates; while colonization is self-explanatory.

differentiated demographic experience portrayed has had significant socio-psychological effects which may remain of importance for some time.[18] There is some confirmation from a psychiatric worker.[19] It may be that Geddes has put his

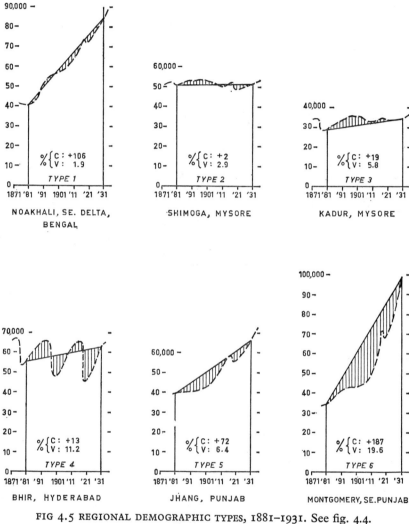

FIG 4.5 REGIONAL DEMOGRAPHIC TYPES, 1881–1931. See fig. 4.4.

finger on one of those socio-psychological blocks to full local participation in community development projects which have been qualitatively described by several

[18] A. Geddes, 'The social and psychological significance of variability in population change with examples from India 1871–1941', *Human Relations*, I (1947), 181–205.

[19] A. Hyatt Williams, 'A psychiatric study of Indian soldiers in the Arakan', *British Jnl Med. Psychology*, 23 (1950), 130–81.

observers. Since he wrote and compiled his map, however, the picture has become much less clear-cut – largely through the complete or partial control of famines, epidemics and not least malaria. Even a study of the period between the

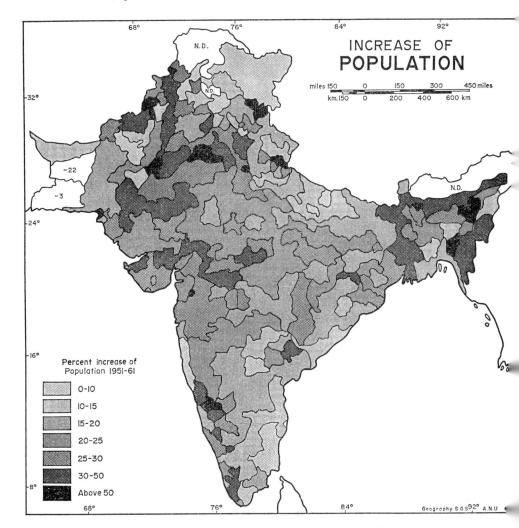

FIG 4.6 INCREASE OF POPULATION, 1951–61.

wars showed some blurring of these demographic regions,[20] and a map of population increase 1951–61 shows that regions of demographic stagnation have been wiped out (Fig. 4.6). There may be a residual in the Cauvery delta, with

[20] A. Geddes and A. T. A. Learmonth, 'Variability in population change and regional variations therein 1921–40', *IGJ* 28/1 (1953), 69–73.

relatively low rates of increase of 5–10%, but all the other regions of stagnation have given way to increases of 15–20% or even 25–30% or more in the Bengal delta (where urban-industrial immigration and refugee influx have contributed). In the forested hilly Malnad o western Mysore, again, formerly very malarious, and from which Geddes's type graph of stagnation was chosen, there are now similar rates of increase. The highest rates of increase of 30–50% or even more over the decade are due to immigration, including refugee movement, and development of fresh resources in areas of population densities relatively sparse in relation to resources – note the contrasting densities within the area of high increase in the Assam valley and in Rajasthan and Kutch. Looking back over a span similar to that studied by Geddes, but later (1891–1951), Trewartha and Gosal point out the significance of a turning point in population trends generally about 1921, with much lower rates of increase (actual decrease in about half the sub-continent) in 1891–1921, and higher rates 1921–51.[21] The first thirty-year period was one of frequent floods, droughts, epidemics and famines, including the last great famine to go comparatively unrelieved in 1899–1900,[22] several plague years and India's heavy share in the world influenza pandemic of 1919–20. The second thirty years was relatively free from these catastrophes, despite the Bengal famine of 1943 and the slaughter accompanying Partition in 1947.

Some population projections indicate that the current, or even a slightly increased, rate of population increase is likely to continue for at least two generations or so. There are indications that the economic level at which family size diminishes, over whole populations, is not beyond the possibilities, for very large masses of the population, within the period of two or three further five year plans – assuming these are successful.[23] Of course, the populations already attaining this modest level of 'middle-class prosperity' may have somewhat different backgrounds and social attitudes as compared with the much larger groups who may reach this level of income over the next ten or fifteen years. So a falling-off in population increase may take rather longer than is needed simply for these income figures to be attained. It is often assumed that urban families tend to be smaller than rural ones, and that this may afford at least to neo-Malthusian thinkers an additional reason for favouring rapid urbanization. Except for limited urban groups, there is little evidence as yet of lower fertility

[21] G. T. Trewartha and G. Gosal, 'The regionalism of population change in India', *Cold Harbor Symposia on Quantitative Biology*, 22 (1957), 71–81.

[22] One cannot maintain, of course, that relief measures were effective in the terrible Bengal famine, markedly concentrated in very densely peopled deltaic country and with many complicating factors, see p. 581. See also C. B. Memoria, 'Growth of population in India', *GRI* 19/4 (1957), 13–26 for an interesting review of the historical geography of population including famines, etc.

[23] P. C. Mahalanobis and A. Das Gupta, 'The use of sample surveys in demographic studies in India', *Proc. World Population Conf. 1954 Rome* (Papers, Vol. VI, UN, New York, 1955), 363–84.

in towns.[24] On the other hand in towns there is some evidence of more rapid adoption of family planning measures, like other innovations, but this is a topic so important that we shall return to it in the conclusion to the chapter.

Medical geography[25]

Regional differences in the incidence of disease have already been discussed, along with important sequelae when disease control became established. No single topic in this field is of greater importance than malaria control.

Large-scale malaria control campaigns in India began in 1947, yet by 1956 serious academic workers new to the country found it difficult to believe that malaria had been an important factor in the lives of the people, and the anonymous writer of the first report in the 1961 Census found it necessary to recall something of the pre-1947 situation for the benefit of the generation who had grown up unaware of the revolution in health and demographic trends so recently and so dramatically effected. Figs. 4.7–4.10 may suffice here to record the changes, and the demographic results have already been outlined. (See also Bibliographical Note, p. 149.)

The great epidemic diseases of India, cholera, plague and small-pox, received a great deal of attention, partly because India is something of a world endemic home of cholera and small-pox, from which the diseases burst forth in occasional epidemic years to bring death and terror in a random harvest of epidemics in all areas and places where the infections find conditions favouring their spread. Yet over the inter-war period they accounted on the average for only about 3% of the total mortality of India, although the figure was higher, up to some 20% or so, in an epidemic year. Plague has been associated for millennia with urban centres of the hillfoot zone of the Indo-Gangetic plains, as an enzootic in rats, epizootic in a cycle of about six years, and with a corresponding tendency towards endemicity in urban human populations, and to epidemic spread from the towns along routes of trade or pilgrimage in epidemic years. These towns are part of a ring of endemic foci including market centres strung around central Asia which contain the reservoir of infection in the 'silent zone' of the disease, the region of enzootic conditions among wild rodents like the marmot. The last great plague cycle came by sea to Bombay in 1896, spreading thence along routes followed by the cotton trade to the cotton collecting and market centres in particular. As well as the short term cycle of six years plague seems also to run in long term cycles.

[24] W. C. Robinson, 'Urban–rural differences in Indian fertility', *Population Studies*, 14 (1960–61), 218–34: for lack of good registration data, the fertility ratio is used, i.e. the ratio of children of 0–4 to 1,000 females, or to 1,000 married females, or 15–39; this ratio was formerly much lower in cities (especially large cities), but the urban–rural differentiation seems to be diminishing, perhaps because of more rapid decreases in infant and child mortality in cities as compared with the country, and perhaps because of a change in the nature of urban populations in the last few decades, from long-term city dwellers of lower fertility to recent immigrants of higher fertility.

[25] A. T. A. Learmonth, 'Medical geography in Indo-Pakistan: a study of twenty years' data for the former British India', *IGJ* 33/1 (1958), 1–59.

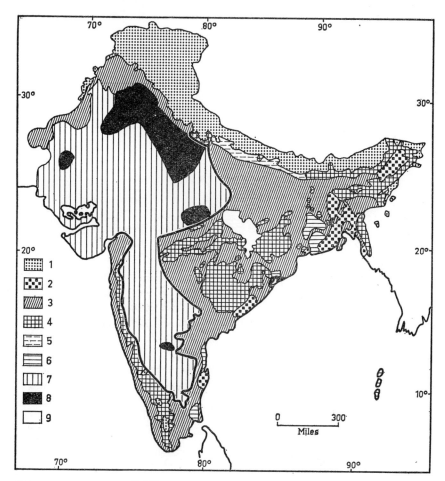

FIG 4.7 MALARIA, 1938. Key: 1, areas over 5,000 ft. (non-malarious); 2, known healthy plains (spleen rate under 10%); 3, more or less static moderate to high endemicity, intensity depending on local factors – seasonal variations moderate, fulminant epidemics unknown; 4, hyperendemic jungly hilly tracts and *terai*; 5, probably hyperendemic hill areas; 6, hyperendemic other than hills; 7, variable endemicity of drier areas, usually with autumnal rise in fever incidence (potential epidemic areas), spleen rate low except in years following epidemics or in special local circumstances, much affected by irrigation conditions; 8, known areas liable to fulminant epidemicity (diluvial) malaria, spleen rate high during and immediately after epidemics, slowly falling to low rates in *c.* 5 years; 9, unsurveyed. The heavy line marks the broad division between endemic and epidemic areas. From *IGJ* 33/1–2 (1958), 12; but ultimately from *Annual Report of the Public Health Commissioner . . . for 1940* (Delhi, 1941), based on work by S. R. Christophers and J. A. Sinton.

This major cycle seems to have been on the decline when the malaria campaign using residual insecticides like DDT seems to have discouraged the plague-bearing rat flea sufficiently to speed the departure of the waning plague cycles. There are up to a few hundred cases a year, but plague has not been an important health problem for a decade or more.

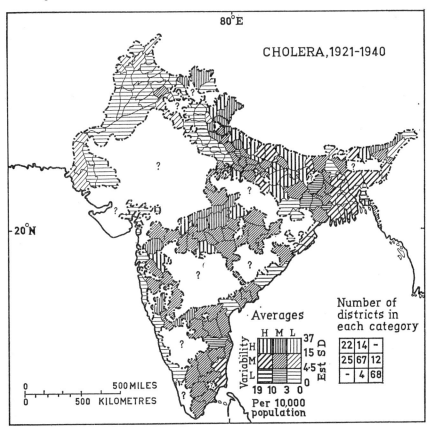

FIG 4.8 CHOLERA 1921–40. The east coast deltas are endemic homes of the disease, showing medium to high average mortality with medium variability; the other areas of high death rates show high variability – these are epidemic areas, to which the infection spreads from the endemic foci in 'favourable' years. There is a rather sharp drop in mortality in the relatively little-affected semi-arid areas, though local outbreaks (perhaps started by a pilgrim carrier) can be unpleasant enough.

Cholera is mapped for British India for the inter-war period as Fig. 4.8. The endemic homes of cholera, a mainly water-borne infection by *Vibrio cholerae*, are particularly low-lying deltas with organic-rich water and a high water table. Even there, cholera vanishes as a human disease causing illness and death in the later years of a cycle of about five or six years. The disease may be present in immune carriers or there may be a cyclic, perhaps genetic change in the virulence of the cholera organism. Illnesses and deaths tend to increase in the endemic homes following this cycle, about every fifth year, and thence to fan out along lines of communications. On many past occasions pilgrimage to the Jagganath (Juggernaut) festival at Puri has caused explosive outbreaks to spread widely, and similarly if a cholera outbreak and widespread rainfall and humid conditions have coincided with one of the particularly large gatherings of pilgrims at Allahabad at the Yamuna–Ganga confluence every twelfth year, or every fourteenth year at Hardwar where the Ganga leaves the mountains. In other years cholera spreads more gradually, more widely, less explosively, from the Ganga–Brahmaputra delta, moving slowly *up*stream on a wide front, and with scattered widespread occurrences rather than highly localized explosive outbreaks round a particular well or other source of drinking water. It has been argued that under these conditions the disease must be fly-borne.[26] Inoculation against cholera is now possible, though not very long-lasting, but over the last thirty years or so the health authorities have attained considerable success in the control of explosive outbreaks dispersing from pilgrim centres through the mass inoculation of pilgrims.[27]

Small-pox, a mainly droplet-borne virus infection, is a disease of squalor and overcrowding, though no respecter of persons, especially the un-vaccinated, in a virulent epidemic outbreak. It is again largely concentrated in the densely populated Bengal delta, including the dreadful urban slums. Again, there is something of a cyclic tendency due to changes in acquired immunity in the population – if only through births and therefore largely in growth of the non-immune and often un-vaccinated – or to changes in virulence of virus, of which many subtypes of different characteristics have been identified. Again it fans out in epidemic years, and the incubation period is such that in these days of rapid travel a single incubating or carrier individual may cause an outbreak in a foreign population low in immunity acquired through previous infection or from vaccination. Many years of mass vaccination campaigns in the Indian sub-continent have met with some failures and with some obstacles set by apathy or by religious objections to vaccination. But these efforts are being intensified, for the sake of internal health as well as external relations.

The great causes of mortality, the major public health problems are much less dramatic than these three epidemic diseases. Among the infections, tuberculosis has been important up to now. A major campaign is being planned using BCG inoculations, and pilot projects under different epidemiological, social and living conditions are being carried out. Bronchitis and associated pneumonia are important causes of mortality, especially in the northern half of the sub-continent, in the cool weather, and among poor, ignorant, ill-clad, ill-fed and

[26] W. C. Ross, 'The epidemiology of cholera', *Indian Jnl Med. Research*, 15 (1928), 951–64.
[27] A. L. Banks, 'Religious fairs and festivals in India', *Lancet*, Jan. 1961, 162–3.

ill-housed groups, in the country and especially in urban slums. Various forms of intestinal infection classed as dysentery, less dramatic than cholera, nevertheless cause much chronic ill-health and inefficiency, and also many deaths. There is an association with fly-breeding and with intimate contacts between flies and family life, especially if the generally poor sanitation is associated with moderate crowding of buildings – wide dispersion permits some poor disposal of faecal

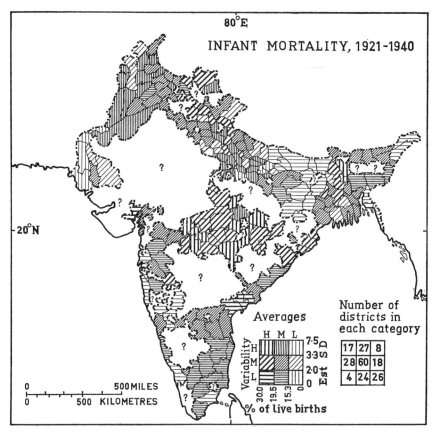

FIG 4.9 INFANT MORTALITY, 1921–40. Infant mortality is regarded as a good index of general conditions of health and hygiene. Rates were generally high by modern standards, but particularly so in central India (liable to variable harvests and epidemics), in the east coast deltas (with lower variability), and in the hills and hillfoot areas, long densely settled, of the north; as also in the overcrowded towns and cities.

matter, while real crowding enforces some systematic disposal of night soil. And there may be a relationship with shallow wells as in much of the Peninsular Block, subject to pollution from run-off rather than fed by water which has undergone thorough filtration through alluvium.

Dysentery will long remain an important public health problem unless a *deus ex machina* is forthcoming as happened with malaria control where only minimal public co-operation with spraying teams is needed. The ultimate remedy lies in improved diet, housing, sanitation and personal hygiene. Indeed, these factors, the very stuff of the improved standards of living sought in the five year plans, will do as much as specific campaigns, it seems, to reduce these remaining major problems of public health. All of these contribute to the still high infant and child mortality rates (Fig. 4.9; Learmonth *op. cit.* in chapter bibliography). As these diseases become less important – and there are hopeful signs from some areas and socio-economic classes – with better general nutrition and infant and child feeding as well as maternal care and welfare, these rates are also gradually improving.

Pakistan – some demographic considerations
The foregoing discussion has been conducted mainly for the sub-continent as a whole – mainly because some of the major sources were written before Partition or maintain this viewpoint in order to follow up the census records of the British period which are good, by comparison with most underdeveloped regions, since about 1881. Pakistan has, however, some particularities from the demographic viewpoint.

The 1961 census revealed a total population of 93,810,000, but a leading demographer working in this area estimates that allowing for under-enumeration, the figure would be 100,000,000 by mid-1961.[28] The official totals of 50,800,000 for East Pakistan and 40,800,000 for West Pakistan plus 2,200,000 in Karachi represent densities of 1,200 per sq. mile (460 per sq. km²) and 130 per sq. mile (50 per km²) respectively. East Pakistan would rank with Java, of the predominantly rural areas, and is as densely peopled as many industrialized countries (Belgium, 785 p.s.m., 302 per km²), though of course with much lower standards of living. West Pakistan, on the other hand, would compare say with Malaya, though it must be remembered that much hot desert is more uncompromisingly uninhabitable than a humid wilderness like interior Malaya; densities of the order of 750 per sq. mile (290 per km²), as in Sialkot and Lyallpur may represent population saturation given existing agricultural techniques and proportions of industrially employed, though granted at rather higher standards of living (and lower population pressure) than are common in East Pakistan.

The recorded rate of population increase 1951–61 was 2·2% per annum, though this may be a little overstated, as some demographers suspect, owing to under-registration (or greater under-registration) in the 1951 as compared with the 1961 census. Even if there is slight overstatement, the increase is considerable, especially since Pakistan's anti-malaria campaigns are only now getting fully into their stride. Rates of increase are higher in West than in East Pakistan;

[28] K. J. Krotki, 'First release from the second population census of Pakistan, 1961', *Pak. Dev. Rev.* 1/2 (1961), 66–71; this article is extensively used in this section.

though the East may have more under-registration, it is the more likely area
to have rates of increase damped down by malaria until the disease is eradi-
cated, and the West to be affected by malaria epidemics (cf. p. 139), so that
the contrast is probably justified. Also the West has had considerable irrigation projects and inward migration. It is likely that one cause of the upward
trend in rates of increase is later marriage (say from early to late teens) which
reduces excessively early child-bearing causing maternal mortality, or sterility
in later years. The upward trend is likely to be maintained, at least for some time,
and the implications for economic planning are serious. As Krotki points out,
investment of 12% of the national income – a high figure outside totalitarian
states – would only keep pace with the population increase, allowing existing and
unsatisfactory standards of living to be maintained – and that on the assumption
of even distribution of benefits from the investment among socio-economic
groups; an investment of 16% would, on such population trends, only permit of
the doubling of the present standard of living by the end of the century.[29]

Conclusion – demographic prospects and policies
There are surely regional demographic differences of academic and practical
importance. The rural population density map today invites not merely an
academic exercise in synthesis, but a systematic study in population capacity –
by no means impossible with modern techniques though it would be expensive
in skill, time and money. A map of urban population invites study both of broad
urban patterns and characteristics and amenities, and of individual city spheres of
influence preferably built up systematically until one can appreciate the complex
and dynamic web of urban influence over the sub-continent. Both of these
studies have been the subject of probing attacks and are certainly practicable.
Regional differences in demographic history are apparently becoming blurred
at present as all parts of the country enter the phase of population increase
differentiated only by degree of rapidity: if there are in fact associated regional
differences in social psychology, as Geddes believes, these may be of academic
and practical importance. But this is a topic difficult to investigate conclusively
because of the extraordinarily complex and multi-dimensional matrix of factors
involved, and equally because of political sensitivity about contemplating some
of them, almost amounting to aversion. Regional forecasts of population using
projections can be done, and may be increasingly necessary should regional
planning be used in the future as a complement to national planning. (Such
regional forecasts might in fact permit greater accuracy in a macro-demographic
projection, or at least a useful check on these.) But naturally enough most concern among educated Indians and Pakistanis and abroad is focused on the

[29] K. J. Krotki, 'Population control – a review article', *Pak. Dev. Rev.* 1/3 (1961), 89–98;
the paper bears a significant sub-title, a quotation from R. L. Meier: 'We cannot be
optimistic and honest at the same time.' See also S. M. Haider, 'Study of population
pressure in relation to agricultural development in Pakistan', *Indian Jnl Econ.* Vol. 38,
No. 153, Pt. 3 (1958), 239–48.

national situation, on macro-demographic problems and policies, specifically on population projections and on family planning programmes, especially in India.

Authoritative projections, made in the 1950s, ranged from 408,000,000 to 424,000,000.[30] India's 1961 population, over 439,000,000, exceeded the highest estimate based on projections, as the preliminary census report points out. More than any other single factor, this discrepancy is due to the demographic revolution effected at a stroke and without much need for widespread public co-operation by malaria control. This underestimate of the upsurge of population was a serious matter particularly in relation to the Second Five Year Plan, many of the benefits of which were eaten up, as it were, by the extra mouths. (While it may be argued that the effort in the Second Plan was maximal and would not be effected by better population forecasts, there is on the other hand the possibility that more foreign aid might have been forthcoming if the full seriousness of the demographic prospect had been realized.) Neither demographers nor planners realized the significance of the effects of malaria control upon both death rates and birth rates, although in a country as near and in some ways as similar as Ceylon, population increase had gone up to 3% per annum within a year or two of the establishment of malaria control, and a very carefully worked out paper on the effects of malaria on mortality had been proved quite wrong.[31] There can be no better example of the need for co-ordinating disciplines in both academic and practical affairs.

Even before the rate of population increase swung up in this way, the government of India had however been greatly concerned about the population problem. After all even an increase of 1·2% per annum as it was in 1951 represented an annual increase of 4,500,000 people – a sufficiently daunting prospect for a nation trying to combat poverty.

There are many strands of thinking, sometimes conflicting, about family planning in India – neo-Malthusian, from the 1920s or even before; Gandhian, with much emphasis on abstinence; anti-colonialist and Marxist, perhaps changing a little as the problems have increased even following Independence.[32] But

[30] R. P. Sinha, *Food in India* (OUP, Bombay, 1961), Ch. IV.
[31] C. A. Gill, 'The influence of malaria on natality with special reference to Ceylon', 1940, *Jnl Malaria Inst. of India*, 3, 201–52; for a recent critical review see H. Fredericksen, 'Economic and demographic consequences of malaria control in Ceylon', *Ind. Jnl Malariology* 16/4 (1962), 379–91.
[32] S. Thapar, 'Family Planning in India', *Population Studies*, 17 (1963), 4–19, gives a very useful history; R. C. Cook, 'India: high cost of high fertility', *Population Bulletin*, 14/8 (1958), for a recent, by no means entirely negative neo-Malthusian view; G. Chand, *Some aspects of the population problem of India* (Patna, 1954), is an extremely well-written socialist view, stressing the need for a positive approach to family size and spacing, and showing resentment of foreign neo-Malthusian views including earlier work by R. C. Cook; S. Chandrasekhar's many works include *Demographic Disarmament for India* (Bombay, 1951), a very clear brief statement, and 'The population factor in economic development', *Population Rev.* (1964), 54–7; see also W. S. Thompson, *Population and Progress in the Far East* (Chicago, 1959).

there is now widespread agreement on the need for population control in order that the very tiny improvements in standards of living of the great bulk of the

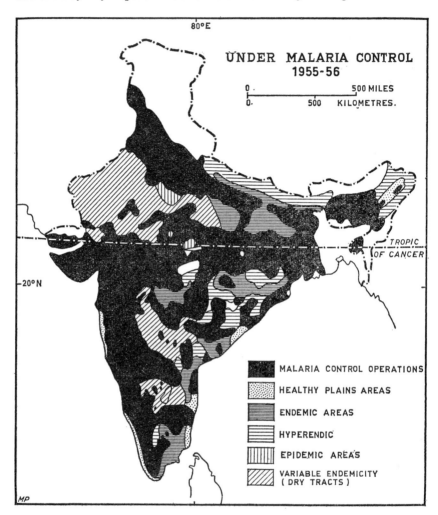

FIG 4.10 AREA UNDER MALARIA CONTROL, INDIA, 1955–56. During the four or five years up to 1956, malaria control had spread very rapidly over the most malarious areas; by now almost the whole country has been controlled and the emphasis has shifted to eradication. Figs 4.8 to 4.10 from A. T. A. Learmonth in *IGJ* 33/1–2 (1958); Fig 4.10 is ultimately from the Malaria Institute of India's 1956 conference.

people since Independence should be much increased in future. So far it has been a matter of running hard to do little better than keep standing still. Family planning has been officially promoted, especially research and experimental work, ever since the First Five Year Plan. Naturally enough there is, on the whole, readier acceptance of the ideas of family planning in the cities where even the poorer groups rapidly become more sophisticated in some respects than their rural cousins. There is not unexpectedly a great desire for family limitation among the women, and fairly widespread acceptance of the idea even among the men. The main difficulty in towns is the cost of any form of mechanical or chemical contraceptives, especially in the poorer groups where the need is greatest. The same groups also suffer from ignorance, illiteracy and notably 'innumeracy' when attempting to apply the rhythm method – a fickle one at best. There is also a widespread demand for treatment for sterility among childless couples, and it is one of the stronger cards of the family planning clinics in establishing *rapport* with their communities that they are frequently able to help with this problem.

In the villages all the problems are large, there is much more conservatism, ignorance, illiteracy even among fairly prosperous groups, much less acceptance from the men of the very concept of the need for family planning; and the crushing burden of ignorance even among actively interested women is illustrated by the now well known example of misunderstanding: beads representing the menstrual cycle differentiating the most likely period for conception – the 'danger period' for the couple with a large enough family or desiring to space the family more widely – were in fact placed around the neck of a goat, in a village near the experimental clinic in Ramanagaram in Mysore, in order to *induce* a caprine pregnancy! Constant effort is applied to improving the methods both of contraception and of communication, and to increasing the coverage of the enormous population by family planning clinics. If as yet there has been no effort comparable to that in China at times when population control is desired by the Communist government, there are some additional problems, such as the linguistic ones, and of course there is no channel of communication comparable in power to the Communist Party caucus and Party member down to village level. At present, success with contraception and the rhythm method has been so limited that the government department concerned has turned, as a desperate remedy, to sterilization, especially of men once they have say three children including at least one son; there is even some tendency to regard the planned increase of medical practitioners as an additional force of potential vasectomists, a sterile objective! From the beginning of the campaign to encourage vasectomy in 1956 to April 1962 the total number of operations performed was only some 98,000 mostly in Madras and Maharashtra. This form of campaign seems doomed to failure, probably implying undesirable social, psychological and international consequences.[33] On the other hand, the time-lag is considerable before improved

[33] S. Chandrasekhar, 'The population factor in economic development', *Population Rev.* 8/2 (1964), 54–7; for a view, not against sterilization, but on the dangers of bad communications concerning it, see E. Wood, 'Science in family planning', *Thought*, 24 (1961), 9.

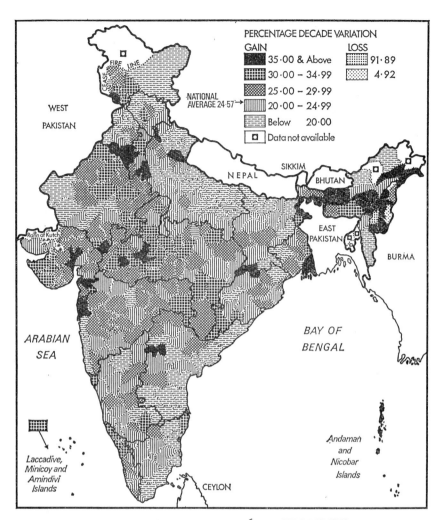

PERCENTAGE DECADE VARIATION

GAIN
- 35·00 & Above
- 30·00 – 34·99
- 25·00 – 29·99
- 20·00 – 24·99
- Below 20·00
- Data not available

LOSS
- 91·89
- 4·92

NATIONAL AVERAGE 24·57 →

WEST PAKISTAN

CEASE FIRE LINE

NEPAL

SIKKIM

BHUTAN

EAST PAKISTAN

BURMA

Rann of Kutch

ARABIAN SEA

BAY OF BENGAL

Laccadive, Minicoy and Amindivi Islands

Andaman and Nicobar Islands

CEYLON

FIG 4.11 INDIA, GROWTH RATES 1961–71 BY DISTRICTS

Note on the 1971 Census of India The provisional totals for the 1971 census have come to hand as the reprint of this book goes to the press. This map has been substituted for that of urban services in Mysore State; we have selected population growth as a complement to Fig 4.6, a somewhat similar map for India and Pakistan 1951–61.

The 1971 provisional total of population for India was 546,955,945 (1951, 439,072,582) – an increase of 107 millions or 24·57% (1951–61), 21·64%. Though, the growth rate is still increasing, the upsurge is in fact rather less than had been expected, and the Census Paper cited notes that death rates had not fallen quite as much as forecast, while family planning may have had marginally greater impact than expected.

The cities or urban agglomerations of over a million had populations and 1961–71 increases as follows: Calcutta 7,040,345 (c. 50%), Bombay 5,931,989 (43%), Delhi 3,629,842 (54%), Madras 2,470,288 (43%), Hyderabad 1,798,910 (48%), Ahmedabad 1,746,111 (45%), Bangalore 1,648,232 (37%), Kanpur 1,273,042 (31%), and Poona 1,123,399 (52%).

standards of education and of material living can be expected to cause a moderation in population increase to rates compatible with the provision of food and a good standard of living (see pp. 137, 281). Assuming continuance of India's five year plans, one can think ultimate success possible, and look forward to a prosperous and relatively stable population in this great sub-continent, but the next generation or two can hardly fail to be very difficult, strained, painful and dangerous. Is there any possibility that a *deus ex machina* may come to solve the problem created by that other *deus ex machina*, the residual insecticide? A really cheap oral contraceptive without side effects on health may be just around the corner. If so, or if the high hopes placed on the 'loop' are realised, the Malthusian spectre may be laid once more.

BIBLIOGRAPHICAL NOTE

The reader wishing to explore this topic should start with Kingsley Davis, *The Population of India and Pakistan*, (Princeton, 1950), though with a sceptical eye on some resources like 'culturable waste': then follow up the footnotes in this chapter. R. P. Sinha, *Food in India* (OUP, Bombay, 1961) is useful as is the *Fact Book of Manpower* (Institute of Applied Research, New Delhi, 1963). The Censuses of India and of Pakistan remain fundamental, and the Indian census publications after the 1961 count include stimulating items like an atlas volume, village surveys, and a monograph series on village crafts. Critical material on demographic and economic data include Krotki's papers cited earlier, J. E. Schwartzberg, *Occupational structure and level of economic development in India: a regional analysis* (University Microfilms, Ann Arbor), and papers in *Population Studies*, published from the Indian Institute of Demographic Studies.

Note on Fig 4.11 The distribution pattern of high rates reflects these high growth rates in the major cities and urgan agglomerations. The eye is drawn to the patchy areas of high increase in hilly but often sparsely peopled tracts in the north and east and again in middle India where they include the Dandakaranya colonization area in the Bastar highlands. Colonization, planned or by family movement, is involved in the Assam plains, the Rajasthan canal tract (including the area in Haryana), and in and around the new steel towns like Bhilai and Rourkela. There are also high increases in densely peopled northern Kerala, in Goa, and in relatively sparsely peopled but highly urbanised western Kathiawad. The areas of *relatively* low increases include areas of emigration and agricultural depression like the plains of Uttar Pradesh, Bihar and the western fringes of West Bengal, North Kanara south of Bombay, and the coastal tracts of Tamilnadu and Andhra Pradesh with access to Madras, Bangalore and Hyderabad.

But the overall picture is of increase *all* of which would have been rated as high only twenty years ago.

Source: A Chandra Sekhar, Registrar General and Census Commissioner India, Paper No. 1 of 1971, *Provisional Population Totals*, Census of India 1971, Series 1, India, Delhi, 1971; our map is after Map 2 p. 9.

CHAPTER 5

The Peoples of the Sub-continent

GENERALITIES

That the diversity of the peoples of India baffles description is a commonplace. Only less frequent is the observation that there is an underlying – or overlaying – cultural unity. This is undoubtedly true of India proper: everywhere, except in some Himalayan and jungle areas, the structure of society and the architectural landscape bear the strong impress of Hinduism. If we think of caste rather than religion, the ambit of common cultural features is yet wider, since even groups whose origin was an avowed or implied rejection of caste still retain traces (sometimes more) of caste attitudes, or are influenced, in greater or less degree by caste spirit: Indian Christians, Sikhs, some fractions at least of the Tribes and even the Muslims. In fact it is hardly an exaggeration to say that the only considerable groups with a culture not at least strongly influenced by Hinduism are the hillmen of West Pakistan, some of the Assam border tribes, and the Buddhists of Ladakh or 'Little Tibet'.

Despite the Pakistani 'Two Nations' theory, the main mass of Muslims have a culture which, if dominantly Islamic, is yet shot through with strands of 'Indianism' (to avoid the word Hinduism). Only Islam has had sufficient strength to exert a reciprocal influence and that has been rather limited, perhaps most clearly seen in the extension of *purdah* (the seclusion of women); and here other sociological factors clearly have their part. In more recent times Christianity has compelled some reassessment of Hindu ideals; like Islam, it had most to offer to those towards the bottom of the caste ladder. But the role of Christianity is difficult to disentangle from that of Westernization in general; Western secular humanism does at least provide some neutral ground on which the adherents of various faiths can meet.[1] Finally it must always be remembered that the religion of the masses – Hindu, Muslim, and Christian – is pervaded by more primitive beliefs.

Ethnic and linguistic divisions do not, in general, correspond to any marked extent; and both are cut across by religion. The division of most practical

[1] It has been pointed out, for example, that some Indian leaders, whose final attitude is known to be essentially agnostic, would by that fact be almost certainly precluded from high political office in the United States. It is 'community' rather than actual belief which counts.

significance is that of 'community': this is for the most part a religious differentiation, but it has some ethnic, linguistic and cultural connotations in the 'Tribes',
and in the 'Scheduled Castes' it recognizes a cleavage within the main religious
community. The minor religious communities – Sikhs, Parsees, Jains – may

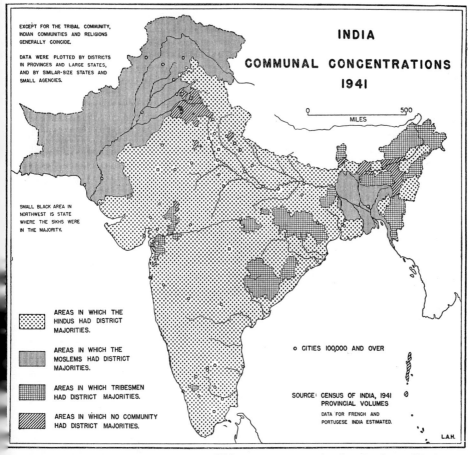

EXCEPT FOR THE TRIBAL COMMUNITY,
INDIAN COMMUNITIES AND RELIGIONS
GENERALLY COINCIDE.

DATA WERE PLOTTED BY DISTRICTS
IN PROVINCES AND LARGE STATES,
AND BY SIMILAR-SIZE STATES AND
SMALL AGENCIES.

INDIA

COMMUNAL CONCENTRATIONS

1941

0   500
MILES

SMALL BLACK AREA IN
NORTHWEST IS STATE
WHERE THE SIKHS WERE
IN THE MAJORITY.

AREAS IN WHICH THE
HINDUS HAD DISTRICT
MAJORITIES.

AREAS IN WHICH THE
MOSLEMS HAD DISTRICT
MAJORITIES.

AREAS IN WHICH TRIBESMEN
HAD DISTRICT MAJORITIES.

AREAS IN WHICH NO COMMUNITY
HAD DISTRICT MAJORITIES.

o CITIES 100,000 AND OVER

SOURCE: CENSUS OF INDIA, 1941
PROVINCIAL VOLUMES

DATA FOR FRENCH AND
PORTUGESE INDIA ESTIMATED.

L.A.H.

FIG 5.1 MAJOR COMMUNITIES, 1941. This map represents the situation immediately
before, and essentially responsible for, the Partition of 1947. *Source:* L. Hoffmann
in *GJ* 91 (1948).

perhaps best be thought of as kiths as defined by Huntington: 'A group of people
relatively homogeneous in language and culture, and freely intermarrying with
one another.'[2]

Ethnic stocks
Only the baldest summary, following B. S. Guha, can be given here; it would be
the vainest of labours to attempt a description of the salient physical and cultural

[2] *Mainsprings of Civilization* (Wiley, NY, 1945), 102 fn.

characteristics of even the main groups in the few available pages. There has been some criticism of Guha's scheme, notably by D. N. Majumdar; but, although the latter has taken blood-group surveys into account, it cannot be said that anything very clear emerges, except that Guha may have overstressed the Negrito element. The populations of the sub-continent exhibit in varying degree characteristics from the four major stocks of mankind: Negroid, Australoid, Mongoloid and Caucasoid.

Of earlier peoples, almost the only known skeletal remains of much significance are those of the Indus Valley civilization: these show very close affinities with those of pre-Sargonic Mesopotamia (Al-Ubaid and Kish). The numerous Megalithic remains of the Peninsula undoubtedly hold vital evidence on the peopling of India; their scientific exploration is but beginning.

The earliest of existing groups are the *Negritos* (Negroids of small stature), of whom the Andaman Islanders are good examples. The Kadars of Cochin, like the Andamanese still hunters and gatherers (except where contaminated by out-side influence), also show some Negrito characteristics; and traces at least of Negrito physical types have been reported from the Rajmahal Hills.

Far more significant are the evidences of *Australoid* stock which appear in the tribal populations of the south and centre (e.g. Mundas, Santals). In varying mixtures, this is the underlying strain in very much of the Hindu population, especially of lower or 'exterior' castes, south of the Narmada–Chota Nagpur line. The Veddas of Ceylon seem to represent a more specialized development from this group, which is also often styled pre-Dravidian; but Dravidian, like Aryan, is better kept as a linguistic term.

The tribal peoples of the north are essentially dissimilar, and, as might be expected, show marked *Mongoloid* characters. They occupy a broad band of Himalayan and sub-Himalayan country from Kashmir to Bhután; in the hills on either side of the Assam valley a long-headed Mongoloid type is dominant; the Burmese are more brachycephalic. The Assam Valley itself has an interesting fusion of Mongoloids (the Shan Ahoms, who were the mediaeval rulers) with Palaeo-Mediterraneans, the bearers of Hindu culture.

The populations which show the most marked evidences of these three major stocks (Negroid, Australoid and Mongoloid) are mainly tribal, though of course these elements are not confined to the tribes, nor are they represented in all tribes. The 'higher' populations are more complex still.

The largest *Caucasoid* element is *Mediterranean*; 'moderate stature, long head, slightly built body, dark complexion'. The Palaeo-Mediterraneans appear to have introduced a Megalithic culture, perhaps originally Neolithic; they form the main component of the Dravidian speakers. Another Mediterranean group, Guha's 'Large-brained Chalcolithic Type', represented by the numerous skeletons of the Indus valley civilization, is dominant in northern India and form a large proportion of the upper classes elsewhere. There is also an 'Oriental' type, mainly in the northwestern hills and the Punjab; it is intrusive elsewhere with upper-class Muslims, descendants of Pathan invaders, and has strong affinities with Anatolian and Arabian groups.

Somewhat later, apparently, than the 'Chalcolithic' type, there was a considerable penetration of Western Brachycephalic types – Alpines, Dinarics and Armenoids. They entered probably via Makran, mingling with the Mediterraneans (they are represented among the Indus valley skeletons), and thence moved as far as Ceylon, while another branch followed the Ganga to Bengal.

Finally, and in many respects more important, there were the great folk-wanderings which brought the *Proto-Nordic* Indo-Aryans. These steppe pastoralists, tall, fair, meat-eating, entered northern India in the latter part of the 2nd millennium BC; together with Mediterraneans they are dominant in the country between the Indus and Bundelkhand, and in Maharashtra form an important element in fusion with Palaeo-Mediterraneans, Alpo-Dinarics, and Proto-Australoids. In the extreme northwest almost blond types are found, and even in Maharashtra almost 10% of the Chitpavan Brahmins have light eyes.

The ethnic history of India is thus complicated, in keeping with the general diversity of the sub-continent. The various stocks have brought diverse gifts, material and cultural, to the common store. The Vedic hymns and the treasury of Sanskrit literature are the obvious contributions of the Indo-Aryans; but the basic concepts of Hinduism seem rather Dravidian, stemming from the Mediterraneans of the Indus valley and the Proto-Australoids.[3]

Language and literacy

There is only a very rough correlation between ethnic stock and language. The Himalayan and Assam tribes speak mainly Tibeto–Burman languages, those of the central hills Dravidian or yet older Austric languages; the south is almost solidly Dravidian, the north mainly Indo–Aryan. That is about as far as one can go; both Indo–Aryan and Dravidian tongues are spoken by representatives of almost all the main racial groups. And even so there are many outliers, of which perhaps the most interesting is the Dravidian Brahui of Baluchistan (cf. p. 184).

The 'racial' element has indeed its importance – a very great importance – in the cultural history of India; it is of little practical significance today. Few Indians (and for that matter few Englishmen) could speak with any degree of scientific accuracy as to their racial origins; everyone knows what language he speaks. Next to religion language is the greatest divisive force in India (and Pakistan) today.

The diversity of tongues was one of the standard imperialistic arguments against nationalist claims. Actually there is not a great deal in it as it was presented. It is true that the 1931 Census showed 225 Indian and Burmese languages; but the great majority of these were mere tribal splinters spoken by a few hundred

[3] See B. S. Guha, *Racial Elements in the Population* (OPIA No. 22, 1944), 27–29, for a brilliant summary; and cf. D. N. Majumdar, *Races and Cultures of India* (Asia, Bombay, 1958).

or at most a few thousand people: very interesting to philologists, but not insuperable obstacles to the unity of over 300,000,000 people. The communist writer Palme Dutt criticized the *Imperial Gazetteer* for citing Andro, spoken by one person only; however, the 1951 Census of India lists 720 languages or dialects with less than 100,000 speakers each, and of these no less than 73 were returned as spoken by one speaker: lonely souls.[4] On the other hand, ten languages accounted for 319,000,000 out of a total population of 357,000,000 – 89%.

There are indeed only some 12 or 15 really major languages, and some of these are closely akin: hardly an alarming total for an area and population comparable to Europe. The most important distinction is that between the Dravidian tongues of the south and the Indo–Aryan of the north and centre. The chief Dravidian languages are Telugu and Tamil (Figs. 5.2, 23.4) with over 33,000,000 and 26,500,000 speakers respectively in 1961, Kanarese or Kannada (14·5 million), and Malayalam, the speech of Kerala (13·4 million). The Indo–Aryan languages account for about three-quarters of the population of the sub-continent, and one of them, Hindi, with its branches ranks numerically as one of the greater languages of the world: in 1935 Western Hindi was spoken by over 105,000,000 people, and it has been gaining rapidly by nationalist and (since 1947) official favour. Other important languages are Bengali with 25,000,000,[5] leader in the literary renaissance in India, Marathi with 27,000,000, and Gujarati, less important numerically (16,000,000) but the main language of indigenous commerce in western India.

Bi- and even tri-lingualism are widespread among all classes except the peasantry of linguistically homogeneous areas. It is probable that there are not many market towns in which the traveller equipped with Hindustani, Tamil and English could not be readily understood.[6]

Yet the problem of a common language remains serious: the world has seen too much use of the linguistic weapon by forces making for disunity. So far English has been the language of most serious scholarship (outside theology) and has been a *lingua franca* for the intelligentsia; but only about 1–2% of the population is literate in English, though English of sorts is understood by many illiterates. Bazaar or camp English is a wasting asset (as well as an insult to Shakespeare's tongue), but the disappearance of academic English would be an intellectual catastrophe of the first order, gravely limiting contacts with the outside world, and especially with the main currents of scientific and social thought. In the past the too-exclusive use of English as a medium of instruction may have impeded learning in other subjects, without always imparting noticeable mastery

[4] There was also, surprisingly, one speaker of Newzealandian.
[5] Figures for India only; Bengali is of course the dominant language of the 51,000,000 people (1961) of East Pakistan.
[6] Cf. G. Slater's remark (*Southern India* (1936), 33): 'Ability to read and write . . . are the Indian census tests of literacy, and by these India makes a very bad showing. If ability to speak and understand a second language were also tested, Madras would show far better results than London. . . .'

in its own use; but there seems to be already some decline in the standard of English in the universities.

Yet it is only to be expected that really creative work will tend more and more to be written in the great mother-tongues of India and, despite expedient delays, the policy of replacing English in provincial and eventually in central

FIG 5.2 LINGUISTIC REGIONS, 1951. The dominance of Hindi in no less than 86 Districts will be noticed. *Courtesy* R. Tirtha.

administration will doubtless prevail in the end. Nevertheless, there are reasonable and serious doubts as to how far the supersession of English should go.[7] Despite its scores of millions of speakers, it will be a long time before Hindi can rank as a world language in the sense in which English is a world language. Its advance to such status is of course retarded by indiscreet Sanskritization instead

[7] Pandit Nehru himself expressed such doubts. For balanced comment, see S. A. Husain, *The National Culture of India* (Asia, Bombay, 2nd ed. 1961), 209–11; Irawati Karve, *Hindu Society – an Interpretation* (Deccan College, Poona, 1961), 131–42.

of transliterating quasi-international technical terms, and by its special script which is, however, one of the factors in its bid to become not only the dominant internal but even the 'national' language.

Nationalist opinion on the whole favours the spread of Hindi as a common language, though it meets with considerable opposition especially in Tamilnad, conscious of its high literary tradition. With its Hindustani form it is undoubtedly the most widely known language; but Hindustani is often a debased *patois*: it has been said, with picturesque exaggeration, that the vocabulary of 'bazaar Hindustani' could be written on a postcard and its grammar under the stamp. High Hindi has a heavily Sanskritized vocabulary and uses the Sanskritic Nagari script. The attachment of the various linguistic groups to their scripts is a serious bar to intercourse, the more irrational in that languages orally more or less mutually intelligible become much more differentiated when written. Yet practically all the Indo–Aryan languages (with the major exception of Urdu) use scripts which stem from Sanskrit characters, and all the Dravidian from those of Pali. They all have the same ancient and very scientific syllabary, but the number of types necessary for printing is excessive (some 450 for Nagari) owing to special forms for joined characters; and they are difficult to write quickly, though aesthetically far superior to any *modern* European scripts. Romanization would seem a feasible and an impartial solution, but for obvious reasons is not likely to be adopted.

The real danger to unity arises not from the existence of hundreds of little languages, but from the rivalries of a few great ones. The agitation for linguistic states was a handy stick for beating the British Raj, but it has been admitted by a Congress committee that its implications were not properly considered. Andhra Pradesh – the Telegu-speaking area – was early accepted as a special case; it was formed from the northern districts of Madras in 1953 and in 1956 absorbed the Telangana region of the former princely state of Hyderabad. Naturally this success spurred on other claimants, and the entire political map of India has now been reorganized.

There are of course reasonable arguments for linguistic states, especially that the mass of the population and its immediate governors should have a common tongue. Nevertheless it is clear enough that the principle carries with it the risk of separatism, and this was recognized by the able *Report of the States Reorganization Committee* (1955) which accepted the risk in face of the high degree of popular expectation which had been aroused. Some changes were carried out smoothly enough: the formation of *Kerala* from Cochin, Travancore and a small Malayalam-speaking area of Madras; of *Mysore* from Mysore, Coorg, the Bombay Karnatak, the Kanaras and the Kannada-speaking Districts of Raichur and Gulbarga in Hyderabad and Bellary in Madras; of *Madhya Pradesh*, essentially the old British Central Provinces minus a Marathi-speaking area and plus many old princely states, of which the most important were Gwalior and Bhopal. But the attempt at combining the Marathi areas of the Deccan with Gujarat broke down completely, and the latter became a separate state in 1960; and there are still tensions arising from the Gujarati commercial dominance in Bombay city, which remains in Maharashtra.

Other states were left as they were, apart from minor mergers and boundary changes; but some of these led to serious disturbances, especially some territorially minor but economically significant changes on the borders of Bihar, West Bengal and Orissa, while there is still some difficulty in the Punjab where the Sikh-dominated west speaks Punjabi rather than Hindi (cf. p. 172).

The linguistic solution cannot of course be complete; there are anomalies such as the queer protrusion of Jhansi from Uttar Pradesh into Madhya Pradesh. More seriously, the principle lends itself to undue local patriotisms, which are likely to be reflected for example in school histories. Allegations of cultural neglect of minority languages provide yet another factional element in already factionalized state politics; but such cross-currents may be some offset to the potentially most dangerous latent separatism, that of the non-Aryan south expressed in terms of 'Dravidastan'.

Apparently as a more formal offset to the inherently fissiparous tendency of linguistic states, the government in 1955 put forward, in a curiously casual way, the idea of forming five (later six) great Zones. Zonal councils group states for planning purposes, for example in relation to the use of common rivers for irrigation or power, and may act as a liaison between New Delhi and the states. It is not clear that this insertion into the bureaucratic structure of another tier of councils and committees has had a great deal of practical effect.[8]

The official language of Pakistan is, or is designed to be, Urdu; similar to Hindi in grammatical construction and basic vocabulary, it developed as the Court or camp language of the Moguls, uses Persian script and largely draws on Persian for its higher vocabulary. The script is also ill-adapted for printing, lithography being still important. It is being introduced into university teaching in West Pakistan, but in East Bengal the hold of Bengali is too strong for its supersession by Urdu to be lightly undertaken.

Literacy has shown a marked increase since Independence:[9] of those over five years of age, in 1951 one in six in India could write a simple letter, in 1961 one in four; for Pakistan the 1961 figure is one in six. Female literacy, though increasing more rapidly than male, still lags: 12·9% and 34·4% respectively in India in 1961, 8·0% and 25·8% in Pakistan. Literacy of course is very unequally distributed both regionally and communally: almost universal among such a small and select group as the Parsees, it is still almost nil in large tribal and peasant groups; in Kerala the literacy rate in 1961 was 46·8%, in Kashmir only 11%. The advance, though irregular, is gratifying; but a good deal of it is by way of adult education and mass literacy campaigns, and at a low level.

[8] For these matters, see J. V. Bondurant, *Regionalism versus Provincialism: A Study in Problems of Indian National Unity* (Univ. of California, Berkeley, 1958).
[9] There is a good review in G. S. Gosal, 'Literacy in India: an interpretative study', *Rural Sociology*, 29 (1964), 261–77.

Education remains badly balanced: the imposing concrete buildings of the universities rest on the timber and brick of the Government High Schools, they in turn on the mud or thatch huts of the primaries. The proportion of literates who have been to a university is higher than in the West (or at least was until the recent mass-literacy drive); but standards are very unequal and wastage appalling. The preference for arts and legal subjects led to the creation of a vast clerical and professional proletariat, too many for available openings and not infrequently driven to miserable shifts for existence; but good technicians are too few for the country's needs. This ill-balance is perhaps due pretty equally to Indian traditions and the British demand for clerks, but its redress is essential, and happily there are some signs of change. Healthy progress will depend also on more serious attention than has generally been given to the elementary schools; the foundations of a building are after all its most vital part. And on a broader view the liquidation or mitigation of many social ills calls for education, particularly in the villages, in the widest and most liberal sense. There is no room for shallow enthusiasm about moral uplift and more literacy drives: their gains have all too frequently been dissipated by lack of *sustained* effort.

Religions and communities

The 'communities' recognized by the Indian Census, in Indian politics, and in daily life[10] are primarily religious divisions, although race, language, caste, geographical localization, and broad cultural distinctions also shape them in part. Thus the 'Aboriginal Tribes' include Hindus, Christians and even Muslims, though the majority follow particularist religions in which emphasis is given to the worship of spirits. The great bulk of the population is of course either Hindu or Muslim; it is important to note that the Partition was not a 'solution' of the communal problem, and (except by a few extremists on both sides) was not intended to be so. Of the 92,000,000 Muslims in All-India in 1941, only 22,000,000 were in West and 29,000,000 in East Pakistan; some 5,000,000 of the remainder were in Kashmir and Hyderabad. This still left some 36,000,000 in India; but although the enforced migrations of the immediate post-Partition period (and after later outbreaks of communal violence) reduced the 'unredeemed' Muslims, and conversely rendered West Pakistan over 97% Muslim, there were in 1961 about 46,939,000 Muslims in India. This is, however, a bare 9·5% or less against the 24% of undivided India, and there is now not a single Muslim majority District in India – excluding Kashmir.

The extent and nature of Muslim invasions and cultural influence are discussed in Chapter 6 (Historical Outlines) and the relevant regional sections.

Hindus in 1961 numbered some 366,500,000 or 83%, including *Scheduled Castes*; but this cleavage will be discussed as part of the general question of caste. We may note, however, that most Muslims in the sub-continent are the des-

[10] Their significance will be diminished, but in practical affairs far from ended, by the abolition of separate communal electorates.

cendants of converts from Hinduism, generally from lower castes, and though some caste attitudes were retained it is probable that the egalitarian elements in Islam formed a great part of its appeal. This is also the case with Christianity, though here too some compromise with caste has at times and places been considered expedient: perhaps more frequently by Roman Catholics, though Protestants have by no means been immune. Moreover, three Indian religions arose largely as reactions against the caste domination of the Brahmins. These are the faiths of *Buddhists*, *Sikhs* and *Jains*.

Incomparably the greatest of these is *Buddhism*, but until the last few years it hardly survived in the land of its birth: only a few monks, mostly Nepalese and Sinhalese, were to be found in the holy places, Buddh Gaya where Gautama received Enlightenment, Sarnath where he began his mission. Early Buddhism had a simple and rational humanistic code, independent of theism and as far from the more pathological forms of asceticism as from hedonism, and with an emphasis on the fellowship, irrespective of caste or station, of men (and women) of good will. When Asoka, desolated by the horrors of his Kalinga war, devoted himself to 'the chiefest conquest' – of the hearts of men – he initiated the great missionary period which has resulted in the survival of the earlier and purer form (though shot through with Animism) in Ceylon, Burma and Thailand. The Graeco-Buddhist sculptures of Gandhara, the ruins of the great University at Taxila, and the colossal cliff-figures at Bamian in Afghanistan, attest the long vitality of Buddhism in the northwest, whence it penetrated High Asia. Deterioration of the creed itself, Brahmin opposition and some persecution, gradually weakened it; by the time of the Muslim invasions it was strong only in its original home, Magadha. But the discontent of the Scheduled Castes or 'Untouchables' with the progress of promised reforms has led to a dramatic change; under the impulsion of a dynamic leader, the late Dr B. R. Ambedkar, many thousands of this community now return themselves as Buddhists, though their degree of informed belief may be doubtful. Whereas in 1951 the Census showed under 200,000 Buddhists, mostly in Sikkim and Baltistan or 'Little Tibet', the 1961 Census showed over 3,250,000, and of these just on 2,800,000 were in Maharashtra. There has also, of course, been a considerable influx of Tibetan refugees into the traditional Buddhist areas of Baltistan and Sikkim.

Jainism antedated Buddhism, and may even represent a continuation of pre-Vedic opposition to Brahminism. It developed an exaggerated asceticism (particularly in the renunciation of clothing) and carried *ahimsa* – reverence for organic or rather animal life – to almost incredible extremes: the practice of wearing a cloth over the mouth to avoid accidentally swallowing insects probably gave rise to the report by the Greek Megasthenes (*c.* 302 BC) of a race which had no mouth and lived on delicate savours. Jainism hardly exists outside India, but its adherents number over 2,025,000. They are strongest in Rajasthan (especially Marwar), Gujarat and Maharashtra, which have about 85% of the Jains; their chief sanctuary is Mount Abu in the Aravallis. Many Jains are traders and financiers, Marwari Chambers of Commerce being powers in the land as far afield as Calcutta; nor, if common repute may be relied on, is their tenderness for physical life reflected in their business ethics: there are few more hardheaded forestallers and usurers than some Marwaris.

The *Sikhs* are much younger; their founder, Guru Nanak (1469–1538) was an eclectic drawing from Islam and Hinduism. Ironically, in view of their later reputation, the Sikhs were originally politically quietist, even pacifist; their military virtues were a response to Muslim persecution after the death (1605) of Akbar, himself the greatest of eclectics. Ideologically they are nearer Hinduism than Islam, but they reject caste; and, though diverse in origin, they have developed by inbreeding and strict discipline into a distinct people, recognizable as such even to the newcomer: their badges are the 'five K's' – *Kesh* (uncut hair and beard), *Kanga* (wooden comb), *Kachh* (shorts), *Kara* (an iron ring in the hair) and the short sword or *Kirpan* which they are (or were) legally entitled to carry – sometimes to the detriment of public order. Rulers of the Punjab under the great Ranjit Singh (1780–1839), they were the last country power of note to be subjugated by the British; and there is little doubt that their feeling of being a chosen people played a major part in the disastrous violence which accompanied Partition. The great majority of the Sikhs (7,845,000) are now in the Punjab, where they form local majorities as a result of the expulsion of Muslims.[11] This concentration, and their rather assertive sense of mission, may present some problems to the state and central governments.

The largest community neither specifically Hindu nor Muslim is that comprehensively labelled 'Tribes'; but it is very heterogeneous and very scattered, with two major zones of concentration: the Assam–Burma Hills and the jungles of central India (cf. Fig. 5.1). It is difficult to say how many people should be regarded as tribal, since recent census policy seems to have led to a great deal of nominal assimilation to Hinduism, and indeed it is impossible to draw any definite line between animism and some forms of rural Hinduism. In general they are shifting cultivators and spirit-worshippers, but Christianity as well as Hinduism has made progress among them, and the passage to a (*soi-disant*) higher civilization has not infrequently been attended by the usual disastrous effects on social culture and individual well-being. It is shallow and imperceptive to write off these often balanced and integrated societies as totally 'savage' because they lack the tricks of technologically more advanced cultures; in the true decencies of life some at least (e.g. among the Nagas) yield to few peoples. We have already mentioned their general racial and linguistic affinities; to attempt to particularize would be hopeless, but special mention may be made of the Bhils, Gonds and Santals. The Bhils are found mainly in the marches of Rajasthan, Maharashtra and Madhya Pradesh; very jungly and great shifting cultivators.

[11] Most of the rulers of these states were Sikhs, but in 1941 they had an absolute majority in only one District (Ludhiana) and a relative one in only one small state (Faridkot). Cf. Postcript, p. 172.

More important are the Gonds (the largest group, most of whom are in Madhya Pradesh); once the rulers of much of central India, forced back into their jungles by stronger powers, they have left the name Gondwanaland as a symbol of their ancient domain. The Santals live on the Bengal–Bihar borderland, and are best known for the rebellion of 1855, provoked by plainsmen taking unscrupulous advantage of legalistic land regulation.

Individuals among the tribal peoples have been able to make the best of both worlds: 'the Gond Raja of Savangar lives in a palace which is equipped with every modern comfort; his well-stocked library includes the works of Aldous Huxley, Bernard Shaw and [significantly] Malinowski; he is a brilliant cricketer and tennis-player. Yet he insists that he is a true Gond; his house is decorated with representations of his totem animal, the tortoise, and in the heart of the palace is a small thatched hut where the cult of the old tribal gods is maintained.'[12] At the other extreme are such groups as the Kadar of Cochin, hardly out of the Stone Age. In between, most tribesmen have often been economically exploited and increasingly morally degraded, admitted to become the lowest stratum of Hindu society, or rescued from that by a Christianity which too often consists largely in destroying all that remains of a once-integrated material and moral culture.[13]

The problem of ensuring reasonable conditions of life is sometimes complicated by wider economic issues: the legitimate interests of the forester and of the shifting cultivator may be hard to reconcile. The British policy of excluding tribal areas from the control of elected provincial legislators was naturally resented by nationalist opinion as another trick to divide and rule; even research was regarded with suspicion since, as Elwin remarks, the official ethnographic surveys were sometimes 'too dependent on facts collected by [untrained] subordinates . . . collections of sensationally interesting but often somewhat discreditable superstitions and customs'.[14]

It is of course true that the hills cannot be artificially fenced from the economic life of the country, to form scientific game-sanctuaries with a human fauna; but there is grave danger, if the barriers to exploitation go down too rapidly in the supposed interests of national unity and development, that the tragic histories of the Santals and the Mundas may be repeated.

Christians numbered about 10,725,000 in 1961, plus 750,000 in Pakistan; about three-quarters are Roman Catholics. It is not, perhaps, a very impressive total after four and a half centuries of missionary effort, it is true discontinuous.[15]

[12] V. Elwin, *The Aboriginals* (OPIA No. 14, 1943), 11.

[13] For instance, by banning animal sacrifices among the Kachins of Burma; as the diviners proportioned the sacrifice to the known wealth of the individual, from a buffalo to a chicken, and as the victim was communally consumed, suppression of this custom cuts down the meat-ration and accentuates economic class-cleavage.

[14] *Loc. cit.* 28.

[15] The EIC took so strict a view of the necessity of non-interference with established religions that in the early 19th century Baptist missionaries (American and British) had to work from Danish Serampore.

Most success has been obtained among the lower Hindu castes and the Tribes – especially, perhaps, those half-Hinduized and beginning to be aware of the disadvantages of coming in at the bottom. Christianity is strongest in the south, where in Kerala it is professed by 3,587,400 or 21% of the population; Madras and Andhra Pradesh have over 3,200,000 Christians. Here they are largely the result of Portuguese mass-conversions and the assimilation to Rome of the Nestorian churches, which claimed continuity from St Thomas the Apostle and are certainly at least fifteen centuries old. Mylapore (San Thomé), just south of Madras, contains the Apostle's reputed tomb, and is still a centre of some Portuguese cultural influence, while some Nestorian or 'Syrian' Christians retain their ancient liturgies and usages.

There are of course innumerable other sects, pure survivals of ancient faiths such as the mysterious 'White Jews' of Cochin, or eclectic crossings of all known beliefs: one person in 1931 'described himself as "spiritually universal", but manifestly could not be distributed to the various heads'.[16] Three numerically minor groups must be discussed: *Parsees, Anglo-Indians, Europeans*.

The *Parsees* numbered only about 112,000, over 80% of them in Greater Bombay. Zoroastrian fire-worshippers, they came, as their name implies, from Fars (Persia) about the 8th century AD, to avoid conversion to Islam. Socially they were regarded as hardly Indian and yet definitely not European; but they escaped the usual disabilities of an intermediate position by virtue of wealth and education, and were indeed a valuable lubricant, contributing greatly to the relative harmony of Indo-British relations in Bombay as compared with Calcutta. Like the Quakers, they have an altogether disproportionate share of economic activity and public spirit; the name of Tata bears witness to their energetic and diverse achievement. But their numbers appear to be kept low by inbreeding and a low birth-rate; proselytism is unknown, perhaps to avoid strain on their very complete internal social welfare arrangements and, again like the Quakers, they are essentially a professional and upper-middle class group.

The *Anglo-Indians* are unfortunately named; the effort to avoid the stigma of 'Eurasian' has deprived us of the useful original meaning of Anglo-Indian – an Englishman who had spent his working life in India. In any case many 'Anglo-Indian' families, including some not the least in standing and social usefulness, are really Luso-Indian. Both Portuguese and British initially adopted deliberate miscegenation policies, to surround themselves as it were by a penumbra of subordinates bound by ties of feeling to the invaders. The history of British attitudes to Anglo-India is distressing; as Cox points out, the existence of caste enabled the British to be virtually a dominant caste, and so 'able to make almost unlimited demands upon the mixed-bloods without necessarily making any concessions to them'.[17] This has not always been so; in earlier days families such as the Skinners and Hearseys were among the most valued servants and soldiers of the EIC.

[16] 1931 Census, Vol. I, Pt. I, 391.
[17] O. C. Cox, *Caste, Class and Race* (Monthly Review Press, NY, 1948), 385.

The change is perhaps to be associated with the opening of the Suez Canal: home leaves became more frequent, and, more important, many more European wives (actual or potential – the cold weather saw the arrival of the 'fishing fleet') came out.

In the circumstances the Anglo-Indians naturally became mere clients of the British rulers; and the community was always liable to erosion at the top as its most successful members managed to 'pass' as Domiciled Europeans, while there was some – though decreasing – accretion at the bottom. Physically, of course, the Anglo-Indians include all shades from 'pure white' to almost black; judging by names and physique, the Portuguese element is more important than is usually allowed.[18]

That mixed ancestry in itself means 'the vices of both sides' it should not be necessary to refute; what matters is the social environment, often more secure where the husband was Indian, the wife European but assimilating. It may be mentioned, as one example of many, that Amrita Sher-Gil, after Jamini Roy perhaps the outstanding modern Indian painter, was the daughter of a Magyar mother and a Punjabi father. But the social scales have been weighted heavily against the Eurasians, and their political fortunes were hitched only too obviously to the British star; as that set, their pleas that they were as Indian as anybody were not unnaturally discounted as death-bed repentances.

Hinduism and Caste

Hinduism and its symbiote, Caste, are entities so complex as to defy definition; as a counsel of despair Hinduism has been defined as 'those beliefs held by Hindus', but this takes us too far and not far enough, as these include all possible metaphysical attitudes (not perhaps excluding solipsism, if that be a possible attitude) and on the theological side everything from virtual atheism in some of the Sankhya school (6th century BC) to pantheism and the spirit-worship of those tribes who have accepted a position in the Hindu scheme of things. Until recently it was roughly true to say that Hindus were those who accepted caste society and Brahminical hegemony; but there are now many who would consider themselves good Hindus but yet would condemn caste, even if they cannot always in practice repudiate it.

Into this maze of jarring sects (far more than Omar's two-and-seventy) and conflicting theogonies we cannot go, even were the author technically competent to do so. But Hinduism as a way of life impinges directly on the relations between men and the Indian environment in two important aspects: the special position accorded to the cow, and caste. The first is more appropriately considered in Chapter 8 (Agriculture); the second must be discussed, with much

[18] Cox is, I think, misled on this point by reliance on the more articulate *Anglo*-Indian writers, for whom 'the call of (British) blood' was an article of faith. The Goanese cross is of course a different issue (below, 669). As for colour, I have seen a man with unimpeachably Saxon names who was better known to his Burmese neighbours as *Kala byu* – 'the *black* black man'.

diffidence, here. But many fundamental questions cannot even be touched upon, such as the movement of castes up and down the scale, *ahimsa*, and the linked concepts of rebirth and *dharma* with its peculiar connotation of both destiny and duty.

There are probably some 3,000 castes in India, and the literature on them is enormous; nor is there any general agreement on the origins and rationale of the system. Any definition can be effectively queried, unless it is so hedged about with qualifications as to fill a book. It would be folly for a novice to attempt even a rough working definition; but from a résumé of some admitted facts and of what appear to be the more tenable hypotheses it is hoped that some idea of the nature and workings of caste may emerge.

The salient features are clear enough. The caste system is the most intensely hierarchical organization of society in existence; the accident of birth is the absolute determinant of a man's caste, and hence of his standing in society. Exclusivism is carried to an extreme; not only is marriage (with rare exceptions) strictly confined within the caste, but normally eating and drinking with members of other castes are banned. The idea of purity is indeed fundamental in the practice of caste. In some cases the cult of ceremonial purity was carried to pathological lengths – in Kerala Nayadis (quasi-aboriginals) could not approach within 72 feet of a Brahmin without occasioning defilement, and as late as 1932 the existence in the same region of an 'unseeable' group, emerging only at night, was reported: these unfortunates washed the clothes of untouchables.[19] On the other hand, ceremonial purity has given rise to some undesignedly hygienic practices, such as the provision in Post Offices of stamp-moisteners to avoid licking, or the use as dishes of leaves or of cheap pottery subsequently discarded.

There are, or at least were, four great caste groupings: Brahmins (priests), Kshatriyas (warriors or, better, rulers), Vaisyas (traders), Sudras (cultivators); together with the lower groups known variously as Untouchables, Depressed Classes, Scheduled or Exterior Castes.[20] The 'Laws of Manu' (1st–5th centuries AD) represent the four as sprung from different parts of the body of Brahma; they have also been equated with *varna* or colour (from light Indo–Aryan to black Dravidian). These seem to be rationalizations; and as *varna* has wider connotations it does not seem that the racial theory of caste origins, so far as built on this equation, has very secure foundations.

Rigid as the system is, in course of time castes may improve their ranking, often by restricting intermarriage to a narrower group within a caste; or they may lose ground. In times of war and revolution energy and ability have carried

---

[19] J. H. Hutton, *Caste in India*. CUP (1946), 70–71.

[20] *Not* 'outcastes': this means no more than those outside the pale (e.g. Englishmen), but carries with it the suggestion of 'outcast' or expulsion – a sanction which may be used on castemen, but these castes, unless by their own volition, are an integral part of the system, with essential ritual duties. Some groups have developed their own *pujaris* (functioning as priests though without benefit of Sanskrit)—a slight qualification of the Brahmin monopoly mentioned below.

men of lower castes to place and power, and the situation may then be legitimated by faking the pedigree, this adjustment being made by complaisant Brahmins. Today individuals have obviously much greater facilities for breaking away, owing to the increased mobility and the increasingly economic values of modern society. Hence the *broad* occupational correlations suggested above have long been practically meaningless, except that only Brahmins can be priests. As Brahmins are essential to many necessary rituals they have an obvious key position, and as the educated class, the clergy, they tended (as the clergy of mediaeval Europe) to monopolize or at least dominate administration. Hindu rulers usually were Kshatriyas, or got Brahmins to say they were;[21] trading castes are still largely Vaisya. But all groups include large numbers of cultivators. It is in individual castes, and still more in the innumerable sub-castes, that the usual Western concept of caste as occupational most nearly holds good. Many caste distinctions based on occupation appear very trifling: between those who yoke to the plough one bullock or two, who make white or black pots, and so on. But in towns at any rate occupational significance, while not unimportant, is of less and less account, except for definitely impure tasks such as those of Dhobis (washermen), Chamars (tanners), Doms (scavengers). In any case the cross-divisions are almost incredibly complex: 'it suggests a division of the inhabitants of England into families of Norman descent, Clerks in Holy Orders, positivists, ironmongers, vegetarians, communists, and Scotchmen';[22] except that the groups are mutually exclusive, and there are no classifications such as vegetarian iron-mongers.

As to origins, it would appear obvious that no simple explanation can possibly suffice. Hutton lists 15 contributing factors, and does not regard this as exhaustive; he inclines to regard the geographical juxtaposition of many differing ethnic groups in India – the end of so many migrations – and beliefs in *mana* and taboo, especially associated with food, as among the most important. This can be supported by a wide range of anthropological evidence, from India and outside. Ethnic and occupational factors clearly play an important part, and the element of deliberate exploitation by Brahmins cannot well be evaded.

What is the objective function of caste? At first sight it appears to be (and indeed it is) a negation of democracy as known in the West: and after all, the values associated with the word 'democracy', while not the peculiar property of the west, are at least so much interwined with Occidental views of the world as to give validity to western judgments on the meaning of the word.[23] To us, then, caste is alien and repellent. Yet it would be superficial to condemn out of hand a system which has met the social needs of so large a fraction of mankind for so many centuries. Loyalty to caste has inhibited the development of national

[21] For a good example – no less a person than Sivaji – see Karve, *op. cit.* 43–44.

[22] J. C. Molony, *A Book of South India* (1926), 106.

[23] On the other hand, of course, social stratification, with only less rigid rules of inter-dining and intermarriage than those of the caste system, is by no means lacking outside India.

patriotisms: but in the conditions of ancient and mediaeval India this was no unmixed evil, since it made adjustments to the constantly changing political pattern so much the easier. There was a place for everybody, for the intrusive conqueror and the aboriginal conquered; the structure was so integrated, so self-regarding, that few groups could long resist the temptation to find their assured niche, humble as it might be. At the same time Cox undoubtedly overstates his case when he claims that 'its practice and theory are in complete synchronization; it does not rationalize its position . . . it has no shortcomings; it does not excuse itself; it is totally excellent. . . . Before the impingement of Western culture upon the system there was no "caste question" in India.' This is to forget Buddhists and Jains and Sikhs, the wide gains of Islam from the lower castes, and not a few Hindu thinkers, poets, and saints who taught that not birth but conduct was the ultimate determinant of a man's right rank in society. But the other phrases from the passage quoted sum up the situation as it was until recently: 'The caste system does not represent a social order in unstable equilibrium; rather a powerful norm towards which social variations tend to gravitate. . . . Resting securely upon universal consensus, the system is taken for granted, and it cannot be legislated out of existence. . . .'[24]

This gift of stability to a highly plural society, always in peril of being shaken to pieces by constant war, is perhaps the most positive argument in favour of caste. On a somewhat lower plane it fulfilled – and to some extent still fulfils – many of the functions of friendly societies and trade unions; its conservatism has acted as a check on despotisms more capricious even than itself. But these are things of historical rather than contemporary significance; the price of stability is too high if it means ossification in a rapidly changing environment; resistance to new forces may indeed be more prolonged, but the ultimate wreck is more disastrous.

It is very difficult indeed to see how any really democratic society can co-exist with such an avowed, not to say violent, assertion of human inequality – not the natural inequality of individuals, but the automatic inferiority of whole classes of men, utterly irrespective of any individual talent or virtue; and rationalizations by such apologists as Radhakrishnan, though eloquent and sincere, are not altogether convincing, even to many Hindus, when they suggest that the role of the lower castes is in fact honoured as being essential. Not all men are philosophers, and much of caste teaching and practice seems to have a demoralizing and certainly has a divisive social effect. Stripped of metaphysic and translated into the terms of day-to-day life, caste retains uncomfortable overtones of *Herrenvolk* and *apartheid*. This can scarcely be afforded in a country committed to modernization on democratic and quasi-socialist lines.

Today, therefore, caste faces what is probably the greatest crisis in its history.

---

[24] *Op. cit.* 22. Buddhism and Sikhism are relegated to a four-line footnote (110); but even if they 'did not seriously change the course of Hindu society', they certainly questioned it sufficiently to induce re-assessments.

The new urbanism has greatly weakened it: without spending a prohibitive fraction of one's time and income on purificatory ceremonies, as a commuter it is simply not possible to escape contamination; and, with all the cultural loss implied in the rootlessness of modern city life, the gift of anonymity does enable the individual to break bonds which are unbearable but unbreakable in a village where all are known to all. Nor can an expansionist industrial economy submit to the occupational shackles of caste, shackles like those of mediaeval guilds, but more rigorous, as Batanagar (p. 596) has shown.

On a different plane the influence of Western ideology and the ideals of secular humanism (probably more than those of Christianity), compel a revaluation of the old attitudes, on the part of the intelligentsia at least. Much of value may be lost in this process of adjustment, and the risk of disintegration and social schizophrenia is profound; but, short of some great and unforeseeable historic catastrophe, it has gone too far to be checked. These factors are clearly seen by most of those in whom leadership is now vested. Some of the earliest legislation of independent India was to enforce the right of untouchables to free access to temples and wells. Articulate opinion has welcomed this overwhelmingly. Yet it is a long way from the Council Chamber at New Delhi to the thousands of villages in the deep South: 'In the city of Bombay, any barber or hotel owner or temple priest who refused admission to a Harijan would soon find himself in the dock. In a Tanjore village the Harijan himself would probably not try to get himself shaved by a caste barber or enter a caste shrine; and if he did, the caste villagers would probably soon bring him to heel, law or no law.'[25]

There is evidence of a distinct decline, especially of course in urban life, of the taboos connected with pollution; but in other ways caste may actually be stronger than it was. The political manipulation of caste groupings in a system of universal suffrage obviously provides a magnificent field for the most complex manoeuvre and chicane; but also for wider caste alliances and a relaxation of the lines between *sub*-castes, since in any one locality the sub-caste will normally be too small to form a politically effective unit.[26] In the village, again, the introduction of producers' co-operatives, the runnings of Community Development Projects, the revival of the old *panchayat* or inter-caste council of (nominally or originally) five representatives, all mean that whereas 'In the past, caste conflict and feud could lie beneath the surface of daily affairs', and those not immediately concerned in a dispute could be neutral, 'Now that overt choices must be made, there is more apparent fragmentation. . . .' To some extent this is offset by wider groupings – inter- rather than intra-village – permitting of more varied and less personal contacts; but it is a main factor in the apparent lack of effectiveness in the panchayat revival.[27]

[25] Taya Zinkin, *Caste Today* (OUP, 1962), 60. This brilliant little essay is perhaps the best introduction for the Western student.

[26] Zinkin, *op. cit.* 62–66; M. N. Srinivas, *Caste in Modern India* (Asia, Bombay, 1962).

[27] H. Orenstein, 'Village, Caste, and the Welfare State', *Human Organization*, 22 (1963), 83–89.

'Perhaps a sceptic whispers, "Such revolutions are not brought about in the lethargic types of Indian climes." Him we only remind . . . that the phenomenon of the conquering Indo-Aryans, who were passionate eaters of flesh and drinkers of intoxicating beverages, settling down as the upper castes of Hindu society and abjuring their food and drink for centuries, is a moral triumph of the people of India, for which there is hardly any parallel in human history. The same people, now called upon to throw off caste, would rise to the occasion and achieve a still greater triumph.'[28]

These are brave and sincere words; but the phenomenon was not a sudden one, and it is a long way back; nor are those conditioned by three millennia of caste 'the same people'.

Caste, then, dies hard; but in anything like its fully developed form it cannot persist indefinitely in the sort of India which most Indians seem to want. The necessary changes are vast, but they are fostered by a great variety of forces, both material and spiritual. The monster may still be lively, but his sharpest teeth have been drawn.

Some social tendencies

A description of the manners and customs of the Indian peoples, or even only those associated with caste, would itself fill an encyclopaedia. Such is their diversity that it has been justly remarked that the only valid generalization about them is that any generalization is both true and false according to *milieu*. The differences are extreme: from primitive tribesmen not far above a Stone Age level to the highly sophisticated urban intelligentsia, from rulers claiming descent from the sun to industrial families such as the Tatas and the Birlas forming economic dynasties in two or three generations. Yet, underlying this diversity, is an unmistakable cultural unity provided by the polymorphic complex of ideas and social and individual observances which is Hinduism, a culture which baffles definition but is everywhere recognizable.

A few leading tendencies may be briefly indicated. India is today the theatre of an indescribably complex interaction between the forces of modern technology (with its own metamorphosing mental outlook) and of an age-old metaphysical tradition. Two examples, admittedly extreme, may illustrate the fantastic inter-digitation – it cannot be called a synthesis – of east and west. The attainment of independence was accompanied by a campaign to prohibit cow-slaughter, even if need be under penalty of death; in Kerala an unexpected result of Communist activity was the emergence of an embryonic sub-caste of Communist bride-grooms, more progressive and so better endowed economically than their fellows, and hence more eligible, and commanding higher dowries.

The love of metaphysic, so often noted, was ascribed by Buckle and other geographical determinists to the influence of the natural environment. It is

[28] G. S. Ghurye, *Caste and Race in India* (1932), 188; cf. his second thoughts in the revised version, *Caste and Class in India* (Popular Book Depot, Bombay, 1957), 238.

perhaps more reasonable to regard it as the natural reaction to centuries, if not millennia, of political absolutism: in one sphere at least, that of cloudy imaginings, man was free. Since the suppression of Buddhism, Hinduism, however rigid in matters of ritual observance, has been extraordinarily tolerant doctrinally – hence its astonishing congeries of beliefs, practically from Animism to atheism. The result has been a metaphysical hangover, shown in the constant tendency among intellectuals to accept an analogy as a demonstration. Moreover, even the most intellectual arguments are not infrequently betrayed into unregulated emotionalism; perhaps not more often than those of Western Europeans, but certainly in a more obvious way.

The hackneyed antithesis of Western materialism and Eastern spirituality, however, is as a rule grossly exaggerated, especially by Western neophytes. The trading castes have a religious sanction to gain almost for its own sake, resembling (but with greater intensity) the attitude of the Puritan bourgeosie in the West. The observer in India certainly does not see any widespread neglect of material advancement in the interests of salvation, and if 'by their fruits ye shall know them' be true, the ethical advantage is not always conspicuously on the side of the East. In the long run it is not likely that the standard patterns of economic and political power-conflicts will differ fundamentally from those of the rest of the world, however exotic their forms of overt expression.

These remarks, of course, apply mainly to the educated and vocal classes of the towns. It must never be forgotten that the vast majority of Indians live in over half a million villages, most of them small and isolated. Here Custom is a king not yet and not easily dethroned (though increasingly tottering), and his laws are enshrined in a multitude of pithy proverbs which, with the religious songs, form a true and remarkable folk-culture. The ancient panchayat or village council, which through all the mutability of dynasties made the villages so many un-federated little republics, became atrophied under British rule, in which administration was legal rather than customary and was far more all-embracing, impinging far more directly on all classes, than under any previous régime. It is doubtful whether, as some nationalists hope, the panchayat can be sufficiently resuscitated to play a very useful function in the epoch of change which has begun to penetrate the Indian countryside (see p. 275 for references to the role hoped for of the panchayat in the Five Year Plans).

In this excessively complex situation it is of course impossible to forecast what changes in the norms of society will take place under a government modelled, in principle, on Western parliamentary democracy and relying for its administration on the inheritance of an immense bureaucratic machine. That there will be both loss and gain appears certain; there may be a loss of formal efficiency mitigated by more ready accessibility to public opinion. But for the latter to be constructive a new revolution of thought is needed, a break from the old traditions of community and caste to new groupings based primarily on economic function and with intelligible and coherent political and economic programmes. And somehow

– this may well be the most difficult task of all – the programmes for the future must be brought to the rural masses and their participation, not just their acquiescence, be assured. In the last resort it is on this more than on anything else that the future, in both India and Pakistan, depends, for without it neither the material struggle for food nor the ideological struggle to create free, active and united nations can be won.

The Pakistani evolution

In contrast to the India of Nehru, avowedly dedicated to the formation of a secular state, the Pakistan of Jinnah was rooted in the belief that there was in the sub-continent a separate religious nation. Rationalistically, many of the points adduced in support of the 'Two Nations' theory may be open to question; but if a sufficient number of people are determined to be a nation, then practically they are one. The history of Pakistan is thus the history of a struggle to transform this feeling of Islamic identity and of the all-pervading social dictates of the faith into a well-knit state; a struggle made peculiarly difficult by the unique division of the country into two unequal parts, separated by 1,000 miles of India, and with very marked differences in language, in cultural tradition, and (though both were agrarian) in economy. There is also the difficulty of reconciling the traditional Islamic element in the polity with the demands of modern administration and economic development. Apart from caste, many of the more social problems of Pakistan are not dissimilar from those of India; but the problem in Pakistan is perhaps more directly political as expressed in the state structure.

Sectionalism in Pakistan is not confined to the obvious division between the West, with the Punjab making the running against more local loyalties and that of the centre at Karachi (or now Islamabad), and the East, more homogeneous in itself (but for the sizeable Hindu minority, some 12%) but on the whole playing a less dynamic and less dedicated role in the making of Pakistan. However, the sectionalisms of West Pakistan seem to have been largely exorcized by its recasting into one unit, and with the greatly enhanced power of the central government under the régime of Ayub Khan, the country seems to have got into as nearly a unitary condition as can be expected when its two major components are geographically so distant and environmentally so different from each other.

The problem of parity remains difficult. East Pakistan has the larger population (51,000,000 against 43,000,000) but is economically not so diversified as the west; yet its jute accounts for up to two-thirds of total exports. The attachment to Bengali sets East Pakistan apart from the main currents of Islamic literary culture as expressed in Urdu; its pre-Partition élite was largely Hindu, and the drive for Pakistan came from the west. During the intense factionalism of the period of constitution making and breaking, East Pakistani politicians had some plausible grounds for expressing, and exaggerating, fears that the East would become merely a colony of the west, while to Karachi they appeared just as plausibly to be irresponsibly trifling with national unity. The present régime seems to have gone a long way in concession to the east; for example, longer tax-free period for new industries in Dacca than in Karachi, and the seating of the legislature (limited as its powers will be) in Dacca. Reservation of official posts in East Pakistan to local personnel, however, though doubtless tactically expedient, may not conduce to real integration.

President Ayub Khan's 1962 constitution, based on indirect election through some 80,000 local units known as 'Basic Democracies', may not fulfil the formal requirements of parliamentary democracy, but may well be more efficient in Pakistani conditions and may enlist wider participation of the people, however indirectly, than the ineffective representative régime. It seems also to have muted the old conflict between Islamic traditionalists and the proponents of a modern state. The extreme position of the traditionalists – back to the golden days of the 8th-century Caliphate – is obviously incompatible with the complexity of modern life, and there is still a wide area for dispute on such matters as the status of women, the rule of secular law, the degree to which minorities (including dissident Muslims such as the Ahmadiyya) may partake of high administrative responsibility, how far traditional Islamic inhibitions against usury may be waived in the interests of capital formation, relations with other Muslim states and the attitude to those Muslims who have remained in India, and so on; while Islamic law on inheritance imposes some difficulties in efforts to prevent excessive fragmentation of landholdings.

Moreover, all Pakistani affairs are overshadowed by the Kashmir dispute with India, and the recent rapprochement with Communist China introduces a certain ambiguity into Pakistan's international position; yet she is very dependent on the west, notably the USA, for economic aid. The setting up of a state in the appalling confusion of Partition was a tremendous achievement in itself, but the gains of Jinnah and Liaquat Ali Khan seemed in danger of dissipation during ten years of political factionalism; a new stability seems to have been attained, but there remain critical difficulties, internal and external.

BIBLIOGRAPHICAL NOTE

Most of the works referred to in earlier editions of this book retain much value; the older standard authors such as J. H. Hutton, Verrier Elwin, W. C. Smith, O. C. Cox, L. S. S. O'Malley, G. S. Ghurye, R. K. Mukerjee, are by no means entirely superseded; still less such essential primary sources as the autobiographies of Gandhi and Nehru or the writings of Muhammad Iqbal and Rabindranath Tagore. Iqbal's 'conversation between Ganges and Himalaya' (in Secrets of the Self, Ashraf, Lahore, 1943), for instance, apart from its poetic greatness, seizes unerringly on the cardinal contrasts between the Muslim and the Hindu genius, the Sheikh and the Brahmin.

However, this literature, vast as it is, is increasing with terrifying acceleration, and any sampling must depend largely on the accidents of local availability and personal taste. Much of the recent literature is far more firmly founded in general sociological concepts than the highly idiosyncratic and subjectivist (but often so much more readable!) works of older writers. Much is owing to the active interest of American students, whose detailed studies show promise of breaking away from older stereotypes about caste and tribal influences. A good bridge between old and new is afforded by N. K. Bose, *Cultural Anthropology* (Indian Asstd Publishers, Calcutta, 1943); of newer books already cited, those of Taya Zinkin and Irawati Karve are perhaps most stimulating.

So much, in the current phase, depends on detailed case-studies rather than 'literary' sources that perhaps the best way to gain some insight into the complex fascinations of Indian society is through co-operative works such as M. Singer (ed.), *Traditional India: Structure and Change* (American Folklore Soc., Philadelphia, 1959); the special number of *Human Organization* (Ithaca, New York, Vol. 22, No. 1, 1963) devoted to 'Contours of culture change in South Asia'; A. R. Desai (ed.), *Rural Sociology in India* (Indian Soc. Agric. Economics, Bombay, 3rd ed., 1961); S. Maron (ed.), *Pakistan: Society and Culture* (Human Relations Area Files, New Haven, 1957); A. F. A. Husain, *Human and Social Impact of Technological Change in Pakistan* (OUP Dacca, 1956). At the opposite pole from the village is the brilliant essay by E. Shils, *The Intellectual between Tradition and Modernity: The Indian Situation* (Mouton, The Hague, 1961). But the list would be well-nigh endless.

On Islam and Pakistan, some good studies have been overtaken by events: I. Jennings, *Constitutional Problems in Pakistan* (CUP, 1957); K. Callard, *Pakistan: A Political Study* (Allen & Unwin, London, 1957); even perhaps L. Binder, *Religion and Politics in Pakistan* (Univ. of California, Berkeley, 1961). R. D. Campbell, *Pakistan: Emerging Democracy* (Van Nostrand, Princeton, 1963) is more up-to-date as to facts (except that he dodges the Chinese issue) but excessively naïve in interpretation. More general works of interest include M. T. Titus, *Islam in India and Pakistan* (YMCA, Calcutta, 2nd ed. 1959); I. Lichtenstadter, *Islam and the Modern Age* (Bookman Assoctes, NY, 1958); I. H. Qureshi, *The Muslim Community of the Indo-Pakistan Sub-Continent* (Mouton, The Hague, 1962).

Postscript. Early in 1966 the Government of India decided in principle on the formation of a new Punjabi-speaking State of Punjab, separated from the Hindi-speaking parts of the existing Punjab which would form a new State of Hariana. Some hill areas were likely to be joined to Himachal Pradesh. The new Punjab, formed in response to Sikh agitation (cf. pp. 157, 160), might have a population of about 12,000,000 (probably around 55% Sikh), Hariana about 7,000,000, some 1,500,000 going to Himachal Pradesh. (*Keesings' Contemporary Archives*, 22/4–7/5/66, p. 21378). The formation of the new States was announced in November 1966.

CHAPTER 6

Historical Outlines

————————➤ ⊂————————

Indian archaeology has made great strides in the past two decades, and there is now a good deal of evidence on the extension of various palaeolithic and meso-lithic cultures, although unfortunately interpretation has as yet to rely more on extensive typology than on intensive stratigraphical analyses. This phase of horizontal reconnaissance is already yielding to more detailed vertical soundings, and the next few years may see discoveries almost as revolutionary as those of Harappa and Mohenjo-Daro.

The Indus civilization

Surface finds of pictographic seals at Harappa in the Punjab had long hinted the existence of an unknown civilization; in 1922 excavations at Mohenjo-Daro ('Mound of the Dead') in Sind disclosed the existence of an urban and basically Bronze Age culture, not dissimilar to that of Sumeria in technical accomplish-ment. The earliest definitely Harappan remains can be fairly confidently dated to around 2500 BC, and there is evidence of trading contacts with Sumeria about 2350–2100 BC; but by this time the civilization was fully developed. Its origins seem thus sudden and obscure, and no less difficult to account for is the fact that, having early reached a high pitch of organization, it then seems to have stagnated for centuries.[1]

It seems to have been a trading 'empire', polarized around the great cities of Mohenjo-Daro and Harappa; and it is now known that, in its later phases, its offshoots spread as far as Rupar on the Sutlej, and southwards into Kutch and around the Gulf of Cambay; these later protrusions may represent a dispersal before barbarian inroads. The cities were impressively, if unimaginatively, planned; what seems to strike most observers, perhaps by reaction to the Indian present, is the high standard of the drains.

Aesthetically, however, the impression is drab, though this may be due to gaps in the record – nothing like the superb monarchic tombs of Sumeria and Egypt has been found. There was a businesslike efficiency, shown for example in

---

[1] Unless indeed we accept the ingenious but not altogether convincing view, based on geomorphological arguments, of R. L. Raikes ('The End of the Ancient Cities of the Indus', *American Anthropologist*, 66 (1964), 284–99), that the main civilization may have endured for only a century or two at Mohenjo-Daro, ending *c.* 2300 BC as a result of earthquake and flooding, Harappa being a subsequent and not a contemporaneous centre.

the standardized layout of workers' quarters with the great grain-mortars massed between them and the granaries. Artistically, the best things are a handful of (rather anomalous) sculptures and especially the splendid stylized animals of the seals. These include tigers, rhinoceroses, elephants and buffaloes, which together with an architecture of kiln-burnt bricks (implying large fuel supplies) suggest a distinctly more humid climate than now prevails. The seals carry an undeciphered script, and their symbolism suggests that some elements in Hinduism, notably Siva-worship, may stem from Harappan culture.

The end of the Indus Civilization is as obscure as its origin. It seems likely that, in the great cities at least, it was a violent one, though too much may have been built on the dramatic evidence of massacre and burning in the last stage at Mohenjo-Daro. Elsewhere, especially in Kathiawad, there may have been some carry-over into the chalcolithic cultures of those dark ages before the lineaments of Vedic India can be clearly discerned. The gap of about a millennium – more rather than less – between the end of the Indus Civilization and the crystallization of the north Indian kingdoms in Buddha's day may soon be closed. Indeed, if the suggestion of a revised date of 1200 BC for the end of Harappan culture is confirmed, it would seem that the civilization must have met its fate at the hands of the Aryan invaders; and decadent successor-states may have lingered on in Kathiawad as late as 500 BC.[2]

The coming of the Aryans

The Aryan invasions, from their date in the middle of the 1st millennium BC, may well have been a part of the great folk-wanderings represented farther west by the Hyksos in Egypt and the overthrow of the Babylonian Dynasty by the Kassites. Be that as it may, the newcomers when settled in their original Indian territory – *Sapta Sindhu* or the Seven Rivers from the Kabul to the Jumna – retained many elements of a pastoral culture: a diet based largely on milk and meat, chariot-racing, the sacrifice of horses. Their religion, expressed in the often obscure but often noble hymns of the *Rig-Veda*, was essentially worship of personified natural phenomena – Sun, Moon, Fire and so on – and at its height tended to monotheism. The Vedic hymns are the only sources of information: the impression is of an initially simple society based on the family and the village, with at least distinct classes of warriors, priests and artisans; divided into monarchical or republican clans, gradually becoming more complex with the growth of towns, trade and crafts.[3] Archaeology is beginning to shed a new, if dim, light on this difficult period, although it suggests that – as in that other Heroic Age which Homer sang – life was ruder than the poets fable.

Larger kingdoms coalesced, and the frontiers of Aryandom were pushed outwards in struggles with the dark-skinned snub-nosed *Dasyus* or *Dasas* – struggles

[2] B. Subbarao, *The Personality of India* (University of Baroda, 2nd ed. 1958), 96, 129–32.
[3] Stuart Piggott, *Prehistoric India* (Pelican, Harmondsworth, 1950), Ch. VII, gives a brilliant interpretation.

in which some have seen the prime origin of caste, though that is probably far more complex. By about the 1st millennium BC the Aryans had passed the Ghaghra, and later pushed through the Vindhyan barrier into the northern Deccan. In Buddha's day (6th century BC) there were four major kingdoms in Madhyadesa, the 'middle country': Kosala (roughly Oudh), Avanti (Malwa), Vatsa (around Allahabad), Magadha (southern Bihar). The last was the most powerful and exerted a certain ascendancy over much of northern India; its later capital Pataliputra is represented by modern Patna, which may thus claim to be the oldest Indian city with a more or less continuous history; but excavations at Hastinapura and Achichchatra, near the Ganga in eastern Uttar Pradesh, 'proclaim the emergence of a comfortable and organized city-life' some centuries earlier.

So far the story has to be pieced out from religious texts and the great epics, *Ramayana* and *Mahabharata*: but the former do not profess to be history or even (until the Jain and Buddhist scriptures) biography, while the epics (especially the *Mahabharata*) are very composite collections of ballads and didactic verse (including the famous *Bhagavad Gita*) containing some material probably not added until the earliest Christian centuries. Socially their content is rich: this is the Heroic Age, an age of myths giving a vivid, if confused, picture of a culture in which cities and arts are increasingly important. The original clan society has developed the complex structure of caste, the austere beauty of the Vedic hymns gives way to elaborate metaphysics; and, by reaction to caste and excessive religiosity, Buddhism has arisen, in its origins simple and emotional, though in turn developing a refined and intellectual psychology and philosophy. But the patterns are shifting, splendid and vague.

The major geographical lineaments of Indian history

Already, however, we can see one of the major structure-lines of Indian historical geography: the Narmada–Chota Nagpur line which has been easily the most persistent internal boundary in India, rivalled only by the terai frontier zone between the mountains and the Indo-Gangetic Plain and by the Bengal march between 'Hindustan' and alien Assam (Fig. 6.1). The Aryans infiltrated beyond the Narmada, but except on the Lavas of Maharashtra the 'Southland', *Dakshina-patha* or the Deccan, is still mainly Dravidian: in the east, Dravidian (and other non-Aryan) languages extend farther north, and the Chota Nagpur–Orissa hill country is very mixed linguistically, while in the west the Marathi (Aryan) and Telugu (Dravidian) boundary shows a remarkable correlation with that of the Deccan Lava (below, Fig. 23.4). North of the Narmada–Chota Nagpur line, then, we have Hindustan, essentially the Gangetic Plain and its outworks in central India; south of it lies the Deccan, essentially Dravidian except on the lavas.

The other major structure-line is more clear-cut in the Muslim phase, but it is, perhaps, dimly foreshadowed in the limitation to the Indus basin of the earliest civilization and of Persian and Greek penetration. This line runs slantwise from

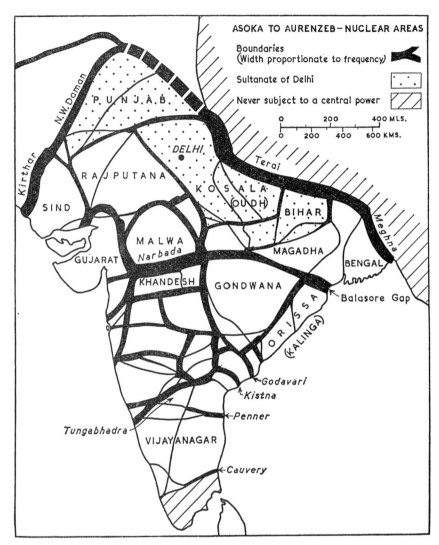

FIG 6.1 ASOKA TO AURENZEB: an attempt to illustrate the relative permanence of boundaries and the persistence of nuclear areas such as Malwa and Gujarat. The evidence permits of rough approximations only, but it is believed that a fair representation is attained. Based largely on maps in C. C. Davies, *An Historical Atlas of the Indian Peninsula* (1949) and E. W. Green, *An Atlas of Indian History* (Bombay, 1937), and on standard histories. Cf. map in W. M. Day, 'Relative permanence of former boundaries in India', *Scottish Geog. Mag* XLV (1949), 113–22.

about Mathura, on the Yamuna above Agra, along the Aravallis to the Gulf of Cambay. North and west of this the generally arid physical environment and the Islamic heritage combine to produce a cultural landscape strongly reminiscent of southwest Asia: it has been said that the true India does not begin before the temples of Mathura, birthplace of Krishna.[4] In the northwest, the mountain girdle of India narrows significantly between Turkestan and the Punjab, and is pierced by numerous passes, of which the Khyber and the Bolan are only the most famous. The importance of this entry is a commonplace and needs no stressing.

We have thus three great divisions: the Indus Valley, open to cultural and political influences from central and southwest Asia; Hindustan, accessible only when the Delhi gateway has been forced, and more receptive than the south, to which it has acted as a shock absorber; the Peninsula south of the Narmada, which, except in Maharashtra, has been far more resistant to influences from Asia: largely, no doubt, owing to mere distance, but to some extent owing to the barriers of hill and jungle, especially in the northeast. It is noteworthy that Deccan Lavas extend far north of the Narmada in Malwa: this is the great passageway from Hindustan into the Deccan, and on its glacis in Maharashtra alike the Aryans, the earlier Muslims and the Moguls established their first serious lodgements in the Southland. The pattern of the sub-continent as a whole – diminishing ripples of alien influence radiating from an entry in the northwest – is thus repeated in the Deccan.

The perennial nuclear regions

Thus early we can also discern the emergence of some nuclear regions or bases of power which are perennially significant in Indian historical geography: Gandhara in the Vale of Peshawar and Potwar; Sapta Sindhu narrowed down to the Punjab, seven rivers to five; Kurukshetra (Sirhind), the Delhi or Sutlej/Yamuna Doab; Panchala in the Yamuna/Ganga Doab and Rohilkhand; Saurashtra (Kathiawad) and Gujarat; the four great kingdoms already apparent in Magadhan times. In the Dravidian south the pattern is more confused, but not without some relatively permanent pieces in the dynastic kaleidoscope: the Kalinga country or Orissa; Andhra, the Telugu country; the Chola (whence Coromandel) and Pandya kingdoms in the Tamil country; Kerala or Malabar, the isolated southwest littoral. There are of course many smaller areas which have preserved an historic individuality, e.g. Bundelkhand, Chhattisgarh, Konkan, Kanara. Some areas again have been debatable marches: such are Khandesh, between Narmada and Tapti, or the Raichur Doab between Tungabhadra and Krishna. It is noteworthy that many of the ancient names survived in the regional

[4] Cf. S. Piggott, *Some Ancient Cities of India* (OUP, 1945), i, 42. Against this is the Hindu as well as Muslim past of Delhi; less seriously, a remark made to the author in Lahore: 'Ah, this is the real India.' As the speaker was a Muslim striving to get as much as possible into Pakistan, the remark has a delightful irony – dare I say characteristically Indian?

consciousness of the people, although not corresponding to any existing political unit, e.g. Kerala, Matsya, Maharashtra, and some are now used as the names of new states of the Indian Union. Research, geographical rather than linguistic, on *pays* names is needed.

These nuclear regions clearly represent the major agricultural areas, for the most part alluvial; intersecting them are arid, broken or jungly refuge areas such as Rajputana and the wild country of the Bhils between it and Maharashtra; the jungly Gondwana country between Son and Mahanadi; Bastar; the Rajmahal Hills in the angle of the Ganga between Bihar and Bengal. These are still the homes of most of the aboriginal tribes, and until the mergers of 1948 the great belt of country between Rajputana and Orissa was a major shatter-zone, a congeries of scores of semi-feudal states.

This pattern is perhaps more clearly grasped if we look at the Indo-Chinese peninsula, where its homologue persisted into our own century. Here we have the great rice-growing basins, deltas or (as around Mandalay, the heart of ancient Burma) irrigated dry zones: these are the bases of organized kingdoms. Around these, on the more or less open plateaus of the Shan country (Burma), Korat (Thailand) and the Laos country (Indo-China), was a penumbra of semi-feudal statelets, subject to Burma, the Thai Kingdom, or Annam, but with an allegiance the quality of which depended on distance from the centre and on the personality, vigorous or effete, of the reigning monarch. And in the wilder mountains, dissected and densely forest-clad, the hillmen lived their ancient and primitive tribal life. In India the Vale of Kashmir and Manipur corresponded to the larger plateau-states of the Shans, formed round an unusually large agricultural base in an old lake-floor silted into a rice-growing lowland.

Three regions have not been mentioned in this survey: the arid northwestern hills; Bengal; Assam. The first were generally dependencies of the dominant power in Iran – Medes, Persians, Macedonians, Parthians, Sassanids and their Muslim successors. Often, indeed, the western Punjab and the Afghan basins were part of the same 'saddle-state', loosely straddling the hills and incapsulating rather than assimilating their tribesmen; power was sometimes based on the Kandahar–Ghazni–Kabul line, sometimes on the Punjab. This Afghan–Punjab relationship, foreshadowed by the Greek Bactrian Kingdoms and the Kushan Empire, naturally bulks larger in the Muslim period: but preoccupation with Hindustan inhibited effective power to the northwest, and vice versa. Often the boundary has been the *daman-i-koh* – 'the skirts of the hills' – the sharp break of slope at the detrital pediment. This, the boundary of the Punjab under the Sikhs, under the British was still that between Administered and Tribal territory in the North-West Frontier Province. The India/Nepal boundary in the terai, the East Pakistan boundary with the Shillong Plateau and Tripura, and many internal boundaries (e.g. that of the Santal Parganas in the Rajmahal Hills) are essentially similar.

As for Bengal, until it became the base for British territorial aggrandizement in the northeast, it was always something of a marchland: beyond lay the Ahom kings of Assam or the Arakanese. Assam itself in early days had something of the Kashmir or Manipur pattern: an agricultural lowland surrounded by hills and jungles, and though the Shan Ahoms were soon Hinduized, Assam remained *mlechcha* – foreign, 'beyond the pale', unsubjugated even by the Moguls.

The Delhi–Agra axis and the Cambay node

One area stands out with peculiar importance: '*The* Doab', a long fillet between Yamuna and Ganga, with Delhi and Agra as its poles. The reasons are clear: at the northwestern end is the gateway between the Aravallis and the Thar Desert on one hand, the Himalayas on the other; to the southeast are the approaches to the great Malwa passageway.

The strategic significance of the Delhi gate is shown not only by the cities – more than the traditional seven – which have intervened between Aryan Indraprastha and British New Delhi, but by its role as the cockpit of northern India. It is the theatre of the great warfare of the *Mahabharata* between the Kurus to the west and the Panchalas to the east of the Yamuna; but at least seven less legendary and more decisive battles have taken place a few marches north of Delhi, where the great highway from the northwestern entry, along the well-watered sub-montane Punjab strip, approaches the Yamuna.[5] The heart of Muslim rule in northern India lay between Delhi and Agra, alike in the great days of the Tughluks and the Moguls and in the decadence under the Lodis (15th century) and the later Moguls. Agra shared with Delhi the prestige of being the Mogul capital, and near it, at Khanua, Babur consolidated his conquest by defeating a powerful Rajput attempt to take over from the discredited Lodis.

Only second in importance to the great highway through the Punjab was the ancient trade route from Agra to the Gulf of Cambay through Ujjain, which by 500 BC was a centre of a Gangetic-type culture. If the views of D. H. Gordon have any validity, the Cambay entry may already have been important in the late or immediately post-Harappan phase in Kathiawad, and may indeed have some bearing on the vexed question of Dravidian origins. In classical times its significance is well attested by Ptolemy's Barygaza (Broach), and the importance of this great commercial entry persisted at least until the 17th century, when the trade of Surat, the most flourishing port of the Mogul Empire, was fought for by Portuguese, Dutch and English: until 1961 the Portuguese enclaves of Diu and Damão, useless as they were in this age, still attested their preoccupation with this entry to the Mogul realms. It will be noted that the two great structure-lines converge here.

[5] Muhammad Ghori's two battles with the Rajputs at Thanesar (1191 and 1192); Babur's victory at Panipat in 1526 and Akbar's 30 years later, the first putting the Moguls on the throne of Delhi and the second securing them there after a usurpation; the Persian Nadir Shah's defeat of the Moguls at Karnaul in 1739; the Afghan victories over the Marathas at Thanesar again in 1759 and at Panipat in 1761, which checked the Maratha flood at its highest tide. Outside Delhi itself Lord Lake defeated the Maratha Sindhia in 1803; and the significance of Delhi in 1857 needs no stress.

Pre-Muslim invasions and empires

After the rich confusion of the Heroic Age, it is a relief to be able to resume the historical narrative with a definite date at last. In 326 BC Alexander the Great, after defeating various Punjab princes, reached his farthest east on the Beas.

The immediate results of Alexander's Indian campaigns were practically nil; not so the long-term effects. The Satrapies formed along the Indus soon reverted to Indian control; even Gandhara, which had been one of the richest provinces of the Achaemenid Persian Empire, was ceded by Alexander's successor Seleucus Nikator to Chandragupta Maurya. But it seems very probable that it was a reaction against the Yavana (=Ionian) invaders that enabled Chandragupta, the Sandrocottos of Greek historians, to seize the throne of Magadha from a decadent dynasty and so to found the first of the great empires which have endeavoured to bring all India under one sway. At its height, under Chandragupta's grandson Asoka (*fl. c.* 250 BC), the Mauryan dominion stretched from the Hindu Kush to the Brahmaputra, and well beyond the Krishna to the Penner. Not all of this area, of course, was directly under Asoka or his viceroys, but frontier kingdoms such as those of the Rashtrakutas (in the Konkan) and the Andhras were subordinate to him. From archaeological evidence it seems plausible that the remarkable south Indian megalithic culture was stimulated by the introduction of iron into a chalcolithic culture, through the medium of Mauryan border kingdoms.

The fragments of the account of India written by Megasthenes, the Seleucid ambassador to Chandragupta, and perhaps some of the traditions embedded in the manual of polity known as Kautilya's *Arthasastra*,[6] attest the high degree of fiscal and administrative organization of the Empire, in which most of the familiar features of Hinduism were firmly established. From Asoka's time onwards brick and stone replace the earlier timber of Pataliputra and other towns. The moral crisis which Asoka experienced as a result of the horrors of his Kalinga war brought him very close to Buddhism, probably actually within its fold; and the later years of his reign were devoted to a pacifist policy (even the royal hunt was abolished) and the fostering of Buddhist missionary activity: the inscriptions of the 'Asoka pillars'[7] and rock edicts scattered over India record missions to Tamilnad, Ceylon and the Hellenistic World. The unique spectacle of a great Emperor publishing (in stone, for all time) his repentance for the sins of his imperialism, and doing all in his power in expiation, makes Asoka perhaps the

[6] The *Arthasastra* is ascribed to Kautilya, adviser to Chandragupta, but in great part at least it is probably of post-Christian date, since the elaborate rules for foreign policy (including alliance with the next state but one, and avoidance of alliance with a stronger state) point to a chaotic 'time of troubles'. Nevertheless it is a most remarkable work whether it is a guide to existing administration or (more probably) a blueprint of what ought to be; it strongly resembles Machiavelli's *The Prince* in temper, though not in conciseness. It is indeed a sort of Gauleiter's Guide, with references, *inter alia*, to the inner ring of spies within and on the secret service, and to the authoritarian control (through gilds) of trade and industry down to the duties, rights and fees of courtesans.

[7] The fine lions from the capital of the Sarnath pillar (near Varanasi) have become the badge of the Indian Republic.

most sympathetic monarch in all history: but, though the mission to Ceylon had results still important today, 'the Greeks apparently were not much impressed by lessons in non-violence', and the wilful decay of the central military power led to provincial disintegration, not checked by Asoka's institution of touring officials analogous to Charlemagne's *Missi Dominici*. After his death disruption set in; the Dravidian south exerted its independence (or rather independences), and in the north the Greeks of Bactria (northern Afghanistan) subjugated Gandhara once more. This Hellenistic domination lasted only a century or so, but to it belongs a fine coinage (a most important contribution to chronology) and the wealth of Gandharan or Graeco-Buddhist sculpture – much of which, it must be admitted, bears the mark of mass production.[8]

Renewed incursions from the northwest – Sakas, Parthians, the Yueh-Chi or Kushans – make the centuries around the beginning of the Christian era a time of troubles. The most important of these 'Scythian' peoples were the Kushans, probably displaced from their homes by Chinese expansion under the imperialist Han dynasty. The Kushan Empire, centred on Purushapura (Peshawar), reached its height under Kanishka (1st or 2nd century AD), whose domains extended from Sinkiang to Varanasi; he carried on the Gandharan Buddhist traditions. During this generally chaotic period a strong Andhra power included most of the Deccan north of the Penner and disputed possession of Malwa – and the Ujjain trade route – with the northern kingdoms.

In the middle of the 4th century AD the Gupta dynasty revived some at least of the Mauryan glories. Under Chandragupta II Vikramaditya (*c.* 385–413), the empire extended, more or less loosely, from the Kirthar Range and the Chenab to Bengal, and south to the Narmada–Chota Nagpur line, with occasional penetrations along the western and eastern littorals. Vikramaditya's court was at Ujjain, centre of a cultural revival which marked the end of Hellenistic influence (except in coinage and astronomy), and the home of Kalidasa, whose delightful lyrical drama *Sakuntala* is perhaps the secular writing in Sanskrit best known to the West. Around 500 the Gupta Empire was shattered by the invasion of the White Huns, who destroyed the ancient Buddhist university at Taxila in Potwar. A long period of anarchy was only briefly mitigated by Harsha (mid-7th century), who seems to have ruled (with considerable local variation in his real power) from the Sutlej to Bengal and the Narmada–Chota Nagpur line. The centre of his power, at all events, was in the Delhi–Agra region, where lay his capital Kanauj on the Ganga.

During these centuries the south was the seat of a bewildering array of dynasties. Between 800 and 1000 India was more than usually disunited, three major and a host of minor kingdoms locked in an indecisive struggle for power. The three were the Gurjara–Pratihara kingdom, within the old Aravalli–Himalaya–Narmada triangle; the Palas of Bengal, Kalinga and the northeast Deccan;

[8] See R. E. Mortimer Wheeler, 'Romano-Buddhist Art: an old problem re-stated', *Antiquity*, 23 (1949), 4–19.

the Rashtrakutas in Maharashtra. The country south of the Penner was, as usual, under its own ever-shifting dynasties, of whom the most generally successful were the Cholas, who in the 11th century held Kalinga and sent armies as far as the Ganga; on the northwest they were held, by the Chalukyas of Maharashtra, roughly on the Deccan Lava boundary in Hyderabad. The Cholas also took much of Ceylon from its native Buddhist rulers – whence a still existing minority problem – and at sea reached out as far as Sumatra.

But, as in Italy, wealth and disunity combined to attract invaders from beyond the mountains; and the newcomers were armed with ideological as well as material weapons. Already in the 8th century the Arabs had conquered Sind, later extending their power as far as Multan and raiding into Rajputana and Gujarat. The stage was set for the great Muslim invasions which

> Cast the Kingdoms old
> Into another mould.

But the changes were political and social rather than geographical: the nuclear regions of power, the great lines of advance, the refuges for the dispossessed, remain the same.

India between East and West

As we have seen, the earliest civilization of India had commercial relations with Sumeria; and it is probable that Solomon's Tarshish and Ophir were southern India and Ceylon. Herodotus knew of northwestern India as part of the Achaemenid Empire, and relates the exploration of the Indus and the Makran coast by Skylax on the orders of Darius (521–485 BC). But Alexander's campaigns, the scientifically organized exploration of the sea route to the Persian Gulf by his admiral Nearchus, and the reports of Megasthenes put classical knowledge of India on a firmer footing. Egypt under the Ptolemies had an active trade with India, which expanded greatly with the luxury demand of Rome. The Greek names for rice, ginger and pepper are Indian, the Sanskrit for tin probably Greek;[9] the Byzantines had an official stationed at Clysma near Suez who visited India yearly to report on trade and political conditions; 'Roman' guards, 'the dumb *mlechchas*', were in demand by south Indian kings owing to their isolation from local faction. All-land routes were subject to interference by Parthia, often at war with Rome and always anxious to inflate transit profits; most trade was by sea, either via Palmyra or Petra and the Persian Gulf, or by Berenice and other Red Sea ports. The chief Indian ports concerned were Barbarikon on the Indus Delta, Barygaza (Broach), Kalyan near Bombay, and Musiris (Cranganore). The drain of precious metal in exchange for luxuries, including spices and sandalwood, is lamented by Roman publicists such as Pliny; evidence of Mediterranean

---

[9] K. de B. Codrington, 'A geographical introduction to the history of Central Asia', *GJ* 104 (1944), 27–40 and 73–91.

exports has been found in the form of warehouses of Roman pottery at Arika-medu near Pondicherry.[10] Ceylon and the extreme south of India were the meeting-places of Graeco-Roman and Chinese traders.

Cultural exchanges, though often indirect, were also important:

'Embassies were exchanged with the Hellenic powers by the sovereigns of Magadha and Malwa. Indian philosophers, traders and adventurers were to be found in the intellectual circles of Athens and the markets of Alexandria. The first of the Mauryas had entered into a marriage contract with a Greek potentate (Seleucus Nikator). His son was eager to secure the services of a Greek sophist. The third and greatest of the Mauryas (Asoka) entrusted the government of a wealthy province and the execution of important irrigation works to a Yavana chief. The services of Greek engineers seem to have been requisitioned by the greatest of the Kushans. Greek influence on Indian coinage and iconography is unmistakable.'[11]

Converse influences were those of Buddhism on the Graeco-Bactrians (their king Menander is the eponymous protagonist of the Buddhist *Milindapanha*); Indian thought may also have had some influence on Manicheism and hence on the early Christian Gnostic heresies. The early legend of St Thomas the Apostle (whose traditional tomb is to be seen in the Portuguese church at San Thomé, Madras) contains an indubitable reference to a Parthian king in the Indus borderland, and the Syrian Christian church of Malabar was possibly in existence in AD 200. Religion apart, the greatest gift of India to the West – and to the whole world – is the 'Arabic' numbers, without which it is difficult to conceive of modern scientific method.

The Western trade was largely in the hands of Asiatics, especially before the 'discovery' of the monsoon (long known to the Yemen Arabs) by Hippalus about AD 50. It is, naturally, much better known in Europe than the Indian expansion into southeast Asia, which began in the 1st and 2nd Christian centuries. Yet this had in a sense a more positive effect, since the beginnings of high civilization in Burma, Malaya, Indonesia and parts of Indo-China were due directly to Hindu and Buddhist traders, colonists and missionaries. Indian dynasties ruled for over a millennium (2nd–15th centuries) in Champa (Annam); Kambuja (Cambodia) at times dominated the whole peninsula beyond Burma, then truly Further India; Sivaism has left its memorial in Angkor Vat, and the culture of Cambodia remains Indo-Buddhist to this day. In Indonesia the Sailendra or Sri Vijaya Empire, centred at Palembang in Sumatra, dominated the archipelago from the 8th to the 11th centuries. Sailendra was Buddhist, deriving its inspiration from Bengal and leaving in the 400-ft.-square terraces of Borobudur (Java) perhaps the grandest material monument of any religion, alike in the superbly massive planning of the whole and in the richness and beauty of the innumerable

[10] R. E. M. Wheeler *et al.*, 'Arikamedu: an Indo-Roman trading station on the east coast of India', *Ancient India*, No. 2 (ND, July 1946), 17–124.
[11] H. C. Raychaudhuri in *An Advanced History of India* (1946), 142.

sculptures. In the 9th century Java (a Hindu kingdom conquered by Sailendra) broke away; in the 13th and 14th the Javanese Majapahit dynasty gradually supplanted Sailendra and in turn controlled the archipelago, only to fall before the Islamic tide in the 15th century. Hinduism survived in Bali, the arts and customs of which reflect, if on a diminished scale, the golden days of classical Hinduism. The *Ramayana* and the *Mahabharata* are still the basis of much popular art – puppet- and stage-plays, poems and folk-tales – in Indonesia and even the Indo-Chinese peninsula.

Naturally the major part in the foundation of these distant sea-states was played by the kingdoms of the eastern littoral, especially Kalinga and the Chola Empire. How false is Lyde's still current concept of an almost solely inward-looking India, with its sea-contacts those of alien traders, may be seen from the fact that the decline of Sailendra was due in large part to an attack by Rajendra Chola II (1012–44); the Cholas were driven out after a century of intermittent war, but in the 13th century a disastrous expedition against Ceylon fatally weakened the power of Sri Vijaya. These armadas presuppose high standards not only in navigation and seamanship, but in naval organization, on both sides of the 1,200-mile-wide waters between Coromandel and Sumatra. Certainly no European power of the day could have dreamt of such oceanic adventure: only the Viking voyages are as impressive, while the Crusading fleets were in comparison mere coastal forays. On the terraces of Borobudur the carved ships of Sri Vijaya still sail, immobile and endlessly, over their seas of stone.

Hindu expansion remained vigorous until about AD 1000–1100; but the declining fortunes of Hinduism in the homeland sapped its strength, and indigenous elements, seconded by Islam, reasserted themselves. Long before then an even greater work had been accomplished from India: by devious ways through mountain and jungle Buddhism had spread over the Far East and High Asia; the Chinese Buddhist pilgrims Fa Hien and Hiuen-Tsang (5th and 7th centuries) give us the first comprehensive accounts of India by outside observers. Buddhism hardly recovered from the devastation of the Huns in its northwestern strongholds, and in succeeding centuries it declined before a Brahmanic revival. By the time it was dead in its birthplace its heirs had developed the strength to stand alone and to evolve the complex cosmogony and psychology of later Buddhism in China, Tibet and Japan, the lands of the Mahayana or 'Greater Vehicle' as opposed to the 'Lesser', the simpler Hinayana form which survives in Ceylon, Burma and Thailand.

The Muslim advance

Apart from the early occupation of Sind, never really followed up, the first Muslim incursions of significance were the almost annual raids of Mahmud of Ghazni, between 1000 and 1030. Mahmud, a first-class soldier and a patron of the arts, was in India no more than a ruthless plunderer; he penetrated as far as Mathura and Somnath (Kathiawad), but only the Punjab – as far as Thanesar –

was held, and that only as the frontier march of a domain covering most of Persia and at times much of Turkestan. But the ferocity of his devastations weakened the economy and morale of the Hindu states, and though there was a respite of 160 years before the arrival of the next great Muslim leader, Muhammad of Ghor in southwest Afghanistan, northern India remained politically fragmented. Muhammad's victory over the Rajput princes near Thanesar in 1192 was decisive; the Delhi gateway was finally forced, the Rajputs split into the petty Pahari (=hill) chiefs of the sub-Himalaya and the better-known princes of the Aravalli fortresses – Rajputana or Rajasthan. Within 10 years the entire Gangetic Plain, as far as Nadia in Bengal, had been overrun; and henceforth Islam was politically dominant in Hindustan.

The Ghaznavid realm, and the new Empire in its first few years, had straddled the northwestern hills. By dynastic accident this Afghan–Punjab relationship was broken in 1206, and the famous Sultanate of Delhi took form, to survive in some sense until 1857, though in evil days the 'Ruler of the World' sometimes ruled effectively 'from Delhi to Palam', nine or ten miles. The Delhi Kingdom now formed a separate entity in the Muslim world, a state at once Indian and Islamic. Under Iltutmish (1211–35), the greatest ruler of the first 'Slave' or Turco-Afghan dynasty, it corresponded roughly with the perennial northern triangle we have already seen as held by the Guptas, by Harsha, and by the Gurjaras; with the difference of a firm hold on the Indus Plains. The heart of Rajputana, and outlying regions such as Kathiawad and Bengal, generally retained a quasi-independence under their own princes or subordinate governors; and internal faction, wars of succession, and at times Mongol raids were constant impediments to consolidation. Under the second dynasty, the Khaljis (1294–1320), forays into the Deccan were frequent, and in 1311 reached Madurai in the far south. The rulers of these dynasties included some able if ruthless leaders, such as the astonishing megalomaniac Ala-ud-Din Khalji, a *soi-disant* 'Second Alexander', who ruled in the most totalitarian manner. Nevertheless the general standards of society and government were probably not very different in degree from those of contemporary Europe, and at Delhi architecture around the Qutb Minar shows an extremely successful fusion of Hindu and Islamic tradition. The Qutb is the highest free-standing stone tower in the world (234 ft., 71·3 m.); it is characteristic of Ala-ud-Din that he began a minar designed to be twice as high.

The Tughluks (1320–1412) represent a sterner and more austere Islam, well shown by the stark cyclopean grandeur of Tughlukabad, only three miles from the Qutb complex but worlds away in spirit. The greatest of them, Muhammad bin Tughluk, was an energetic despot who would have been enlightened in the European 18th-century manner had any enlightenment been to hand. Like the Khaljis, he had a bad press, since he based his politics on the world as he saw it rather than on Quranic commentaries (again a parallel with mediaeval Europe, i.e. the Emperor Frederick II). Muhammad extended his power almost to the southern extremity of India; it was in pursuance of a policy of definite conquest, rather than the mere depredations of preceding rulers, that he transferred the population of Delhi (or a large part of it) to Deogir in the Deccan, renamed Daulatabad and provided with spectacular fortifications. But although his domains were equalled in extent only by Asoka's before him and Aurenzeb's after, 'it was impossible to control the Deccan from an external centre in Hindustan, just as it was equally impossible to rule Hindustan from Deogir'[12] – the same problem as faced the Hohenstaufen in Germany and Italy, or Ghaznavids and Moguls in their relations with their Iranian holdings; realization of this probably accounts for so many invaders reaching Delhi and turning back, e.g. Timur, Nadir Shah, Ahmad Shah Durrani. Despite these and other aberrations Muhammad was a man of large ideas in many directions, not least in his conciliatory policy towards the Hindus. His successor Firoz Shah was more orthodox in this respect, taking piety indeed so far that he endeavoured to spare the blood of believers; an ineffective policy. He has at least the merit of initiating large-scale irrigation canals in the Punjab. Disintegration had set in before Muhammad's death – especially (as usual) in the south and Bengal, and after the death of Firoz (1388) the prestige of the Tughluks was irretrievably ruined in 1398 by the ferocious sack of Delhi by Timur (Tamburlaine). Centrifugal tendencies were scarcely checked by the weak successors of the Tughluks, the 15th-century Sayyids and Lodis.

In the south a strong new Hindu power, Vijayanagar, arose on the ruins of the older Dravidian dynasties, shattered by the Tughluk incursions, and made head against the Muslim princes, whose revolt had set into motion the disintegration of Muhammad bin Tughluk's Empire. In the Deccan, between Tapti and Tungabhadra, the Bahmani kingdom split off from the Tughluk dominions, and in turn split into five Deccani Sultanates: Ahmadnagar, Berar, Bidar, Golconda and Bijapur; the broken country of the northeastern Peninsula was left to Gond tribal chieftains. Gujarat, at the height of its commercial importance, was an independent Muslim kingdom, as were Khandesh south and Malwa north of the Narmada, Sind and Multan in the west, Bengal in the east and for a few years even Jaunpur in the heart of Hindustan. All these were under Muslim rulers, but the Rajputs formed a confederacy under the leadership of Mewar, threatening the diminished Lodi realms, which at best formed a belt from the Punjab to Bihar, but were often not much more than the Delhi–Agra region.

Thus, after 300 years of Muslim conquest and attempted consolidation, all the old patterns of pre- and post-Mauryan India have once more emerged. Nothing better illustrates the perennial significance of the geographical factor in Indian history than this continual re-assertion of the nuclear regions as the power-bases of political entities. But two mighty forces were looming on the horizon of Indian politics: in 1526 Babur, who began his career as a boy of 12 dispossessed of his petty principality of Ferghana, utterly overthrew the Lodis at Panipat; and already in 1498 Vasco da Gama had reached Calicut, precursor of yet stronger

[12] C. C. Davies, *An Historical Atlas of the Indian Peninsula* (1949), 34.

and more alien powers who were to rule as much by economic chains as by the sword.[13]

The Mogul synthesis

The key significance of the Delhi–Agra region is strikingly illustrated by the incidents of early Mogul rule. By 1529 Babur was in possession of Bengal; he died in the next year and his son Humayun, after an expedition as far as Cambay, was defeated at Kanauj in 1539 and expelled from Hindustan. His supplanter, Sher Shah, was a very capable ruler, who laid out the Grand Trunk Road from Bengal to the Indus, and whose principles of land revenue administration influenced, through the Moguls, British practice. Disputed successions enabled Humayun to return in 1555 after a victory at Sirhind; but in 1556 his son Akbar, on any reckoning one of the world's great men, succeeded at the age of 14 to a military situation in which Delhi and Agra had been lost. Once more the field of Panipat saw a Mogul triumph. The old significance of these sites – Kanauj, Sirhind, Panipat – will be remembered.

Before his death in 1605 Akbar had secured not only Hindustan and the north-west, but had crossed the Narmada as far as the Godavari, and in the east held Orissa; between these salients the wild Gondwana country remained under independent or tributary chiefs. Territorial expansion, however, was the least of Akbar's achievements, nor, splendid as were his capitals at Agra and Fatehpur Sikri and his patronage of artists and scholars, were these his greatest. His administration was one of the best India had known, at least in its principles: but in all these vast empires, even-handed and accessible as might be the sovereign, he could not be accessible and effective everywhere, and there was much local tyranny. Nor were communications adequate to avert such natural disasters as the Gujarat famine of 1632; and the Empire was hardly so strong as it looked: in the later 17th century Tavernier estimated that 30,000 good European troops could march through it. Nevertheless it is impossible to visit Delhi, Agra and above all Fatehpur Sikri without an involuntary comparison with the Versailles of Louis XIV – a comparison unfavourable to the latter. Man for man Akbar was immeasurably the greater of the two, and he was as well served by men as able and loyal as Colbert or Vauban. But with all this, social organization was essentially semi-feudal, and India lacked the Enlightenment: when it came it was through the distorting prisms of an alien rule.

The grasp of Akbar's mind is the more astonishing when it is recalled that an excellent memory had to serve him in the place of formal literacy. He advanced from the tactical alliances of expediency with Rajput chiefs to a real tolerance and some degree of synthesis of the two great cultures, Hindu and Islamic: in

[13] See A. J. Toynbee, 'The Unification of the world' (*Civilization on Trial*, OUP, 1948, esp. 65–71). This is a very penetrating analysis of the situation; as always with Toynbee brilliantly written, and getting to the heart of the relations of geography, history and technology much more effectively than usual.

his last years indeed he went so far as to foster an eclectic creed drawing from these and even from Christianity; but this artificial construct had only a temporary following of courtiers. Under his successors Jahangir and Shah Jahan the policy of toleration was still followed, with less conviction, and advances were made in the Deccan, as far as Bijapur and Golconda, though effective action here was hampered by preoccupations in Afghanistan.

With Aurenzeb (1658–1707) the Empire reached its greatest extent: from Kabul to the Cauvery. But the seeds of disruption, always latent, were fertilized by Aurenzeb's intolerance, which completely alienated the Rajputs, by this time probably the most valuable military elements in the Empire. More serious was the situation in the Deccan. Here, after long wars centring round the Raichur Doab, the allied Sultanates had in 1565 finally crushed Vijayanagar at Talikota, southeast of Bijapur; only to fall in turn to the ceaseless Mogul attrition, advancing by the historic Malwa–Khandesh–Maharashtra route on the Deccan Lavas. But long before the definitive Mogul conquests of Bijapur and Golconda (1686–87) the Western Ghats were overhung by a cloud, at first no bigger than a man's hand, but destined in the next century to sweep over nearly all India. And behind the Marathas another cloud was setting in from the sea.

The founder of Maratha power, Sivaji, son of a minor noble of the Ahmadnagar Kingdom, from his little fief of Poona had won fortress after fortress in the wild Ghats country; when he died in 1680 he held the Konkan less Bombay, the Portuguese towns and Janjira – the last a holding of the Abyssinian Sidis, nominally the Bijapur and later the Mogul admirals. The core of Maratha power was a belt of country along the Ghats and as far east as the Bhima; and they had also various outliers in the south – Bellary, Bangalore, Tanjore. Sivaji's rise was of course aided by the extraordinary perfidy of Deccani politics, a tangle of ever-shifting alliances: war was generally triangular and might be polygonal. And the Moguls were long past their best: their Hindu subjects were sullen or in revolt; their armies were vast, cumbered with camp-followers, in a war of movement no match for the tough and mobile Maratha light horse; their leaders, no longer dominated by an Akbar or a Babur, but by a politician at once shifty and bigoted, more and more played their own hands. The stage is set for the chaos and anarchy of the 18th century; and by now the coasts from Diu to Chittagong were dotted with the trading stations and forts of Portuguese, Dutch, French, Danes and English.

The Mogul collapse

European expansion in India can be understood only against the background of 'country powers'. The successors of Aurenzeb were all ineffective, and the throne of Delhi became the plaything of internal and alien factions. Such morale as the Empire retained was shattered by the almost unopposed invasion of the Persian Nadir Shah and his savage sack of Delhi in 1739.

The Marathas represented the effervescence of a long-fermenting Hindu revival. Initially they kept tight discipline and were conscious of a mission as the liberators of Hinduism; but this element of idealism faded as they found their account in manoeuvres among the distracted factions of Muslim India. As their power expanded it became looser, a confederacy headed by the Poona Peshwas, ministers and supplanters of Sivaji's heirs; but the centre had influence rather than power. That was in the hands of the great warlords: the Gaekwar in Baroda, Bhonslas in Nagpur and Berar, Holkar in Indore (Malwa), most powerful of all Sindhia in Gwalior. Even Calcutta had its 'Maratha Ditch'. At the same time Mogul and other Muslim warlords set up for themselves.

Thus by the 1750s Haidar Ali subverted the Hindu dynasty in Mysore; the Viceroy of the Deccan had become the Nizam of Hyderabad; Bengal and Oudh were but very nominally subject to the ghost of empire at Delhi. Sind and the trans-Sutlej Punjab were under Afghan domination, and there was a separate Afghan state so near Delhi as Rohilkhand. So low had the Empire fallen that the Hindu Jats – little more than an armed peasantry – could dominate the Agra–Mathura region, plundering the Taj Mahal and Akbar's tomb near Agra.

Already in 1719 the Marathas had marched to Delhi as allies of one of the king-making Mogul factions. Before the repeated invasions of Ahmad Shah Abdali, founder of the Durrani dynasty which still rules Afghanistan, the Muslim rulers of the Punjab, unsupported by their 'government' in Delhi, called in the Marathas, who as a mere incident took possession of capital and Emperor. But they alienated the Rajputs and the rising Sikh chieftains, while Ahmad Shah rallied the Rohillas and Oudh. In 1761 Panipat once more saw the climax of the drama, when the Marathas were utterly overthrown, losing thousands of their best men and nearly all their best leaders: 'Two pearls have been dissolved, twenty-two gold Mohurs have been lost, and of the silver and copper the total cannot be cast up.' This was a decisive check to Maratha expansion; although Afghan affairs prevented Ahmad Shah from consolidating his power, the Sikhs filled the gap. Originally a quietist, even pacifist, reforming Hindu sect, Mogul persecution forged them into a nation, and under the extraordinarily tough one-eyed Ranjit Singh (1780–1839) they rose to dominate the Punjab. The Marathas remained dominant at Delhi, the Emperor being merely Sindhia's puppet. But Muslims and Marathas virtually cancelled each other out; four years before Panipat, Plassey had been fought, and the future, for nearly two centuries, lay with its alien victors.

Europe in India: Portugal

The British Empire in India was only the latest phase of four and a half centuries of European intrusion. This long history falls into distinct periods: Portuguese monopoly (1500–1600); the age of conflict between the European powers (1600–1763); the rise to power of the East India Company and its Indian Summer before the Mutiny (1757–1857); the unchallenged hey-day of the British Raj (1858–c. 1900); and the struggle for independence.

It is important to remember that Vasco da Gama's voyage was not only the climax of decades of patient African discovery; it was also a part of the Iberian crusade against Islam. Once the road was known experience soon taught the value of the monsoons to Portuguese fleets, which developed regular sailing habits, leaving Lisbon in time to reach Moçambique (where Lourenço Marques founded his colony in 1554) for the southwest monsoon to take them across to Goa. But it was certainly not timidity which led da Gama to work up the east African coast as far as Malindi (north of Mombasa) before striking into the open ocean: the journey (c. 1486–90) of Pero da Covilhan by the Red Sea to Calicut and down the African coast to Sofala (20°S) had taught the Portuguese of the Arab hold on the Indian Ocean trade and something of navigation conditions; da Gama knew that on this coast he could find a pilot to bring him through.

The Portuguese fixation on western India was thus influenced by sailing conditions; but in large part also by their preoccupation with the 'Moors' as well as with the monsoon. This bias is suggested by the title adopted by the King of Portugal: Lord of the Conquest, Navigation and Commerce of Ethiopia, Arabia, Persia and India. The 'Moors' fought tenaciously for their monopoly, with the support of the Muslim rulers of Bijapur and Gujarat, of Egypt and of the Turks after their capture (1518) of Alexandria, hitherto the great emporium of eastern trade. Afonso de Albuquerque, greatest of the Viceroys (1509–15), saw the key points for domination of the Indian Ocean: Goa, Malacca, Aden.[14] Goa was an island site, defensible behind its tidal creeks yet large enough to give a local agricultural base; it controlled the valuable trade in Arab horses for the armies of the Deccani kingdoms: it was taken in 1510. In the next year Albuquerque took Malacca, guarding the approach to the Spice Islands and the Far East. At Aden he failed, though the moral effect of his expedition beyond Bab-el-Mandeb was great; but he secured Socotra and Ormuz, the latter guarding the alternative seaway to the Levantine portages. With the fortification of Ormuz, Albuquerque's last act before he died in Goa harbour, Portuguese domination in the Indian Ocean was complete: it was only seventeen years since da Gama's arrival at Calicut. The Portuguese achievement was secured against very heavy numerical odds, and with a much lesser margin of technical superiority than that enjoyed by later Europeans: by the time of the great sieges of Diu in 1538 and 1545 there was little that Europe could teach the 'Rumi' (Turkish) gunners in Indian service. But there have been few better geopoliticians than Albuquerque.

Besides Goa and a number of minor stations on the Konkan, Malabar and Coromandel coasts, the Portuguese held by 1540 the flourishing ports of Chaul, Bassein, Damão and Diu; in the east they were established – more precariously – at San Thomé (Madras), Hooghly and Chittagong; they had forts in Ceylon

[14] Four and a half centuries later these were the only important points on the Asian mainland shores of the Indian Ocean to remain in European hands.

and were beginning to dominate its politics; they were in official contact with China and freelance adventurers reached Japan in 1542 –

E se mais mundo houvera, lá chegára.[15]

But the royal trading monopoly was always cumbrous and usually corrupt; ill-paid officials made their fortunes where they could find them; the bigotry of the ecclesiastics often wrecked promising political combinations; the administration, in theory tightly organized, was as a rule ramshackle in practice – to find money for the rebuilding of Diu after the second siege the Viceroy D. João de Castro had to pawn his beard as security for a loan from the citizens of Goa. On the other hand, the archaic theocratic outlook of the Portuguese fitted into the Asian scene better than the secular temper of their supplanters, and, together with their tolerance of miscegenation, accounts for the deep cultural impress of Portugal in Ceylon and parts of the Konkan.

Decay had set in before the catastrophe of 1580, when the crown passed to Philip II of Spain and Portuguese holdings were open to Dutch attacks, without any compensating aid from Spain. The Portuguese effective was locked up in too many scattered small garrisons; at Tuticorin 'the Captain-Major of the Fishery Coast' points to 'what is little more than a hut: "The fortress is that house in which I live. All the Portuguese consist of myself."'[16] Yet the old Lusian spirit flared up in gallant last-ditch defences, as when Bassein fell to the Marathas in 1739; and indeed the *Novas Conquistas* of Goa were won in the 18th century.

Europe in India: the age of conflict

In 1600 the English East India Company was founded, in 1602 the Dutch: more efficient commercial mechanisms than the Portuguese monopoly, backed by the more modern ideology of energetic and youthful bourgeoisies rather than the inept control of a half-feudal state. In the struggle which ensued the English played a minor part, though they helped the Persians to capture Ormuz in 1622. But after this they and the Portuguese were as a rule on fairly friendly terms: after all, the Dutch might be Protestants but were obviously more dangerous trade rivals. As for the Dutch, they were greatly interested in the Spice Islands and not at all interested in warring with the enemies of Christendom: they based themselves well to the east, at Batavia, founded in 1619 to guard the Sunda Straits breach in the island barrier between the Indian Ocean and the Far East.[17] Malacca they took in 1641, Colombo in 1656, and Goa itself was blockaded in the open season for several years from 1639. Cochin was taken in 1653 and other

[15] 'And had there been more of the world, they would have reached it' – Camões, *Os Lusiadas*, VII. 14.

[16] João Ribeiro, *The Historic Tragedy of Ceilão* (1685; trans. P. E. Pieris, Colombo, n.d.), 238. This simple, stout-hearted captain speaks much more sense on the decline than is found in either the modern Portuguese rhetorical historians, or in the traditional Popery-and-immorality English view of Portugal in the East.

[17] The Dutch normally sailed with the Westerlies to about 100° E before turning north, which led them to the discovery of western Australia – for two centuries 'New Holland'.

Malabar forts in 1661–64. By this time Portugal was finished, and Bombay after it became English (1661–66) soon outstripped all other European bases on the western littoral.

Nevertheless the Portuguese had pre-empted this coast, and except at Surat, terminal of the Malwa trade-route, and the pepper coast of Malabar, it was hardly worth while turning them out. Dutch and English factories at Surat date from 1616 and 1612, and both fought the Portuguese in Swally Roads off the port. But the main interest turned to the east coast, where the 'country powers' were weak and disunited. The Dutch had stations at Pulicat (1610), Chinsura on the Hooghly (1653) and Negapatam (1659); the English at Masulipatam (1611), Armagaon (1626), and above all Madras (Fort St George, 1639) and Calcutta (Fort William, 1691–98). In the 18th century the Dutch, weakened by the long struggle with Louis XIV and now definitely a junior partner to their British allies, gradually lost ground in India and concentrated on Indonesia, though Chinsura was not ceded to the EIC until 1825.

In the meantime a far more serious competitor had appeared. In 1668 the first French factory was established at Surat – then nearing its decline – followed in 1669 by one at Masulipatam; and while they were dispossessed of San Thomé by the Dutch in 1673, the same year saw their establishment at Pondicherry, and 1690–92 at Chandernagore. This initial development, largely due to Colbert, was not followed up, and the years of Marlborough's wars saw a general decline in French activity. In the 1720s, however, Mauritius, Mahé and Karikal were occupied.

At this stage the French, like the Dutch and English, were content with 'factories': small extra-territorial holdings granted by the local ruler, and if possible further secured by a *firman* from the Mogul Emperor. Here, within a fortified *enceinte*, were offices, warehouses, official residences; and sometimes there were jurisdictional rights over native settlement attracted by the trade (and the security) afforded by the factory. All were managed by monopolistic chartered companies, an organization adopted by other countries which took a hand: Sweden, Austria (the Ostend and Imperial Companies, 1722–44 and 1781–84), Prussia (the Emden Company) and Denmark. Only the last had any significance: Danish Serampore and Tranquebar were not sold to the EIC until 1845, and were important missionary centres when the EIC took its policy of non-interference in religion to the point of discouraging Christian zeal; Tranquebar has still a Lutheran Bishopric, with an Indian Bishop.

The Franco-British struggle for power was in appearance no more than a side-show to the War of the Austrian Succession (1744–48) and the Seven Years' War (1756–63). But it laid the foundations of an Empire which at its height included some 1,750,000 sq. miles and 410,000,000 people (including Ceylon and Burma).

Ever since 1505, when the Captain of Colombo reported to the King of Kandy of the Portuguese strangers that 'their guns were very good', European military aptitudes had been held in respect; but they had been mainly confined to the defence of fortifications. A chance clash in the open field between a small French and a large local force opened the eyes of all parties.[18] The Europeans were now courted for military assistance; and in the whirlpool of Indian politics the possible gains were immense. Always liable to be cut off from France by superior British sea-power, the French under Dupleix and Bussy tended to fall back on this game, played with vigour and skill. There was a ding-dong struggle in which both Pondicherry and Madras changed hands, and at times it seemed that French influence would dominate the Deccan. But lack of steady metropolitan support ruined their chances. After 1763 there was never a serious French menace, though the British were long nervous of possible French-inspired coalitions, such as those suggested by Napoleon's intrigues with Tipu Sultan of Mysore.

Territorial rise of 'John Company'

The serious beginnings of British territorial power were the acquisition of the Northern Circars (Madras–Orissa coast) and the 24 Parganas around Calcutta in 1757–59. There is truth in the traditional view that the subsequent advance was to some extent involuntary, since the anarchic turmoil of war and intrigue beyond the Company's borders made advance essential for security. Yet the appetite grew by what it fed on, and within 20 years of Plassey (1757) the Gangetic Plain as far as Kanpur was either directly under Company rule, or under clients such as the Nawab of Oudh. In the west the Marathas were a more solid obstacle than the effete Mogul succession states of the northeast; here even Salsette Island, immediately adjacent to Bombay, was not occupied until 1775–76. The great years, in which it became clear that no likely combination of 'country powers' could withstand British arms, were those of the Napoleonic Wars. Mysore, a serious menace under the vigorous and able soldiers Haidar Ali and Tipu Sultan, ceased to be so on the defeat and death of the latter in 1799; the Nizam of Hyderabad (one or two lapses apart) had been Our Most Faithful Ally almost from the beginning; the Marathas, rarely able to co-ordinate their powers, were finally defeated in 1818. By 1849 the last serious opponents (and perhaps the toughest of all), the Sikhs, had been subjugated, but the early disasters of the First Afghan War (1839–42) were a clear warning of the limits on this side. Apart from Baluchistan, annexed in part as a reaction to the Anglo–Russian crisis over the Balkans in 1878, Lower Burma (1852), and Upper Burma, annexed in 1885–86 to forestall French penetration from Indo-China, India was substantially as it stood in 1947, except for the separation of Burma in 1937.

'The actual distribution of British territory is too significant, in the broad, to be a mere absent-minded accident, although no other explanation will account for some of its fantastic local fragmentations and aberrations. The bases lay in the great Presidency provinces of Bengal, Madras, and Bombay,

[18] See Sir J. Fortescue, *A History of the British Army*, II (1910), 184–5.

securing all the coasts with the unimportant exceptions of those of Travancore and Cochin in the southwest, one or two tiny states south of Bombay, and arid Kutch, Kathiawad, and Baluchistan (and the Oman outlier at Gwadar) in the northwest; apart of course from the Portuguese enclaves of Goa, Damão, Diu, the French of Mahé, Karikal, Pondicherry, Yanaon, and Chandernagore, the total area of these amounting to under 1,750 square miles. The entire alluvial crescent between the Ganges and the Indus deltas, a few enclaves apart, was British, and the three bases were linked by practically continuous bridges, with a wedge of the United Provinces reaching down to contact the Bombay–Calcutta corridor of the Central Provinces. The two great states of Mysore and Hyderabad were neatly cut off from the sea and from each other. From Kathiawad through Gujarat, Rajputana, and Central India, as far as the Orissa hinterland, stretched great but broken blocks of states' territory; but no single state in these groups exceeded 36,210 square miles or 3,050,000 inhabitants in 1941, and the political fragmentation (now largely swept away by the Union) was indescribable verbally and well-nigh unmappable: it was as if the feudal map of England in the anarchy of Stephen's reign had been frozen. In the northwest money, diplomacy, and arms, in adroit and ever-varying combinations, held a disjointed buffer-strip firmly under British control; and the key points, Peshawar and Quetta, were in British hands.'[19]

The Indian Empire

'There have been in Asia, generally, from time immemorial, but three departments of Government: Finance, or the plunder of the interior; War, or the plunder of the exterior; and the department of public works . . . the British have neglected entirely that of public works.' This indictment by Marx was ceasing to be true when he wrote it in 1853, as indeed he himself points out; but it is no unfair description of the India of Warren Hastings. In the next century came the economic catastrophe of the free entry of Manchester goods, ruining the old craft industries. Against this must be set an administration which at least set its face against corruption, and, in most times and places, a general peace which must have been unspeakably comforting after the atrocious warfare of the post-Mogul anarchy.

Yet revolutionary changes were afoot in 1853. Railway development had but begun – a few miles at Bombay. At least, according to Marx, the British were 'laying down the material premises' for emancipation and social improvement: 'They intend now drawing a net of railroads over India. And they will do it. The results are incalculable.' This laying of the foundations of a modern state in India was the historic task of the British Raj, however blindly, and sometimes reluctantly, carried out.[20]

[19] W. G. East and O. H. K. Spate (eds.), *The Changing Map of Asia* (Methuen, London, 4th ed. 1961), 131.

[20] See pp. 180–94 of *A Handbook of Marxism* (Gollancz, London, 1935); a vigorous and astonishingly acute analysis. Lest Marx's attack should seem overdrawn, cf. the even more severe contemporary judgements of Sleeman and Lawrence (both British officials) cited in L. S. S. O'Malley (ed.), *Modern India and the West* (OUP, 1941), 76–77.

Nevertheless, after the EIC lost its trading function in 1833, it stagnated in a *laissez-faire* world, improving its administration, but doing little else: the Heroic Age was over with the defeat of the Sikhs. Into this Indian Summer crashed the tremendous thunderstorm of the 1857 Mutiny – or War of Independence.

Uniting, if imperfectly, the most diverse factions, it was complex in its proximate origins: resentment at Dalhousie's high-handed 'doctrine of lapse', whereby several states had passed to the Company in default of male heirs, but in disregard of Hindu adoption law; the grievances of the landowners of Oudh, which had recently been annexed on account of the chronic misgovernment of its rulers; the famous scandal of the greased cartridges. Yet perhaps at bottom it was simply the last rally of the old indigenous India, a gigantic protest against a revolution from above and to the profit of an alien race. Delhi – significantly on historic and geographical grounds – was the major storm-centre. It ended in the death of one Empire and the birth of another. The last Mogul, Bahadur Shah, a blind old poet hardly understanding his proclamation by the mutineers, was taken to Rangoon to die; the discredited Company was superseded by the direct rule of the Crown, and twenty years later Queen Victoria was proclaimed Empress of India.

Nationalism

The first fifty years of the Empire saw much material change – the spread of railways and telegraphs, the initiation of great irrigation works; the cotton boom of the American Civil War years (1861–65) gave an impetus to commercial speculation; the Suez Canal (1869) brought England and India nearer;[21] large sectors of the peasantry were now tied to the world market. Yet it was possible to maintain that the fundamentals of Indian life and society had changed little, beneath the surface layer of public works, though in two directions forces of great significance were stirring. The necessity of staffing an enormous adminis-trative machine led to the production of a vast clerical army trained (however inadequately) in Western techniques, and far too large to be profitably employed: hence the frustration of the unemployed intellectual, and the schizophrenia of those no longer believing in the old gods, yet with no secure place in the new world.[22] And by the turn of the century a vigorous capitalist class was growing, as yet industrially weak, almost confined to the cotton mills of Bombay and Ahmedabad, but conscious of potentialities and girding at fiscal restraint in the interests of Lancashire. These provided the sinews of war, the intellectuals the ideology, the young men of the urban middle-class (and increasingly the town workers) the rank and file; and at times sections of the peasantry gave massive

[21] And, by facilitating the coming of English wives and the development of more exclusively English social life, contributed to detach the English in India yet farther from their subjects. The old officials were not infrequently kept in good touch with Indian feeling by alliances, temporary or permanent, with Indian mistresses.
[22] On this, see G. Wint, *The British in India* (Faber, London, 1947), (a most acute analysis); L. S. S. O'Malley, *op. cit.* 763–97; East and Spate, *op. cit.* 25–29.

weight to the attack. The Indian National Congress travelled fast from its innocuous beginnings in 1885; and in 1905 the Japanese victory over Russia ended the automatic acceptance of European invincibility.

This nationalism began in the 1890s with Tilak's appeal to Maratha traditions and gained strength from the agitation against Curzon's partition of Bengal in 1905. It was thus largely Hindu in tone, and after the collapse of the Hindu–Muslim united front in defence of the Caliphate in 1921 this bias was on the whole strengthened by the ideology of Mahatma Gandhi. The distress and disturbances of the years after 1914–18, culminating in the appalling bloodshed at Amritsar in 1919, and the great mass Civil Disobedience movement of 1931, showed that the temper of articulate India was far ahead of the reforms, which seemed doled out in niggardly instalments. In 1937, however, Congress decided to work, at least temporarily, within the 1935 Constitution, and Congress governments in nine major provinces gained valuable experience and showed both the potentialities and the limitations of constitutionalism. The automatic entry of India into the war in 1939 without consultation with Congress led to a decisive breach; and the Japanese successes of 1941–42, bringing them to the very borders of India, gave point to the dictum (whether or not Gandhi uttered it) that the Cripps promise of Dominion status (with right of secession) was 'a post-dated cheque on a failing bank'. At the same time Congress blunders, the communal struggle for patronage, resentment of the fact that the numerical majority controlled an even greater share of the economic life of the country, fed Muslim separatism.[23] At the end of the war two things were inescapably clear: British rule could by no possibility be said to retain or to be able to regain the consent of the governed, and could be maintained only at the cost, unthinkable morally and materially, of a 'super-Palestine'; and no settlement within a single state could meet the demands of the Muslim League, which now represented the political mass of Muslims. The Gordian knot was cut by the British government, and on August 15th, 1947, the Dominions of India and Pakistan came into their inheritance. On January 26th, 1950, the Indian Union declared itself a Republic and five years later Pakistan became an 'Islamic Republic'; both within the British Commonwealth. By a strange irony the fragments of Portuguese and French dominion survived, for a little while, their mighty supplanter the British Raj.

BIBLIOGRAPHICAL NOTE

The standard large work, superseding *The Cambridge History of India*, is the multi-volume *History and Culture of the Indian People*, edited by R. C. Majumdar and published by Bharatiya Vidya Bhavan, Bombay; a co-operative work of massive scholarship. There are numerous shorter histories, of which R. C. Majumdar, H. C. Raychauduri and K. Datta, *An Advanced History of India*

[23] For fuller discussion see O. H. K. Spate, 'Geographical aspects of the Pakistan scheme', *GJ* 102 (1943), 125–35; and 'The partition of India and the prospects of Pakistan', *GR* 38 (1948), 5–29.

(Macmillan, London, 1946) is perhaps the best, full and balanced, if rather text-booky in style. J. Nehru, *The Discovery of India* (Doubleday, Anchor Paper-backs, 1946) is a highly stimulating nationalist treatment. On the cultural side, H. Zimmer, *The Art of Indian Asia* (Pantheon, NY, 1955) is authoritative and lavishly illustrated. C. C. Davies, *An Historical Atlas of the Indian Peninsula* (OUP, Madras, 2nd ed. 1954) has useful maps and brief but acute notes.

On pre- and proto-historic India, the best introduction is R. Mortimer Wheeler's *Early India and Pakistan* (Thames & Hudson, London, 1959); more specialized are D. H. Gordon, *The Prehistoric Background of Indian Culture* (Desai, Bombay, 1958), A. H. Dani, *Prehistory and Protohistory of Eastern India* (Mukhopadhaya, Calcutta, 1960), and H. D. Sankalia, *Prehistory and Proto-history in India and Pakistan* (Univ. of Bombay, 1962). B. Subbarao's *The Personality of India* has a strong geographical framework, and another stimulat-ing survey published by the Maharaja Sayajirao University, Baroda, is Y. A. Raikar, *Indian History: A Study in Dynamics* (1960).

Turning to later times, for the Mogul period (which administratively formed the mould for the British Raj and even, in some respects, for the present Republics), the 17th-century travels of Bernier, Tavernier and especially Nicolo Manucci (*Storia do Mogor*) are available in good libraries and throw much light on social conditions, as well as being exceedingly good reading. W. H. Moreland's economic histories, *India at the Death of Akbar* and *From Akbar to Aurengzeb* (London, 1920, 1923) are classic pioneer works in a field which Indian scholars are now tilling. It was time, however, that the Eurocentric bias of Indian (and Asian) historiography was redressed, though it may be questioned whether K. M. Pannikkar's *Asia and the European Dominance* (Allen & Unwin, London, 3rd ed. 1961) does not tilt too far on the other side.

Works on the British period are often, and naturally enough, tendentious on one side or the other. Perhaps the most candid from the British side is G. T. Garratt and E. Thompson, *The Rise and Fulfilment of British Power in India* (London, 1934). Philip Woodruff's *The Men Who Ruled India* (Cape, London, 1953, 1954) gives a vivid picture of the British Raj at work, occasionally too nostalgic but at least not sinking into hagiography.

For the origins of Pakistan, ideological and political, see W. C. Smith, *Modern Islam in India* (Gollancz, London, 2nd ed. 1947), R. Symonds, *The Making of Pakistan* (Faber, London, 1950), and the works cited in the preceding Biblio-graphical Note. The Partition and its immediate effects are well presented in E. W. R. Lumby, *The Transfer of Power in India and Pakistan* (Allen & Unwin, London, 1954) and in the first-hand narratives of an actor in these affairs, V. P. Menon, *The Story of the Integration of the Indian States* (Longmans, Green, London, 1956) and *The Transfer of Power in India* (Princeton Univ. Press, 1957). Two excellent books are H. Tinker, *India and Pakistan: A Short Political Guide* (Pall Mall Press, London, 1962) and I. Stephens, *Pakistan: Old Country, New Nation* (Pelicans, Harmondsworth, 1964).

CHAPTER 7

Village and Town in India

I. THE INDIAN VILLAGE

Of the 1961 population of India, about 360,000,000 – 82% – lived in villages. Altogether there were 564,258 villages, of which about 4,200 had over 5,000 people, and no fewer than 349,195 had under 500. Pakistan is even more dominantly rural. Some general remarks on the villages and their life seem desirable, although settlement patterns, house-types, and so on are treated in some detail in the regional chapters.

The village in general

The great majority of the country folk live in small or large nucleated settlements, and areas of dispersed habitations are few: the Himalayan zone is perhaps the only extensive area of true dispersal, of the type found in European highlands; elsewhere, even in the hills, the normal unit is the small hamlet rather than the homestead. In the arid west this is enforced partly by the paucity of water-points, partly by the needs of defence – still visibly attested by the watch-towers of Pathan villages. In the Assam–Burma Ranges defence is also an important factor: villages are on hilltops or spurs, often stockaded; it must be remembered that in these jungly hills the valleys are extremely malarial, and the communication is easiest along relatively open ridgeways. The Bengal Delta – especially the East – is *sui generis*: there is indeed much settlement that is not nucleated, but 'dispersal' appears an exceedingly inappropriate term for the dense stipple of separate homesteads, hardly isolated except in the most literal sense of the word when, during the rains, each is an island on its little earthen plinth.[1] Other more or less dispersed zones are found in the Konkan, in areas of recent or temporary reclamation by squatters in the Assam jungles, or in the great floodplains by farmers using the rich khadar for high-value crops after the rains. But in both groups the very small hamlet – say 6 to 12 huts – is the rule, rather than true dispersal; and in the latter case the huts are often only temporary, inhabited during the dry weather by people normally resident in big villages on the bluffs above.

[1] See J. C. Jack, *The Economic Life of a Bengal District* (1916), 16–38; and below. Figs. 19.6 and 19.7.

These are anomalies: in the great homogeneous plains nucleation is almost invariable. In the past defence played its part, and in areas open to constant disturbance (e.g. the Sutlej/Yamuna and Yamuna/Ganga Doabs, Rohilkhand, the fringes of central India, Khandesh, the Raichur Doab) villages are often grouped around a petty fort; and even today the close-packed houses, with blank outer walls and low doorways, massed into a ring with few entrances, present a defensive aspect. Often there is not much in the way of site selection; one place is as good as another, and the village rises are as often as not their own creation, the rubbish of generations. But any discontinuity, any break in the almost imperceptible slope, produces linear settlement patterns: especially notable are the bluffs above floodplains and the margins of abandoned river courses. The bluff villages tend to be larger than those on the drier interfluves; they have the advantage of two types of terrain, the upland doab and the valley-bottom with its tamarisk brakes and the excellent soil of its *chars* or *diaras* – the floodplain islands – submerged in the rains and liable to disappear completely in floods, but cropping up again sooner or later. These alluviated areas are often given over to cash crops of high value; near large towns they are often used for market gardens, easily irrigated by wells taking advantage of the high water-table.

Settlement lines tend to occur also at the marked break of slope where steep residual hills grade into a fan, which has usually a fairly high water-table. Lateritic shelves along deltaic margins are also important building sites, poor in themselves but offering rough grazing, scrubby woodland (the source of a great range of minor necessities from timber to illicit alcohol), and providing space for dry crops, the flats below being entirely given over to paddy. They form as it were neutral ground between the jungly hills and the waterlogged paddy-plain. Here not only the general arrangement of settlements but also the village itself is often linear; islands of lateritic and older alluvium in the deltas are often completely ringed with houses. Linear settlement is also, of course, prominent in the deltas and wider floodplains themselves, strung out along levees or artificial embankments, and in places (e.g. Kerala and the Contai area of southwest Bengal) along old beach ridges. Very often such sites are the only dry points in the rains and the only water-points in the hot weather.[2]

There is in general very little that looks like a 'plan', other than that dictated by such site factors as alignment along bluffs or levees, grouping round a fort or a tank; but within the seemingly chaotic agglomeration there is, as a rule, a strong internal differentiation, that of the separate quarters for various castes.

A village in detail: Aminbhavi (Figs. 7.1 and 7.2)

These points are best brought out by a close view of a specific village, not indeed 'typical' (no single village could be that) but certainly the most random

[2] For analogues cf. G. T. Trewartha, *Japan* (Univ. of Wisconsin, Madison, 1945), Figs. 64 and 68; E. H. G. Dobby, 'Settlement patterns in Malaya', *GR* 32 (1942); O. H. K. Spate, 'The Burmese village', *GR* 35 (1945).

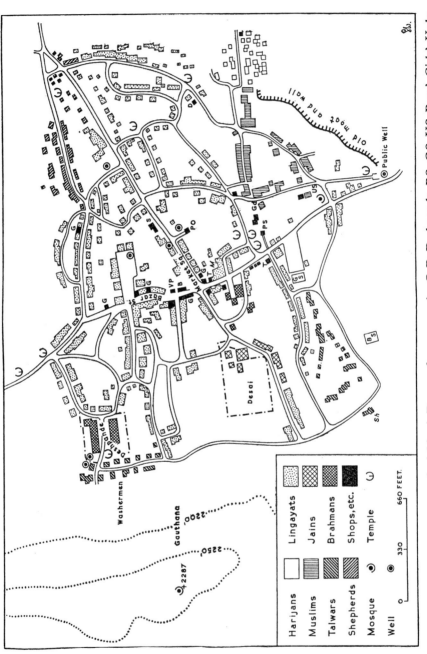

FIG 7.1 A VILLAGE IN DETAIL. Aminbhavi, Deccan, from survey by C. D. Deshpande. BS, GS, US, Boys', Girls', Urdu Schools; G, B, T, Grocers', Bania's and Tea-Bidi Shops; PO, PS, Post Office, Police Station; D, Dispensary; Gd, ; VP, Village Panchayat; M, Lingayat Math; Sh, Shikalgars.

of samples.[3] Our example is in the Deccan, more precisely in north-western Mysore.

Aminbhavi lies 7 miles NNE of Dharwar; an old settlement, going back at least thirteen centuries, originally walled and moated. Essentially its site is governed by the junction of the Dharwar rocks, forming poor red soils around the mosque-crowned hill to the west, with the crystallines which have weathered into deep black cotton soils in the east. It is a typical black soil agricultural village, with a rainfall of about 24 in. (610 mm.), devoted mainly to dry crops (cotton, jowar, wheat, pulses, safflower, in that order), tending to become a satellite of Dharwar, the market of its dairy and agricultural produce. On the poorer land to the west is rough grazing, supporting a few shepherds, and immediately west of the village the common or *gauthana*, an essential part of its economy, the centre of all harvesting.

Caste and community largely govern the layout. Of its 4,106 inhabitants, Lingayats, the sturdy agricultural caste of the Karnatak, number some 2,650. Next come 550 Muslims, an unusually high proportion, but the place was of some importance in the days of the Bijapur Kingdom. But the culturally dominant groups are the Jains (250) and the Brahmins (75); an *Inam* (landlord) village, most of it belonging to the Desai (Jain) and Deshpande (Brahmin) families, whose *wadas* (more or less equivalent to manor houses) stand on the best sites, within large compounds. The Desais provide the village *patel* or headman. For the rest, each caste tends to occupy a solid block of contiguous houses in a lane named from the caste; where, as with the Lingayats, several lanes are occupied, each is named from the leading family residing in it. Besides those mentioned, there are 300 Talwars (domestic servants and agricultural labourers), 200 Harijans ('untouchables'), and smaller groups of other low castes: Wadars (quarrymen), Shikalgars (backward semi-nomadic casual labourers), washermen, and so on. These groups live on the circumference of the village, or even beyond the old moat. (Fig. 7.1.)

Occupations likewise are still mainly on a caste basis: the Lingayats provide the bulk of the tenant-farmers, Talwars and Harijans landless agricultural labour; carpenters, smiths, cobblers, washermen, barbers are all separate castes. Apart from these crafts and agriculture, there is some handloom cotton weaving, a subsidiary occupation of the Lingayats.

Houses are generally built on to each other, or at least the mud walls of the compounds are continuous. The house layout (Fig. 7.2) is as standard as in any English working-class street. In front is a porch (*katte*), used for drying agricultural produce, as a formal reception room, as 'a place of female gossip when the

---

[3] The coincidence of the writing of this chapter and a correspondence with Dr C. D Deshpande then of Dharwar led me to appeal to him for a sample survey; the choice was left entirely to him. Nothing could be more random and free from preconceived choice. I am deeply indebted to Dr Deshpande and his students for the very full and admirable maps, photographs and notes on which this section is entirely based. For the general setting, see 703–5 below. Cf. also the Addendum to this chapter.

master of the house is out', and above all as a sleeping-room in the stifling summer nights. Behind this is the main room, some 25 ft. (7·6 m.) square, part

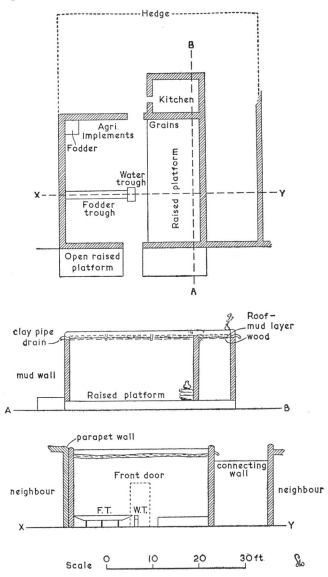

FIG 7.2 AMINBHAVI HOUSE PLAN. *Courtesy C. D. Deshpande.*

of which is a cattle pen, at threshold level; the remainder, raised some 2 or 3 ft., is the general living-room, for sleeping, eating, more intimate entertainment of guests, and perhaps handicrafts. The most prominent object is the pile of grain stored in gunny bags and sadly depleted towards the end of the agricultural year. Behind is a separate kitchen (with a corner for the bath) and the backyard with manure-pits and haystacks. This is the standard pattern; construction is similar in all groups (except the lowest), differences in economic status being reflected merely in size, except that the well-to-do have more separate single-purpose rooms. Jains and Brahmins do not live so tightly packed as the rest, either in the spacing of the houses or within them.

The poorest castes live in wretched one-room wattle huts with thatched roofs. Apart from these all houses have walls 1 or 2 ft. thick of mudbrick, with few (and high) or more likely no windows: Indians in general have a doubtless well-founded burglar-phobia. The flat roof is supported by wooden posts and made of mud on a framework of crude beams and babul (acacia) branches; they have rounded mud parapets and clay rain-water pipes.

As for services, these are mostly grouped around the main village lane: market-place for the weekly bazaar, eight shops (four grocery, two cloth, one tailor, one miscellaneous) and a number of booths selling tea and *bidis*, the cheap crude cigarettes of the Indian masses. Near the market-place is the room of the village *panchayat* or caste council, an ancient institution generally fallen into desuetude but now being fostered as the first step in local government. Associated with this tiny 'urban core' are the government establishments – Police Station, Post Office, grain warehouse. There are three mosques, one giving its name to the Idgah hill in the west, and eight temples, including that of the Deshpandes, as well as the Lingayat *math*, a centre of religious and charitable fellowship. The professions are represented by an Ayurvedic (indigenous) dispensary, an Urdu school for the Muslims, and separate schools for boys and girls. The boys' school is the most modern building in Aminbhavi, its stone walls and red-tiled roof standing in sharp contrast to the monotony of mud walls.

Finally we may note the large masonry-lined public well, sunk in what was once the moat; it is no mean excavation, an apt reminder of the all-importance of water-supply in Indian life.

Once more, no one village can be typical of the whole sub-continent; but many of the features detailed above can be paralleled over and over again in most parts of India. Our random sample is at least very representative.

The village : its aspect and life

The aspect of the village varies not only with the general regional setting, with building materials and house-types, but with social factors. The generally greater emphasis on caste in the south takes social fragmentation allied with spatial separation to the extreme, segregating the untouchables in outlying *cheris* or sub-villages, sometimes located several hundred yards from the main villages of which they are service-components. This is indeed the climax of geographical differentiation; *apartheid*. A typical *cheri* may consist of two rows of huts with a narrow central 'street'; in the middle this widens to make room for a tiny temple. The huts have thick mud walls, roofed with palmyra thatch, and low mud porches scrupulously swept. To enter one must bend double; the only light comes from the door and from under the eaves, and the furniture consists of a few pots and pans, a couple of wooden chests, and the essential paddy-bin, 4 to 6 ft. high and 3 to 4 in diameter, raised from the ground to escape the rats, and built up of hoops of mud. Poor as they are, these dwellings are yet homes, and obviously loved as such: their cleanliness, the surrounding mangoes, coconut and palmyra palms, redeem them from utter squalor. The nadir is reached in the bustees of Calcutta and the revolting camps of casual tribal labour found on the outskirts of the larger towns: shelters (they cannot be called even huts) of matting, of rags, of petrol tins beaten flat, on waste spaces open to the sun and reeking with filth.

A geographical study of Indian house-types (Fig. 7.3) would be a work vast in scope and rich in instruction; a few of the more striking instances are mentioned in the regional chapters.[4] Social factors are no less important than environmental, at least once we go beyond the fundamental antithesis of the northwestern (or southwest Asia) type and the thatched gable of the more humid areas. Not only the site and layout of the village, but the 'geography of the house' often reflects age-old religious and magical traditions: the round huts of some lower castes in Telangana, with bold vertical stripes of white and rusty red, are clearly culturally rather than geographically influenced. At the other extreme from the rude massive huts of Bundelkhand we have the elaborate courtyard house of the richer Uttar Pradesh farmer, with some pretensions to elegance – the survival of decayed traditions – in doorways and arcading. Some Indian domestic building indeed reaches a high standard of artistry: the carved timber of Kumaon or of the small towns of the Konkan, the restrained but excellent brick details and the very pleasant white bungalow-style houses, with low gables of semi-cylindrical tiles, found in small Maharashtra towns. Environmental influence is well seen in the flat-roofed blank-walled box standard in the Punjab and western Uttar Pradesh – so strongly reminiscent of arid southwest Asia, and fitting so well into the four-square planned villages of the Canal Colonies. Against these may be set the Bengal house, matting-walled, with thatched gables pitched high to shed the rain and ingeniously designed to take the strain of cyclonic gales. In Madras

'we see flat-roofed stone houses in the Ceded Districts (Deccan), so constructed as to protect the dwellers from the severe heat of the sun, the rocks and slabs locally available being used. In contrast we find in Malabar timber entering into the construction. Here the buildings are on high ground and have sloping roofs, both necessitated by the high rainfall. . . . In the Tamilnad we have tiled brick houses with open courtyards, reflecting an equable climate and moderate rainfall'.[5]

[4] The most comprehensive survey for a large area I have seen is Enayat Ahmad's unpublished London Ph.D. thesis, 'Settlement in the United Provinces' (1948).

[5] K. M. Subrahmanyam, 'Four main house types in south India', *JMGA* 13/2 (1938), 168–75.

As for what life in the Indian village is really like, who knows save the Indian villager? The insight of officials like M. L. Darling and of some devoted social workers, Indian and European, Christian and otherwise, has now been supplemented by much sociological research, some of it excellent; and from this the lineaments of village life (and especially the role of caste groupings) may be drawn, and now and then something of the psychological reality. The alien may perhaps glean something from that rich harvest of salty rural proverbs (a comparative anthology of them would be fascinating) which are as vital a part of India's cultural heritage as the lyrical and metaphysical visions of her sages. Not that this latter strain of culture is absent from the village: the great epics *Ramayana* and *Mahabharata* pass from lip to lip in folk-versions, to some extent at least every man is his own poet, and not a few of the noblest figures in India's predominantly devotional literature sprang from the village rather than the schools: Kabir the Weaver, Tukaram. The things that strike the outsider, then, are not perhaps ultimately the most important: the flies and the sores, the shrill clamour of gaunt pi-dogs, the primitive implements, the utter lack of sanitation.

At its worst the Indian village is infinitely depressing: in the plains where so much ground is cultivated that the scanty village site cannot grow with its growing population, or where a few miserable huts cling to shadeless stony rises in the drier parts of central India or the Archaean Deccan. Yet cheerfulness keeps breaking in, in the most unfavourable circumstances; fatalist as he is and must be, the peasant often displays an astonishing resilience and refuses to be broken by his often bitterly hard geographical and social environment. And over much of the land the villages have their amenities, even their beauties: in the plains and deltas they rise out of the sea of cultivation, emerald or gold or drab grey in the stubble season, like dark green islands, shaded in mango or orange trees, tamarinds, bamboos, palms. The tank or the well, the shade of the great banyan or the porch of the headman's hut, are essentially free clubs for the women and the menfolk respectively. Though the substratum of life – the gruelling round of the seasons – remains and will ever remain the same, though a miserable livelihood exacts an exorbitant price in endless toil, there have been great changes, material and psychological, since Edwin Montagu, Secretary of State for India, spoke in 1918 of the 'pathetic contentment' of the Indian village. Pathetic it still too often is; contented, less and less; which is as it should be. As Marx put it, 'These idyllic village communities confined the human mind within the narrowest possible compass.' This is overstated: there *were* the epics and the proverbs; but the horizons were far too narrow for a full life. Now new motifs are changing the tempo of life in the large villages: perhaps a radio, perhaps a mobile film unit, more and more frequently a school. Despite the weaknesses in Community Development projects, all are helping to break down the isolation and lack of information which rendered the villager so helpless a prey to the moneylender, the retailer and the grain-broker – often all three being one and the same person. Perhaps the most powerful agent of change is the battered, ramshackle motor-bus, packed to the running-board and coughing its way through clouds of dust along the unmetalled roads to the nearest town. There may be loss as well as gain in all this; but it is idle to bewail the break-up of integrated codes of life – too often integrated by religious, social and economic sanctions which were a complete denial of human dignity. In any case the

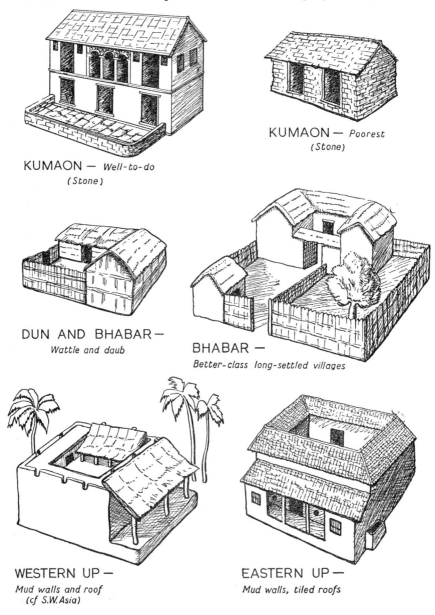

KUMAON — *Well-to-do*
(*Stone*)

KUMAON — *Poorest*
(*Stone*)

DUN AND BHABAR —
Wattle and daub

BHABAR —
Better-class long-settled villages

WESTERN UP —
Mud walls and roof
(*cf S.W.Asia*)

EASTERN UP —
Mud walls, tiled roofs

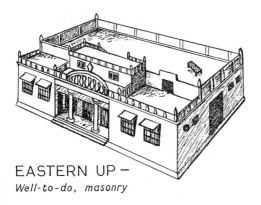

EASTERN UP –
Well-to-do, masonry

EASTERN UP –
Poorest, mud walls, tiles

BUNDELKHAND –
Mud walls, tiled

BUNDELKHAND –
Stone, stone slab roofs

BENGAL (CONTAI) –
Well-to-do, bamboo and thatch
on mud plinth. Double roof

BENGAL – *Poorest,*
Bamboo . thatch

FIG 7.3 SOME NORTH INDIAN HOUSE TYPES. Redrawn by Marjory Fowler from illustrations in theses by E. Ahmad and B. Mukerjee.

disintegration set in long ago, with the impact of the world market; and it is high time that new horizons should be opened, that the villager should see whence the forces that have subverted his old life have their origins, and what of good they may bring.

II. THE INDIAN TOWN

Some general characteristics

Urbanization is considered demographically in Chapter 4; the greater cities receive separate treatment in the regional chapters. There would be little point in classifying the towns of India and finding that after all they occupy similar positions and perform similar functions as do their compeers in the rest of the world. The fossil stronghold and the place of pilgrimage are perhaps commoner than in most countries: Carcassonne and Lourdes occur over and over again. The purely railway town is common, as in North America. The most distinctive Indian contributions to modern urbanism are the hill station and the cantonment: but even these have their analogues elsewhere.

It would also be possible to describe the aspect, function and morphology of a hypothetical generalized town: but its characterization would certainly be inadequate to convey the real richness of the Indian urban scene. It seems more profitable and interesting to examine in some detail four scattered and very diverse towns which the author knows at first hand. Before doing so, however, it may be as well to make some points of general application which are in fact largely specific to the towns of India.

1. *The agrarian setting*. It hardly needs stressing that the great majority of 'census towns' have still very strong agricultural elements within them; this holds, at the very least, for the 1,926 Indian towns (out of a total of 2,689 in 1961) which had under 20,000 inhabitants; the proportion of such towns in Pakistan would be higher. The smaller ones are indeed little more than large market villages, with some very local administrative functions added; perhaps two or three central streets inadequately paved and lighted give the semblance of an urban *cachet*. Even in so large a city as Agra herds of dairy buffaloes are driven out in the morning, back in the evening 'hour of cow-dust'.

2. *Administrative uniformity*. A large number of the towns are primarily administrative; they may have been local commercial centres and market villages picked as headquarters of Districts or their subdivisions mainly on account of centrality. Many of these go back at least to Mogul times as District headquarters; the somewhat bureaucratic motif of the territorial structure is shown by the fact that 242 of the 304 Districts of India are named from the chief town, and nearly all those of Pakistan. They have a strikingly uniform cast. The same official buildings occur; the architecture of the Public Works Department is standard practically everywhere, and Economy has obviously been the watchword.

3. *Building types*. These, of course, vary with local materials and traditions;

but there are certain very widespread features, ancient and modern. Of the former the bazaar streets with open booths raised 2 or 3 ft. above the pavement are typical. Middle-class Hindu town residences tend to have a verandah-plinth on the street, perhaps pillared, perhaps a mere recess between the party walls; there is usually room for a rope bedstead or two, used for daytime lounging and at night by the *durwan* or watchman. By the door is a little recess for a light; sometimes this is virtually a tiny shrine, but often it has degenerated into a vestigial niche, too shallow to perform its original function. On the modern side, new shopping areas are strikingly similar: box-like concrete shops-cum-houses, with cast concrete balustrades and so on. The glaring whiteness is often offset by pastel colours, very sensibly in view of the noonday dazzle. The monotonous architecture of the Public Works Department has been touched on; the railways are sometimes more imaginative, but with results often even more disastrous, until really ambitious efforts like Bombay's Victoria Terminus can hardly be described as other than Indo-Saracenic-Byzantine-Italo-Gothic-Baroque.

4. *Incomplete internal differentiation.* Most Indian cities (and large sections of even the greatest of them) have not separated residential and other functions to the same extent as Occidental towns. Well-to-do merchants still live over their shops and offices; and a large proportion of day-to-day consumer needs is still met by artisans living or working in tiny shops at street corners or in the bazaar area. Very often, as in mediaeval Europe, all of one trade will live in one or two adjoining streets: this, of course, links up with caste segregation. But differentiation by class and wealth is also not so advanced – on the whole – as in the West: of course in the Civil Lines and similar areas there will be very few poor people other than domestic servants, and at the other extreme there are homogeneous slums; but in the older and more indigenous parts of the towns opulence and indigence often live cheek by jowl.

5. *Community quarters.* Yet if the separation of work from residence often hardly exists, there is a very strong tendency (at all levels from village to metropolis) for members of each religious community, caste or race to live together. This is only to be expected in the general social context of India. Notable examples are the *pols* of Ahmedabad (see below, p. 653) and the Parsee housing estates of Bombay; and where there are very large numbers of Chinese, as in Calcutta, there is a Chinatown – as indeed happens universally.

6. *Western elements: cantonments, civil lines, railway colonies.* The British in India as it were fused this communal separatism with their own emphasis on class. Large Indian cities generally consist of two entirely distinct areas: the old Indian city, a squalid but picturesque confusion, and the monotonously planned open-developed town of European-style bungalows in large gardens along straight, broad roads, aloof and boring in a high degree, and absolutely dead in the heat of the day. These two are very often separated by the railway which – in some cases apparently by design – forms a broad barrier with few crossings: the motivation of 'internal security' is obvious. The 'Civil Lines' contain the

official residences of the local bureaucracy and such hangers-on as the more flourishing lawyers; architecture is European, with an interesting climatically induced variation: absence of chimneys (except in the northwest) and presence of a carriage-porch, essential in the rains. The European population is now generally very small indeed. The Railway Colony is generally planned on a far less generous scale, but on mathematically rectilinear lines. The Cantonments explain themselves; but they generally had a little Indian enclave, the bazaar to serve the needs, material and sometimes other, of the troops: this was necessary as for the most obvious reasons the Indian city was strictly Out of Bounds.

Generally the cultural divide made by the railway lines is sharp; but sometimes there is a transitional zone, as in the Mall and Anarkali Bazaar at Lahore: here are European and European-style shops, banks, offices, cinemas, some official buildings and a variety of places of resort, from the first-class (in price at least) hotel to the seedy eating-house.[6]

Four representative towns

We may now consider our four towns: in order of antiquity (which is approximately the order from south to north) Kanchipuram, Poona, Qadian and Simla. They form a good sample from several points of view: the geographical scatter is wide, Tamilnad, Deccan, Punjab, sub-Himalaya; two are well-known and typically Indo-British, two of much less note and representing almost solid Hindu and Muslim communities. They include a minor commercial and religious town, Kanchipuram; a great military, administrative and educational centre, Poona; the queen of hill stations, Simla; and in Qadian the headquarters of a religious sect. Qadian is at once unique but typical, since the particular ruling group is unique, but the phenomenon itself is not uncommon: one interesting example is Chettinad in Madras, seat of the remarkable Chettiar banking caste whose children lisp in numbers and accounts, inheriting a tradition of business acumen which enabled them to dominate indigenous finance and actually secure control of about one-third of the rice lands in Lower Burma.

Kanchipuram (Fig. 7.4)

Kanchipuram, 40 miles (64 km.) southwest of Madras on the Palar River, lies in a gently undulating countryside, paddy-floored bottoms and lateritic rises largely under poor grass and scrub. Agriculture is largely dependent on tanks; Kanchipuram lies in the heart of the Pallava kingdom (4th–9th centuries AD) and many of the larger masonry-bunded tanks were built by the Pallava kings, whose engineers had an uncanny flair for detecting the slightest usable drainage-line.

It is a fairly widespread town of 82,714 people; a market for the agricultural produce of its *umland*, with some hand industry, notably the weaving of silk

---

[6] Many of the points in this section are illustrated in O. H. K. Spate and Enayat Ahmad 'Five cities of the Gangetic Plain', *GR* 40 (1950), 260–78; cf. O. H. K. Spate, 'Aspects of the City in South Asia', *Confluence* (Chicago) 7 (1958), 116–28.

nearly a century it was the seat of
federacy possessed; their decisive o
river at Kirkee in 1817. The core

saris; pottery, basketry and bamboo crafts are also carried on. But it is far more famous as a religious centre, the shining or golden city; popular tradition assigns

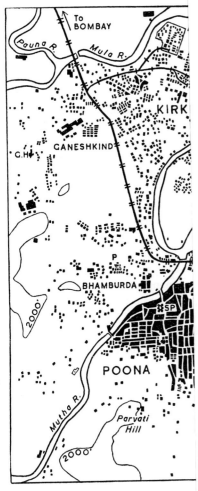

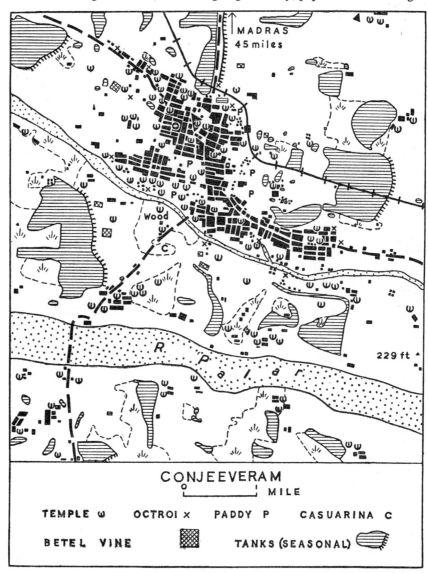

FIG 7.4 KANCHIPURAM (CONJEEVERAM). Heavy broken lines are main roads. Surrounding country mainly paddy; streams seasonal. *Courtesy* SOI.

FIG 7.5 PC

have been added the great Cantonn
Kirkee; these form three distinct ur
expansion, including industrial esta

The general level is about 1,80c
plain broken by a few remarkably sy
terrain is of course Deccan Lava. '
mesas at about 2,000 ft. abut directl

it a thousand temples, not without exaggeration; indeed the thousand pillars of the great hall in the Sivaite Ekambaranath temple are really only 540. But the great temples – largely dating from Vijayanagar times – are very impressive

indeed, culminating i
covered with innumer
Buddhist associations.

Not unnaturally, the
Muslims in 1941, and
ing villages; European

The most notable th
got one: the town is int
due not so much to *a*
accommodating the cr
haul the huge temple c
with solid wooden w
great streets are found
common; the general
thoroughly typical. H
layers of semi-cylindi
niches by the doors: v
There are the usual n
invariable Public Wc
light carts with a se
bullocks; goods trave
bus is recognized by
petrol shortage, the
scrabbling for the ci
Hardly a golden city

Poona (Fig. 7.5)
Poona is in itself by f
significance is more
concentrates on histo

The primary reasc
miles (77 km.) to the
and the town is nov
Poona and the Bhor
century that Poona b
of the Mutha-Mula c
temples. Sivaji, four
(fief) of his grandfat
nagar sultan; but his
a typical site on the
and the Deccan. Po

⁷ A vivid sketch of S
Grand Rebel.

and finally British power, until the great revelation to Mirza Ahmad.[10] For nearly forty years (1908–47) Qadian was as it were a miniature Vatican; not sovereign, but something of a state within a state. Crime in Qadian, for instance, was invariably reported first to the Ahmadi office and then to the police.

Qadian lies in the Bari Doab, on the Indian side of the border 35 miles (56 km.) northeast of Amritsar. The old town, still called 'the Fort', and retaining traces of a town ditch, is like hundreds of others in southwest Asia: some

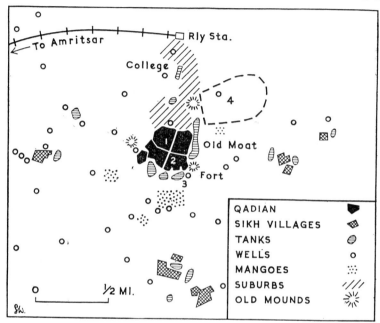

FIG 7.6 QADIAN. Based on SOI44M/5 (1913) with additions from personal observation. 1, Bazaar; 2, Ahmadi admin. and religious centre; 3, Ahmadi cemetery (guest-house, etc., between 2 and 3); 4, modern planned area (villas, offices). The nearer suburbs are closer-built and more industrial than the northern protrusion to the railway. Mounds (15–25 ft. high) mark old settlements. The area lies midway between the Kasur and Sobraon branches of the Bari Doab Canal.

12–15,000 people (the great majority were Ahmadis) living on the area of an English village of 2,000; narrow twisting alleys, encroached on by stalls and swarming with children and donkeys; two bazaar streets, covered with rough awnings of sacking (poor relations of the Damascus *suqs*), and significantly a Hindu enclave; mud-walled houses, windowless, built round courts where spinning, milking of buffaloes and all women's work is carried on; flat roofs

[10] 'I tell the tale that I heard told,' and have no means of checking it; it is inherently not improbable, though some of the embellishments perhaps are so, e.g. that at one time during the Mogul decadence the Ahmadis were thought of for the throne of Delhi. But then, anything is credible of a family which speaks of an ancient quarrel with the House of Timur for all the world as if Tamburlaine the Great were a rather unfriendly uncle.

littered with rope bedsteads, where the men smoke and gossip in the cool of the evening. A few large brick houses rise like monadnocks out of a peneplain. These include the Ahmadi offices, in a house once belonging to a wealthy Hindu, as is architecturally obvious from the details of the extremely beautiful brick façade and doorways, perhaps 18th century and certainly built when the now-decayed traditions of Hindu architecture were still vigorous; exterior windows are few and small – significantly – but within is a galleried court. Here was the vault containing the treasury, and the offices of a bureaucracy under seven 'Secretaries of State', including one for Entertainment of Guests, whose department was wonderfully efficient. An important feature was the guest-house, a caravanserai of courts and cubicles and cookhouses (more hygienic than many in the British Army), where disciples from all the Islamic lands endlessly commented on the Quran and the writings of Promised Messiah.

From the 120-ft. minar of the mosque all this warren lay at one's feet: to the north stretched the open modern development; to the south, on the rich fields of the Bari Doab, half a dozen large villages, darkly shrouded in mango-groves, seemed to enclose Qadian in a ring: all were Sikh.

In the new town, as in the old, women were in the strictest *purdah*; there were few other common features. Apart from an industrial fringe on the edge of the old town, this area was laid out in wide streets, with strict zoning and regulated densities. Architecture on the whole was poor, but sanitation superior to that in Lahore's best hotel. The most grandiose building was the big college, PWD Mogul in style, and well equipped especially in physics and chemistry labs. Between the town and the railway lay the industrial area, largely powered by Mandi hydro-electricity. On the fringe of the old town factories were largely private enterprises, but in the more open areas the community was building more modern workshops for vegetable oil, paint and varnish, and plastic industries – linked with research in the college labs. The most important activities actually existing were hosiery and knitwear, and all sorts of light electrical goods, all on a small scale (e.g. plastic presses electrically heated but hand-operated) and with apparently rather happy-go-lucky management; in which Qadian very faithfully reflected conditions in a large sector of Indian industry.

In a sense Qadian was a sociological freak, a combination of modern enterprise with fundamentalist theology; one might compare it with Salt Lake City. But the material expression of this duality was by no means un-typical. The day-to-day life of the old town stood on the ancient ways, life as it has been lived in many Asian lands for centuries or millennia. The new, in its slapdash planning, in its architectural tawdriness or rawness (whether the 'style' was traditional or modernistic), in its mixture of considerable drive and adroit improvisation with a certain lack of poise and stamina, can be paralleled over and over again on India's expanding industrial frontiers. But rarely are the contrasts of ancient and modern so sharply pointed within such narrow room; and yet in this too Qadian could stand for an epitome of India, if not of Asia.

Simla (Figs. 7.7 and 7.8)

The most famous of Indian hill stations lies at over 7,000 ft., (2,133 m.), 175 miles or 282 km. north of Delhi, approached by motor road and mountain railway from Kalka on the edge of the plains. Nearly half of the railway has a gradient of 1 in 33, and it has 103 tunnels; Fig. 7.7 shows its necessarily roundabout entry into Simla.

The building and maintenance of a town of some size – approaching 20,000 in the hot weather – on such a site was something of a *tour de force*. Every piece of metal had originally to come up the cart-road from Kalka; even today the internal transport services are mostly human, rickshawmen or porters bent double under tremendous packs. Both the Indian and the Punjab Governments used to migrate annually to Simla, and until 1912 this involved, for the Central Government, the 1,115-mile journey (1,794 km.) from Calcutta. Army Headquarters was permanently located there. The clerks in some offices had to climb 800 ft. (244 m.) in a quarter of a mile to reach their work: this in a climate with nearly 35 in. (889 mm.) of rain in July and August together. Other services had a yet inferior situation: laundry-men had a pull of 1,000 ft. from their dhobi-ghats to their customers. There can be few places in the world where the upper ten was so literally upper; the Viceroy and the Commander-in-Chief had naturally the best peaks. But all these inconveniences were subordinated to mean summer maximum temperatures of 67–82°F. (19–28°C.) compared with 110–120 (43–49°) in the plains below.[11] And, if Englishmen (and women) set the fashion, beginning in 1819, well-to-do Indians soon found Simla essential to physical and still more to social health.[12] Yet in a sense the whole place was a parasite.

The plan (Fig. 7.8), very typical of Indian hill stations, resembles nothing so much as a dissection of some invertebrate, an elongated tangle of guts and nerves with two or three ganglia. Roads tend to run sub-parallel to contours, and of course nearly all junctions are acute forks. Traffic would be a problem were it not nearly all banned (even bicycles, which could be used along the Mall) in the interests of rickshaw-men and porters – or their masters. The main axis lies along a saddle between Jakko (8,040 ft., 2,457 m.) in the east and Observatory Hill (7,050 ft., 2,150 m.) in the west; on the latter is what was the Viceregal Lodge. The hub of Simla lies under Jakko, on the broad Ridge between the Town Hall and Christ Church; here are the chief cinemas, libraries, and so on. The main road, the Mall, runs from end to end of Simla; the part of the Mall immediately below the Ridge is the only real shopping street, for all the world like the shopping street of some very minor English inland resort, say Crowborough. And indeed the whole atmosphere is like that of a watering-place without any waters.

[11] In winter, indeed, it is inconveniently cold, with mean minima below freezing in December–February. Absolute maxima and minima are about 95 and 17°F., 35 and 8°C. Communication with the plains is sometimes blocked for 3 or 4 days by snow.

[12] Some hill-stations like Dalhousie have declined, others, like Naini Tal and Ootacamund, continue to flourish. In 1965 in West Pakistan a new hill-station called Ayubia, after the President, was developed to add to the facilities of nearby Murree.

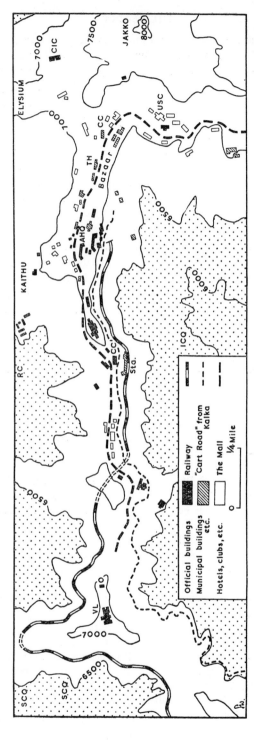

FIG 7.7 SIMLA: GENERAL PLAN. AHQ, Army HQ; CC, Christ Church; CC¹, Council Chambers; CIC, Commander-in-Chief's residence; I (S) CQ, inferior (superior) clerks' quarters; O, Observatory; RC, Racecourse; TH, Town Hall; VL, Viceroy's Lodge; USC, United Services Club. Based (as in Fig 41) on SOI plan on scale 1/7920. *Courtesy* SOI. Under 6,500 ft, stippled.

Below the eastern Mall is the Bazaar, the only close-built area, approached by roads at each end but transversely by steps in narrow winding alleys, a good deal steeper than those of Clovelly. The Bazaar area is a mass of tin-roofed houses clinging to what seems an impossibly steep hillside. Southwest, towards the railway station, is the office quarter. Here the hill is so steep that many buildings can be entered by a short bridge on to the top-floor back, while the ground-floor front entrance is half a mile or so away by road. Around this central belt is a great penumbra of villas and bungalows, for the most part on south-facing slopes but with two protrusions northwards along the Kaithu and Elysium spurs. Underneath Kaithu is the racecourse, sunk in a shadowed and gloomy combe.

Apart from its setting of forests and ravines, which is splendid, and its suitability as a centre for anthropological study of Indo-British tribal customs, there was not much of interest in Simla. Architecturally, besides the nondescript or Swiss-chalet bungalows, there were three main styles: baronial chateaux with corrugated-iron roofs (one or two, seen against the sunset, not so awful as it sounds); dull but relatively dignified Tudor-Gothic; and concrete and cast-iron boxes which did not even pretend to be 'modernistic'. The Bazaar was dull, apart from some good silversmiths and the Sikh woodworkers of Lakkar Bazaar north of the Ridge; itinerant Tibetans and Ladakhis sell various barbaric but effective ornaments, especially necklaces and bracelets of rough turquoise.

Simla has still some official functions under the new régime; the physical atmosphere is perhaps conducive to the efficient conduct of conferences. But the glory, such as it was, is departed.

ADDENDUM TO CHAPTER 7

Recent changes at Aminbhavi

A note received from Dr L. S. Bhat gives some interesting details of recent changes at Aminbhavi; these came to hand too late for incorporation in the body of the text, and in any case it seems better to maintain the original account so that the contrast should stand out more clearly.

The village is now a real satellite of Dharwar, separated by only four miles from the nearest suburb, and marginal village lands are cultivated by Dharwar residents. About 150 travel daily to markets, courts, schools and entertainments in Dharwar, and this figure rises to 5–600 for the Tuesday market. Bus traffic on a good asphalt road is increasing; vegetables, flowers and dairy products go to the Dharwar bazaar.

The population is now 5,538 and the village council has become a Town Panchayat. Community proportions remain much the same: 2,950 Lingayats, 650 Muslims, 350 Jains, 100 Brahmins, 300 Talwars, 300 Harijans. The last group has now a separate planned colony, and the Shikalgar housing has also improved, with tiled roofs. Services now include another Ayurvedic and a Homaeopathic medical practitioner, a Government Rural Medical Practitioner and trained midwife, as well as telegraph and telephone facilities.

There have been changes in land use: groundnuts have partly replaced cotton

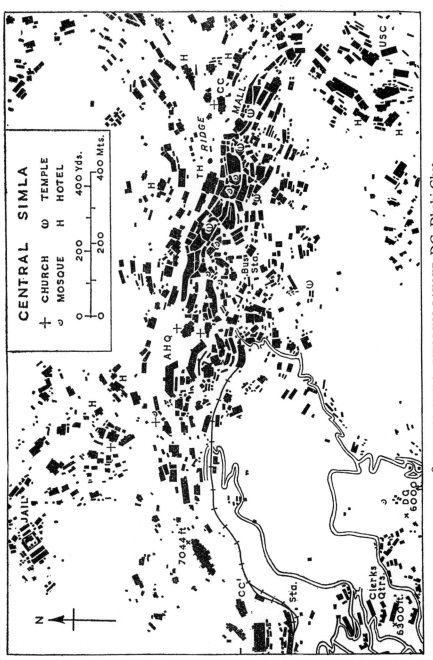

FIG 7.8 CENTRAL SIMLA: BUILDING LAYOUT. DG, Dhobi Ghat.

as a cash crop, partly owing to quick returns in the middle of the year just before the Diwali festival; increasing quantities of vegetables and flowers are grown under the influence of the Dharwar market. Pump irrigation, chemical fertilizers, better seeds, insecticides, composting, are being used by a few of the better-off and more progressive farmers, but poverty and debt still inhibit their spread among the mass of the peasantry. Those who can apply these improvements estimate an all-round increase in yields of about 10%.

On the whole, the changes seem to show Aminbhavi as still a microcosm of rural India: increasing mobility, increasing urban influence (this not so typical), better diffusion of information about the world through mobile libraries and so on, a definite, but very uneven, increase in productivity so far largely confined to the already well-found and progressive farmers. Two Community Development officers sum up – and in view of Aminbhavi's locational advantage, this may well stand as a comment of very wide application: 'It is too early to say anything about the impact in terms of cash or buildings and things like that, but there is a change in the outlook of the villagers. Nothing more can be said at this stage.'

BIBLIOGRAPHICAL NOTE

The settlement geography of the sub-continent has attracted a good deal of attention in the last few years; in addition to Enayat Ahmad's excellent study already mentioned (summarized in his 'Rural settlement types in Uttar Pradesh', *Annals Asstn American Geogrs* 42 (1952), 223–46), articles too numerous to mention, and on regional scales as well as of specific cases, are scattered through the Indian and Pakistani journals. The increasing sociological interest has also produced many studies, and several of the references to Chapter 5 apply here also. Special reference may be made to M. Marriot (ed.), *Village India* (Univ. of Chicago, 1955). An important critical paper is H. Tinker, 'Authority and community in village India', *Pacific Affairs*, 32 (1959), 354–75.

A fascinating illustrated survey of the 'material culture' of the countryside, from village types to shoes and carts, will be found in *Peasant Life in India*, (Anthropological Survey of India, Memoir 8, Calcutta, 1961).

There are also a very large number of studies of towns; some of the more important are referred to in the appropriate regional chapters. Perhaps the best study of a single town in modern geographical terms is R. L. Singh, *Banaras* (Nand Kishore, Banaras, 1955), and a most important general work is R. Turner (ed.), *India's Urban Future* (Univ. of California Press, Berkeley, 1962); this contains a very full review of recent literature by B. F. Hoselitz. For the 'feel' of town and village life, more creative writers are invaluable, e.g. novels such as Ahmed Ali's *Twilight in Delhi* or R. K. Narayan's many books set in 'Malgudi', which is Somewhere in Tamilnad. On the village side, there are M. L. Darling's unmatched 'Rural Rides' in the *Punjab*, or Kusum Nair's *Blossoms in the Dust* (Praeger, NY, 1962).

Where available, the Survey of India's 'Guide Maps' (1/21,120 or larger scales) are invaluable for the chief towns.

PART III

The Economy

CHAPTER 8

Agriculture and Agrarian Problems

Comments on the data

India, and even more Pakistan, will remain predominantly agrarian countries for many years or decades; and over the millennia they have evolved an indescribably complex mosaic of tenures and techniques which defies generalization. More-over, the various aspects of rural life and its problems are inextricably inter-woven, so that the organization of even the most generalized account is a matter of great difficulty. The volume of the literature is enormous, even though some important topics such as farm management and marketing are neglected; but the single Report of the Royal Commission on Agriculture in India (RCAI) of 1928 runs to 755 closely printed pages, and even so contains hardly any detail on crop distributions, no statistical tables, and no discussion at all of the extremely intricate matter of land tenure – a subject strangely barred by its terms of refer-ence. And it is extremely difficult to separate the grain from the chaff in this literature, while some fields have been ploughed over and over again, and one suspects that diminishing returns long ago set in: some studies are tendentious and many more unbearably repetitious.

In recent years the churning of the ocean of facts contained in official reports has been more assiduous than ever, while since Independence vast surveys of such topics as rural indebtedness and agricultural labour have been issued. There are now many more, and more competent, first-hand village and regional surveys than were available fifteen years ago; qualitative material on everything from lac to leather is to be found in a vast mass of official papers, and in a plethora of private reappraisals of all aspects of the agrarian situation. All that can be done in a limited space is to set out some of the basic facts, to sketch rather than to discuss some agrarian maladies, and to indicate some recent developments. The fundamental factors of climate and soil should need no recapitulation.

Crude statistical data are superabundant, but subject to serious limitations. Despite the spread of sampling, too many official figures still depend on the conscience and efficiency of half a million or more badly paid and not very literate village officials; there are of course some checks, and the pious hope that errors cancel out. But too often real accuracy is sacrificed to 'a formal kind of precision'; 'roughly two-thirds' may be much more accurate, and much less misleading, than '68·2%'.[1] In some cases the anomalies are glaring on the face of it: when one finds that the acreage irrigated by wells in the single District of Bhagalpur (Bihar) is given for nine years running as 9,752, to spurt to 100,000 in the tenth and collapse to 500 in the eleventh year, one is tempted to scrap the lot.[2]

It is simply not possible for the most perfect bureaucracy to know the actual output; the surplus after deducting grain for family use (and a large wastage from attack by rodents, insects and moulds) is largely dissipated in millions of petty sales. Probably something between a quarter and a third enters the commercial market. Here again the village official is at the bottom of a shaky pyramid; his estimates are in their nature impressionistic and subject to bias. Yield figures in particular are open to grave doubt; the discrepancies between those obtained by actual crop-cutting samples and those obtained by dividing area into recorded output have amounted to over 36%; two official estimates of the gross value of crop output, those of the National Income Committee and the Rural Credit Survey, were Rs 4,887 crores and Rs 2,921 crores respectively, a difference of 67%.[3] Sampling will give better results in the future, but of course any comparative study over a long term is rendered hazardous by the non-comparability and varying reliability of the earlier data. All yield figures, and arguments based on them, must be used with circumspection, as *relative* approximations and indicators of trends and intensities, and not taken as absolutes.

The National Sample Surveys, conducted by the Indian Statistical Institute under the leadership of Professor P. C. Mahanalobis, have now been running for some 15 years; they cover an enormous range of information on many aspects of economic life, though many findings are of sociological rather than geographical significance. The NSS apart, however, not all surveys under official auspices can be taken at face value: apart from what seem questionable sampling techniques, as for instance in the All-India Rural Credit Survey, the capacity and training of some of the host of enumerators are very probably inadequate, and it seems certain that many farmers – and this would apply in countries much more literate than India – cannot really understand all the questions or recall all of the large assemblage of facts demanded from them.[4]

With all their limitations, these statistical assemblages do represent a big achievement. Bearing in mind always that they are indices rather than absolute statements, they are useful enough in regional or crop comparisons and as evidences of trends. The wonder is not that there should be large errors, but that so large a mass of data should exist. But in view of the vital importance of forward planning for food, this does not absolve the governments from making every effort to improve their statistical machinery.

[1] Cf. D. J. M. Hooson, *A New Soviet Heartland* (Van Nostrand, Princeton, 1964), 15.
[2] P. Dayal, *The Agricultural Geography of Bihar* (London Ph.D. thesis, 1947), xii–xiii.
[3] D. and A. Thorner, *Land and Labour in India* (Asia, Bombay, 1962), 208–9.
[4] For a severe but apparently justified critique of some recent enquiries, see D. and A. Thorner, *op. cit., passim.*

I. GENERALITIES

Classification of area

The primary division of the land is shown in Table II (p. 391); it will be seen that the *oikoumene*, represented by the area 'from Village Papers', amounts to about 90% of the geographical area of India, and of this about 45% is sown, or allowing for multiple cropping over 51%. For Pakistan the position is different: some 36% of the total geographical area is 'not reported', and there is a very striking difference between the two wings: a mere 631,000 ac. (255,000 ha.) of East Pakistan is not reported, only 1·8% of total area against 42·5% in the west. The net sown areas (NSA) in East and West Pakistan are 58·5 and 27·4% of the reporting area, but the west has only 15·8% of its total area under crop. Multiple cropping brings the total cultivated area (TCA) of East Pakistan up to almost three-quarters of the total area, but to only 31·4% of the reporting or 18% of the total area in the west.

The breakdown of the Indian figures has been improved since the old days when about one-fifth of British India – some 90,000,000 ac. (36,400,000 ha.) – was returned as 'Culturable Waste'; a figure patently absurd and, as the RCAI remarked, 'calculated to give rise to misconceptions'. With no undue haste, the government met the Commission's demand for a more reasonable classification by simply re-naming the 'Culturable Waste', which became 'Other Uncultivated Land excluding Current Fallows'. More recently the old term has been used again, but applied to a much more limited area – 51,000,000 ac. (20,600,000 ha.), though it is doubtful whether many even of these diminished acres exist at all, and still more whether most of those which do exist could be cultivated without an inordinate capital outlay. Perhaps about half might be reclaimed in a not impossibly distant future. 'Other Uncultivated Land' also includes permanent pasture and grazing and land under miscellaneous tree crops, though apart from village fruit groves and so on it is not very clear what these are.

In 1950–51 a uniform distinction between current and other fallow was adopted: 'Current Fallows' are those lying fallow for less than one year, 'Fallow, other than current' has been unploughed for between one and five years, and anything above that is distributed into Culturable Waste or miscellaneous tree crops and groves. It would seem that there is room for a good deal of subjectivism about such classifications.

Perhaps the most striking aspect of the Indian figures is the very small proportion – 4·5% of Village Papers area – under permanent pasture or grazing; and this in the country with the largest bovine population in the world. Of course much of the Culturable Waste – and probably not a little of the 'Not Available' – is grazing of a sort: roadside verges, rough rocky patches of scrub, and so on. Much of West Pakistan's 'Other uncultivated land' is rough (very rough) grazing. The Pakistani poverty in forests, as against India, will be noted, though a good deal of the 'not reported' area is more or less forested.

The most essential fact in Table II, however, is that even allowing for multiple cropping, only a little over half of the more settled area of India is cultivated. By 1961–62 the TCA had reached 347,300,000 ac. (140,650,000 ha.), and this amounts to under three-quarters of an acre (0·303 ha.) for each person in a population in which 73% of the work force is *directly* dependent on the land for livelihood.

For Pakistan the man/land ratio is of the same order: overall, 0·66 cultivated acres per person, with a distinct disparity once more between east and west, with 0·53 and 0·8 ac. respectively (in hectares, 0·27, 0·21, 0·32). Yet the dependence on the land is as strong as in India; 70% of the civilian labour force is engaged in agricultural pursuits, and in East Pakistan, with about half an acre per head (allowing for multiple cropping!) and scarcely any scope for expansion of the cropped area, this figure rises to 85·25%.

When we add the further fact that in both countries unit yields for virtually every crop are below, and often very much below, world averages, the keynote of the whole agrarian problem is at once struck by these simple but terrifying figures.

Types of farming: Kharif and Rabi

Farming practices are considered in some detail in the regional chapters; broadly speaking the types of cultivation in India may be grouped as follows:

    1. Shifting hill cultivation.
    2. Sedentary peasant agriculture:
        (*a*) food crops, dry or irrigated;
        (*b*) cash crops, dry or irrigated;
        (*c*) arboriculture and gardening.
    3. Capitalist farming:
        (*a*) estates;
        (*b*) plantations.

The first and last may be briefly dismissed; the second is the norm of Indian farming, and forms the staple of this chapter.

Shifting agriculture – the *jhum* of Assam, the *kumri* or *podu* of the Peninsula – conforms to the standard pattern so widespread in tropical regions.[5] Dry rice, buckwheat, maize, poor millets, sometimes poor tobacco or sugar-cane, are grown on burnt-over clearings; in, say, two to five years, when the ash-given fertility dwindles, new clearings are made, preferably in new forest as the dense twisted scrub of abandoned jhums is often less tractable than untouched high forest. Obviously this can usually support only a sparse population, but on all

---

[5] E.g. *taungya* in Burma, *chena* in Ceylon, and so on; agreement on one name (or two, to cover the distinction between the 'nomadic' and the 'long fallow' types) is most desirable. For a general discussion, see P. Gourou, *Les Pays tropicaux* (Presses Universitaires de France, Paris, 1948), and H. G. Conkling, 'The study of shifting cultivation', *Current Anthropology* 2 (1961), 27–61.

the borders of Assam and in the wilder parts of central India it is dominant, while on the Western Ghats and the sub-Himalayan slopes both shifting and sedentary cultivation are carried on, as well as intermediate forms recalling 'run-rig' or the long fallowing (15–20 years) of south-central Africa.

Dry deciduous forest is obviously especially suited to jhuming, and as it is also the most generally valuable commercially, this devastating practice is frowned on by authority; moreover it may initiate severe soil erosion. But in some areas it is the only cultivation topographically possible, and in many there is at present no alternative to a considerable amount of controlled jhuming, sometimes turned to account by making the planting of commercial timber on abandoned fields a condition of licensing.

As for *capitalist farming*, there are or were a few large estates run on modern lines, though often cultivated by tenants; these include military dairy and vegetable farms, and some factory estates for sugar, cotton and oilseeds. Interesting as these estates are, they are alien to the whole structure of Indian farming, and can hardly play a decisive role in agricultural advance. *Plantations* are almost entirely for tea, rubber and coffee, and are therefore dealt with in Section II.E of this chapter; it may be added that in the prevailing climate of Indian opinion, there is little scope for extending plantations, which may indeed have some difficulty in holding their own.

Our second type is by far the most important. The overwhelming majority of Indians living by the land are smallholders, usually very small indeed, or landless. It is clear from Table III that their major activity is the growing of cereals (2a), though in some areas oilseeds, sugar and fibres (2b) are nearly as important to the economy as are foodgrains, and locally minor branches (2c) are significant: market gardening, spices, sericulture, perhaps even lac-collecting come under this head.

Two vitally important cross-divisions are those between (i) wet and dry crops and (ii) the autumn (*kharif*) and spring (*rabi*) harvests.

(i) Irrigation demands a separate place, but we may note here that 'wet' crops are not necessarily irrigated. While in much of West Pakistan crops of any sort are virtually impossible without irrigation, at the other extreme East Pakistan cultivation is wet enough but practically independent of irrigation.

(ii) Kharif is the monsoon crop, sown soon after the onset of the rains (June–July) and harvested in autumn: rice, jowar, bajra, sesamum, cotton (though this is long on the ground), jute. Rabi crops are sown after the rains and harvested in spring: wheat, barley, gram, linseed, rape and mustard. Kharif and rabi may be, but as a rule are not, sown on the same ground; rabi is essentially the crop of doabs and uplands, kharif of flood-plains and the areas under tanks. A given crop need not fall exclusively into one category, and in the southern half of the Peninsula, and particularly in Tamilnad with its October–December rain, the distinction is blurred; and sugar, which may be 10–18 months in the ground, clearly does not fit in. Locally, of course, there are minor harvests, especially in

Bengal and Bihar, where the relations of the two (or even three) crops are exceedingly complicated.

Irrigation (Fig. 8.1 and Table V)

Altogether about 9% of the total area of the sub-continent is irrigated – over 130,000 sq. miles (336,700 km^2), an area nearly half as large again as the entirety of Great Britain. Irrigation of some sort has been practised since time immemorial – the Grand Anicut on the Cauvery, a million cubic feet of masonry, was built in the 11th century; but most canal development is the work of the last hundred years. With a net irrigated area of around 60,000,000 ac. (25,000,000 ha.), India uses about a quarter of her estimated usable flow, and this may increase to about a third by the end of the Third Plan. Canals account for about 42% of the irrigated area, tanks 20%, wells 29%, the balance being accounted for by minor weirs and so on. About two-thirds of the TCA of West Pakistan is irrigated, and only a small fraction of the total 24,000,000 ac. (9,700,000 ha.) under irrigation is in the E st. Canal irrigation is dominant in West Pakistan, though there is an important area of well-irrigation in the sub-montane strip of the Punjab, and in Baluchi tan *karez*, irrigation tunnels, are common (below, p. 485).

(i) *Canals* fall into two groups: inundation canals, mere cuts parallel to the rivers in the flood-plains, and perennial canals fed by elaborate headworks, with regulated flow, generally aligned along the doabs so as to command a wider area. Many of the former date from Mogul times, a few even earlier, but the perennial systems, a creation of the British period, now cover a much wider area (cf. Fig. 17.6). Details of the layout and working of a modern canal system are given in Chapter 17.

Inundation canals merely fill with the rising river, and if it does not rise enough they remain empty. They are thus liable to fail precisely when most needed. Their offtakes silt readily. Perennial canals also have disadvantages, of which the most important is that their headworks may trap much of the silt so valuable to the ill-manured fields. Again 'it is just as important to get the water off the land as to get it on, and few ryots still seem to know it. The water comes to the cultivator without much labour on his part, and the high esteem in which he holds it leads to over-irrigation without adequate drainage'.[6] Hence waterlogging and the formation of alkali pans – menaces which have reached alarming proportions in parts of West Pakistan and northern India leading to very serious losses of cultivated land. By the late 1950s the situation in West Pakistan was extremely serious, by official figures something like 15,000,000 ac. (6,000,000 ha.) being water-logged or saline and another 11,000,000 (4,450,000 ha.) having saline patches; altogether about 70% of the cropland was more or less affected, and in

[6] G. Kuriyan, 'Irrigation in India' (*Journal of the Madras University*, 15, No. 1, Sec. A, 1943), 167; payment by volume has been suggested, instead of by area irrigated as at present; for objections to this, see RCAI, 336.

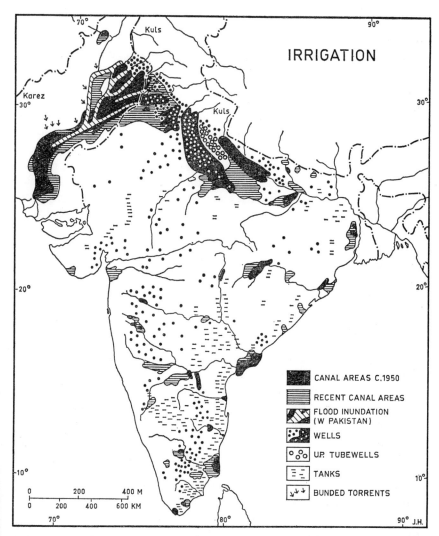

IRRIGATION

70° 90°

Kuls

30° Karez Kuls 30°

20° 20°

CANAL AREAS C.1950

RECENT CANAL AREAS

FLOOD INUNDATION
(W PAKISTAN)

WELLS

U.P. TUBEWELLS

TANKS

BUNDED TORRENTS

10° 10°

0 200 400 M
0 200 400 600 KM

70° 80° 90° J.H.

FIG 8.1. IRRIGATION. Apart from the classic areas of canal irrigation in the Indo-Gangetic Plains, the areas of close well-irrigation (especially by tube-wells in Uttar Pradesh) and the tank-fed areas of Telangana, Mysore and Tamilnad stand out. Compiled from various sources.

the Rechna Doab (between the Ravi and Chenab Rivers) 15% of the area had gone out of production. A vigorous effort in pumping and drainage has been started, but to deal effectively with the problem may well cost Rs 500–600 crores. A detailed analysis of the complex difficulties met with in the long-cultivated Cauvery Delta in consequence of changing from direct (inundation) to perennial irrigation will be found on pp. 764–67. When all is said, however, such great achievements as the Punjab Triple Project form a most impressive memorial of the British Raj.

(ii) *Tanks* are illustrated in some detail in Figs. 25.11 and 25.12. Their siting speaks to a wonderful flair for detecting the minutest variations in the terrain. A reliable tank needs a considerable catchment, which is usually waste; rice is the usual tank-fed crop, on gently falling terraces designed to secure an even flow of water over the fields. Often a whole stream is reduced to a string of tanks, the lower ones trapping the surplus water from those above. The high water-table below the tanks supplies good wells, used either for security in bad years or a second crop in good ones.

Nevertheless tanks are on the whole unsatisfactory. The water-surface is large in relation to volume, so that loss by evaporation is high, as is that by seepage; relatively few tanks hold water throughout the year (cf. Fig. 25.12). Sooner or later they silt up; the bed will retain some ground-water, held up by the bund, and for a while at least be very fertile; but the problem of a new supply remains.

Irrigation tanks must be distinguished from the small rectangular tanks for domestic water-supply. These are often built-up as much as excavated, rain- and not stream-fed, and except in wet areas like East Bengal (where they occur in tens of thousands, as a by-product of excavating mud for house-plinths) are obviously very likely to fail in the hot weather.

(iii) *Wells* of course command individually small areas; even in the Punjab, where they are large and permanent, the average area is only 12 acres (4·9 ha.). But in aggregate they are exceedingly important, and not only quantitatively.

A *pukka* – masonry or brick-lined – well is costly to construct, and the use of any well makes great demands on human and animal labour; well-irrigation is thus six or seven times as expensive as canal, and so tends to be reserved for high-value specialized crops – vegetables for urban markets, sugar, or, where soil is good, really first-class cereals. This is in fact garden cultivation; over-watering is obviously unlikely, and the well can be used exactly when needed, which is by no means always so with other methods. The small areas lend themselves to fencing and individual care, and are usually well weeded and manured.

Several types of lift are used. The simplest, for shallow wells, is the *picottah* (=Egyptian *shaduf*), merely a weighted pole pivoted on an upright; for lifts of over 15 ft. bullocks are used. In the north, and especially in West Punjab, the 'Persian wheel' is common: an endless chain of pots on a vertical wheel geared to a horizontal and worked by bullocks endlessly circling the well. Also common is the *mhote*, a steep ramp up which the bullocks are backed to depress the bucket, raising it on the forward downhill movement. In Tamilnad the *kabalai* is an ingenious variant (below, p. 753).

Oil-driven pumps have been used, but unless they can be worked for four hours a day – which would probably exhaust most wells rapidly – they are no more efficient than the *kabalai*, and to be economic they would demand large holdings of 10–15 ac. (4–6 ha.).[7] This last argument, however, loses much of its force when put against the general high cost of well-irrigation, which means that only large holders could contemplate such methods anyhow. The introduction of cheap electricity is already causing major changes, and there is an increasing demand for electric pumps in the areas served by Pykara and other south Indian hydro-electric plants. Another development of great significance is the introduction of tube-wells tapping the huge resources of water at depth beneath the Indo-Gangetic Plains; here Uttar Pradesh has led the way (below, p. 554).

(iv) *Other Sources* consist for the most part of small temporary dams and channels (e.g. the *ahars* and *pynes* of south Bihar), the 'spring channels' of Tamilnad river-beds, mere water-holes in flood-plains, direct lift from rivers, and so on. The most interesting type – Iranian rather than Indian – is the *karez* of Baluchistan (Fig. 16.2), tunnels constructed by connecting lines of shafts sunk in the detrital fans of the piedmont, which has a relatively high water-table. *Karez* may be a mile long, but most are much smaller, and the best probably do not discharge more than 9–10 cusec. In this semi-desert zone much of what little cultivation exists is by means of bunds across the drainage-lines of the hill-slopes (Fig. 17.3). This holds up the ground-water and is water-conservation if not irrigation.

The area under wells and other sources is capable of rapid, if temporary, expansion and fluctuates widely, being especially important in years of deficient rain.

II. MAJOR CROPS AND THEIR DISTRIBUTION[8]

A. FOOD AND FODDER

1. Cereals and Pulses

(i) *Rice*. About a quarter of the net cultivated area of India, and over 45% of that of Pakistan, are under rice; East Pakistan indeed would be almost monocultural were it not for the competition of jute. The Indian acreage has risen fairly steadily of recent years and now runs at about 85,000,000 (34,500,000 ha.); that of Pakistan is around 25,000,000 (10,000,000 ha.), some 92% of which is in the eastern wing; however, the wheat-eating West has a surplus of 100,000–200,000

---

[7] Kuriyan, *loc. cit.* 56. Ch. VI of *Imperial Gaz.* Vol. III (1908) is still valuable for a discussion of the indigenous types of irrigation.

[8] Reference may be made to the distribution maps in the *National Atlas of India* (Ministry of Education, 1957, unfortunately in Hindi) and the *Indian Agricultural Atlas* (Ministry of Food & Agriculture, 1958, in English).

tons a year available for East Pakistan. Indian output of cleaned rice from 1955–56 to 1960–61 averaged about 29,500,000 tons, that of Pakistan about 10,000,000. There is, of course, much wastage, and the deduction for seed alone must be of the order of 5,000,000 tons of paddy (rice before any treatment).[9]

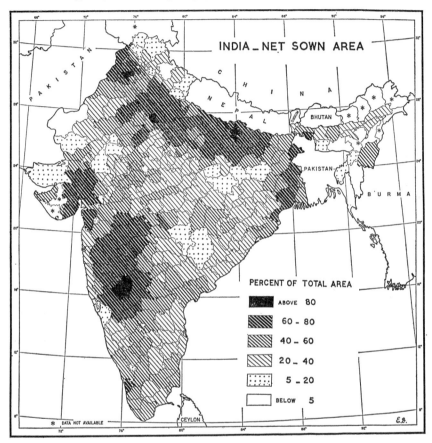

FIG 8.2 INDIA: NET SOWN AREA. Figs 8.2, 8.3, 8.6 to 8.8, 8.10, 8.12 to 8.14, are by courtesy of S. S. Bhatia and are based on statistics for 1950–52; see *Economic Geography*, 41 (1965), 39–56.

The high temperature and water requirements of paddy – except the practically negligible dry hill rice – make it dominantly a crop of the deltas and flood-plains, and the dominant crop there. It is at its best when the growing season has a mean temperature of 75°F. (24°C.) or more and, in non-irrigated areas, 60–80 in. (1,524–2,032 mm.) of rain. The fact that rice is so pre-eminently a 'wet crop' is responsible for the not uncommon fallacy that it is grown almost entirely by

[9] The remainder of this section is largely based on G. Kuriyan, 'Rice in India', *IGJ* 20/1 (1945), 28–36, 76–84, 110–26 – a very comprehensive account.

irrigation. The plant certainly can mature satisfactorily only if it grows in a few inches of water; a five-month crop will need about 70 ac.–in. But in the great domains of paddy this is supplied by the rain on the fields themselves or by natural flood, and is simply retained by the low mud field-walls (bunds); whereas

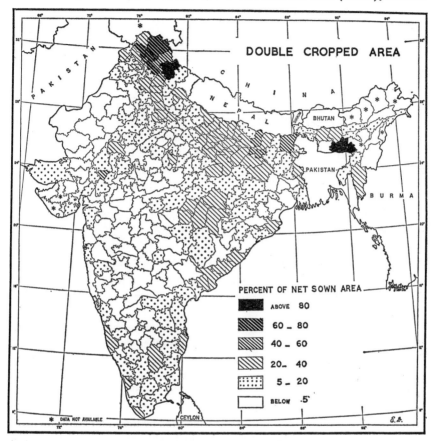

FIG 8.3 INDIA: DOUBLE CROPPED AREA.

'irrigation' surely implies an artificial supply. This is necessary wherever the rainfall is below 40–45 in. (1,016–1,143 mm.), and at least very desirable at 50–55 in. (1,270–1,397 mm.). Paddy favours rather heavy soils – clays, clayey loams, the clay-with-silt of the deltas and is fairly tolerant of salinity (hence its tendency to expand in waterlogged areas—for instance in the Punjab).

As a rule it is sown soon after the beginning of the rains and harvested in November–January, but in Bengal there are three crops: *aus* (harvested June–September), *aman* (November–January; *c.* 75% of acreage), and *boro* (February–May). This last is grown on the shrinking margins of lakes and swamps and has a very small acreage. Broadcasting is used, in Bengal for about half the crop, but more generally seedlings are raised in heavily manured beds and transplanted; this is back-breaking work, often done by the women. The soil is puddled and tends to become very heavy; organic and especially green manures are useful, but probably most paddy-fields get little fertilizing except the burning of the stubble and sometimes of branches and twigs.

Of the complexities of paddy cultivation and the rice trade there is no end; in India alone some 4,000 varieties are known, each with special requirements and qualities. An increasing area is under improved strains produced by the agricultural research institutes.

The grading of paddy for sale and milling is a fine art. Rice is not in itself a very good food, with only fair though easily assimilated protein content. Unfortunately the taste for polished rice – purely a matter of prestige – seems to be spreading, though of course village consumption is mostly home-ground or pounded in mortars and retains much of the valuable husk. Coolies often eat cheap parboiled rice, which is steamed before milling; this is valued as it keeps well when cooked, and the vitamins and minerals of the husk are not lost to such an extent as in ordinary milling. A diet based on milled rice, deprived of vitamin B, definitely predisposes to beri-beri, one of the most serious deficiency diseases of India, and not confined to the quantitatively under-fed. The famous experiment on rats fed on diets typical of provinces from the Punjab to Madras also shows the low dietetic value of poor rice diets.[10] But these qualitative failings are offset by heavy yields per acre – nearly twice those of jowar and bajra – and rice retains its place as the staple food of the wetter areas, and of the better-off classes nearly everywhere.

Paddy has developed a strikingly individual landscape, broadly similar from the Ganga to the Yangtse: myriads of tiny mud-walled fields, in the rains with only the bunds and the villages rising above the grey water through which the young paddy shows like thin flames of a most wonderful glowing emerald; in the hot weather a grey expanse of baked mud and thin stubble, dotted by the threshing-floors with their bamboo tripods whence swing open-meshed baskets into which the threshed grain is thrown to be winnowed by the wind. Here and there are the gaunt corrugated-iron roofs and spindly chimneys of small rice mills. More significant are the social correlates of this landscape so intensively moulded by man. If intensive rice farming draws much energy from the soil, much energy must also be put in, and 'the investment of effort required to develop paddy land immobilizes the population itself. . . . Industrial development may enable a people to levy on the produce of other lands and develop a denser population than any agriculture will support', but no other way of life (except the not dissimilar economy of Egypt) has led to the evolution of a cultural system

---

[10] The average body-weights of the rats of each diet group (in grams) at the end of the experiment were: Sikh 235, Pathan 230, Maratha 225, Kanarese 185, Bengali 180, Madrassi 155. The Maratha/Kanarese drop is most significant, as these areas adjoin, the Marathas being practically confined to the wheat and jowar-bajra Deccan Lavas. See R. K. Mukerjee, *Food Planning for 400 Million* (London, 1938), 167-8.

so stable and so permanent as that associated with the great paddy-plains of Monsoon Asia.[11]

(ii) *Wheat*. The distribution of wheat shows an even more marked climatic correlation than that of rice, but inverse to it. Of the total acreage (*c.* 37,000,000 ac., 15,000,000 ha.) two-fifths are in arid West Pakistan, and about half of the rest in East Punjab and western Uttar Pradesh. Wheat extends down the Ganga as far as west Bihar, and across Malwa into the drier northwestern quadrant of the Deccan; beyond these limits it is negligible. In the Peninsula, wheat is usually a dry crop on black soils; in the Indo-Gangetic Plains, irrigated on alluvial loams. The few inches of winter rain in the sub-montane strip of the Punjab enable good rabi crops to be grown. Most Indian wheats are hard.

The export of wheat through Karachi always fluctuated, falling off sharply in years succeeding a bad monsoon and has now dwindled to almost nil. The reason is obvious, and it is not likely that there will ever again be much significant export from the sub-continent.

(iii) *The Millets*. The total millet acreage perhaps equals that of rice, jowar and bajra alone having a combined area of 70,000,000–75,000,000 ac. (28,000,000–30,000,000 ha.). Yields, however, are on the whole low, the output of these two being only 10,000,000–12,000,000 tons. In location millets are intermediate between rice and wheat, jowar and bajra, for example, being usually rain-fed, in areas with *c.* 25–40 in. (635–1,016 mm.). Nothing displays more strikingly the contrast between the two Pakistans, wet in the east and dry in the west, than the fact that their acreage of these 'intermediate' crops is almost negligible. The concentration of jowar and bajra in the Deccan is also striking; ragi, the third of the more important millets, has a rather wider spread.

The idea, often held in Europe, that the millets are spindly plants little better than grasses, and of inferior nutritive value, will hardly bear analysis. Jowar and bajra grow 6–8 ft. high, or even more, and jowar indeed looks like a field of bulrushes. Table VII shows clearly that in many respects lesser millets are better-balanced as food than is rice, and bajra ranks high indeed – level with wheat and oats in calcium content, between them in phosphorus, and with five and two times as much respectively of these minerals as even home-pounded rice. Yet there is a strong prejudice against them and as they are generally grown on poorer soils and in the precarious 25–40 in. (635–1,016 mm.) rainfall zone, yields are insecure.

(*a*) *Jowar (Sorghum vulgare)*,[12] known as cholam in the south, is both kharif and rabi. As kharif it needs 30–40 in. (762–1,016 mm.) of rain and is grown mainly on black soils, often rotated with cotton and usually mixed with pulses or sesamum. Rabi jowar is less often mixed with other crops; it needs moisture-retaining soils which have received good rain in September–October, and is

---

[11] G. Kuriyan, *loc. cit. ad fin.*

[12] The 'bread sorghum' of American writers, who apparently do not count it among the millets. American and British usages of the terms 'millet' and 'sorghum' are difficult to disentangle; here standard Indian usage is followed.

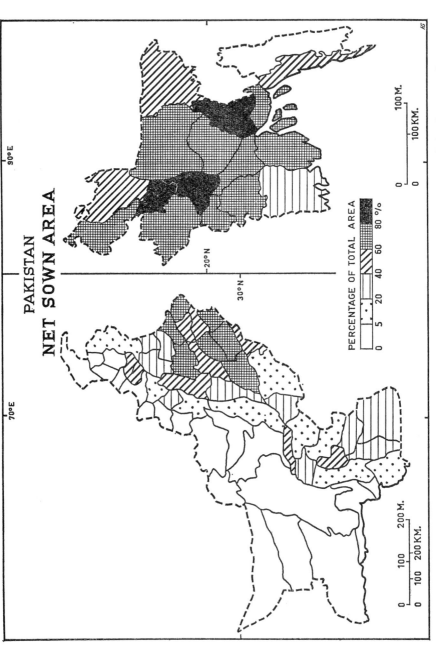

FIG 8.4 PAKISTAN: NET SOWN AREA. Figs 8.4, 8.5, 8.9, 8.11 and 8.14 are based on statistics for 1959–63.

perhaps most notable in Tamilnad – where, of course, the 'rabi' is the monsoon crop. Jowar stalks form valuable fodder; the yield per acre may be 500 or more pounds of grain plus 100–200 lb. of inter-grown pulse and anything from 1,000–3,000 lb. of fodder (100 lb./ac.=112 kg./ha.). When grown specifically for fodder, as in Gujarat, parts of the Deccan and Coimbatore, jowar is sown very closely to make it run to stalk; in the Deccan a rude pit silage is practised.

(b) *Bajra* (or bajri, in the south cumbu or cambu, *Pennisetum typhoideum*) tolerates lighter soils than jowar, and is therefore grown extensively on the poorer Deccan Lava uplands, and on sandy or stony soils generally. It is nearly all kharif, but too much rain is harmful, and it is usually sown after the first force of the rains is spent. As a rule it is mixed, usually with pulses,[13] so that rotation is less necessary; but it may be 'rotated' with jowar in years of weak monsoon. Its nutritional value has been noted.

(c) *Ragi* (marua or madua, *Eleusine coracana*) ranges from the Himalayan slopes almost to the extreme south. Again it is a kharif crop, which may be transplanted; sometimes irrigated, in the Archaean Deccan it is often grown under tanks. Dry ragi is usually intercropped but not irrigated ragi. The highest yielder of the millets, with improved strains and careful culture it can give as much as 1,500 lb. per ac. (1,681 kg./ha.) or more; but as a rule only the nurseries receive much manure.

Ragi is perhaps the most important, though far from the most esteemed, food in such poor regions as Telangana. Although it is in some respects a better food than rice, with a remarkably high calcium content (0·33%), 'it is often regarded as food suitable for poor and ignorant villagers – also as the food of prisoners in the jails'.[14] He who rises in the world exposes himself to beri-beri, while the diet and physique of the convict are generally better than those of his less enterprising fellows. It is often eaten as balls of the hard small seeds, dipped in a sauce of pulse or spices to impart flavour.

(iv) *Other Cereals: Pulses.* Apart from wheat, the only temperate cereals grown on a really large scale are barley (8,000,000–10,000,000 ac., 3,250,000–4,000,000 ha.) and maize (up to 13,000,000 ac., 5,250,000 ha., plus probably a good deal unrecorded). Half to two-thirds of the barley and a quarter of the recorded maize are in Uttar Pradesh, largely in the sub-Himalaya; in the higher Himalaya ordinary barley and the naked Tibetan variety (*grim*) are staples. The Ford Foundation Agricultural Team which visited India, briefly, in 1958 attached great importance to hybrid maize (at least seven of these thirteen advisers came from the Corn Belt), but little seems to have come of this. The pulses, served in innumerable attractive forms, are of great importance in protein intakes, and are probably of greater importance than the statistics suggest; they are often, perhaps usually, sown mixed, and the only ones for which separate figures are available are gram (25,000,000–30,000,000 ac., 10,000,000–12,000,000 ha.) and

---

[13] Thus further, and indeed insolubly, complicating the statistics.
[14] National Nutrition Research Laboratories, *Rice* (Bull. No. 28, Coonoor, 1940), 16.

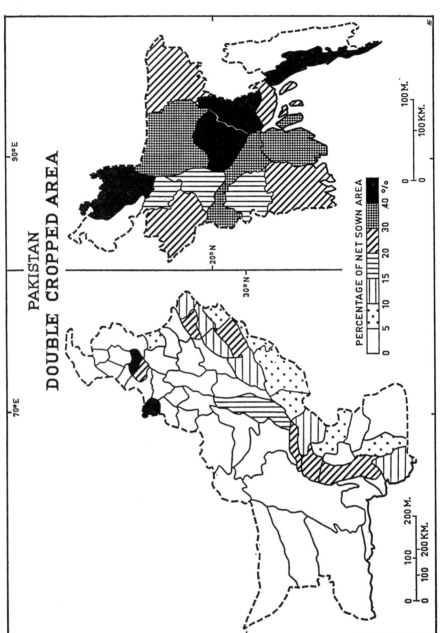

FIG 8.5 PAKISTAN: DOUBLE CROPPED AREA.

tur, rather over a quarter of the gram area. The main areas for gram are Uttar Pradesh and East Punjab, each with around 6,000,000 ac. (2,500,000 ha.) and in Pakistan the Punjab with about half this area. The pulses are useful as catch crops on poor soils or in bad years, and they are of course extremely valuable as

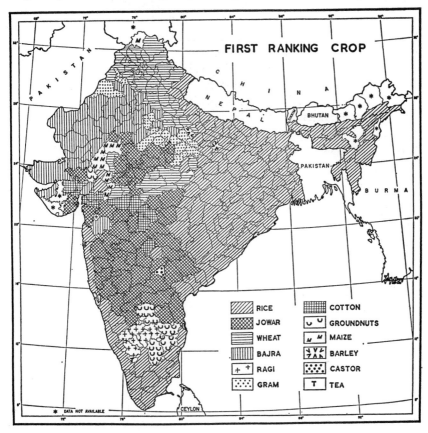

FIG 8.6 INDIA: FIRST RANKING CROP.

'nitrogenizers'; the extension of their use as green manure is desirable. As *dal*, a sort of lentil purée, pulses form an essential adjunct to most Indian curries.

2. Other Food Crops

Sugar and edible oilseeds demand separate treatment; no other crops cover a large area individually, the area returned under fruits, vegetables, spices and miscellaneous tree crops being divided among plants far too numerous to be listed, except perhaps for coconuts, which account for 1,700,000 ac. (700,000 ha.) in India alone. Except on some specially favoured areas such as floodplains near large cities, or around hill stations, horticulture is generally neglected: lack of storage and transport facilities, and of purchasing power in potential markets, account for this dietetically deplorable situation. Mangoes, however, are all but universal, oranges – small and loose-skinned – and plantains (bananas) widespread; the Himalayan regions and the western border hills grow most temperate fruits, including grapes, and in the northwest Himalaya apricots are an essential food. The fruit industry is best developed in Kashmir and around Peshawar, and there are possibilities of extension in Baluchistan. A dried- and canned-fruit industry may develop in West Pakistan.

Condiments such as chillies, essential to give a specious appearance of variety to a poor rice diet, are grown almost everywhere; spices mainly along the Western Ghats and the coast south of Goa; pepper is probably still the most important. In the better rice diets of the predominantly vegetarian south, plain boiled rice is served on a banana leaf (or a silver or, nowadays, stainless-steel plate) with a number of small dishes containing a variety of 'hot' or spicy soups and vegetable sauces; a ball of rice is mixed with a chosen sauce and eaten with the right hand. Curds, slightly sour like yoghourt, are often taken as a chaser after a hot-spicy mouthful; south Indian languages have a special term for 'hot-spicy'. Coconuts are officially oilseeds, but have too many uses to be easily categorized; other palms of value include dates in West Pakistan (the ubiquitous wild date has a practically useless fruit, but is tapped for toddy); palmyra, widespread but especially important in the extreme southeast, used for toddy, sugar and thatching; and the areca palm with its associate the betel vine, sources of the red *pan* chewed by high and low, Hindu and Muslim. There is some export of cardamoms, pepper and areca nuts.

3. *Fodder Crops*

Little, unfortunately, need be said about these: some 10,000,000–12,000,000 ac. (4,000,000–5,000,000 ha.) only, nearly half in the Punjab and nearly a quarter in Maharashtra. Even allowing for the larger areas of rough, and usually very poor, grazing, this is exceedingly low for a country which contains nearly a third of the world's cattle, but the reason is distressingly simple: few peasants will devote land which might grow food for men to grow food for beasts, and indeed such are the demands on the scanty holdings that the ryot often cannot do so even if he would. The results, however, are directly deplorable for the bovine population, and ultimately for the human. To this problem we shall return.

B. FOOD/CASH CROPS: OILSEEDS AND SUGAR

These occupy an economic position intermediate between the cereals and the fibres; some oilseeds, such as castor and linseed, are exclusively for industrial use, while rape, mustard and sesamum are mainly foods, and the internal consumption of groundnuts is rapidly increasing. Sugar is distinguished from the purely food crops by the strong industrial element in its development.

1. *Oilseeds*

Pakistan's share of oilseeds is slight – neglecting cottonseed, some 2,000,000 ac. (809,000 ha.), almost all rape and mustard. In India oilseeds acreage for the decade before 1945 was fairly steady at 20,000,000–23,000,000 (8,000,000–9,000,000 ha.), about 9% NSA, of which four-fifths were edible – sesamum,

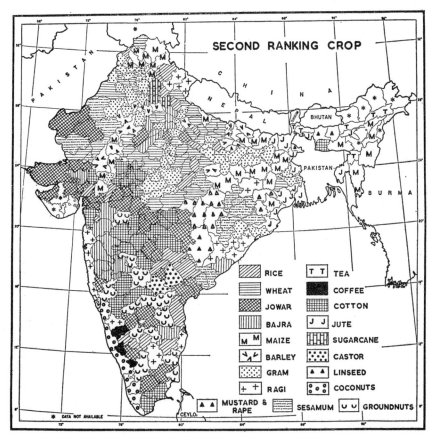

FIG 8.7 INDIA: SECOND RANKING CROP.

groundnut, rape – and the rest mainly linseed and castor. Within the group the most striking development was that of groundnuts, insignificant before 1913. The Indian oilseeds area is now about 32,000,000 ac. (13,000,000 ha.), of which nearly half is devoted to groundnuts, which have a considerably larger area than sesamum and rape combined.

Groundnut is a crop of the Peninsula, about half being grown in the Deccan (with a strong concentration behind Pondicherry) and about a quarter in Gujarat. Its export value has led to its receiving marked attention from the

Agricultural Department, and a main factor in its spread has been its suitability to light sandy soils, of little use for cereals or cotton; it is a kharif crop. *Sesamum* (til or gingelly, *Sesamum indicum*) has rather more than a third of the area of groundnut, but is far more widely distributed, being significant everywhere except in the wetter Peninsular margins and Pakistan. It is the source of the most widely used cooking oil; in Bengal and Assam mustard is the staple. It can be grown as kharif (usually mixed) on light soils and as rabi, rotated with jowar and cotton, on heavy. Of the coconut area, the bulk is in south Madras and Kerala, with a subsidiary concentration in East Bengal.[15]

2. Sugar-cane

Sugar is probably indigenous to India, the word itself apparently coming from Sanskrit through Hellenistic Greece. In terms of raw cane, India is the largest producer in the world, but the low saccharine content of the cane and perhaps poor techniques bring its output in terms of sugar (including the semi-refined fudge-like *gur*) to third place, after Cuba and Brazil. The annual output of 3,000,000 tons or so comes from about 5,500,000 ac. (2,200,000 ha.) of which some 60% is in Uttar Pradesh, followed by Bihar and East Punjab. Pakistan has about 2,000,000 ac. (809,000 ha.), three-quarters of it in the West, where the factory at Mardan in the Vale of Peshawar is one of the largest in the sub-continent, if not in Asia.

The distribution shows some peculiarities. Northern India is the largest producer of cane-sugar in the world *outside* the tropics; and although in the south temperature régimes are closer to those of other cane-producing countries, and southern canes produce 2·5 to 3 tons of sugar per acre[16] against 0·6 (Punjab) to 1·5 (Bengal) in the north, yet 80–90% of total output comes from Indo-Gangetic regions, with thin, probably indigenous, canes in contrast to the thick varieties, perhaps Pacific in origin, of the south. One point in this low standing of the south is lack of humidity: the really heavy producers – Java, Cuba, Hawaii, Mauritius – all have insular climates to which the nearest Indian homologue would probably be coastal Kerala, already entirely devoted to paddy and with no room for a cash crop. But for several physical reasons costs of production are much higher in the south than in the north. Outside the middle Ganga Plains (Bihar and eastern Uttar Pradesh) sugar-cane must usually be irrigated, and irrigation is as a rule much easier and cheaper in the Indo-Gangetic Plains than in the Peninsula; moreover, the loamy alluvium, with sufficient lime and potash, does not need manuring to anything like the extent necessary in the south. The Godavari–Krishna deltas, indeed, approach optimum conditions, with ample cheap irrigation and rich alluvial soils; but here frequent cyclonic storms compel the use of some 5,000 bamboos per acre to protect the canes, and the

[15] The vegetable oil industry is discussed in Chapter 10, coconut culture in Kerala in Chapter 22.
[16] One ton per acre=2,510 kg. per hectare.

cost of this in 1942 was Rs. 80–150 per acre, the latter figure being half the cost of cultivation. Further, although the main cane research station in India is at Coimbatore, work was originally on the thin varieties, improved strains of which were in general use in the north by 1938, when trials of new tropical canes were not complete. Finally there were few other cash crops suitable to Uttar Pradesh

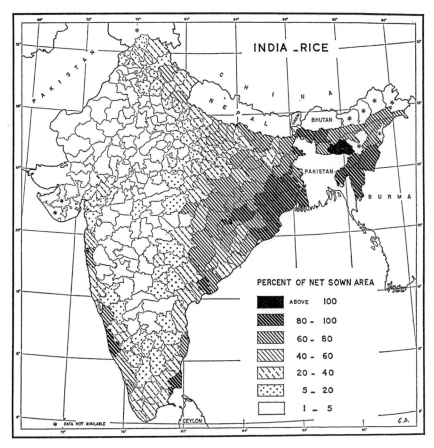

FIG 8.8 INDIA: RICE.

conditions, after the collapse of indigo cultivation, and hence cane is grown in solid blocks; the more sporadic distribution in the south has inhibited the growth of refineries, in turn restricting demand while the north was building up a great industry.

The main risk in the northwest, as far as eastern Uttar Pradesh, is frost; in Meerut losses of up to 20% are likely every five years or so, and in extreme cases losses of 50–80% have been reported. Frost is a menace as far south as Ahmadnagar and Nasik, at 1,600–1,800 ft. (490–550 m.) in the upper Godavari basin;

here also water-logging and saline efflorescences have put over a third of some canal-irrigated areas out of cultivation.[17]

Indian yields are generally low, averaging about 3,000 lb. of raw sugar per acre (3,363 kg./ha.); this is less than a quarter of Javanese and Hawaiian yields, though not very far below those of Cuba and Brazil. This figure is not so likely to be understated as cereal yields.

C. FIBRES

Here at last Pakistan holds a strong position, even if one rather less commanding than it used to be. In 1947 she had c. 80–85% of the area and output of jute, and about one-fifth of the area but one-third of the output of cotton. After an almost catastrophic war and post-war decline in the Indian cotton figures, there has been a considerable revival and they now exceed the immediate post-war acreage for both countries together. Pakistani yields, however, remain higher, producing about 2,000,000 bales a year against about 4,500,000 from India, but from less than a fifth of the Indian acreage, and including much of the higher quality fibre.

In jute, which is a notoriously fluctuating crop, there has been a striking change in the relative position of the two countries: whereas before Partition areas now in India had about one-third the area and little over one-quarter the output of East Pakistan, friction between the countries led to a remarkable expansion in India, as well as the introduction of *mesta*, which is now of considerable importance. Indian jute output is several times the pre-war average and, on a roughly equivalent area, is now about two-fifths that of Pakistan; the latter shows little expansion owing to the competition of paddy in the overcrowded Bengal delta.

Both raw cotton and raw jute are now overshadowed as Indian exports by their manufactures, and there is a large import of raw cotton, while Pakistan has made a beginning in the export of jute and cotton goods.

1. *Cotton* (Table IX)

The cotton of West Pakistan is entirely an irrigated crop, grown on about 3,500,000 ac. (1,400,000 ha.); in India only about 12·5% of some 17,500,000 ac. (7,100,000 ha.) is irrigated, it being essentially a rains-sown crop in the 25–30-in. (635–762-mm.) rainfall zone, usually grown on the deep, heavy, moisture-retentive black soils (regur) of the Deccan Lavas, the Gujarat alluvium, and pockets on the Archaeans. Cotton is again probably aboriginal to India, grown and woven from the earliest times. The indigenous (*desi*) cottons, of which the 'Tinnies' of the southeast and 'Oomras' of the Deccan are perhaps best-known, are short-stapled – only $\frac{1}{2}$–$\frac{7}{8}$ in. Efforts to increase staple have resulted in a considerable extension of the area under improved strains (especially Cambodia,

[17] This discussion is based on Chapters 8 and 9 of T. R. Sharma, *Location of Industries in India* (Hind Kitabs, Bombay, 3rd ed. 1954).

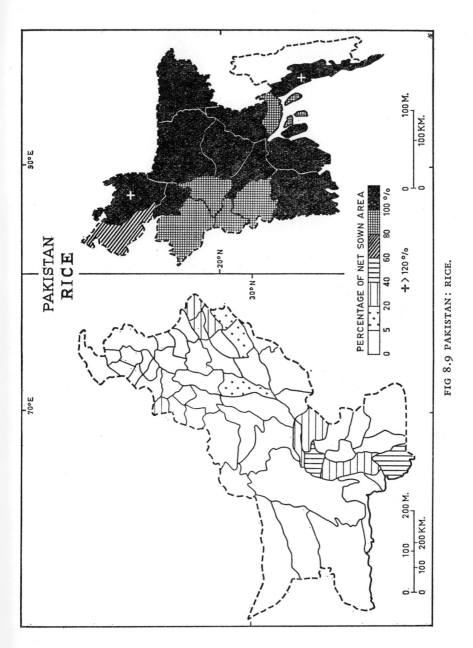

PAKISTAN
RICE

PERCENTAGE OF NET SOWN AREA

0   5   20   40   60   80   100 %

+ > 120%

100 M.
100 KM.

200 M.
200 KM.

FIG 8.9 PAKISTAN: RICE.

$\frac{7}{8}$–1 in.), but it is difficult to maintain standards owing to adulteration, especially in ginneries. On the whole, however, the proportion of long- or medium-staple is increasing. In West Pakistan development for export came later, with the Canal Colonies rather than with the American Civil War boom, and American varieties (staple 1–1$\frac{1}{16}$ in.) predominate, accounting for the higher output in relation to area.

2. *Jute* (Table X)

Before Partition Bengal held practically a world monopoly of jute production:
the nature and requirements of the crop are thus perhaps best dealt with in
Chapter 19. The significant spread of jute in India since Partition is clearly a

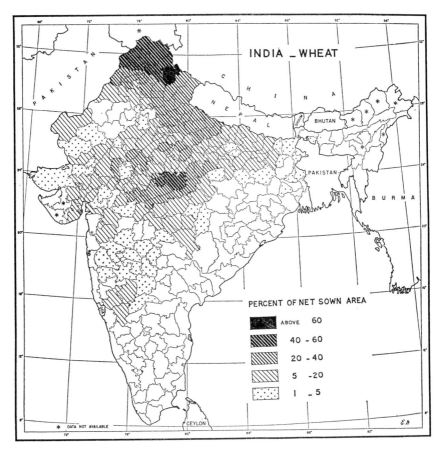

FIG 8.10 INDIA: WHEAT.

matter of nationalist rather than rationalist economics. It may be noted, however,
that apart from the Orissa delta the main extension has been in Assam and along
the terai in Bihar and eastern Uttar Pradesh. Here, on newly cleared land settled
by refugees from East Pakistan, the claim that jute extension does not encroach
upon the food area is doubtless justified; but it is difficult to think that this can
be so in the other areas, and from the Indo-Pakistani ratio of area and yield it
would seem that a good deal of this new cultivation is in rather marginal areas.
But this is a part of the wider dilemma of food *versus* cash crops.

The indigenous grass *mesta* has been developed in India as a jute substitute or mixture: not shown in the *Statistical Abstract* before 1953–54, by 1961–62 it covered 950,000 ac. (385,000 ha.) and had an output of 1,700,000 bales, over 27% of the volume of jute output. It is grown mainly in West Bengal (35%), Bihar and coastal areas of Andhra and Maharashtra. It may be noted that the considerable linseed cultivation in India, as in other sub-tropical areas, is entirely for oil and not for fibre.

3. *Wool*

For the sake of a general view we may deal here with animal fibres. Of these wool is more important than silk. In 1961 India had about 40,000,000 sheep, half of them in Andhra, Madras and Mysore, and 7,000,000 in Rajasthan; some 10,000,000 must be added for West Pakistan. Kashmir, Rajasthan and West Pakistan produce nearly two-thirds of the annual clip, and it would seem that the Pakistani share would be fully 30%, and that again including most of the better grades from the hill sheep of Baluchistan and the Northwestern Hills. The northern wools are usually white, those of the south anything from off-white through red to black, and also coarse and hairy.

About half the clip was exported for coarse manufactures such as carpets, felt and rough blankets; for good woollens the Indian industry has to import most of its requirements from Australia.

4. *Silk*

It seems probable that the silkworms of ancient India were generally not mulberry-feeders (*Bombyx* spp.), though *Bombyx mori* from China is of old standing in Manipur. Mulberries are grown and the true silkworm reared along the western Himalayan slopes, especially in Kashmir, and on paddy-bunds in Bengal. In addition, 'India has three well-known purely indigenous silkworms: the *tasar*, the *muga*, and the *eri*. The first is widely distributed in the lower hills, more especially of the great central table-land, and feeds on several jungle trees. The second is confined to Assam and eastern Bengal, and feeds on a laurel. The third exists in a state of semi-domestication, being reared on the castor-oil plant'.[18] The EIC early took an interest in sericulture, exporting to England either fabrics or raw silk in accordance with changing economic or political circumstances.

A small proportion of cottage-produced tussore is of high quality, but the worms are generally badly cared for, and indeed much of the cocoon production is wild, collected in the forests. Nevertheless, the long decline in Indian sericulture seems to have been checked. Annual production of raw silk is about 3,300,000 lb. (1,500,000 kg.), and exports and imports in 1961 were of about equal value. About one-fifth of production is from the indigenous tasar, muga and eri.

[18] *Imperial Gaz.* III (1908), 208.

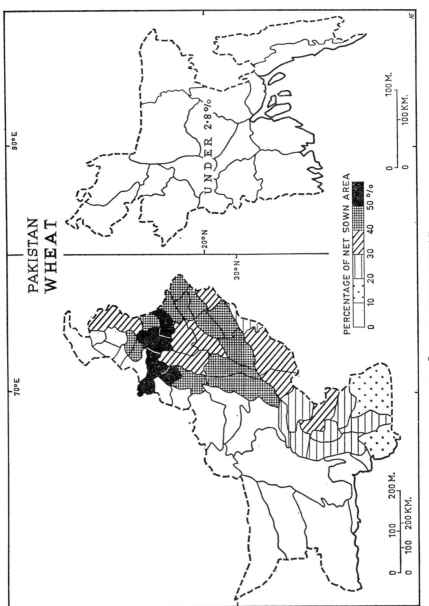

FIG 8.II PAKISTAN: WHEAT.

D. MISCELLANEOUS PEASANT CROPS

It would be hopeless to attempt even to enumerate the enormous variety of interesting special crops, from the saffron of Kashmir to the senna of Tirunelveli. It may be noted, however, that two of the most famous of Indian products are now all but extinct: *indigo* and *opium*. In 1897 synthetic indigo became commercially practicable, and in fifteen years the area under the crop fell by 90%. It rallied in the First World War, but in 1939–40 only 40,000 ac. (17,000 ha.) were cultivated, mainly in Bihar, and it is no longer given in the returns. Opium had in 1939–40 about 7,000 ac., against over 600,000 before export to China was stopped in 1907; under 3,000 ha. against 243,000. The destruction of the industry was thus a deliberate, though not immoral, political act. Opium is consumed in India, especially in the Himalayas and the Assam Hills, but is rigorously controlled, though there is probably sporadic illicit cultivation in the hills. The social effects of opium smoking in Himalayan India, however, are hardly serious. Indian hemp (*ganja*) is far more dangerous.

Tobacco is grown in all Indian states, but mainly in Andhra, which has 40% of nearly 1,000,000 ac. (400,000 ha.); in Pakistan there has been a marked decline in the last 10 or 12 years, from 350,000 to 200,000 ac. (142,000 to 81,000 ha.), mainly in the east. Probably there is a good deal of unrecorded cultivation. Tobacco is grown to some extent all over the country, and in the north is a favourite crop on the rich silts of temporary alluvial islands; but Madras has over a third of the Indian acreage. Smoking is universal – cheroots, hookahs, English and American cigarettes (some manufactured in India with imported tobacco) or the appalling *bidis*, the cheap smoke of the masses. By and large Indian tobacco is poor stuff, and the divine if financially deplorable habit is far from playing the part in the national life that it does in Burma. The main cheroot-making centres are Dindigul and Trichinopoly in Madras, but even those brands which bear English (or Anglo-Indian) names are hardly as good as the humbler product of the petty shops of Burma, innocent of machinery or publicity.

E. PLANTATION CROPS

Plantations are almost confined to tea, coffee and rubber, with a little cinchona in the Nilgiris and Darjeeling. (Table XI.)

1. *Tea*

The wetter Himalayan slopes and their gravelly piedmont fans, and the hills of the extreme south, offer admirable conditions for tea; indeed when the EIC began planting with Chinese seed in 1834, a wild variety was found in the Assam Hills. Tea is grown in the south at elevations of over 4,000 ft. (1,200 m.) and in Darjeeling to 7,000 (2,135 m.), but generally speaking yields are smaller, though quality is better, on the higher plantations. Most of the larger plantations in Bengal and Assam are on the terai (here 'Duars') or its equivalent.

Of the total area of 865,000 ac. (350,000 ha.), which is about 40% of world area excluding China, East Pakistan has some 9%, Assam and West Bengal two-thirds, and most of the rest is in Kerala and the Nilgiris. Plantations in these areas are large, 450–550 ac. (180–220 ha.), but along the Himalayan slopes as far as East Punjab tea is grown on holdings of 4 or 5 ac. (2 ha.) or less; but their share of output is negligible.

The plantation economy is somewhat alien to the new India, but two-thirds of Indian tea is exported, and this amounts to about a fifth of the value of exports.

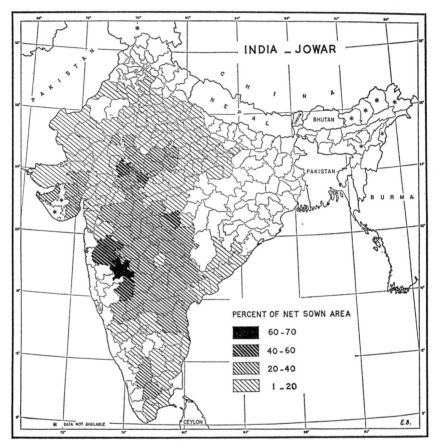

FIG 8.12 INDIA: JOWAR.

Owing to the static condition of the industry in Pakistan, and rising internal demand, Pakistani exports are not now important; with an export of 200,000–225,000 tons a year, India accounts for about half the world trade.

2. *Coffee*

Coffee was introduced by a 17th-century Muslim saint returning from Mecca, who gave the plant and his name to the Baba Bhudan Hills in Mysore; but real development began in the 1830s. By 1885 there were 237,500 ac. (96,000 ha.), but borers, leaf-blight and Brazil brought catastrophe, and in 1877–87 no fewer than 273 plantations were abandoned. Coffee estates are usually small, only about 50 ac. (20 ha.) and there are holdings of under 10 ac. which do not appear in the statistics. The area has increased since 1947 and is now about 250,000 ac. (100,000 ha.); about a third of the output of some 95,000,000 lb. (43,000,000 kg.)

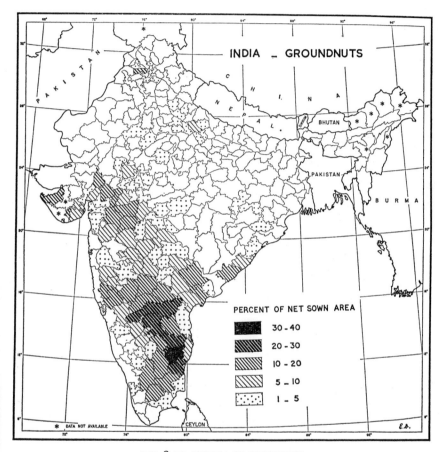

FIG 8.13 INDIA: GROUNDNUTS.

is exported. Coffee gardens are very narrowly concentrated in southern Mysore and adjacent uplands of Kerala and Madras; coffee is much drunk in the south.

3. *Rubber*

Only in Kerala, with high but equable temperatures and a dry season of only three or four months (and those not rainless) are conditions reasonably suitable for rubber, and even there they are not ideal. Yields are low, less than half those of Malaya, and this may be due as much to poor management as to environmental disadvantages; but there has been a remarkable increase in area, over 120% in the decade 1951–61. There are now about 264,000 ac. (107,000 ha.) with an output of about 24,000 tons. This expansion is probably due to the rising internal demand fostered by industrialization. Rubber is also grown, as yet experimentally, in the Chittagong area of East Pakistan.

III. ANIMAL HUSBANDRY

The cattle problem

The sub-continent, or even India alone, has to support the largest bovine population of the world: the 175,000,000 oxen and 50,000,000 buffaloes of India are nearly a quarter of the world's horned livestock. Altogether the sub-continent has at least 270,000,000 head of cattle. These numbers are undoubtedly excessive, perhaps by at least a third. *The First Five Year Plan* (1951, pp. 109–10) pointed out that there was probably roughage for only 78% of the (then smaller) cattle population, and of course a far smaller proportion of concentrates, and that only about 750 good stud bulls were bred annually, against a total need of about 1,000,000.

The agriculture of India differs fundamentally from that of Japan and most of China in that it is firmly based on the use of draught animals. Sacred as the cow is, the bullock is of more mundane importance; there are about five bullocks to every four cows, and they do most ploughing and almost all carting. 'The essential equipment of the peasant farmer includes a pair of bullocks or buffaloes to do the ploughing and draw the cart; a cow to propagate the species and quite secondarily to give milk.'[19]

Paradoxically enough, no branch of Indian agriculture is worse managed than animal husbandry. Except for the fundamental taboo against taking the life of the cow, this is not so much the peasant's original sin as the result of strictly geographical conditions. To take one example, Indian 'hay' is really dried grass which has lost its seeds and so is little better than straw, rather than hay in the European sense: it is too wet for hay-making when the grass (such as exists) is up towards the end of the rains, and after that the peasant is too busy with kharif harvest or rabi sowing. Where rainfall is too light to inhibit hay-making there is precious little to make hay with, and in any case – probably as a natural consequence of these conditions – the ryot 'has been a grass-cutter, but a hay-maker never, and he finds it hard to begin'.[20]

By and large the cattle, being essentially working rather than food animals, are where the men are, and in these areas pressure of population is so intense that often the village-site itself can hardly be squeezed into the sea of arable, and so

[19] L. D. Stamp, *Asia* (ed. 1944), 230.
[20] RCAI, 205–6; the whole of Chapter 7 remains of great interest.

obviously there is no meadow, no permanent pasture, no fodder crops: only the waste, which in the worst parts of the Ganga plains is reduced to mere wayside scraps. Elsewhere such fodder as there is – mainly paddy, wheat and millet stalks – goes mainly to the working cattle, the bullocks; the cow must fend for herself.

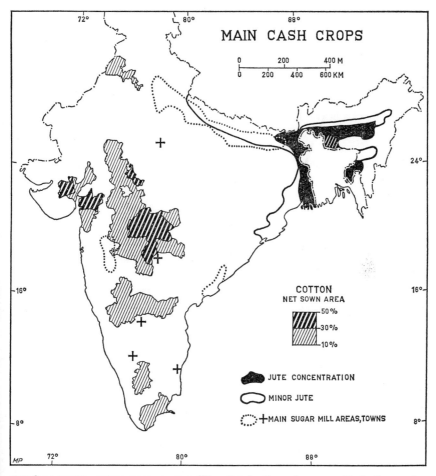

FIG 8.14 INDIA: MAIN CASH CROPS. The distribution of sugar mills indicates the main areas growing cane as a cash crop.

By April and May, the height of the hot weather, there is likely to be very little stalk left, the stubble has been grazed off, in many areas there is very little leafage on the trees, and finally the scanty vegetation of the waste, at best coarse, tussocky and of little food value – or guarded by a fierce array of thorns – has been reduced in effect to a mass of dry cellulose. The general appearance of the cattle in most

255

parts of India is then simply horrible – skeletons wrapped in hide, tottering to whatever patches of shade may be.

Some areas, it is true, look at first sight as if they could support more cattle, farmed on pastoral lines: such are the less arid parts of Rajasthan, in Malwa. But soils are thin, rainfall irregular, grass poor except after flushes of rain; any considerable stocking would probably result in heavy erosion. Moreover pastoralism as such is at a discount; the long distances to wretchedly poor urban markets render dairying uneconomic, and there is obviously no sale for beef.

Such a state of affairs would be bad enough even were the stock healthy. But the country is unenclosed, there is still a great lack of eugenic practices, and too often feeble bulls beget at will upon diseased cows. Veterinary services, despite recent expansion, are terribly inadequate, and epidemic disease such as rinderpest still takes a heavy toll.

The over-population, however, is not solely the result of an irrational apotheosis of the cow. Paradoxically there is often an actual deficiency in the cattle-power needed to work the land; the numbers are there, but the bullocks are simply not strong enough for their work. Hence more are bred, which implies more cows and young stock – strictly speaking useless mouths – and the circle of starvation is complete. Yet, while one sizable and healthy animal will consume about half the food needed by two weaklings and may yet produce more dung, 'when it comes to the threshing of corn and the puddling of rice fields, eight feet are decidedly better than four. . . . [Again,] the chance of losing half of one's capital against an equal chance of losing it all, is one that would be preferred by any sound business man. The chance of one bullock falling down a well, or getting its leg broken, or being eaten by a tiger, is just half the chance of the same thing happening to two.'[21]

Since Independence, and against the views (however guardedly expressed) of central planning bodies, some States have enacted bans on cow slaughter. *The First Five Year Plan*, recognizing that wholesale slaughter was just not practicable, suggested (p. 111) that in areas 'where the fodder supply to-day is unutilised' (but where are they?), *gosadans* or camps of refuge for aged and infirm cattle might be set up, where they could end their days in peace and yet contribute something through arrangements for the collection of manure and the hides and bones of the carcasses. Some *gosadans* were created, but the experiment has not been very successful. Even without cattle slaughter, however, something can be done. The difficulty of diverting land from foodgrains to fodder is obvious, even though there would be an increase in milk supply; the Ford Foundation Agricultural Team, which estimated the annual loss from keeping useless cattle at Rs 70 crores, recommended a graduated tax on such animals and the control of open grazing. Steps have been taken to improve the breeding of bulls and to extend castration, sterilization, segregation and even artificial insemination. Progress has been made on these lines, but not nearly enough.

[21] G. Williamson, in U. N. Chatterjee (ed.), *Developing Village India* (Orient Longmans. Bombay, 1951), 173–4.

However counter to average Indian opinion, the conclusion seems inescapable: the essential improvement of cattle cannot be attained without limitation and even actual reduction of numbers; but sentiment and policy act in a contrary direction. Even to a non-Hindu there may be something of a moral problem here; man has after all called into existence these millions of sentient beings for his convenience, to be liquidated when inconvenient. But on a different level we have the old dilemma of not being able to afford short-term what it is necessary to afford long-term: there are too many cattle in the gross, but most individual farmers may have too few to carry on with.

Better breeds

As so often, these malpractices are virtually forced upon the husbandman, either by the weight of immemorial social pressures, or by sheer necessitous poverty; and they are not universal. Indian cattle in normal conditions are well adapted to their trying environment in that they have amazing powers of endurance and recuperation, and the use of the zebu or humped ox for crossing as far afield as South America attests its inherent suitability to the leaner tropical grasslands.

When he is able to do so the ryot takes good care of his stock, and in some favoured localities really good strains have been evolved. These are mainly draught animals, such as the Kankrej of Gujarat, the Kangayam of Coimbatore, and the famous Amrit Mahal breed fostered by Haidar Ali of Mysore for military mobility. But they include milkers such as the Gir and Sindhi, and dual-purpose breeds such as the Hansi or Hariana of East Punjab. A few scattered groups are indeed pastoralists rather than cultivators: the few hundred primitive Todas of the Nilgiris, the Alambadi breeders of the Mysore forests. In the extra-Peninsular mountains, of course, a different type of pastoralism, based on sheep and goats, is common.

Dairying

Despite the enormous numbers of cows milk plays a pitifully small part in Indian diets; in Saurashtra daily consumption per head is about 19 oz., in the Punjab it is only 10, nowhere else consumes more than half as much, and in Madhya Pradesh the amount is under 1 oz.! The Indian average is 5·5 oz. (0·16 kg.), against 40 (pre-war) in Britain. The urban milk supply is almost everywhere entirely deplorable in quantity and much worse in quality, even when (if ever) not deliberately adulterated. Much of it is produced in foul conditions within city limits, the herds being driven out each morning to the ragged fetid waste found around all large towns. Climatic conditions are at least partly responsible for the low direct milk consumption, since it is obviously impossible to keep milk for long; over 40% of it is in fact converted into *ghi*, butter clarified over a slow fire, for which cowdung is the best fuel. Hence buffaloes are often preferred to cows as milch cattle, since their milk contains up to 50% more butterfat than that of the cow; buffaloes supply about 45% of total milk output. As might be expected, milk yields are almost incredibly low, except on a very few military or

257

capitalist dairy-farms; in India they average 413 lb. (187 kg.) a year for cows and 1,100 (499 kg.) for buffaloes; with 61,000,000 milch cattle, nearly twice as many as all Europe outside the USSR. Indian milk output is only about one-fifth the European total.[22]

[22] *India Record* (London), II/39 (22/11/1950); improvement since 1951 is not likely to have affected relative and per capita figures significantly.

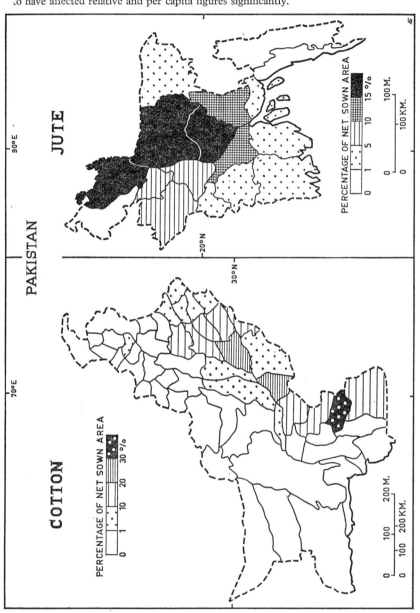

FIG 8.15 PAKISTAN: COTTON AND JUTE.

Hides and skins

Even though shielded from sacrilegious hands, the cow sooner or later dies and must be disposed of. This task is left to Muslims and the untouchable caste of Chamars or leather-workers. Something over 20,000,000 cow and 5,000,000 buffalo hides are produced annually, to which must be added 25,000,000 goat and sheep skins. Before 1939 some 40% of the hides and 50% of the skins were exported, about half the former as semi-tanned 'kips'. In the 11 years 1929–40 an annual average of 70,000 tons of hides, skins and more or less tanned leather was exported; 'for some time past India has been not only the most important exporting country for hides and leather but has constituted the only reservoir for the drawing of the large supplies of light hides by the world mar ets' ;[23] in 1960 the value of hides and skins exported was over Rs 10 crores.

Exports of bones were also very large, though their retention for processing (for bone-meal and so on) is increasing.

Other livestock

These need not detain us long. In addition to the 50,000,000 or so *sheep* there are over 61,000,000 *goats* in India and in Pakistan. Again Madras leads, followed closely by Uttar Pradesh, Bengal and the Punjab. Goat 'mutton' is probably the most widely consumed flesh food.

Horses are scarcely used for agricultural traction or indeed for any cartage, but they draw the light traps (*tongas* or *ekkas*), the taxis of the lower middle class, largely replaced in the south by the bullock-drawn *jutka*. *Donkeys*, in the mountains *mules*, and in the higher Himalayas even sheep, are used as pack animals; pack bullocks are also seen. *Camels* are still important in West Pakistan and Rajasthan, but hardly known elsewhere; in Karachi they do a good deal of the port cartage, hauling large rubber-tyred floats. *Poultry*, small and tough, are ubiquitous, but the *pig*, so conspicuous in China, is conspicuous only by his absence in most parts of India. Universally common to both countries are the village scavengers, lean mongrels of repulsive aspect: the traveller's entry into the village is invariably signalized by a clamorous reception committee of pariah dogs, and one thinks, not unreasonably, of rabies.

IV. OTHER RURAL OCCUPATIONS

It remains to glance briefly at other ways of life in the countryside. First in numbers and importance are the village artisans who, despite factory competition, in many lines still provide very essential services. Apart from these the most important rural occupations are those connected with the forests, sericulture (already discussed), and fishing.

[23] Sharma, *op. cit.* 168.

Forests and forest products

Forestry proper is almost entirely a government monopoly, either by direct exploitation or by licences. The most important timbers are noted in Chapter 3. Indian outturn is about 110,000,000 cu. ft. (3,125,000 m³), two-thirds of it from Madhya Pradesh, Maharashtra, Mysore, Kashmir and Uttar Pradesh; the accessible and exploited forests of Pakistan are mainly in the east, apart from small plantation areas in the Punjab. The recorded outturn of firewood is thrice that of timber. Pulp wood output is increasing, though bamboo and *sabai* grass are as yet the main bases of the paper industry. More important in the day-to-day life of those villagers who live within reach of woodland is the enormous range of 'minor forest products'. Many of these can be directly used or collected on payment of small fees; sometimes they are free by immemorial custom. Such items include foliage for use as fodder or leaf-manure; materials for thatching, mat-making and basketry; grass-cutting and grazing rights; fuel-wood; bamboos for individual use. The right to collect commercial products has naturally to be paid for, except in unreserved jungle: these include a multitude of dye- and tan-stuffs, drugs and nuts.

Among the more important, in which there is already some export, are acacia gum, artemisia (source of the vermicide santonin), beeswax, canes, cardamoms, cashew nuts, chaulmugra oil, cinnamon, cutch, Indian kapok, lac, lemon-grass oil, myrobalans, nux vomica, resins, sandalwood, senna and tamarinds.[24] Sugar and alcohol are obtained from the toddy and nipa palms and from the edible flowers of *mahua* (*Bassia latifolia*); this tree is so common and so luxuriously florescent in the northeast Peninsula that it has been suggested as a source of power alcohol.

Lac is no longer the most important of these products, but remains one of the most interesting. It is a gummy excretion from the body of the lac-insect, which infests several species of trees, notably dhak (*Butea frondosa*). The lac forms a crust on the twigs, which are collected and sold as 'stick-lac', and after processing shellac is produced. Shellac is an essential ingredient of some varnishes, of sealing-wax and similar compositions, and has also a wide range of uses in indigenous arts and crafts. Lac collecting is particularly important in Chota Nagpur and adjacent areas, where it provides a useful subsidiary income to a large number of villagers. Competition from plastics has caused decline.

Fishing

Even though the numbers of India's people are so great that it would seem that a large proportion of them would in any event be condemned to a poor life, the neglect of fisheries seems another striking example of what seems almost a masochistic tendency to make the worst of a bad world. Religious factors play a part:

[24] S. Krishna and R. L. Badhwar, 'Exploitation of Minor Forest Products' (5th British Empire Forestry Conference, Dehra Dun, 1947), 2.

the caste status of fishermen, who automatically take animal life, is very low. Climate also is obviously unfavourable to marketing any but dried fish far away from coast or river-bank.

The total production in India is not much over a million tons a year, a quarter of it fresh-water fish; this is under 6 lb. (2·7 kg.) per head of population. Obviously fish-foods can never attain the importance they have in truly maritime countries, but there is ample scope for expansion in both sea and inland fishing. The continental shelf in Indian waters is about 115,000 sq. miles (298,000 km²), and the coast is dotted with fishing villages; but sea-fishing is rarely carried on beyond 5 or 6 miles offshore. In both India and Pakistan, however, steps are being taken to increase the number of powered boats and to expand and improve the generally very inadequate shore installations. Real deep-sea fishing is as yet in its infancy. Of the inland fisheries the most important and best-used are those of Bengal; many of the deltaic and estuarine fish are excellent, especially the *hilsa*.

Government assistance and co-operative marketing could probably lead to a great increase in the output of the inland fisheries by 'fish-farming', and this without undue difficulty; it is surprising that more has not been done in 'fish-farming' with such species as *Tilapia*; here East Pakistan has admirable opportunities, which are beginning to be taken up. The improvement of sea-fishing is a harder problem, though in some cases technological innovation has been acceptable, e.g. in the use of nylon nets. The Indian government is devoting considerable attention to fishery research and development, aiming at a four-fold increase in the catch under the Third Plan; but given the poverty of the fishing communities the lines of advance open would seem to be (*a*) large-scale capitalist fishing or (*b*) state working thinly disguised as co-operation. The former is socially undesirable and in any case unlikely as returns are at present problematical, and there is no real interest in it; the latter would probably be 'improvement from above', and unduly costly in relation to the nutritional gain. There might, however, be possibilities in canning, using wastes as fertilizer, and extracting shark-liver oil.

Apart from the delta fisheries of East Bengal, the situation in Pakistan is much the same as in India, but distinct progress is being made in both sea and inland fishing, the latter in West as well as in East Pakistan.

V. AGRARIAN PROBLEMS AND PROGRAMMES

Much more than in any Western country, the wealth of the sub-continent lies in its fields – fields often fragmented into mere rags of land, torn by erosion, tilled for so long without rest or fertilization that over large areas they seem to have reached the ultimate base-level of infertility; and yet ultimately responsible for the sustenance of some 550,000,000 souls. Advances in agricultural technique, while not entirely lacking, affect but a small fraction of the farming, and with increasing pressure on the land either sheer need or the reduction of cash crops has led, in some areas, to a lowering of standards in such matters as rotations. Until recently, the owner-cultivator was increasingly forced into tenancy, the small tenant to become a landless man. The pressure of the cattle population is as bad or worse, with results ultimately disastrous to man and beast. There can be no possible doubt, then, that the rehabilitation of agriculture is by far the most pressing problem facing both India and Pakistan; more important even than industrialization which has a vital part to play in that rehabilitation, yet cannot be truly successful without the markets of a thriving countryside. This at once suggests what is indeed the fact, that every step forward seems enmeshed, as in 'concertina wire', by a tangle of interlocking vicious circles.

This interlocking of the problems renders the writing of a coherent account extremely difficult. But we can, perhaps, get a reasonably articulated picture by separating out (i) problems of technique, (ii) problems of social organization and (iii) the general problem, resuming all others, of the ratio between food output and mouths to feed. Finally, in succeeding chapters, we may survey recent developments and plans. But it must always be remembered that this breakdown is arbitrary, all specific problems having both technical and social aspects, as is obviously true, for example, of fragmentation and the cattle position.

A. PROBLEMS OF TECHNIQUE

1. *Sub-division and fragmentation*

The average Indian farm is very small, probably uneconomic if we admit any element of welfare into economics. The position is complicated by the distinction (not always made) between ownership and cultivation holdings: the man who farms his own land, neither more nor less, is probably rare in the more settled regions. The following significant figures based on about 10,000 households are given by the National Sample Survey (Eighth Round, 1954–55):

Acres occupied*	% of households	% of cropped area occupied
none	6·3	—
under 2·5	48·5	5·9
2·50–4·99	15·9	10·9
5·00–7·49	9·3	10·5
7·50–9·99	5·6	9·1
10·00–14·99	5·5	12·6
15·00–24·99	4·9	17·7
25 and over	4·0	33·3

[*5 ac.=2·02 ha.]

It will be seen that while 4% of rural families occupied a third of the cropped area, over 6% were entirely landless. On the other side it is possible to support a family on a very small area indeed of good rice land, and many of the tiniest cultivating holdings are worked by people whose main livelihood comes from some non-farming employment; are in fact allotments, not farms, tokens of attachment to the land rather than the main business of life.

Since overheads do not, of course, decrease proportionately as the size of holding goes down, the peasant with such an exiguous basis for his support is practically forced to overwork his land by neglecting fallows and by excessive double-cropping. Without venturing on the vexed and highly technical question of what an 'economic holding' might be, we may think it clear enough that the opening statement of this section errs if anything by moderation.

All this is the result of *sub-division* of property among all the sons, a practice sanctioned by both Hindu and Muslim laws of inheritance, but less invoked when the 'joint family' system was in full strength, or in old days when, in Jathar and Beri's phrase, 'it was land that ran after tenants'. Growing population and the substitution of the cash nexus for customary status have led to an insistence on individual rights which may reach fantastic extremes, and accentuates the allied, but distinct, *fragmentation* of one man's ground into scattered tiny parcels. In places this reached almost incredible proportions; to cite again some often-cited figures, in one Punjab village 12,800 ac. (5,184 ha.) were divided into 63,000 'fields'; in another 28% of holdings had each over 30 separate fields.[25] Even if physical division is impossible, partition between heirs has been insisted upon down to a half-share in a tree. To some extent this is understandable; he who has little must cling to what he has. But it is none the less deplorable, resulting, together with the multiplication of debt and tenancy suits, in a staggering burden of litigation. In 1939 nearly half the nearly 1,900,000 civil suits were directly concerned with the land, and over 1,000,000 were for Rs. 50 (£3. 15s.) or less. Unfortunately lawyers – and too often witnesses – must be paid, whence more debt. Recent land reforms may offer even more scope for litigation.

Fragmentation does not, of course, arise solely as an incident of sub-division. It is deeply rooted in the old communal principle of fair shares, and has sometimes still some economic justification, as for example to secure to each holding a balance of kharif flood-plain and rabi upland, to enable the farmer to plant two or more crops on different soils and so to insure against the weather, or to enable a better spread of working days than would be possible on a compact holding limited by soil and water factors to one or two crops in any one year. Nevertheless the general effects are often evil: waste of time in journeying to and from the fields, and of space in the boundaries; the prohibitive expense of fencing the small parcels, so that the cultivator is bound to follow the régime of his fellows or else see his standing crop destroyed by cattle grazing on the stubble; difficulties of

[25] See e.g. M. B. Nanavati and J. J. Anjaria, *The Indian Rural Problem* (Bombay, 3rd ed., 1947), 46–47; RCAI, 134.

water-supply. All these again give ample cause for dispute and litigation. Nevertheless, as B. H. Farmer argues, to look only to inheritance laws and so on is to mistake the occasion of sub-division for its cause and to tackle the symptom, not the disease: 'The disease is an economic system . . . and the answer lies, if it lies anywhere, in economic development.'[26]

Consolidation of holdings is the obvious answer; a little too obvious. Clearly it applies to fragmentation rather than to sub-division; it is one thing to exchange enclaves, another to surrender land, and, in the absence of alternative employment, compulsory formation of economic holdings could result only in an increase in the numbers of the most wretched rural class.[27] These are the landless labourers, condemned to work part of the year for minute wages and for the rest to exist in unemployment, from which the only 'escape' may be the acceptance of an extra-legal and unavowed, but in effect real, state of serfdom, in return for a pittance from better-off peasants. In some States a fair beginning has been made in the task of consolidation through co-operative societies; in East Punjab, where conditions are perhaps unusually favourable, rapid progress has been made in the last few years; from the air much of the area between Delhi and the Sutlej appears gridded into large squares, with the old irregular boundaries showing up beneath the new. Altogether perhaps some 40,000,000 ac. (16,200,000 ha.) have been consolidated in India, and in West Pakistan about 7,000,000 ac. (2,800,000 ha.).

2. The fertilizer problem

Even if we follow the authority of Sir John Russell and add 25% to Indian yields, they remain pitifully low: rice 900–1,000 lb. per ac. (1,009–1,121 kg. per ha.; Japan 2,250 lb. per ac., 2,802 kg. per ha.); wheat 750–800 (760–785, about 40% of British yields, or equivalent to the yields of *extensive* farming in Australia); cotton 89 (102), against 300 (336 in USA). Moreover, if the figures mean anything at all, they show a marked fall in productivity in this century: the average rice yield was 982 lb. per ac. in 1909–13, about 840 in 1926–38; in kg. per ha., 1,101 against 942. It must be remembered that these are pre-Partition figures and Pakistan took over some of the most productive areas. Recently, and on really comparable figures, there has been some recovery, but not nearly enough. For India, the average rice yield in the five years ending 1956–57 was only 740 lb. per ac. (830 kg. per ha.); in the next five years it was 838 lb. per ac. (940 kg. per ha.); for wheat the figures are respectively 642 (720) and 714 (800).[28]

[26] See his very important paper, based on Ceylon experience, 'On not controlling sub-division in paddy lands', *Trans. Inst. of British Geographers*, 28 (1960), 225–35, and also S. M. Ali, 'Field patterns on the Indo-Gangetic Divide', *Panjab Geographical Review*, 1 (1942), 26–35, for cases in which consolidation is either unfeasible or undesirable.

[27] Thus *The First Five Year Plan* admits (p. 102) that a main objection to rationalization is that it would throw large numbers out of work, and that 'hasten slowly' must perforce be the motto.

[28] *Statistical Abstract of the Indian Union*, 1962, Table 20; *Pakistan Economic Survey 1963–64*, Table 12.

Pakistani rice yields are much the same as India's, wheat rather greater, cotton twice as much (for mainly irrigated as against mainly rainfed cotton).

The main cause is simply failure to fertilize the fields; but again this is not mere stupidity or even ignorance. It is clear enough that the peasant with a tiny holding can hardly afford to grow a nitrogenous crop for the luxury of ploughing it in: the gain in output next year will not keep him alive in this. As a general rule he is far too poor to be able to buy artificials. Stubble may be burnt, but often it is needed for grazing. Where there is access to woodland, leaves and branches are burnt on the fields or leaf-mould collected; mud from tanks may be used; oilcake is sometimes applied. But in areas of greatest population and greatest need such resources, if available at all, are hopelessly insufficient. For social reasons it is unlikely that India will ever emulate Chinese thoroughness in the use of human waste-products, though around some large towns night-soil, poudrette and sewage have been exploited, and the universal use for natural purposes of the fields abutting upon the village-site has actually led to their up-grading in revenue assessments.

There seems little point in such picturesque impressionism as F. L. Brayne's remark that 'if we could rescue the cow-dung from the housewife' (whose duty it is to make it into flat fuel-cakes), then something like a third of India's agrarian poverty would be wiped out at a stroke.[29] As a matter of fact more cow-dung is actually used as manure than is generally realized; some 20% is simply lost, 40% burnt, and perhaps 40% spread on the fields;[30] the use of compost is spreading, if slowly. One factor in the burning of cow-dung is the preference for a slow-burning fuel for making *ghi*; but, quite apart from this, over much of the Indo-Gangetic Plains there is hardly any alternative fuel. Such 'forest' as exists is needed for grazing and produces very little wood, and it may be added that the lack of decent fodder in itself lessens the organic values of the cattle-manure. Sir Herbert Howard, in *A Post-War Forest Policy for India* (1944), pleaded for the planting of thousands of small fuel and fodder forests to meet this situation; but without a numerous police these might not survive human and animal assault during infancy, though perhaps with intensive propaganda co-operatives or *panchayats* (village councils) could give some protection. It is precisely where additional grazing and alternative fuel are most needed – in the Gangetic plain – that there is least room to provide them; indeed there is hardly room enough to expand the village-sites except at the expense of arable. And that expense can ill be afforded. It may be that there is promise in the use of cow-dung to produce combustible gas – the sludge would retain considerable manurial value; there are obvious problems in the organization and capital required, but in principle this is a fairly simple and even elegant operation.[31]

[29] Should we not rather wish to rescue the housewife from the cow-dung?
[30] *A Food Plan for India* (RIIA and OUP, 1945), 47n., 19, but cf. conflicting figures on p. 9.
[31] See S. V. Desai in *Developing Village India*, 140–3, and below, 291.

The conclusion seems inescapable that artificials must be supplied, and lavishly, even at financial loss to government; a loss which might in time be recouped financially by increased taxable capacity, but which would certainly be worth while in terms of welfare.

There has indeed been a great expansion in fertilizer output and use, but a disproportionate share has gone to plantations and special cash crops. A very much larger effort is needed, as is very obvious when the sale of 86,000 tons of fertilizer in nine months for the 26,000,000 (10,500,000 ha.) cultivated acres of East Pakistan can be officially described as 'a major break-through'. West Pakistan uses rather over 250,000 tons of artificials a year; India's use of ammonium sulphate amounted, in terms of nitrogen, to 230,000 tons in 1961, about half of which was home-produced, while superphosphate used was the equivalent of 70,000 tons of P_2O_5. The Third Plan would increase these four-fold and six-fold respectively; but these seem almost trifling beside the consumption of say Japan and Egypt on much smaller areas, and indeed are well below official estimates of needs.[32]

3. *Tools and seeds; roads and markets*

The manifold inefficiencies of Indian agriculture are probably less the responsibility of the peasant than of nature and of society: of precarious seasons and poor soils, of the immemorial load of exploitation. Doubtless the Indian farmer is on the whole conservative, and on the whole he has had need to be so: for ages past his farming practices have been so closely adjusted to their environment that there could be little need or possibility of change – until the whole fabric of his myriad little closed societies was shaken by the impact of the tightly-administered British Raj and of the world market. 'That in many places the system of agriculture followed has attained a very high standard is a matter of common knowledge; the cultivation of rice in the deltas, for example, has reached a marked degree of perfection, and the wisdom of many agricultural proverbs stands unchallenged by research.'[33] Now that change is imperative sheer poverty too often inhibits it, and perhaps more often than mere conservatism; but it must be admitted that, especially in the harder or more precarious areas, apathy and fatalism have struck deep and sapped away the vitality of the people precisely where change is most needed.

It is essential to see that innovation is really improvement; condemnation of 'the plough that merely scratches the soil', for instance, is too facile. The RCAI cites two widely held opinions to account for the cultivator's tenacious adherence to his ancient models: (i) a light plough is all that his bullocks can draw, and (ii) he prefers a plough which he can carry on his shoulders to and from his often scattered fields. These reasons are valid and important; but the RCAI itself held

[32] S. Thirumalai, *Post-War Agricultural Problems and Policies in India* (Indian Soc. of Agric. Economics, Bombay, and Inst. of Pacific Relations, NY, 1954), 170–1.
[33] RCAI, 14. A careful correlation of rural saws with the environmental conditions they reflect would be both fascinating and instructive.

that the main factor is a realization of the importance of conserving moisture. Whether this is consciously felt may perhaps be doubted, but the RCAI's conclusion is noteworthy: while deep ploughing is essential for some crops and soils, 'it has certainly not been established that it would pay the cultivator in all kharif conditions. Indeed, the contrary is more probable', as it might well lead to loss of moisture in areas of light rainfall, to the reverse in humid areas, in either case jeopardizing germination.[34]

Nevertheless many implements could be much improved, and some new ones are desirable: seed-drills, cheap threshing and winnowing appliances, better water-lifts, more efficient cane-crushers and oil-expellers. Mechanization in the normal sense is difficult, indeed probably impracticable while the farm unit, even if compact, is so small. The use of tractors is indeed increasing; in 1961 there were 34,000 used for agricultural purposes in India. These have been most successful on government clearing schemes, or preparing the ground for tillage in new irrigation areas such as the Thal; they are obviously beyond the means of most individual farmers, but can perhaps be made available by co-operatives. Except for actual tillage, indeed, there is not likely to be much need for mechanization, since harvesting machinery does not itself increase production; it may save a crop threatened by weather, but this is too slight a risk to be insured against at so heavy a premium. Tractors might also be used for transporting pumps, small presses, and so on. But if tractors are wanted for a part only of their possibilities, the question arises whether it is economic to use them.

Mechanization, after all, is labour-saving, and in the sub-continent it is not so much a saving of man-hours that is needed as an improved labour efficiency; by no means the same thing. And there is the problem of servicing: 'of the villages in which manufacturers would normally establish the chain of dealers and sub-dealers . . . not one in a hundred (and according to some estimates, not one in a thousand) has anyone capable of undertaking the responsibilities involved.'[35] Coming as it does in a generally optimistic survey, this admission has great weight.

On the other hand, a persuasive argument in favour of a large-scale shift from bullock to tractor farming has been put forward by K. W. Kapp; he discounts the effect on employment and points to the gains, financial and nutritional, from a change to milk cattle, as well as more general economic advantages. Here again reliance is placed on co-operative organization. It may well be questioned, however, whether all of Kapp's assumptions (e.g. on depreciation) are realistic.[36]

[34] RCAI, 110–12; a discussion of great importance. Those who condemn the light plough are not often in the habit of carrying agricultural machinery on their shoulders.

[35] *Report of the UK Industrial Mission to Pakistan* (1950), 31–40 (refce at p. 35). It should be noted that the Mission included no representative of agriculture; and the words 'soil erosion' do not occur in this most interesting discussion. Cf. G. Slater, *Southern India* (1936), 57–58, on 'labour-saving'. But for an opposite view, see W. Klatt, 'Agricultural planning in East Pakistan', *Pacific Affairs*, 25 (1952), 263–7.

[36] See his *Hindu Culture, Economic Development and Economic Planning in India* (Asia, Bombay, 1963), 144–62.

The application of cheap electric power to pumping (whether for irrigation or drainage), oil-pressing, and so on has great possibilities and has made a promising start. Great economies could be effected by improving bullock-carts; in some areas wheels are still all but solid and the weight of the cart ridiculously large compared with its capacity. The increasing use of rubber tyres is a notable advance.

Much research has gone into the production of improved crops; the most notable achievements are probably in sugar-cane and the introduction of Cambodia cotton and the development of strains from it. But there is substance in the frequent criticism that activities have been too much devoted to cash crops. However, since 1947 much more attention has been given, by both India and Pakistan, to improved seed for foodgrains, including jowar and maize. Many seed multiplication farms have been set up, but it is difficult to assess the actual results: as the Ford Team pointed out, it was 'unable to get what we felt was clear verifiable data on the extent to which improved seeds are actually used . . . in rice and wheat, a very high percentage is alleged to be planted to improved seeds. Yet only limited progress in some States has been made in increasing rice and wheat yields'.[37] It seems likely that there is a good deal of carelessness in distribution, and adulteration is probably widespread. It is difficult to reconcile the statement by the Grow More Food Enquiry Committee (1952) that 100% of rice land in East Punjab was under improved varieties, against 0·9% in West Bengal, with the higher yields of the latter State. Possibly double-cropping may account for this particular case, but there seems no relation at all between the ranking of States by 'improvement' and by yield, even where environmental conditions are not dissimilar.

A more vigorous attack on plant diseases, insects, fungi, wild pigs, rats and monkeys is urgently needed. Crops such as sugar-cane, grown more or less homogeneously, are of course especially liable to diseases and pests. Both India and Pakistan are devoting a good deal of effort to meeting the vital need for adequate storage godowns.

Rural communications are nearly everywhere inadequate: this is a major factor in the slight development of dairying and of fruit and vegetable crops, a large increase in which is exceedingly desirable to offset the excess of carbohydrates in Indian diets. Bad roads or rather tracks also impose a severe strain on bullocks, especially where kharif marketing coincides with rabi tillage. It is not surprising that the construction of feeder roads is often a main preoccupation of Community Development Projects, though if all the villagers contribute their labour, the lion's share of the returns is likely to accrue to the better-off farmer with a surplus.

Market facilities in India are in general poor. In some areas and for some crops (e.g. cotton in Maharashtra) there is a good network of officially inspected mar-

[37] *Report on India's Food Crisis and the Steps to Meet It* (Ministry of Food and Agriculture, ND, 1959), 194–5.

kets, though even so malpractices are not unknown. Elsewhere the peasant is often at the mercy of unscrupulous traders, and there are too many brokers and middlemen. As the farmer has usually very slight storage facilities and so no holding power, and is often without access to reliable market information, efforts to by-pass the broker can easily be broken by rings and boycotts, though here and there co-operatives have scored notable successes. But as a rule the peasant is exploited by secret bidding between the buying and the selling brokers, arbitrary deductions for alleged deficiencies, false weights, unwarranted commissions, and so on. Local governments are increasingly publicizing current prices, in part over village radios, in part by posters at markets; the importance of 'literacy drives' is obvious in this connection. Very much more remains to be done; there were only 978 regulated markets in India in 1962 – an increase of 248 over 1961.

B. PROBLEMS OF SOCIAL ORGANIZATION

1. Land reform in India

Land tenures and kinship systems are perhaps the most complex of all social phenomena; and when caste intricacies are interwoven with the vast variety of tenurial relationships produced by the diverse regional and local societies, histories and geographies of the sub-continent, it is obvious that any general account – even were half a volume rather than part of a chapter devoted to it – must be drastically simplified; yet some sketch is absolutely essential to any understanding of the agrarian *misère* of the countryside. Moreover, since Independence immemorial relationships have been, in theory at least, completely subverted by law – and not by a single body of central legislation, but by the many separate enactments of fifteen Indian States, not to mention Pakistan.

An officially optimistic article by a member of the Indian Planning Commission's Advisory Committee on Land Reform begins by remarking that 'It would be no exaggeration to say that never before in the world history of land tenure reform has so much legislative action, with such wide social and economic ramifications, been undertaken'; and this is certainly true if we exclude such totalitarian changes as those in Russia and China. The article ends, 'Hereafter, the major task . . . is to devise machinery for the effective implementation of the comprehensive legislation';[38] and that is even more certainly true, for the gap between enactment and enforcement is at the heart of the agrarian crisis. With all the vast literature, it is extremely difficult to evaluate what changes have actually taken place in the countryside, as distinct from changes in the law, and what their social and economic effects have been.

There was a distinction in British India between *ryotwari* areas, where the peasant held directly from the State, and *zamindari*, where the land was held by owners who were often absentees or, probably more often, resident but still exploiting gentry. Especially in areas under the Bengal 'Permanent Settlement' of 1793, which was designed to set up a class of 'improving landlords' on the

[38] M. L. Dantwala, in *Indian and Foreign Review* (ND), I/21 (15/8/64), 14–16.

contemporary English model, there developed a fantastic number of inter-mediaries between the rack-rented peasant and the final landlord who paid a fixed revenue assessment; and in many princely states, notably those of central India and Hyderabad, local notables held large grants or *jagirs*. Even in *ryotwari* areas there were often numerous petty tenancies; under the British Raj, land had become a market commodity for investment, and overwhelmingly investment of rentier rather than entrepreneurial type. With growth of population and ever-increasing land-hunger, the better-off, usually of higher caste, were able to build up estates. The variety of titles, tenures, rents and services was bewildering.

It is unfortunately not easy to have much confidence in the official figures on tenure. The 1954 Census of Landholding, so far as carried out, in effect eliminated joint-family holdings by simply instructing its officers to show separately the nominal share of each person; 'land under personal cultivation' included land not leased out for a year or more – and very much of this would be cultivated not personally by the owner but under oral arrangements, seasonal crop-sharing, and so on; while an area 'owned by A but worked under occupancy right by B will be shown as B's land'. The net effect was to inflate the number of 'owners' and to whittle away landlordism at one end of the scale, and to diminish the extent of sharecropping and tenancies-at-will at the other; but these are among the most important factors in the situation. Somewhat similar criticisms apply to the Census figures. In 1951 these showed 249,000,000 people dependent on agriculture; of these only 2·1% were rentier landlords, 67·2% were 'owner-cultivators', 12·7% 'tenant-cultivators', and 18% labourers. Labourers *and their dependents* num-bered 44,800,000; a figure difficult to reconcile with the total of 25,511,000 (1961: 31,482,000) just for labourers. All this before land reform; and as Daniel Thorner remarks, why, if these figures give a reasonably accurate picture, is there so strong and persistent a demand for reform throughout the country?[39]

Land reforms fall essentially under three closely related heads: the elimination of intermediaries between the cultivator and the State – this is often referred to as *zamindari* abolition; the setting of ceilings on individual holdings; and the protection of tenants by providing for security and fair rents. The history and details of legislation vary from State to State; in most cases, however, it is not unfair to remark that the length of the legislative process gave much time and opportunity for such evasions as the nominal splitting-up of joint holdings and securing the 'voluntary' surrender of occupancy rights. While the relatively few really large estates have been severely shorn (against compensation) and in some cases tenants have gained more security, the consensus of informed opinion seems to be that in many areas evasion took place on a large scale, and it seems quite possible that there has been an actual, though concealed, increase in share-cropping and what are in effect tenancies-at-will. These are matters difficult to police in any case, even were there no collusion by local officials, who are often badly underpaid or drawn from classes adversely affected by reform, or both.

[39] For all this, see D. and A. Thorner, *op. cit.*, Chapters 10–13, *passim*.

The big *zamindar* may be on the way out; but the *malik* or middling proprietor may have gained; and while a few *kisans* ('working peasants') may have improved their position and perhaps even graduated to the *malik* class, the *mazdurs* or labourers, often 'attached' by debt-slavery, are probably as wretched as ever.

The evidence for this view is scattered, but it comes from too many sources to be ignored.[40] Thorner, writing in 1955, was of opinion that there had been 'some perceptible change' in the then States of Bombay, Hyderabad, Madhya Bharat, Punjab and Punjab States Union, Saurashtra and Uttar Pradesh; the rest of India showed little or no change, with the significant exceptions of Kashmir and Andhra: here change was greatest, and here there were obvious political factors – the presence of Pakistan and the Communist agrarian rising of 1948–51 in Telangana.[41] On the other hand there has been more legislation since 1955, especially as regards rent fixing, though some of this is probably plugging of loopholes after the damage has been done; and a detailed survey of Saurashtra, while perhaps glossing over the amount of resistance and evasion, comes to definitely favourable conclusions.[42]

To what extent land reforms have actually improved production is an even more difficult question. One factor in the delays and changes of policy has been the apprehension, especially in bad years, that a too rigorous application of ceilings on the size of holdings might prejudice production by depriving the larger, better-equipped, and more commercially-minded proprietors of needed land, and also of incentives. Looked at in cold blood, it might indeed appear that a strengthening of the *malik* – or 'kulak' – class would, economically considered, be the best thing for production;[43] but this runs counter to the *mystique* of land reform, though as we have seen it may not be so unconformable to its *practice* in the countryside. Even setting aside more idealistic and humanitarian considerations, however, it seems unlikely that the rural masses can be enlisted for a really wholehearted economic effort without some vigorous reform, despite what Iyengar terms its 'cumulative diseconomies'.

2. *Bhoodan, Gramdan and co-operative farming*

The Bhoodan or 'land-gift' movement initiated in 1951 by the Gandhian idealist Acharya Vinobha Bhave has appeared to some as a way out. Vinobha based himself on a direct missionary appeal; he estimated that about a sixth of the land, 50,000,000 ac. (20,230,000 ha.) could meet the needs of the *mazdurs* and could be made available if only the landed would recognize their rightful obligation to

[40] Cf., for example, the essays (on widely scattered areas) in A. R. Desai (ed.), *Rural Sociology in India* (Vora, Bombay, 3rd ed. 1961), 489–505; and, in the same volume (424–6) an example of actual *loss* of land rights by low caste people in Madhopur village, UP.

[41] *The Agrarian Prospect in India* (Delhi Univ. Press, 1956), 29–53.

[42] R. B. Mishra, *Effects of Land Reforms in Saurashtra* (Vora, Bombay, 1961). Annual summaries of legislation are perhaps most conveniently found in *India: A Reference Annual* (Ministry of Information, ND), though in themselves they are not very revealing.

[43] See S. K. Iyengar, *A Decade of Planned Economy* (Indian Academy of Economics, Mysore, 1961), 114–15, 178–97, for a typically iconoclastic view.

the landless, and in the first few years the sincerity and emotive appeal of himself and his disciples elicited a remarkable response: by 1957 over 4,000,000 ac. (1,620,000 ha.) had been donated, half of them in Bihar. But he relied on a *continuity* of generous response which has not been maintained; often (and naturally enough) the land given was the most marginal in the village – and sometimes the gift was merely the surplus over the legal ceiling, which would have been forfeit anyhow; and Vinobha gave much too little thought to equipping the *mazdur* (with bullocks and so on) to become a *kisan*. There has been no increase – rather a slight decrease – in the cumulative totals of land donated, and although practically no new land came in after 1957, in the 10 years to 1962 only a quarter of the land given had been distributed.

The later phase of the movement is known as Gramdan, or the communalizing of entire villages; so far over 5,000 villages have accepted the movement, but nearly half of these are in the hill country of Orissa where there is plenty of land for shifting cultivation and the people are probably simply returning to tribal traditions. Gramdan may help in Community Development and have lessons for co-operative farming; but with all respect for the devotion of Vinobha and his followers, it is difficult to take their economic thinking seriously. Gramdan seems a desperate expedient to revitalize a movement which had already become stagnant.[44]

Faced with the general impasse, official thinking seems to be turning towards large-scale co-operative farming. It is admitted that even in rural credit, where most has been done, the achievements of co-operation have been disappointing, but it is hoped that with such strong government backing collective production, if not ownership, could be successful. Obviously much could be done on these lines in the way of supplying seeds and fertilizers and in running machinery; and some co-operative colonies have been established for refugees from Pakistan in East Punjab, the terai and Rajasthan. But clearly it is one thing to set up a collective of displaced persons on new land, backed by a definite government responsibility for rehabilitation; and quite another to reverse the strong and accelerating century-old trend towards individualism in the territorially and socially tight-packed villages of say the Gangetic Plains or Tamilnad, with their intense caste factionalism. Although financial provision is being made under the Third Plan for such development, detailed programmes do not seem to be readily available.[45]

[44] There is a large literature; statistics are given in the *Reference Annual*, and Desai, *op. cit.* 567–632, includes essays by both supporters and critics. It is perhaps significant that Srimati Kusum Nair does not so much as mention Vinobha, Bhoodan, or Gramdan in her excellent first-hand sketches of rural India, *Blossoms in the Dust: The Human Factor in Indian Development* (Praeger, NY, 1962).

[45] There is some discussion in Tarlok Singh's essay 'India's rural economy and its institutional framework' in J. P. Bhattacharjee (ed.), *Studies in Indian Agricultural Economics* (Indian Soc. of Agric. Economics, Bombay, 1958), 300–16, and *Towards a Self-reliant Economy* (Ministry of Information, ND, 1961), 186–92. For criticism, even more scathing than usual, see Iyengar, *op. cit.* 118–19, 186–90.

Readers of *Blossoms in the Dust* or of many sociological studies of Indian village life will not be optimistic; and yet this may seem the only way to render possible the application of those other necessities (which by themselves are but palliatives) such as improvements in technique and 'rural uplift'. As Wilfrid Malenbaum puts it, 'the devices proposed for closing the gap are exciting; as of the end of the second plan, they remained imprecise – and untested.'[46] They may have a hard time in what Thorner calls 'the world of organized subterfuge'.

3. *Debt, credit, co-operation*

Nearly all agrarian societies developed beyond subsistence level are debt-ridden, since (except for market-gardeners, dairy farmers and the like) the farmer's resources are liquid but once or twice a year, after harvest, while his outgoings recur throughout the year, often with peaks around sowing-time and at the harvest itself. Nowhere is debt so crushing as in the peasant societies of Asia.

After the depression of the 1930s the total volume of rural debt in British India alone was estimated to exceed Rs 1,200 crores or about £900,000,000.[47] Divided by scores of millions, the debt might seem small in terms of individuals, but it probably approximated to, if it did not exceed, the average annual income in the countryside. The high agricultural prices of the Second World War, together with the shortage of consumer goods, undoubtedly resulted in a considerable liquidation of indebtedness, but it seems highly probable that this affected mainly the middle and upper strata of rural society; there is evidence that since 1945 the volume of debt has again risen, and this time it is mainly the lower ranks that have been most adversely affected.[48] The All-India Rural Credit Survey of 1954–56 estimated that 69% of cultivating families were in debt to the average extent of Rs 526.[49] Most of the debt is non-productive; even for 'big cultivators', only about one-third is for capital outlay, and 'family expenditure' rises to nearly 60% for the smaller cultivators: the financial impact of the social conventions governing such expenditure does not fall proportionately with status.

The causes of indebtedness are manifold. Fundamental are the small holdings, the perversity of the seasons, the peasant's lack of information and of storage which compel him to a quick and blindfold disposal of his harvest. He has no reserves to meet sickness, drought, flood, cattle diseases; his savings account is in his wife's few poor rings and bangles, and when natural calamity comes and everybody is selling at once, these do not fetch much. The unco' guid and the well-to-do condemn his undeniable extravagance when his son is born or his

[46] *Prospects for Indian Development* (Allen & Unwin, London, 1962), 226. See also the balanced remarks in R. P. Sinha, *Food in India* (OUP, Bombay, 1961), 131–8.

[47] G. B. Jathar and S. G. Beri, *Indian Economics* (OUP, Bombay, 7th ed. 1942), I.283.

[48] Thirumalai, *op. cit.* 186, gives totals for both 1937 and *c.* 1953 of Rs 1800 crores.

[49] This vast report seems not to be available in Australia; there is a summary by V. M. Jakhade in J. P. Bhattacharjee, *op. cit.* 249–99. The sampling and general conduct of the enquiry are severely criticized by D. and A. Thorner, *op. cit.* 188–224.

daughter married: but in a round of drudgery and privation, these are the socially sanctioned opportunities for a little colour and gaiety, a few days of uninhibited projection of his personality, new clothes and good food; and it is hard to blame him over-much.

All this would be bad enough were the agents of credit impeccable; notoriously they are not. According to the Rural Credit Survey, about a quarter of all loans come from better-off agriculturalists, *maliks* and the like, and this often leads the poorer peasants and labourers into something very like almost permanent debt-slavery. Nearly half the total borrowings came from professional moneylenders. These people may also be the village grainbrokers and shopkeepers; they have funds for retaining lawyers and local officials, and command the services, as witnesses or strong-arm men, of numerous clients. Since the poorer borrowers are more likely than not illiterate, the cards are stacked against them. There is no doubt that the rigid legalism of the British Raj played into the moneylender's hands, and, despite much protective legislation (before Independence as well as since), it is not at all certain that things are greatly better now. In thirty-three of the seventy-five sample Districts covered by the Rural Credit Survey, over half the moneylenders' loans carried interest at over 18%.

The natural answer would seem to be co-operative credit societies. It is not a new one: the chequered history of such societies in India goes back to 1904. Their success has been by no means commensurate with the effort put into them; the Rural Credit Survey found that the 'utter insignificance' of the movement's share in rural financing – after fifty years, 3·1% – 'was perhaps the most startling revelation' from its enquiry. It is not easy to understand this surprise at what everybody knew, nor are the reasons obscure. The societies, bound by regulation, are faced always with the dilemma of too rigid management, or too lax; the moneylender is bound by no such rules, he is on the spot in almost the smallest village and knows his clients thoroughly, he imposes no formalities or delays, and he is as a rule quite content to receive interest to eternity rather than to foreclose or to be repaid. Co-operatives cannot – or at least should not – lend to support more borrowing; their rates are much lower than the moneylender's, but they are not nearly so obliging.

Perhaps nowhere is the gap between the official and the actual so wide as in this field. It is officially estimated that in 1961 about 39% of the population was served by the co-operative movement, but what this really means is hard to tell. It is claimed that 33% of agricultural production is covered by co-operative arrangements, and the Third Plan target is 60%; it is disconcerting to see a Third Plan target of 100% for coverage of villages, when no comparative figure is given for the end of the Second. Undoubtedly there has been a big increase in activity in the last ten years: all forms of co-operative societies rose from 185,630 in 1951–52 to 332,488 in 1960–61, membership from under 14,000,000 to over 34,000,000; and whereas before 1947 co-operation was almost overwhelmingly in the form of agricultural credit societies, there are now many for marketing, production (especially of sugar-cane), irrigation, fishing and so on. Two facts in relation to agricultural credit societies may be significant: though working capital per society rose from Rs 4,190 in 1952 to 14,808 in 1962, deposits per member were the same in both years – Rs 9; and while in 1960–61 such societies lent Rs 203 crores, outstanding loans were 218 and *overdue* loans over 44 crores.[50]

With all their shortcomings, credit societies have done something to keep interest rates down by providing an alternative source of credit. However, as so often, it is the bigger and stronger men who can best take advantage of them; the poor and weak, who need them most, are just those who cannot provide security and cannot afford the delays and limitations in their working. There is a complicated system of co-operative banks and other quasi-governmental financing agencies, and the Third Plan envisages very considerable expansion. Some critics appear to think that this will amount to throwing good money after bad,[51] and the Committee of Direction of the Rural Credit Societies itself was impelled to admit some truth in a definition of Indian co-operation as ' "a plant held in position with both hands by Government since its roots refuse to enter the soil." More than the roots of Co-operation, it is the tentacles of private economy that have acquired grip. . . .'[52] Yet it seems inescapable that, if there is a way out from the agrarian tangle, it will need massive financial assistance from government, and it is difficult to see any other practical method of deploying it. In Pakistan similarly, the *Five Year Plan Draft* summed up: 'Although it may be argued that co-operation has failed, it must nevertheless be resolved to make it succeed.'[53]

4. *Community Development and Panchayati Raj*

From all that has gone before, it will be apparent that the body social of the Indian countryside labours under a complication of ills; there is an appalling deadweight to be lifted. The agrarian problem seems hydra-headed; it is essential to establish priorities, and yet so many and so urgent are the tasks that there is always a danger of dissipating energy, or of 'solving' one problem at the price of raising up others: the history of land reform bears witness.

Before Independence, many attempts had been made to break through the cycle of rural poverty, rural apathy, rural poverty. . . . Notable among these were F. L. Brayne's village propaganda and M. L. Darling's co-operative work in the Punjab, Rabindranath Tagore's educational effort at Santiniketan, Mahatma Gandhi's village uplift in Gujarat. Such efforts, usually on a very local basis, lacked extension and continuity; often they tended to follow up one pet line. Striking results might be obtained, to be dissipated when the particular servant of the people departed and the village relaxed into the old comfortable ways.

---

[50] Figures in this paragraph from the 1963 *Reference Annual*, 225–31.
[51] Cf. Iyengar, *op. cit.* 141–74.   [52] Cited Desai, *op. cit.* 511.
[53] Cited in J. R. Andrus and A. F. Mohammed, *The Economy of Pakistan* (OUP, Karachi, 1958), 143.

Those carried out by British officials, however devoted and sympathetic, were still alien in inspiration; conversely, it is not unfair to say that many Gandhi-inspired efforts (of which Vinobha's Bhoodan is but the latest example) lacked a sense of the practical. Some residue of better living was usually left, but perhaps more important in the long run was that this experience produced a large literature on 'rural uplift', often indeed impractical enough, but in sum doing much to define problems and to evaluate techniques.

The Community Development Project, launched in 1952, set out to give large-scale government backing, organization, and continuity to what had been a sporadic movement. It was much encouraged by the very striking results obtained by an American-inspired project in Uttar Pradesh;[54] but pressures of opinion, internal and external, led to a pace of expansion which seems to have paid insufficient attention to the matter of diminishing returns ('what will happen when *every* village woman has been taught to make four-anna trinkets for sale to her neighbours?') and to the need for more careful observation and record of trial in diverse environments. The statistics of Community Development are impressive, but in that fact is hidden one source of weakness: the movement has of necessity evolved a sort of rural Welfare State bureaucracy, alongside or over-lapping with the normal administrative machine, with its own inevitable frictions and frustrations and a pressure to produce paper 'results'.[55]

Community Development is based on blocks of about 100 villages, say 60–70,000 people; there are now over 5,000 blocks covering practically the entire country. The aim is to enlist the effort of the people themselves in a wide variety of improvements – the use of fertilizers, better seeds, composts; better stock management, including castration; development of village industries; physical ameliorations such as properly lined wells, latrines, street drainage, school building, construction of feeder roads, provision of village radios and so on. The main agent is the *gram sewak* or trained Village Level Worker; unfortunately it is likely that only too often the multiplicity of interests which he – or she – is expected to encourage precludes really thorough training; on the other hand, undue specialization at this level could only increase bureaucratic stresses. At the next level, a Block Panchayat Samiti is in general control, formed of the heads of village panchayats and co-opted representatives of women and depressed classes, and assisted by the Block Development Officer and his specialist Exten-sion Officers. The Presidents of these Block Panchayats, together with local elected representatives, form the Zila Parishad, which is in general control at District level, and the old officials in charge of sub-divisions (tahsils, taluks, or thanas), including the minor revenue officials, are brought into this set-up. This last point emphasizes that a great experiment in decentralization is in progress,

---

[54] See A. Mayer, *Pilot Project, India* (Univ. of California, Berkeley, 1958).
[55] Iyengar (*op. cit.* 124–5), critical as usual, makes the point that 'nothing is easier than boosting village figures for the simple reason that verification is impossible on account of area and numbers'.

which it is hoped will lead to Panchayati Raj, the long-desired revival of the old virtual village self-government by the Gram Panchayat. These were councils of five which, with the assistance of the headman and village clerk, in the past represented the main caste groupings, but are now to be enlarged and remodelled on elective lines, and also given the responsibility for expending a large share of the local land revenue.

The weaknesses and failings of Community Development are obvious. It has been over-extended and energies have been diffused into improvements which should be, but too often are not, co-ordinated. The dangers of bureaucracy have already been stressed; in some cases the new Panchayats, with their elected lower castemen, may really only rubber-stamp the behind the scenes decisions of the old petty oligarchies. Most serious is the fact, probably inherent in the nature of things (and by no means only in India), that a programme meant for the benefit of all, but especially the masses, in actuality plays into the hands of the already fairly well-off farmers. This is natural: the *malik* is the man with the resources to obtain the most benefit from better techniques and ameliorations such as feeder roads, to which, however, the whole village will have contributed, if only by its more or less voluntary labour. There are not wanting suggestions that this *shramdan*, or spontaneous labour contribution, sometimes tends to slide over into the old *begar*, or more or less forced labour at the behest of local magnates and officials. *Jis ke pas jitna hai, utana use milta hai*: precisely, To him that hath much, shall much be given.[56]

On the other hand, there have been undeniable successes, and the best blocks are surely inspiring. Whatever discounts may be made, it is surely no mean achievement that the people themselves have contributed, in cash, kind, or labour, some 40% (Rs 112 crores, to March 1962) of the total costs. Pukka wells, latrines, schools however poorly equipped, are at least tangible additions to the amenity of life. For this reason, doubtless, the official Evaluation Report of 1957 found that, while benefits varied greatly with such factors as the accessibility of villages and accrued more to those with bigger holdings and some financial resources, real understanding and active participation were stronger for the 'constructional' than the institutional aspects of the programme. These physical ameliorations are of course very good and very much needed, but they are not *directly* conducive to increased production; at best they offset the bigger direct dividend to the *malik* or kulak groups.

The true effect of Community Development on agricultural production is impossible to assess: there have been so many other factors, multipliers or depressors, at work; but in many places, at least, there has been some more general diffusion of improved techniques. Many communities remain sunk in

[56] Cited D. and A. Thorner, *op. cit.* 10. Good reviews from several points of view are given in Desai, *op. cit.* 531–66; Official evaluations and hopes may be found e.g. in *The New India* (Macmillans, NY, 1958, for the Planning Commission), 168–79, and *Towards a Self-reliant Economy*, 181–6. H. Tinker's 'Authority and community in village India', *Pacific Affairs*, 32 (1959), 354–75, underlines some fundamental assumptions and realities.

apathy and highly suspicious of all 'improvement'; in others, the major change as yet has been some acceptance of the concept that change of any sort is possible; in some there have been real self-help and even local initiatives. It is impossible to generalize. (Cf. pp. 342–3.)

It would be delusive to assume that techniques alone are the answer, or on the other hand, as the followers of Vinobha seem to believe, that only a spiritual revolution will help and that this is possible simply by appeals to conscience. Panchayati Raj, for example, is undoubtedly an appealing concept; sometimes it does open the way to real participation in affairs by the lowly and oppressed; too often it simply formalizes, on the local plane, the political intrigue to which caste factionalism, a culture very hospitable to that virus, gives such immense scope. To understand what is really happening in India one must penetrate behind the statistics and the official reports, behind the tendentious essays of the publicists, and fall back on such scattered samples as are available in the increasing number of scholarly studies in rural sociology, and in such honest reporting as Kusum Nair's *Blossoms in the Dust*. The picture is inevitably a confused one of success and failure, enterprise and frustration, hope and apprehension.

5. *Agrarian reform in Pakistan*

At Partition, the land situation in Pakistan was naturally as complicated as in India. Three-quarters of the cultivated land in East Pakistan was under the Permanent Settlement; in the Punjab, the Canal Colonies had a reasonably strong class of direct government tenants on sizeable holdings, but elsewhere *zamindari* was strong; Sind was officially *ryotwari*, but intermediaries had developed to such an extent that most actual cultivators were *haris*, tenants without occupancy rights and working on the *batai* share-crop system which gave them a nominal half, but often an actual third, of the crop. Partition led to a great exodus of non-Muslim landowners, but brought in many landless refugees; according to the 1951 Census, nearly half of the Punjab's 3,400,000 cultivators owned or claimed to own all the land they tilled, but this probably included many refugees resettled on evacuee land who 'regard[ed] themselves as owners, regardless of legislative definitions'.[57]

The objective in East Pakistan is the abolition of intermediaries altogether; *zamindars* are limited to a personal holding of 33 acres (13·3 ha.). One effect of the consequent strengthening of the position of former occupancy tenants, now in effect *ryots*, seems however to have been a weakening in that of non-occupancy tenants or *bargardars*, who are now in the position of landless labourers. Information on the full effects of legislation in East Pakistan is lacking.

In the West, Punjab legislation set a ceiling of 50 acres (20·2 ha.) for the landlord's personal cultivation, gave the option of purchasing proprietary rights to occupancy tenants and some security to non-occupancy tenants, and fixed a general proportion of 40% as the landlord's share of crop, water rate, and land

[57] Andrus and Mohammed, *op. cit.* 123.

revenue. In Sind, a certain amount of relief was given to *haris*. It was officially admitted that this led to more tensions than it allayed.

The Ayub Khan régime appears to have approached the problem in a manner at once more limited and more forceful. Individual ownership is limited to 500 acres (202 ha.) of irrigated or 1,000 acres of dry land; 2,200,000 acres (890,000 ha.) were resumed by government and by 1964 over half of this had been distributed to cultivators. When it is recalled that the cultivated area of West Pakistan is some 41,000,000 acres or 16,581,000 hectares, it is obvious that much remains to be done. At the same time, a vigorous programme of consolidation has been launched, and sub-division below 12·5 acres (5·1 ha.) in the former Punjab and 16 (6·5) in Sind has been prohibited.

One result of Partition was the disappearance of many non-Muslim money-lenders; although some Muslim groups, for example some Pathans, did practice usury, this was mainly in towns – before the war, as far afield as Rangoon. In Sind, the *hari* was entirely dependent on the *zamindar* for credit – on what terms may be imagined! – and the *zamindar* in turn on grain dealers; this was a factor in the extremely weak development of co-operation in the province, the Punjab being much stronger in this respect. In East Pakistan the number and membership of co-operative societies fell in the five years after Partition, and their working capital fell by a much greater percentage than their membership, which probably reflects the exodus of better-off Hindus. With the disappearance of many Hindu *banias* or moneylenders, the credit situation in East Pakistan thus became very serious, the only recourse of the small cultivator being sale or mortgage, a factor in the increase of *bargardars*.[58]

In West Pakistan, at least, there has been a considerable improvement. The Agricultural Development Bank, founded in 1961, works in both wings and is an important source of rural credit; in West Pakistan, rural credit co-operatives advanced Rs 11 crores in 1961–62, against 31·5 crores from the Bank and 1·8 as direct loans (*taccavi*) from the government. There has also been a considerable development of other forms of co-operation, including an experiment in co-operative mechanized farming covering 120 villages and 120,000 acres (49,000 ha.), of which over a third are already under mechanized farming.

The Pakistani equivalent of Community Development was initially the Village Agricultural and Industrial Development (AID) Programme; its methods and objectives were much the same, and it perhaps relied even more on (usually married) women helpers. With the institution of the Basic Democracies, AID has been subsumed into their activities, while many of its trained personnel have gone into the Agricultural Development Corporations of each wing: these are responsible for procuring and distributing fertilizers, implements, improved seeds, pesticides, and so on, as well as agricultural extension activities.

It is not likely that the results of such activities differ significantly as between Pakistan and India: against the general background of poverty, small holdings,

[58] See Andrus and Mohammed, *op. cit.* 136–56, for conditions in the mid-50s.

and backward techniques, regional differences within each country, the resultant of very diverse physical and social environments, are likely to be much more significant. For both countries, the general problem can be summed up by returning to the man/land or more precisely the man/food ratio.

V. THE GENERAL PROBLEM

Depressing as the agrarian picture is in both India and Pakistan, there are, especially in the former, some signs of more encouraging trends in what may be called the middle term, that is for the next ten or fifteen years, beyond which it would be useless to speculate. Fig. 8.16 suggests that the effort of the Indian Plans is at last beginning to show some results; the gap between targets and attainment is so far not desperately large. It must be remembered that, while the population curve has no actual dips and is likely to rise at a somewhat accelerating rate until the early 1970s (when the rate may begin to slacken off), the curve of food output is subject to marked ups and downs; even if the general prognosis is reasonably favourable, there may be very difficult spells, as for instance in the rainy season of 1964 and again 1965–66. The position is still generally marginal and sometimes critical. Nevertheless the fact that the area under foodgrains has risen less markedly (though more steadily) than that for output is in itself encouraging, bearing witness to an increase of productivity in the last few years, an increase not yet reflected in the available figures for unit yields. Better marketing and procurement may also have contributed to the gross apparent improvement.

It is however much too soon for optimism. The best of the possibilities for expansion have probably been taken up already; more and more the food for the ever-increasing population will have to come from intensification on already cultivated land. Both approaches, intensification by more fertilizers and better techniques, and expansion by irrigation and reclamation, are costly, and especially in the latter diminishing returns must always be reckoned with as more marginal options have to be taken up. Even before the shock of the 1961 Census, which showed a population well above most good projections, R. P. Sinha's careful study showed that only on very optimistic assumptions would there be any prospect of India reaching self-sufficiency in food by 1975–76; his conclusion after the Census was that, depending on the rate of rise of national income, the demand for food in the early 1960s would be between 94 and 115% greater than that of 1955–56.[59] This implies continuing food imports, which in the last resort must be paid for by exports, and it is clear that very careful adjustments must be made in the application of India's capital resources as between field and factory, private and public sectors. The machinery and the programmes for the development of India's mixed economy will be the subject of the succeeding chapters.

[59] *Op. cit.* 138–50, 183–5.

The prospect for Pakistan seems as difficult in the long term. Population increase is at least as great as in India; expansion of area has been much less proportionately, and it is very difficult to see how it can take place on any significant scale in the East, while in the West it must depend to a great extent on large and costly irrigation projects – and indeed on large-scale reclamation of waterlogged

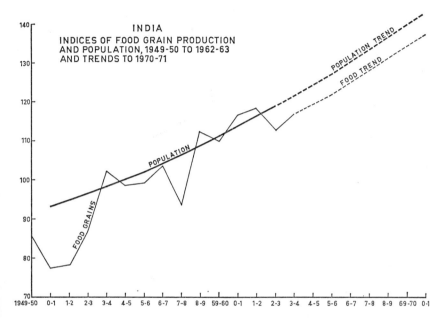

FIG 8.16 INDIA: TRENDS OF FOOD AND POPULATION. Based on figures in S. E. Johnson, *India's Food Situation and a Look Ahead* (Report to Ministry of Food and Agriculture, 1963). The food situation has improved since 1968–69; there was record grain production in 1969–70.

and salinized land if it is not to remain static. On the whole Pakistan is much poorer than India in resources and, perhaps to a lesser extent, in know-how; and in both the situation is much worse in East than in West Pakistan. West Pakistan has the makings of a well-found if dominantly agrarian country; it is impossible to be very hopeful about East Pakistan, despite its recent (but, objectively considered, still slight) industrial development.

Industry has a great part to play, not only on its own account but in the rehabilitation of agriculture; it is not, however, a simple panacea. It is not likely to develop rapidly enough to be able to do much more than take off new surpluses, the new cohorts of job-seekers, without making very great inroads on the vast pool of un- or under-employed labour in the countryside; and, while in time urbanization may be expected to have a large effect on fertility, this effect does not come about, even in Japan, in decades so much as in generations. Moreover industrial development itself will depend to a considerable extent on rural demand: its primary market is in the rural population, but one so far so depressed by poverty that industrial development itself must be inhibited if agrarian standards do not rise. The agrarian problem thus lies dead centre to all the workings of man in the sub-continent, and it is against an agrarian background that the drama of planning must be played out.

Postscript. Attention is drawn to two important recent articles. M. Harris, 'The cultural ecology of India's sacred cattle', *Current Anthropology*, 7 (1966), 51–66, is an authoritative discussion of many angles of this complex problem; J. G. Crawford, 'Planning under difficulties', *Australian Jnl of Politics and History*, 12 (1966), 155–76, talks of planning in general but pays special attention to the food/population problem.

CHAPTER 9

The Industrial Base: Power and Mineral Resources

INTRODUCTION

As long as agriculture directly supports 70% or more of the population, the agrarian problem will remain as the obvious and basic drag on progress towards a better living standard. Long term hopes and plans however lie as much – perhaps more – with industrialization. Agriculture and industry are symbiotic; the rural population provides both a market and labour supply, though limitless cheap labour does nothing to raise wages, efficiency or conditions. Conversely, industrial products are needed for the dams and power houses, fertilizers and machinery necessary for rural improvements. Equally important are the resources of power and minerals available. In assessing these, India and Pakistan are discussed separately with an analysis of power first, followed by minerals grouped according to their principal industrial users.

I. INDIA

A. POWER

1. Coal

With about 3% of world output, India shares eighth place with Japan. From a production of 500,000 tons in 1868, output increased to 6,000,000 tons by 1900, 30,000,000 tons in 1945 and has more than doubled since Independence; it is now over 60,000,000 tons a year and should reach 90,000,000 tons by the end of the Third Plan. Reserves are reasonable for the medium and poorer qualities (about 70,000,000,000 tons) but relatively low for the essential coking coals (2,500,000,000 tons), and of the total reserves, Fox's original estimate of only 20,000,000,000 tons less than 2,000 ft. (610 m.) deep and with ash content less than 25% still holds good, although it is now considered that workable coal goes down to 4,000 ft. (1,220 m.). In addition, there are reserves of about 10,000,000,000 tons of Tertiary coals. Most of the Lower Gondwana seams, which yield 95% of Indian coal, are fragments, preserved, by faulting, of four great Permian basins in the north of the plateau.[1] Linear series of exposures run along the Damodar,

---

[1] J. Coggin Brown and A. K. Dey, *India's Mineral Wealth*, (OUP, 3rd ed. 1955) is the source for most of the genetic information on minerals.

east-northeast/west-southwest to include minor fields in tributary valleys south
of the Son, thence along the southern side of the Narmada structural valley
where they are partly concealed by Deccan trap, but appear as small scattered
coalfields. A second series, running southeast/northwest from Talchir in Orissa
up the northern side of the Mahanadi valley, coalesces with the first in Baghel-
khand. Westwards, a less well marked series, also trending northwest/southeast,

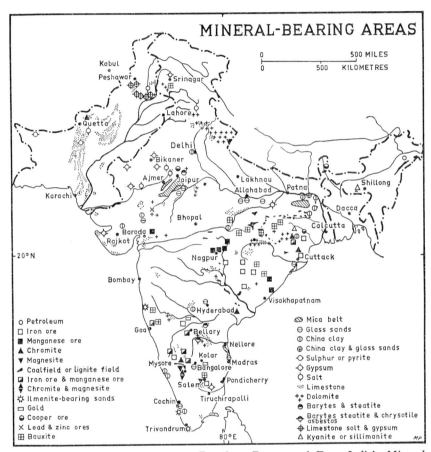

MINERAL-BEARING AREAS

o Petroleum	⊗ Mica belt
□ Iron ore	⊖ Glass sands
▣ Manganese ore	⊕ China clay
▲ Chromite	⊕ China clay & glass sands
▼ Magnesite	-O Sulphur or pyrite
◢ Coalfield or lignite field	-◇ Gypsum
◪ Iron ore & manganese ore	◊ Salt
♦ Chromite & magnesite	∴ Limestone
✫ Ilmenite-bearing sands	+:+ Dolomite
◻ Gold	● Barytes & steatite
⦿ Cooper ore	⬡ Barytes steatite & chrysotile asbestos
X Lead & zinc ores	⊕ Limestone salt & gypsum
⊞ Bauxite	△ Kyanite or sillimanite

FIG 9.1 MINERAL-BEARING AREAS. Based on Brown and Dey, *India's Mineral
Wealth* (OUP, 1955).

gives the minor fields extending from Chanda in Madhya Pradesh along the lower
Godavari to beyond the mining town of Singareni. The Damodar fields still
dominate; the easily mined seams, often over 80 ft. (24 m.) thick, of the Jharia
and Raniganj–Burdwan fields produce over 60% of the total; in the same area are
the Bokaro, Ramgarh and Karanpura fields, the latter with important new coking
reserves. Singareni, recently greatly developed by the National Coal Develop-

ment Council, produces some 5% from relatively undisturbed beds. Northwards, the fields of Madhya Pradesh, yielding about 10% of the total, are also
being developed partly by the NCDC to feed the new steel plants of Bhilai and
Rourkela; one of these, Korba (discovered by Blanford in 1870), is now linked by
rail to the main line 25 miles (40 km.) to the south near Bilaspur. One or two
small fields are being developed in Maharashtra.

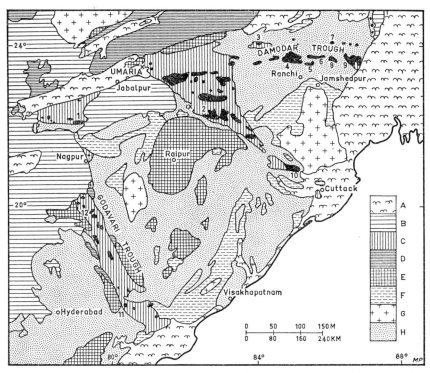

FIG 9.2 NORTH EASTERN PENINSULA: GEOLOGY AND COALFIELDS. Geology: A,
alluvium; B, Deccan and Rajmahal Lavas (Cretaceous-Tertiary); C, Gondwana
(Jurassic to Carboniferous, including marine Jurassic of coast and Umaria); D,
Vindhyan, etc. (Cambrian to Algonkian; E. Cuddapah and equivalents (Algonkian);
F, rocks of Dharwarian age (Huronian); G, Archaean crystalline and igneous rocks;
H, mainly ancient gneisses and granites. X, X, occurrences of marine Jurassic in
Peninsula. Coalfields in solid black; those mentioned in text: 1, Pench valley; 2,
Korba; 3, Daltonganj; 4, Karanpura; 5, Ramgarh; 6, Bokaro; 7, Jharia; 9, Rani-
ganj; 10, Talchir; 11, Singareni; 12, Chanda. Cf. Fig. 21.7.

Otherwise, there is some Eocene sub-bituminous and highly sulphurous coal
in Assam, and some reserve but virtually no production from the highly faulted
anthracite beds of Riasi in Jammu, and in the Rangit valley in Sikkim. Much
more important than either of these are the lignites of Rajasthan, under Eocene

limestones in Bikaner, which have been briquetted for railway use since 1898; and those of South Arcot in Madras associated with Miocene sandstones. Although discovered in 1934, exploitation only began here in 1961 as part of an integrated power, briquetting and fertilizer scheme at Neiveli. The *karewas* of Kashmir contain considerable low-grade deposits yielding some 5,000 tons a year.

Exploitation of coal began tentatively at Raniganj in 1774, but real development came only with the railways, still the main single consumer taking about 25% of output. But iron and steel plants are increasing their demand, and already take about another 18–20%. Power stations use 8% and other industries 20%, leaving the rest for bunkering, exports, and domestic consumption.[2] Development, apart from collieries owned by steel firms or the railways, was erratic and uncontrolled, with short term leases by the zamindars to inadequately capitalized syndicates. Some 80% of the output is still produced by the private sector, and the public sector concentrates on less profitable but strategically important developments. Efforts to rationalize some of the chaos of small workings have had only local and limited effect.

Labour problems remain acute, with the tribal people, who are an important element in the work force, returning to their fields at busy times. Housing conditions are only slowly improving, and mainly at the larger collieries, where provision of small holdings helps to stabilize the workers. On the physical side, problems of the industry stem from the shortage of coking reserves, and have led to attempts to conserve supplies – as well as to reduce subsidence: compulsory sand stowage instead of pillars in the thick, deep seams (fortunately with plenty of local raw material) and blending at the coke ovens; the Durgapur plant for instance uses only 20% of coking coal. The concentration of Indian coal in the northeast corner of the peninsula has always been a handicap, and today bottlenecks and storage, more than actual pithead output, appear as problems in attaining planned targets.

2. *Petroleum*

There appears considerable promise for oil potential in the general structural relations of the Indus–Ganga–Brahmaputra foredeep to the Himalayas, by analogy with Iran and Iraq, and with Burma; in the deltaic basin structures of the Indus and especially the Ganga–Brahmaputra, by analogy with the Gulf Coast of the USA, and to a lesser extent in various synclines of Tertiary rocks marginal to peninsular India.

The oldest exploited oilfield is in Assam. After one or two precocious and short-lived attempts at oil mining and even refining between 1879 and 1883, in the Upper Coal Measures near Jaipur and Makum, drilling was transferred to

[2] Figures throughout this section are averaged and approximated and are taken along with much useful information from the *Indian Minerals Yearbooks*, Indian Bureau of Mines, Nagpur.

the Digboi area in 1888; oil production began in 1892 in what has proved to be a very long-lived oilfield in an east-west anticline in Miocene impure sandstones, shales and clays.[3] The oil company opened a refinery at Digboi in 1900. Since Independence the company has continued exploration in the area under licence, and finding considerable further reserves at Nahorhatiya and Moran is developing these in partnership with the government, to supply the new refineries at Noonmati near Gauhati and Barauni in Bihar, by pipeline. Oil exploration in West Bengal from 1953 to 1960 added a great deal to geological knowledge, but no trace of oil was found.

In 1955, the government set up the Oil and Natural Gas Commission and widespread oil exploration has been carried out, with a good deal of technical collaboration from Roumania and particularly USSR. A further oilfield has been found in Assam, at Sibsagar, but the main new prospect opened out so far is in Gujarat. Geological and geophysical prospecting has revealed a down-faulted *graben* structure underlying the Tertiary sediments and alluvia of the plans around the head of the Gulf of Cambay; over a floor of Deccan Traps are some 5,700 ft. (1,900 m.) of alternating limestones and sandstones, shales and clays, from the Eocene to post-Miocene in date, within which are minor folds, including some oil or gas bearing anticlines, some slightly faulted. The Cambay or Lunej field appears likely to produce initially some 250,000 cu. m. of gas per day; reserves have not been estimated, though an early indication was of easy exploitation of shallow deposits rather than large reserves comparable to those of Sui in West Pakistan.[4]

The Anklesvar field may yield some 1,250,000 tons of oil per annum; reserves are not fully determined. The Kalol field contains oil and gas, but is not fully explored. A refinery has been built with Russian help at Koyali near Baroda.

In the Jurassic and Cretaceous shales, sandstones and limestones the slight anticlinal structure of Kutch are worth exploring further, though the probabilities seem to be against large accumulations of oil. But in Rajasthan the generally slight dip to northwest or westnorthwest is promising; hydrocarbons have been proved down-dip in Pakistan, and some may have migrated up-dip and may have been trapped in anticlines, etc., concealed by desert sands.

Exploration of the sea-bed off Kutch, Kathiawad and Cambay is regarded as well worth while, and several other possibilities on land and on the continental

---

[3] Legend has it that the Assam Railways and Trading Company was led towards buying up the oil rights from the earlier unsuccessful explorers by an elephant which returned to camp with traces of oil on its feet (*The Eastern Economist*, ND, 27 Dec. 1963, 133; this publication is a source for much of the quantitative data used). The Digboi field yielded some 1,558 million gallons of oil between 1892 and 1950 (Brown and Dey, *op. cit.* 100).

[4] United Nations, Proc. Second Symposium Development of Petroleum Resources of Asia and the Far East, Mineral Resources Development Series, No. 18, Vol. 1, New York, 1963, 239; this work is a major source for the following paragraphs. See also W. B. Metre and Y. Nagappa, 'Oil prospects in India', *India Quarterly*, 14 (1958), 154–65.

shelf may be considered together: (1) if the coast of Travancore was subject to down-faulting in mid-Miocene times, as Krishnan suspects, there may be a sequence of Upper Tertiary to recent sediments off-shore which may contain oil: (2) the sediments of the Thanjavur basin, Gondwana, Cretaceous and Tertiaries, thin on the western margin with the Archaeans, but up to 5,000 ft. (1,524 m.) deep on land, may continue under Palk Strait and the Gulf of Manaar and both land and sea-floor are worth exploring; (3) the continental shelf off Orissa may similarly include Cretaceous and Tertiary sediments worth exploring as also the whole of the submarine delta of the Ganga–Brahmaputra whose sediments may range from the Tertiary to the present.

To sum up, reserves at about the end of 1962 were some 45,000,000 tons in Gujarat and about the same in Assam. Production was just over 1,000,000 tons of crude petroleum, total home production just over 6,500,000 million, all petroleum-based products, i.e. including refining of imported petroleum mainly at dockside refineries; and total demand just over 9,000,000. Though demand is increasing about threefold per decade, production of crude oil is increasing at the moment a little faster, and the country's position is at least much stronger than might have been anticipated ten or fifteen years ago.

3. *Electricity*

The water power resources of the continent are considerable though not without limitations. The survey by J. W. Meares in 1918–24 arrived at an estimate of 12,680,000 kW as the potential at minimum flow; of this it was thought that 2,650,000 could be developed within twenty years. But by 1944 the total generating capacity was only 1,280,000 kW, and of this only 500,000 was hydro. Considering India's coal position this laggard pace is difficult to explain and perhaps not easy to defend.[5]

It is generally reckoned that Meare's estimate was less than half the real potential – current estimates range from 25,000,000 to 40,000,000 kW – and indeed schemes projected or under investigation already exceed his total.[6] Of course, it is not likely that all of these will be executed. Present total capacity is 6,030,000 (steam plant c. 3,500,000 kW, hydro-electric 2,000,000), the current target is 12,500,000 kW.

Since electricity was introduced to Bombay and Calcutta in 1899 over 2,000

[5] For a basic, even though dated, geographical account of high quality, see G. Kuriyan, *Hydro-electric Power in India* (Ind. Geog. Soc. Monograph No. 1, Madras, 1945); an up-to-date account is M. Datta, 'Electricity supply in India and its future', *Science and Culture* (Calcutta), 30 (1/1/64), 11–19.

[6] The Central Water and Power Commission's estimate is 40,000,000 kW at 60% load factor, or about 210,000,000,000 kWh annually, equivalent to 150,000,000 tons of coal. It is significant that one of the world's greatest single potentials is just within Tibet, at the Brahmaputra gorge and elbow through the Himalayas: it is estimated that an 11-mile headrace tunnel with a head of 7,500 ft. and a minimum unregulated flow of 30,000 cusecs (1 cusec=102m^3 per hour) would yield about 130,000,000,000 kWh per year, or about six times the present Indian total (Datta, *loc. cit.*).

thermal stations, mostly very small, have been set up for town supplies. About 1943 Bombay and Calcutta alone used 42%, and adding Kanpur and Ahmedabad, four cities with 1·5% of population accounted for over 50% of the total

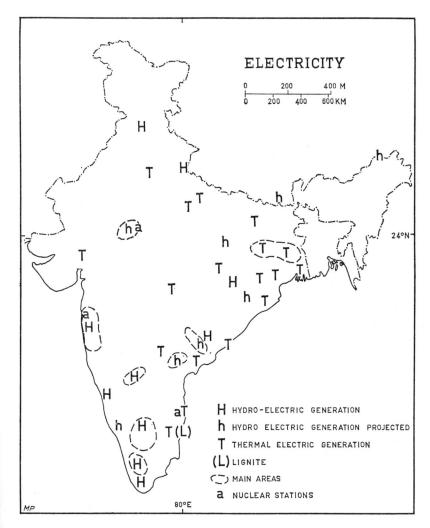

FIG 9.3 INDIA: ELECTRICITY. Hydel development so far is mainly along the Western Ghats and the Nilgiri-Annamalai group, and in montane Punjab; scheduled projects are largely in the Eastern Hills, with lower heads and larger rivers than on the Western Ghats. The very large potentials of the Himalayas present considerable engineering difficulties. Thermal power so far is related largely to urban markets, but location on fuel resources has begun in the Damodar and on the Neiveli lignite field in Madras (cf. Fig. 25.5).

electricity energy of India – which equalled a week's supply of the USA.[7] The concentration of coal in the Damodar kept costs high, on account of the long rail hauls, and it is not easy to generate centrally near the coal since water supplies are inadequate.[8] Hydro-electricity started fairly early. In 1902 Mysore opened the Sivasamudram installation, powering the goldfields 90 miles away – a notable achievement in its day. By 1915 about 130,000 kW were generated, 45,000 at Sivasamudram and 60,000 in the Tata schemes behind Bombay. Subsequent development and the main projects are shown on Fig. 9.3.

The main zones of hydro-electric potential are: (i) a belt along the Himalayas from Malakand to Assam (with an outlier on the Shillong Plateau); (ii) the Western Ghats; (iii) the Southern hills, especially on the Nilgiris and the middle Cauvery. In 1947 the three Tata plants above Bombay accounted for 47% of the total hydro-electric capacity of India, the Cauvery basin for 29%.

The main, and most obvious, limitation is the very pronounced seasonal variation of the rivers. All along the flanks of the Peninsular plateaus there are many sharp falls, some several hundred feet high, with an immense volume of water in the rains; but in the dry weather they are mere dribbles. Thus the Ken, a right-bank tributary of the Yamuna, varies from 300,000 to 5 cusecs, while even in sub-Himalayan Kumaon the Tons, with a maximum of 400,000, has fallen to 45.[9] Reservoirs must be large, and, as a rule, allow for a high rate of silting. In the Himalayas the slippery contorted shales which form much of the terrain are liable to slipping, and this is also the great seismic zone of India: earthquakes can be guarded against, but only by expensive specialized construction. In the Gangetic Plain, the deep Uttar Pradesh tube wells depend in part on thermal electricity but increasingly on that elegantly developed by concentrating the 146 ft. (44·5 m.) drop of the Ganga Canal into little falls of 8–12 ft. (2·4–3·7 m.); a principle which could obviously be extended at least in new canals.[10] When the first edition of this book was written, financial stringency was holding up developments and though there was obvious promise in the application of electricity to large and small scale industry, to lift irrigation and to village life, the general tone lay between caution and pessimism. Despite large development since then, the present position is of continued shortage of power. Plan targets have almost been fulfilled, but the generally dynamic tendencies of the economy tend to outstrip even this. The country has moved from using 'hydel' as a catch-word to a position where hydro-electricity must be considered in relation to new sources of thermal power, including lignite and nuclear energy. This broader strategy of power is better discussed under Planning (Chapter 11).

[7] P. J. Thomas, *India's Basic Industries* (Orient Longmans, Bombay, 1948), 134, 142.
[8] But half the electricity to be generated by the Damodar scheme will be thermal, using the great reservoirs of the project.
[9] T. R. Sharma, *Location of Industries in India* (Hind Kitabs, Bombay, 2nd ed., 1949), 213.
[10] For a useful regional account in detail, see A. S. Jahauni, 'Development of electric power in north west India', *NGJI* 2/1 (1956), 48–67.

4. Total energy budget: domestic fuel; the burning of cow-dung; alternative sources.[11]

The recent estimates of India's total energy budget give a total of 166,000,000 tons in coal equivalent. Commerce and industry consume 67,000,000 or 40%, (coal 55,000,000 or 33%, oil 10,000,000 or 6%, hydro-electricity 2,000,000 or 1%), while domestic consumers use 99,000,000 tons of coal equivalent or 60% (dung 46,000,000 tons or 28%, wood and charcoal 35,000,000 or 21%, various waste materials 18,000,000 or 11%). The total domestic use of energy for fuel, light, etc., is about 0.25 tons per capita per annum, and is similar to that in Latin America.

Wood and dung have the lowest thermal efficiency (17% and 11%), hence the highest real cost. Wood is derived from roadsides and wastelands, too often causing accelerated soil erosion, rather than properly maintained woodlands; if it could be properly controlled and charcoal manufactured so that the by-products are collected for use, this part of the pattern would be less wasteful. The dung used in this way is only 40% of the total dung: perhaps 30% is lost, though some of this may benefit the soil, while the 10% *systematically* applied as manure – increasingly composted with leaves and refuse – is much greater in areas with a good proportion of forests (which also have sources of green manure) than in largely treeless tracts. Taking the All-India average proportion burned as an index ratio of 100, well forested States like Madhya Pradesh or Himachal Pradesh may burn as little as 10 to 15%, ill-forested States like Uttar Pradesh or Bengal 180% to 220% or even more.

A satisfactory household plant for the production of dung gas for cooking and (less satisfactorily) for lighting, has been produced by the Indian Agricultural Institute in New Delhi. The cost is Rs. 350, though only Rs. 80 is for mechanical parts that could not be produced locally in a village. It will produce 100 cu. ft. (2.8 m³) of gas daily – ample for the needs of an average family – from the dung of four animals, and the manurial value of the dung is not lost. In the cities, the processing of sewage for gas production could yield similar results – for Delhi 90% of the fuel needs for cooking could be met in this way. It is estimated that if dung burned could be saved, the equivalent of the output of twelve Sindris in manurial value could be applied to the fields in ammonium sulphate equivalent alone, while there are also phosphates present. So considerable capital investment would be justified; the great difficulty is that twelve Sindris would be easier to control than a myriad family plants in over 500,000 villages. But it is difficult to think of a more constructive task for Community Development.

---

[11] This section is compiled from: P. Pant, 'The development of India', *Scientific American*, 209 (1963), 189–206; *Domestic Fuels in India* (Natl Ccil Applied Economic Research; Asia, Bombay, 1959); J. Kishen, 'Domestic fuel consumption in India', *Jnl Sci. & Indl Research* (ND), 18A/10 (1959), 458–66; E. G. Rao, 'Evaluation of the domestic fuel situation in India . . .', *Jnl Inst. Engineering India*, 44 (1963), 49–66. Cf. also fn. 30 to Chap. 8.

B. MINERALS

Apart from the serious shortage of coking coals India has a rich endowment for heavy metallurgy: not only reserves of high grade iron ore hardly to be matched anywhere in the world, but good resources of alloy minerals, fluxes and refractories. She is weaker in the non-ferrous metals as a group, especially copper, although bauxite resources are good. She has almost a monopoly of mica and holds a strong position in the sources for atomic energy.

Juxtaposition of down-faulted sedimentaries including coal, with the rich concentration of iron and alloy minerals in the Archaean metamorphics, gives the peninsula its dominant position, especially the plateau fringes of Chota Nagpur. It seems unlikely that the hegemony of the northeast quarter of the Peninsula will ever be seriously challenged, but prospecting and the development of power are producing important mining areas in the south and will eventually make much more of the mineral resources of the Himalayas.

1. Bases for iron and steel

The Dharwarian and Cuddapah rocks of the eastern half of the Peninsula contain some of the world's largest reserves of *iron ore*, mainly haematites and magnetites of high iron content – 60–70% Fe. The most important exploitation lies on the northern flanks of the Orissa Hills, in what were the states of Keonjhar, Bonai and Mayurbhanj and in Singhbhum District, Bihar.[12] Here 'there is what appears to be a range of iron running almost continuously for 40 miles', and this alone is estimated to hold 2,700,000,000–3,000,000,000 tons of metallic iron – 'thought to be the largest and richest deposits of iron perhaps in the world, surpassing in magnitude the Lake Superior ores.'[13] The ores occur in close association with banded haematite quartzites in the Dharwar schist series within the Archaean, probably because of secondary enrichment of the iron content of zones within volcanic series by re-arrangement of iron by later solutions.[14] This ironfield extends southwards into Chhattisgarh, Bastar (which jungly District has at least 600,000,000 tons), and southern Madhya Pradesh, where whole hills of haematite several hundred feet high are found; Madhya Pradesh has at least 1,100,000,000 tons. In the Damodar Valley the ironstone shales of the Raniganj coalfield have reserves of about 400,000,000 tons of lower-grade ore (35–40% Fe). Mysore has 250,000,000–600,000,000 tons, all over 42% Fe, and 100,000,000 about 65%. The magnetite (35–40% Fe) resources of Salem are unknown but at least to be reckoned in hundreds of millions of tons.

After this it seems an anti-climax to note the vast quantities of lower-grade

[12] The ores were discovered by a pioneer Bengali geologist, P. N. Bose, in 1904 (Brown and Dey, *op. cit.* 178); for a regional account, see below, 713–15, and also P. P. Karan, 'Iron mining in Singhbhum and Mayurbhanj Region', *Economic Geography*, 33 (1957), 349–61.

[13] G. B. Jathar and S. G. Beri, *Indian Economics* (OUP, Bombay, 7th ed., 1942), I.29–30; D. N. Wadia, *Geology of India* (Macmillan, London, 3rd ed. revised, 1961), 476.

[14] Brown and Dey, *op. cit.* 179–80, where other theories are also quoted.

(25–40% Fe) lateritic ores; the magnetite sands of the Konkan beaches, derived from erosion of the Deccan lavas and used for primitive smelting; the Dharwarian ores of Goa and Ratnagiri (Maharashtra); the large deposits of 40–60% Fe in Kumaon; and the association of poorer ores with the Tertiary coal of Assam.

Reserves of the major deposits of high grade ores amount to about 8,000,000,000 tons, but reserves of lower grade ores are very large and the Third Plan quotes total reserves of almost 22,000,000,000 tons. So superfluous is this richness that the Jamshedpur and Asansol furnaces for long did not use ore much below 60% Fe content, and some consignments are 69% Fe, 'the theoretical composition of pure haematite being 70% iron and 30% oxygen'.[15] However, the trend is towards less selective mining followed by careful mixing in the sintering process, to conserve resources. The main drawback of Indian ore is that much contains too little phosphorus for the relatively cheap Bessemer process, though some Deccan ores may have as much as 0·15% phosphorus. Fluxes are usually available. Large new ironfields are being developed, some for new iron and steel plants, others for ore exports mainly to Japan and Eastern Europe. Thus the Kiriburu field in Bihar and Orissa developed with Japanese aid has yielded ores for export, though it will be used eventually for Durgapur and Bokaro plants. It will be replaced, for export purposes, by a new field in Orissa where the Bailadila Range cliffs of haematite are being developed in association with a Japanese steel firm, and a rail link is being built to Visakhapatnam. It is possible that one of the new Fourth Plan steel mills may be built in this region; reserves here amount to some 3,500,000,000 tons with some limonite in addition. Similarly Mysore, which has rich reserves within 100–200 miles of the west coast ports, has recently explored new ones with reserves of 120,000,000 tons. The easily exploited ores of Goa, recently acquired by annexation, have a somewhat lower iron content. Again a future steel plant is being considered for either Goa or Hospet. Similar ores with a half million ton reserve are being developed at Ratnagiri. It is clear that even with the current output of 12,000,000 tons a year considerably increased, India's iron ore reserves can be reckoned in millennia rather than centuries.

Manganese, as Sondhi points out, has been an Indian export since 1891, second only to iron ore as an earner of foreign exchange.[16] With a production of well over a million tons she is equal to South Africa, and together they are second to USSR. Production has fluctuated with world demand and competition and still tends to do so in spite of increased home demands as steel making progresses. The chief problem is the reduction of the phosphorus content and the beneficiation of low grade ores to meet export standards under Indian conditions.

The ores are widely distributed in peninsular India in either tabular deposits in pre-Cambrian metamorphics, or subsequently formed or enriched deposits from weathering of manganiferous rocks or lodes. The Keonjhar Hills of Orissa

---

[15] A. M. Heron, *Mineral Resources* (OPIA, No. 28, 1945), 13.
[16] V. P. Sondhi, 'Manganese ores in India', *Indian Minerals*, 11/3 (1957), 167–84.

provide about a third, the northwest Districts of Mysore and Balaghat in Madhya Pradesh about a fifth each, Bhandara in Maharashtra and Rajasthan the remainder. Reserves are in the region of 185,000,000 tons of which under 50,000,000 are of high quality.

2. *Other minerals used in the engineering industries*

Unfortunately, the non-ferrous metals are not so well represented in Indian resources; some are completely lacking, such as tungsten, cobalt, and nickel, and others are inaccessible or difficult to work. *Lead and zinc* have largely to be imported. The only producing area is at Zawar in Rajasthan with an output of about 150,000 tons and reserves of 8,000,000–10,000,000 tons. Lead is smelted at Tundoo in Bihar and a little silver obtained in the process. The zinc, until now sent to Japan for refining, will be processed at the plant now under way at Debori near Udaipur. *Copper* too is a deficit mineral: only 10% of needs are produced from the 80-mile (129 km.) copper belt along the Subarnarekha southeast of Jamshedpur, where there are reserves of 3,000,000–4,000,000 tons. But there are reserves of 20,000,000 tons in Khetri and Dariba Districts in Rajasthan, and a smelter and refinery are under way. Some exploitation of the Sikkim copper is in progress as a joint venture with the Sikkim Government. Expansion of the existing refinery at Ghatsila in Bihar, with the new one at Khetri, may ultimately produce up to half India's needs for alloys and electrical industries; but these are always growing. It will also produce useful side-products of nickel, sulphur and selenium. Other, more doubtful, reserves have been found in Hassan (Mysore), and in the outer Himalayas. All Indian ores are low in copper content – about 2% only.

Of the abrasives, *corundum* is obtained from surface deposits in Sidhi District in Madhya Pradesh and to a lesser extent from Salem (Madras) and Hassan (Mysore), while *garnets* from Sikar District (Rajasthan) are still cheaper than the synthetic product; the Panna *diamonds* (Madhya Pradesh) provide only a quarter of needs, the rest being imported.

Chromite production also fluctuates with overseas demand, for over 95% of production is still exported to Japan and Europe for alloys. The bulk comes from ultra-basic intrusions in the Baula Hills of Cuttack and Keonjhar in Orissa, which also have the biggest proportion of a total reserve of 4,000,000–5,000,000 tons. Total output is in the region of 45,000 tons, the rest coming from Singbhum (Bihar), Bandhara (Maharashtra) and Hassan (Mysore). Within India chromite is only used at present for chemical (mainly tanning) and refractory uses. The main problem is the beneficiation of low grade ores to a marketable standard. *Vanadium* is not exploited although interest and exploration are increasing with the demand for alloys and atomic energy. There is a reserve of over 20,000,000 tons, along with the iron ores of Singbhum and bordering parts of Orissa; but it can also be obtained from steel slag and alumina sludge.

There are also adequate resources of refractory materials: *fireclays* are exploited in Sambalpur to provide Jamshedpur's needs, and there are significant quantities produced in the Damodar coalfields, Jabalpur (Madhya Pradesh), and South Arcot and Tiruchchirapalli in Madras. There is a small export to Pakistan and Burma. Production of *magnesite* has greatly increased to over 200,000 tons a year, from the open cast workings occurring as veins in the intrusive masses of the Chalk Hills near Salem in Madras; but there are big reserves here, in Mysore and in the Almora hills, the last to be opened up. Some 15% is exported, and the rest used for furnace linings and some chemical processes. *Asbestos* is however in short supply, all but 5% being imported; home supplies come from Rajasthan but there are fair deposits of chrysotile asbestos in the Andhra Cuddapah series. *Kyanite* from perhaps the largest deposit in the world, at Lapse Buru near Jamshedpur, is taken mainly from surface deposits and exported; only a little is used in India for high-grade refractory bricks, and for insulator and heater elements. *Sillimanite* is also a silicate of aluminium, and shares the very high heat resisting qualities of kyanite which make both suitable for purposes where fireclays break down. It is, however, a controlled export since the reserves in the only workings (in the Khasi Hills) are not large. Limestone for flux is plentiful and new deposits are being developed for instance in Durg District (Madhya Pradesh) for Bhilai, and Sandigarh's calcite marbles in Orissa for Rourkela (see also building materials, below). Quartz for ferro-silicon is also abundant.

3. Minerals used in the electricity industry

The chief user of aluminium is the electrical industry, especially since its substitution for the costly and scarce copper is desirable; it is important too for innumerable consumer goods including ubiquitous drinking vessels and plates. With plentiful reserves, in the region of 270,000,000 tons, of which some 73,000,000 are of high quality, India exports *bauxite* to Japan, Australia and Europe, while importing about two-thirds of her aluminium needs; such a situation reflects of course an early stage of development of an industry, in this case linked with the high power needs for the conversion of purified alumina to aluminium. Bauxite is obtained from the scarp faces of thick lateritic blankets on the peninsular plateaus; a situation making exploitation difficult. The main source of this type is in west Bihar, where workings feed the ore first by aerial ropeway and thence to the Lohardaga railhead. Similar deposits in Orissa await access, and in Madhya Pradesh those at Amarkanatak may be developed with Rihand power. The high level deposits of Kolhapur (Maharashtra) and the Shevaroy Hills (Madras) will be exploited with Koyna and Mettur power. Processing takes place at the integrated works at Jaykaynagar near Asansol, using thermal power; ore is also purified to alumina at Muri and converted by hydro electric power at Hirakud in Orissa and at Alwaye in Kerala, involving high transport costs in the latter case, in order to benefit from cheap power.[17]

[17] P. Dayal, 'Location and development of the aluminium industry in India', *NGJI* 4/2 (1958), 67–78.

Low level laterites, being more accessible, have been worked for many years at Katni in the Son Valley in Madhya Pradesh and still supply the cement and refractory industries; reserves are good. But the leading producer in this rapidly changing and developing industry is Gujarat; here low level laterites round Kaira provide bauxite for export from Okha port.

All the exploited peninsular bauxites have aluminium content between 50% and 60%; near Riasi and Poonch in Jammu are Eocene fossil laterites which reach 80%; unfortunately they are at heights from 2,000 to 5,000 ft. (610–1,525 m.), and lack at least existing power development; it seems Bhakra will have none to spare.

Bauxite production has expanded from under 20,000 tons in 1947 to over 500,000 tons. There is sufficient caustic soda for the alumina plants from the growing heavy chemical industry; the essential catalyst, cryolite, has previously been entirely imported from Greenland, but progress is reported in the home manufacture of a synthetic cryolite.

India produces almost 90% of the world's *mica* – one of the fundamentals of the electrical industry – and exports almost all her annual output of about 30,000 tons. About half of this comes from the Bihar mica belt, lying along the northern fringes of the Chota Nagpur Plateau in Hazirabagh; the other half comes almost equally from Nellore in Andhra and Bhilwara in Rajasthan. In Bihar, mica is obtained from innumerable primitive workings under difficult conditions along the forested scarps. Exploitation has shifted steadily eastwards over the last fifty years, echoing in a way the shifting cultivation of the hill tribes who comprise the work-force, and following similar laws of diminishing returns due to primitive exploitation.[18] There is increasing attention to quality control and export incentives to beat the potential competition from Brazil and from synthetics, not easy to bring home to the jungle miner or cottage worker splitting 'books' of mica.

India is very well placed for the raw materials necessary for atomic energy. Although known to exist for more than fifty years, it is only recently that workable deposits of *uranium* have been identified in Singbhum and Rajasthan, associated with pre-Cambrian thrust planes. More erratic sources are the mica-bearing pegmatites of Bihar. But her greatest strength lies in the *monazite* which is one of the minerals won from the black sands of the western littoral of south India.[19] *Thorium* from the monazite was first exploited by German, then British, interests for gas mantles; this use has now been superseded by the rise of thorium as an even more important factor in atomic power production than uranium itself.[20] Placer deposits in Bihar may double the known beach sand reserves of 1,500,000 tons in Travancore. Even higher amounts of thorium are

[18] P. P. Karan, 'The Bihar mica belt', *NGJI* 4/1 (1958), 16–34.

[19] P. Viswanathan, 'Beach sands of South India', *Science and Culture*, 27/1 (1961), 16–21, recounts the discovery of the Kerala beach sands in Kerala by C. W. von Schomberg, after walking in vain along the east coast from the Godavari to Tuticorin.

[20] D. N. Wadia, 'India and the Atomic Age', *Science and Culture*, 23/6 (1957), 264–70.

found in the rare *cheralite* also obtained from the black sands along with *zirconium*. The latter, comprising some 6% of the sand, is essential in reactors as a refractory, as well as having ceramic uses; and resources which are the world's largest are now naturally jealously guarded. *Graphite* is also a strategic mineral now, because of its use in reactors; although it can be obtained from the chimney deposits of oil-fired power stations, research is going on along the Eastern Hills in the Khondalite series analogous to the graphite bearing rocks of Ceylon.

4. *Minerals used in chemical industries, and for glass and ceramics*

These are multifarious and only a broad review can be given; but from the humble but basic common salt, to the vital sources for fertilizers, they are of fundamental significance. *Salt* has historic associations and a wide range of modern industrial uses. It also is exported, mainly to Japan. Over 80% of the annual output of some 3,500,000 tons is from the evaporation of sea water in the tidal flats of Kutch and Maharashtra, with important contributions from Andhra and Madras coasts. The delta coast of Bengal is too wet for evaporation and the sea is too fresh; hence a small export to East Pakistan. Some 7% is produced from Lake Sambhar and the Pachbhadra beds of Rajasthan, and developments are planned in refining and even iodising to provide for the goitrous hill tracts. The magnesium chloride from the Kutch salts is also exported. There is a small output from the rock salts of Mandi (Himachal Pradesh), with further development planned.

Gypsum is used as an agent to retard the setting of cement, but two-thirds of the output are now used in the converting of ammonia to ammonium sulphate, and as a direct source for sulphuric acid; this is important since India lacks any sulphur resource. The pure gypsums of Jammu and Garwhal are used in plaster of Paris and as paint fillers, but production is negligible. Over 90% of the gypsum produced comes from the Bikaner, Barmer and Nagaur Districts of Rajasthan, and has increased by some 200% since supplies from the Salt Range were cut off in 1947. Reserves are good, but are becoming more difficult to work as the accessible manually quarried beds are depleted; the gypsum goes to Sindri, but a local fertilizer plant is planned. Tiruchchirappalli and Coimbatore, both in Madras, provide about 4% each of the total. In all, India is self sufficient, but there is some anxiety about the future as demands increase.

Sources for phosphatic fertilizers are much more deficient. India is able only to produce some 10% of her needs, and her twenty or more super-phosphate factories rely on imports from North Africa. Of the native output, over 90% comes from manually quarried lenses of *apatite* associated with the copper, uranium and magnetites of Singbhum; it is owned and chiefly utilized by Indian Iron and Steel in the making of the highly phosphorous pig iron. There is a small production from similar rocks in Visakhapatnam, and investigation is proving fair quantities of phosphatic nodules in Cretaceous clays in Tiruchchirappalli although little is exploited yet and there are problems of beneficiation. Some phosphate is obtained from monazite at the Rare Earth plant at Alwaye in Kerala. These sands too contain *ilmenite*, a major source of titanium oxide for pigment. Some 95% is exported, unlike the carefully guarded strategic monazite from the same source. The concentration is high – even the tailings from previous workings have a higher proportion of heavy minerals than the virgin sands exploited in Australia; yet poor methods and standards have led to economic difficulties in export.[21]

Several minerals are used as fillers in paper, textiles and paints; of these *barytes* (obtained from fissure veins associated with trap sills) from Kurnool has an export surplus, and a plant to produce barium chemicals is planned at Kothu-gudum in Andhra. *Steatite*, which is tending to replace kaolin and is used also in fertilizers, is also exported to Europe; the bulk comes from large pockets in the metamorphics of Anantpur and Chittoor in Andhra, which with Sirohi in Rajasthan also produces an increasing quantity of calcite as a filler and for insecticides. Adequate quantities of *Fullers earth*, used in bleaching and purifying oils, are found in Jaisalmer and Jodhpur and may even have a potential export value; it is of course the *dhobi* or washerman's main raw material, apart from a slab of stone or concrete. Another bleaching clay, with increasing demand in association with oil drilling, is *bentonite* found in Gujarat.

Felspar supplying the potteries of Jabalpur is mined from the pegmatites of Ajmer, and can be exported given better freight rates, and quartz has already been mentioned.

5. *Building materials*

The great majority of houses are built directly of mud (*terre pisé*) or of mud bricks, and stones may be set in mud-mortar or in lime derived directly from *kankar* concretions in the alluvium or from rock. The most important large scale exploitation is that of limestone for the cement industry rapidly expanding to meet the demands of today. There seem to be almost inexhaustible reserves in the Vindhyan limestones of the Son Valley; their relationships to steel needs have already been mentioned. In the south the deposits in Tiruchchirappalli are mainly used for cement. The bulk of the output, now in the region of 15,000,000 tons a year and planned to reach 30,000,000 tons by the end of the Third Plan, comes from the relatively small number of big concerns; but there is a multitude of small-scale quarries. India's building stones are justly famous: good *granites* and *slates* (the latter mostly Himalayan), the unique Porbandar *miliolite* and many meretricious *marbles*. *Deccan Lava* is a sombre material, giving dignity to even unimaginative architecture, and there is perhaps no more beautiful stone in the world than the Vindhyan *sandstone* of Akbar's rose red palaces. Nor should the humble *laterite* be forgotten, whether squared for tanks, temples or new village housing, or crushed to rubble and red dust on the local roads.

And so, finally to *gold*, impossible to class with any of our groups, but so

[21] P. Viswanathan, *op. cit.*

important to the Indian; for it is even – perhaps especially with toaay's anxieties – his personal bank. Its national importance is clear – and at times of crisis the government appeals to women especially to give gold jewellery to their country. It is mined solely from the Dharwarian quartz reefs of Mysore: at Kolar, which still produces three-quarters of the output, yields have been steadily decreasing as the mines extended to deeper and less productive levels; some go down 9,000 ft. (2,743 m.). The Hutti mines (Raichur District) are increasing output, and there is active exploration of the possibilities of re-opening the old fields of the Wynaad on the Mysore–Madras border and in Andhra.

It has been said that India is a rich land inhabited by poor people. The present balance sheet of India's power and mineral resources is given in the table below. The dominance of iron, manganese and mica in the export list, and of petroleum in the import list, is clear; but of course minerals can be vital even though not needed in large quantities, as with copper or nickel. Japan is the principal trading partner, followed by the countries of Eastern Europe, but USA and UK are important customers for manganese and mica.

INDIA'S MINERAL BALANCE SHEET

Self-sufficiency	Exportable surplus in order of value	Imports necessary in order of value
Coal	Iron ⎫ 60%	Petroleum (75%)
Limestones	Manganese ⎭	Copper
Bentonite	Mica (20%)	Zinc
Calcite	Coal	Lead
China Clay	Teminite	Asbestos
Fullers Earth	Kyanite	Apatite
Garnet	Magnesite	Tin
Ochre	Chromite	Diamonds
Vermiculite	Bauxite	Nickel
	Sillimanite	Tungsten
	Barytes	Wolfram
	Fireclay	Cobalt
	Felspar	

II. PAKISTAN

A. POWER

I. *Coal*

Coal reserves, estimated variously, but probably between 160,000,000 and 200,000,000 tons, are concentrated in West Pakistan.[22] Mainly sub-bituminous Eocene coals, they are friable, with high sulphur and ash content, and non-

[22] R. R. Platt (ed.), *Pakistan: A Compendium* (American Geogl Soc., NY, 1961). Although already partly out of date, this is a useful source used throughout this section along with J. R. Andrus and A. F. Mohammed, *The Economy of Pakistan* (OUP, 1958).

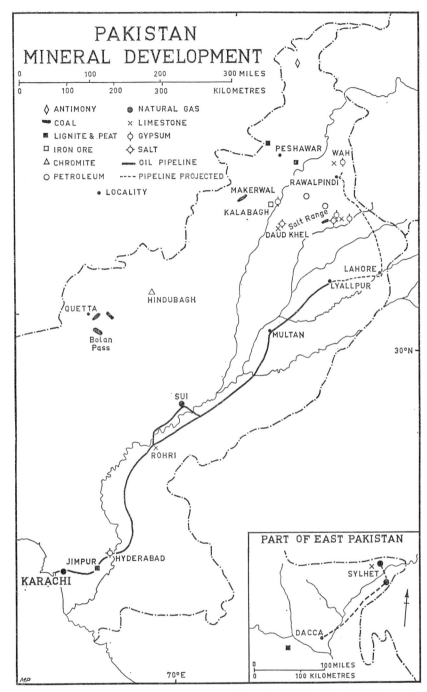

PAKISTAN
MINERAL DEVELOPMENT

| 0 | 100 | 200 | 300 MILES |
| 0 | 100 | 200 | 300 | KILOMETRES |

◊ ANTIMONY   ◉ NATURAL GAS
▬ COAL   × LIMESTONE
▪ LIGNITE & PEAT   ◊ GYPSUM
▢ IRON ORE   ◇ SALT
△ CHROMITE   ── OIL PIPELINE
○ PETROLEUM   ---- PIPELINE PROJECTED
● LOCALITY

PESHAWAR
WAH
RAWALPINDI
MAKERWAL
KALABAGH
DAUD KHEL
Salt Range
LAHORE
LYALLPUR
HINDUBAGH
QUETTA
Bolan
Pass
MULTAN
30°N
SUI
ROHRI
PART OF EAST PAKISTAN
SYLHET
JIMPUR HYDERABAD
KARACHI
DACCA
70°E

| 0 | 100 MILES |
| 0 | 100 KILOMETRES |

MP

FIG 9.4 PAKISTAN: MINERAL DEVELOPMENT. Based on K. S. Ahmad, *A Geography of Pakistan* (1964). The pipeline should be shown as gas, not oil.

coking; exploitation is difficult because beds are thin and tilted, and the fields remote. Improved methods and intensive investigation of new reserves have almost doubled production in the last decade, to close on a million tons a year, but this is still only half of requirements, and higher grade coals are imported. Briquetting plants at Quetta and Rawalpindi produce fuel usable in foundry and factory from the poor quality lignites.

The highest production comes from Makerwal, the trans-Indus continuation of the Salt Range fields, themselves worked for over eighty years. But the biggest reserves are in Baluchistan, where the Khost–Sharig field along the Sibi railway has Pakistan's only coking coal, and her largest reserves. A newly developing field in the Sor Range, just east of Quetta, is seen as a useful asset to a backward region, and new roads and increased capacity on the Bolan railway are planned to meet its needs and those of the Mach field in the Bolan Pass area.[23]

Apart from these areas, there is some exploitation in the Kohistan region in western Sind, and of the poor lignites of the far northwest. East Pakistan has only the waterlogged peats and lignites of Sylhet,[24] Mymensingh and Faridpur, difficult to dry and of poor quality; coking coal is reported from Bogra too deep to mine, and there are high quality deposits in Paharpur which are thought to be extensive and economically viable, a continuation of the Bihar belt.

2. *Petroleum*

The most prolonged and expensive exploration by American and British companies, and now by the Pakistan Oil and Gas Development Commission which uses Soviet technicians, has failed to find commercial deposits beyond those of the small Potwar field; this in spite of the seemingly favourable geological conditions in the Tertiaries of the old 'Sind Gulf' in the west, and of Assam in the east. Drilling and access are difficult in the western deserts and the eastern jungles. Only a fifth of the country's quite modest needs (half of it used for diesel locomotives) are produced from the five small fields in the Punjab. The newer Bikasser wells produce more crude oil than the older Kaur and Dhulian fields, but it is of poorer quality and too thick to pipe to the refinery at Mogra; it is railed there. The Dhulian field has a small quantity of associated gas, now exploited.

One big refinery at Karachi will be joined by another within a short time; both relying on supplies from the Persian Gulf. East Pakistan so far imports all her oil ready refined.

3. *Natural gas*

In the course of oil prospecting in 1962, natural gas was discovered at Sui in the barren Bugti Hills 350 miles (563 km.) north of Karachi. Four other fields were

[23] F. Hussein, 'Structure and coal reserves of the Sor Range–Doghari Coalfield', *Oriental Geogr.* (Dacca), 5/2 (1961), 137–44.
[24] N. Ahmad, 'Peat deposits of the Faridpur District, East Pakistan', *ibid.* 5/1 (1961), 59–62.

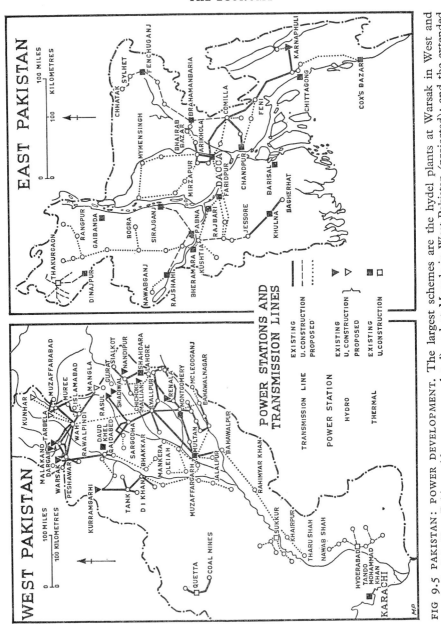

FIG 9.5 PAKISTAN: POWER DEVELOPMENT. The largest schemes are the hydel plants at Warsak in West and Mangla in West Pakistan (projected); and the extended

soon found in the same region, and a big step was taken in solving Pakistan's fuel problems. Reserves would last four hundred years at present rates of consumption; even with vast increase, there is not less than fifty years supply.[25] A pipeline to Karachi, something of an engineering masterpiece as it crosses incredibly difficult terrain, began operating in 1955, serving industrial users at Hyderabad and Rohri. A branch goes to Multan 200 miles (322 km.) to the northeast from a point near the Gudu Barrage. At Karachi, the gas supplies both domestic and industrial needs as well as providing raw material for big new petro-chemical plants, and natural gas runs power stations at Karachi, Multan, Sukkur, Hyderabad and Lyallpur. The Multan branch will one day reach the new capital of Islamabad and serve the Punjab towns, supplementing the seasonally variable hydro-electricity and scarce coal reserves. The local tribal people in the new gas fields have benefited by lease payments and the new townships are bringing changes from a nomadic to sedentary way of life. In East Pakistan, natural gas has been found at four places in the Sylhet region; of purer quality but inferior quantity to the western supplies, the gas so far only supplies the Fenchuganj fertilizer plant (where again it is raw material as well as power) and the Chattak cement factory. There will be a pipeline to Dacca.

4. *Electricity* (Fig. 9.5)

From a very meagre consumption of power in 1947 (about half coming from Indian sources), Pakistan now has an installed capacity which is outstripping demand, although increasing industrialization and decreasing costs of production should soon reverse this position. There has been a big change too from almost complete dependence on thermal plants to the development of hydro-electricity and natural gas, but steam plants still play a very important part. West Pakistan again dominates, with an installed capacity of about 500,000 kW in 1963, three-fifths of which is accounted for in almost equal amounts by the Warsak multi-purpose project and the Multan natural gas plant which is now being doubled. Integrated development of water and power was undertaken in 1958, and great strides have been taken since then. Natural gas also supplies fuel for plants at Hyderabad, Sukkur and Karachi. The old hydro-electric plant at Malakand in the northwest has been doubled in capacity. And three new canal fall projects have been added to the Rasul scheme, on the Jhelum and Chenab Canals. All the stations are linked by a Primary Grid ensuring continuity of supply throughout the country.

East Pakistan has about half the installed capacity of the west, the biggest single contributor being the Karnaphuli project. But thermal plants still dominate in total output, the bulk being in the Dacca–Narayanganj region, and in other urban centres. There is as yet no widespread grid although one is planned to distribute Karnaphuli power.

[25] G. Whittington, 'Natural gas resources of Pakistan', *Tijdschrift voor Econ. en Soc. Geografie*, 53 (1962), 163–4; also Table XIII.

B. MINERALS

Unfortunately Pakistan's mineral resources can be quickly summarized; she lacks coal and iron in anything like the quantity needed for major industry, and remoteness is a serious drawback to developing such minerals as she has. There is, however, a good base for chemicals in the Salt Range complex. And the discovery and development of natural gas, first in the west and now in the east, has given tremendous impetus to power and industry.

The only known deposits of high grade *iron ore* lie in two extremities of the country – in Chitral and in northwest Baluchistan where they are too remote to exploit. Low grade ores (35–45% Fe) have been found in Mianwali District and experiments to determine their commercial value are in progress. *Chromite* is the only metallic ore mined in any quantity. The source is an ultra-basic intrusion in the Zhob valley worked since 1903, by primitive methods, and exported to Japan and UK. But production is a pathetic drop in the bucket of world output and it is subject to market fluctuations. The *antimony* mines of Chitral send small quantities across 175 miles (282 km.) of mountain road to a railhead. There are reported to be workable *manganese* deposits in the Las Bela region in the south of Baluchistan. *Fire clays* are being produced in increasing amounts from the Salt Range.

The chemical industry has a much firmer base: *salt* from the Salt Range and its trans-Indus continuation has been a government monopoly since Mogul times at least, and has been mined for over 1,000 years. The Khewra mine is the most mechanized of the three major workings which extract the salt from the vast, thick beds that stretch from Jhelum to Indus and beyond. Other centres are Warcha and Kalabagh, the latter now only of local importance; the layers here are thinner. Associated with the salt beds are large masses of *gypsum* mined for cement and also for the ammonium sulphate plant at Daud Khel (p. 502) further very large resources are as yet untouched in Sibi District in Baluchistan. *Magnesite* and *potassium* are found in workable amounts in the Salt Range and *alum* at Kalabagh. The *sulphur* in the volcanic craters of Koh-i-Sultan on the Afghan border is no longer worked; the Karachi refinery imports its supplies more cheaply. *Barytes* in Kalat (Baluchistan) and in Hazara District west of Rawalpindi now supplies all the needs of Pakistan's paint industry, and *bauxite* deposits in Hazara and in Azad Kashmir and Sibi are being assessed, and *silica* sand for glass comes from Sind. The lovely *marbles* of Peshawar region and the green *aragonite* marbles of Chagai are the basis of a small polishing industry, with a small export. But every one of these is in West Pakistan; the east has little but some glass sands in Mymensingh. And the position of the country as a whole offers little hope for new indigenous bases for industry, though those already exploited have considerable scope for expansion.

CHAPTER 10

The Evolution of Industry

I. FROM HANDICRAFTS TO FACTORY TECHNIQUES

The historical background

During those centuries when sailing ships, water-mills and handlooms were the most complicated machines in existence, India shared with China and Byzantium the leadership of the world in technical ingenuity, economic organization and volume of manufactures. Few finer textiles can ever have been produced than the 'woven wind', the diaphanous muslin of Dacca, and the wrought-iron pillar at Delhi, dated at latest AD 415, would rank as an outstanding technical achievement in any century before our own. For about 150 years after 1600 Indian textiles were a main staple of Eastern trade, and quite capable of capturing Western markets from local producers; so at least thought the London calico-printers when they rioted against the EIC's imports in 1721, and so secured protective legislation.

The decline from this position was abrupt, and with the rise of Lancashire and the fall of the princely Courts India collapsed into industrial insignificance, complete but for the hard-hit village crafts. In its external relations the whole Indian economy was geared to that of Britain, whether as market or as source of raw materials. The first steps towards a modern industry were indeed taken a century ago, but on the whole progress was irregular in time, space and the internal structure of industry. By 1957 India ranked about fifth among the industrial countries of the world, but this was a function of size rather than of development: coal and steel outputs were a fraction of those of the great industrial powers, output per head of population a fraction of that of minor industrial countries.

Yet perhaps only Brazil and China offer such scope for industrialization, and the technical bases have been laid. The main obstacles to advance are now probably social: low purchasing power, 'cheap' labour inefficient to the point of dearness. These are clearly linked factors, though unfortunately urban enthusiasm still seems to regard industry and agriculture as autonomous sectors of the economy, except that agriculture can be milked for raw materials.[1] Much Yamuna water has flowed past the Red Fort since Agarwala wrote, but residuals

[1] How strong this view is may be seen from the very odd arguments against it in A. N. Agarwala (ed.), *Position and Prospects of India's Foreign Trade* (Allahabad, 1947), 34–41.

of the controversy remain, and not entirely without reason: on the one hand, progress under the Five Year Plans has been imperilled by food shortages and other shortfalls in the agricultural sector; on the other, under existing conditions rural investment is very difficult to control, returns from it are *ipso facto* problematical, and yields are also vulnerable to monsoonal vagaries.

The crafts

It is hardly necessary to recount the dispossession of the artisan by the mill, whether the latter was British or, later, Indian – or Japanese;[2] in fact it is more to the point to indicate the limitations to this process. The town artisan, working for a market readily accessible to alien trade, suffered first and most; the village craftsman held out longer and in some areas, such as Assam, where communications are poor he has still a fairly strong position. Furthermore, distinctions must be made within the general category.

Those crafts with the highest survival value appear to be (*a*) services following population; (*b*) some luxury trades; (*c*) at the other extreme some crafts which have as it were a market sheltered by its poverty, or which deal in raw materials not worth processing by modern methods. Within all groups, in proportions varying with the technical cast of each trade, there is a wide range of organization, from the true independent artisan owning both tools and raw materials, through all the variants of piece-work for entrepreneurs, putting-out, and so on, to workers in what is in effect an embryonic factory. The pages of Lipson or Cunningham take on visible flesh and blood in this laboratory for the economic historian.

(*a*) The village servants include smiths, carpenters, tailors, potters. In the old days of self-sufficiency these were supported by a definite assignment of land or by a fixed annual payment in kind, in return for which they met all normal requirements through the year, but these customary arrangements have been largely superseded by payment for the job. Except where they do piece-work (knives, locks, etc.) for petty town entrepreneurs, the smiths are now less makers than fixers, and the same is true, to a less extent, of carpenters: they are the village repair and maintenance men, and 'it is the smith and the carpenter who make the Persian wheels go round'. The increasing use of simple machinery may actually improve their position, given some elementary technical education. Potters have to meet the demand for very cheap wares necessitated by the custom of smashing food-dishes after use (especially on ritual occasions) in order to obviate the risk of caste defilement; this is of course losing ground, but obviously no factory process could market at a sufficiently low price to meet the need. This custom is doubtless responsible for the striking lack of an important ceramic in Hindu civilization, perhaps alone among the great cultures of the world.[3]

[2] One of the most celebrated cases, if only on account of Marx's notorious onslaught on the EIC, is the decline of the once world-famous Dacca muslin industry; see N. Ahmad, *An Economic Geography of East Pakistan* (OUP, 1958), 94–102, and below 585.

[3] There is some attractive modern factory-made pottery, e.g. from Gwalior, but it is hardly equal aesthetically to the pots turned out in hundreds in any small Burmese town.

(b) The luxury crafts include the makers of the finest silk *saris*, of gold and silver-thread embroideries, really skilled jewellers, ivory-carvers, and so on. The old Court demand is all but dead, owing in part to the liquidation of the old aristocracies and in part to the apeing of bad European taste by the survivors, and only in a few places are classic standards more or less maintained. There is a strong tendency for these crafts to turn to workshop organization and the tourist market, with results more deplorable than describable.

(c) A vast demand at the lowest possible price-level is responsible for the survival of such trades as the making of *bidis*, the ersatz 'cigarette' of the masses; the units of sale are so petty as to be not worth much capital equipment so long as there is a reserve of cheap labour. *Bidi*-making is essentially a sweatshop industry using female and child labour; it could of course be put-out, but the entrepreneurs prefer the adulteration to be done for their own profit. The factory leather industry has made notable advances, and improved methods are found in some small rural tanneries and training centres, but the formerly untouchable Chamars still produce millions of half-tanned 'kips' from their crude vats; the hides of diseased and half-starved cattle, riddled by sores and ticks, are hardly worth tanning by modern methods. 'Like many other Indian handicraftsmen, the untouchable tanners remain because of the presence of low-grade materials and a market for cheap products.'[4]

The *charkha* or spinning-wheel and the handloom raise a number of difficult and much-canvassed questions: can they survive in the face of mill competition? if so, how? and is it really worthwhile to save them? The values involved are as much human as economic, and the answers therefore subjective; and the economic arguments are too technical to be discussed here. The whole question is studded with sociological man-traps, and the more sentimental devotees of the *charkha* simply ignore, or distort, the comparative costs of mill and home production. Nevertheless it would be socially very desirable to provide some relief to the seasonal un- and under-employment of the countryside, and perhaps even morally beneficial, as Gandhi held; this element in Gandhian thought was sufficiently strong for the spinning wheel to be placed centrally in India's national flag. Improvements to the *ambar charkha* and to handlooms are spreading, and a compromise solution may be possible by decentralising the machine spinning industry to provide cheaper yarn, and fostering cottage or small workshop weaving with electric looms.

Other rural crafts and trades, at present strictly speaking uneconomic, might be salvaged and become economically worthwhile given a sufficiency of *cheap* power; and since the expansion of large-scale industry cannot hope to take in all the increasing surplus of rural population, some such development, if attainable, might provide a way out of the impasse of an increase of population at a rate

---

[4] D. H. Buchanan, *The Development of Capitalist Enterprise in India* (Macmillan, NY, 1934), 94; his whole Chapter V is a very fair discussion of the craft *vs.* machine question, and still valuable.

disproportionate to the expansion of agricultural and factory output. But obviously there are no short-cuts on these roads, and no easy salvation for India's ancient crafts.

Phases of industrialization

Broadly speaking, India's industrial revolution falls into five phases:

(i) *c.* 1854–1914: the provision of a railway net, the usual initial concentration on textiles;

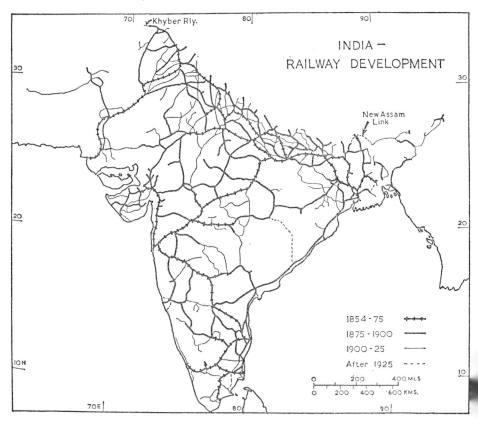

FIG 10.1 GROWTH OF THE RAILWAY SYSTEM.

(ii) 1914–21: (*a*) recognition of India's potential significance and actual insignificance to Imperial military economics; (*b*) political unrest and the attainment of fiscal autonomy;

(iii) 1921–39: experiments in protection, rise of iron and steel and of sugar industry, considerable but uneven progress generally;

(iv) 1939–50: involvement in a world war under the colonial power, the struggle for independence, the first uncertain years of a new nation;

(v) 1950 to date: India in the era of planning; it is a measure of the importance of this phase that it has been seriously claimed (though it might be difficult to substantiate the claim) that more progress has been made since the Plans began in 1951 than in the preceding half-century.[5] This last phase is the subject of the succeeding chapter.

1854-1914: Cotton is King. In the 19th century the EIC itself did virtually nothing for Indian economic development, except to foster opium cultivation for the China trade, to introduce tea-planting from China, and to give some support to the long-drawn-out attempts at exploiting Salem iron ores (below, 754); it left the field clear for private enterprise to flood India with Manchester goods, to extend tea and indigo plantations, and to build up a great export trade in cotton, jute, hides and oilseeds. Before 1850 a few steam-engines had been set up in docks, flour-mills and so on, mainly around Calcutta.

But the decade 1854–64 was critical. Politically the Mutiny led to the end of Company rule; economically two distant wars led to the founding of Indian factory industry: the Crimean War by cutting off hemp supplies to Dundee (which had been experimenting with power-woven jute since 1835) and so creating a great demand for raw jute; the American Civil War by producing an even more inflationary demand for raw cotton. With money pouring in and fibres pouring out it would have been strange indeed had nobody turned his mind to local manufacture. The major economic effect of the Mutiny was to render urgent, for military reasons, the extension of the two or three fragments of railway which existed in 1857, and this played a part in the general quickening of economic activity, not least by the establishment of railshops and collieries. But for sixty years at least railways rate policy favoured the export of cash crops and hampered industrial development away from the three great ports.

In 1854 a jute mill was opened at Calcutta, a cotton mill at Broach and another at Bombay;[6] the pioneers were respectively English, American and – significantly – Parsee. By 1861 Bombay had eight mills with nearly 200,000 spindles and a start had been made at Ahmedabad; the frenzied finance of the cotton boom was succeeded by merited catastrophe, but the Suez Canal (1869) was a stimulant and by 1877 there were fifty-one cotton mills with nearly 1,250,000 spindles, though only 10,385 looms. The jute manufacturing boom came later, with a jump from five to eighteen mills in 1873–75. From the first, however, weaving was important in Bengal, while Bombay devoted itself primarily to spinning, largely for the hand-looms of China. Apart from the local raw cotton – offset by the necessity of importing coal from England – the major factor in the lead taken by the west coast was historical. The sixty years which intervened between Plassey

[5] S. R. Sen, 'History of planning in India', *India 1962* (Information Service of India, London, 1962); the claim might be justified by the increase of 100% in the index of industrial production, 1950–60; only one index, but significant of achievement. See also P. Pant, 'The development of India', *Scientific American*, 209 (1963), 189–206.

[6] An unsuccessful cotton mill was set up at Bowreah, Calcutta, about 1818 (Buchanan, 128, 136). The Bombay mill is often dated 1851.

and the overthrow of the Marathas were those of the most ruthless economic aggression by the commercial oligarchs of Calcutta, seated in the entry to Hindustan and with their attention fixed on the richest plains of India. The very active trade of Bombay had a stronger element local to the Arabian Sea, and was hence more largely shared by indigenous groups such as Parsees and Khoja Muslims; indigenous enterprise was never so stifled as in the east. It is significant that the Managing Agency system is strongest in Bengal, where indigenous capitalists – quite rightly – showed an entire lack of confidence in their own managerial capacity. Hence while, except for the great Sassoon interests, British participation in cotton was from the start very slight, it is only in the last few years that British interests in jute have been bought out, and the executives of the industry are still in part Scots.

Apart from the growth of coal mining and of the service industries (foundries, etc.) of the ports, the last quarter of the 19th century was marked mainly by the spread of cotton mills to inland centres – Ahmedabad, Nagpur, Sholapur. By 1900 factories employed some 500,000 workers, of whom 160,000 were in cotton.

By 1900 also there was a significant hardening of nationalist feeling; Congress was soon to change its tone from 'we respectfully submit' to 'we demand'. A main part in this change was played by resentment against the government's adoption in 1883 of a virtually complete Free Trade policy; where the small revenue tariff could have assisted Indian manufactures (e.g. $3\frac{1}{2}\%$ on cotton goods) a countervailing excise was imposed. This certainly gave colour to suspicions that the whole policy was rigged in favour of Lancashire. The placing of India on the gold standard (1893–98) was a severe blow to the yarn trade with China, which adhered to silver; but this may have been a blessing in disguise since it impelled an increase of weaving and a better balance within the industry. There was neither disguise nor blessing in Lord Morley's doctrinaire refusal to sanction the Madras Government's industrial experiments. From the Indian point of view Free Trade was decidedly illiberal.

Yet despite all difficulties expansion continued: on the eve of the First World War coal output was over 12,000,000 tons, factories with over fifty hands employed some 900,000 workers, and few important towns had not been reached by a railway. And in 1911 the first pig iron had flowed into Jamshedpur moulds.

1914–21: the empty arsenal. The First World War brought an abrupt fall in imports from the warring countries and a boom demand for Indian raw materials, while the important campaigns in Mesopotamia and Palestine cried out for stores which could have been supplied by an integrated Indian industry, had that existed. The stage was set for large expansion, but the prime weakness of India's industrial structure was at once apparent: an almost complete lack of machines to make machines.

The growth of consumption industries had been favoured by untaxed machinery imports – some offset to 'Lancashire interference' – but this inhibited the development of production goods. As a result purely extractive industries boomed, Jamshedpur was sheltered at a critical phase, and existing industries worked to capacity; but except for jute, for which Calcutta engineering firms managed to produce some plant, very little expansion was possible. Government now paid heavily for its policy (in bland disregard of its own rules) of purchasing stores in England even when, with little inconvenience, they could have been had in India; a policy at once discriminatory and lacking discrimination. As it was, Britain's loss in the Indian market was only in small part India's gain; the lion's share went to Japan. Exports also were affected: in the Chinese yarn trade the India : Japan proportions of 77 : 23 in 1906 were exactly reversed by 1924. No better justification could have been found for the thesis that fiscal control from London was indefensible.

The post-war boom-and-slump was aggravated in India by violent fluctuations of the rupee. Nevertheless in 1922 factory employment was 1,360,000, and it is significant that the share of cotton had fallen from a third in 1902 to a quarter. At this point India gained fiscal autonomy.

1922–39: 'Discriminating Protection'. The new powers were exercised with discretion, rather strict interpretation being given, for instance, to the principle that an industry to receive protection should have such natural advantages as adequate home supplies of raw materials; this ruled out the glass industry for lack of soda ash, though matches, dependent on imported splints, received protection. The following figures illustrate the progress of the chief protected industries:[7]

	Steel	Sugar	Paper	Cotton Piecegoods	Matches
		1,000 tons		1,000,000 yards	100,000 gross
1922–23	131	24	24	1,725	8
1939–40	1,070	1,242	70	4,013	220
Increase %	717	5,075	192	132	2,850

The depression of the early 30s slowed expansion, but there was little actual retrogression, in part doubtless because there was so much leeway to make up. Cotton, for instance, added to both spindles and looms in every year until 1937.

Progress, however, was on a very ragged front, the most serious laggard being perhaps heavy chemicals. The leading developments of the inter-war years were: (i) changes in the cotton industry – an increased proportion of higher counts, especially in Ahmedabad; a relative decline in the position of Bombay Province, with an actual fall in the number of mills in Bombay Island; a rapid expansion in Mysore and Madras, especially at Coimbatore, consequent on the use of Jog, Nilgiri and Cauvery power;[8] (ii) the expansion of Jamshedpur as a metallurgical

[7] J. Matthai, *Tariffs and Industry* (OPIA No. 20, 1944), 9–12.

[8] In 1921 western India had 68·6% and southern India 9·3% of 280 mills; in 1937 the percentages were respectively 56·3 and 17·7 of 419 mills (T. R. Sharma, *Location of Industries in India* (Hind Kitabs, Bombay, 3rd ed., 1954), 30.).

centre; (iii) the rise of the sugar and cement industries; (iv) a proliferation of minor consumption industries. This last was in the nature of things, but was powerfully aided by the nationalist boycotts of British goods.

In 1939 coal output was 28,000,000 tons, steel had topped the million, and industrial employment (excluding government ordnance and railshops, and seasonal gins and presses) was 1,809,000. Cotton again accounted for nearly 33%, probably owing to Tamilnad's entry into the 'first phase'. Allowing for the multiplied mechanization of the second war, India was far better equipped in 1939 than in 1914, and this was reflected in a marked, if highly uneven, expansion not only in heavier industry – where, for instance, Jamshedpur developed some armament lines – but also, despite all difficulties of supply, of consumption industries.

Some general features

(a) *Mistries and Managing Agents.* The old territorial patchwork, the *morcellement* of the fields, the ladder of sub-tenancies from ryot to zamindar, the vivi-section of society by caste – all these suggest that 'fragmentation' is a main motif in the life of India. Nor is even modern industry altogether exempt, despite such great integrations as the House of Tata. There seems a curious tendency to depute and re-depute responsibility: at one end of the scale labour is recruited and controlled by contractors, at the other executive functions are farmed out to Managing Agents, and exchanges in between are in the sticky hands of multiple hordes of middlemen.

There was originally, doubtless, good reason for this fragmentation of functions, just as there was for caste, but it can hardly be doubted that it is now a burden on industry, with endless delays, frictions and confusions, as well as the direct cash charge for services rendered. Thus the labour jobber or *mistry* – there are other names for him – who beat up a gang of labourers was useful enough in the earlier phases; he is now often an unscrupulous exploiter of both sides, at times even a strike-leader, more frequently a strike-breaker. He adds to legitimate commissions innumerable exactions from his workers, bound to him by initial advances, and thus secures his hold to the serious detriment of good and stable labour relations.

At the top is the Managing Agency system. This again was natural enough when Indian capitalists with no technical experience wished to start an industry; the importers who provided the plant would set it up and recruit technicians and managers; they would also buy stores and raw materials and market the product. This was, as it were, insurance against inexperience; but when in time one Agency came to run scores of firms, with perhaps a dozen of them in the same line, and was paid largely by commissions on both purchases and sales (or, much worse, on output sold or unsold) and took policy decisions for the 'directors' to rubber-stamp, the possibilities of abuse became enormous.[9] There are now

[9] See Buchanan, 165–72, and especially the extraordinary balance-sheet at p. 171.

Indian Agents, and there is still some case for the system. While the Government's commitment to a 'socialistic pattern of society' would not suggest this, it is also pledged to economic expansion, and meanwhile Managing Agencies further this by providing or attracting risk capital and by expanding existing businesses.[10]

(b) *Industrial psychology.* Indian industry has suffered from being initiated, as a rule, by men whose inherited aptitudes were commercial rather than industrial; hence a tendency to go all out for quick profits, often dissipated in speculative extensions. There is often a fantastic diffusion of energy and money into any number of petty unrelated projects – more fragmentation! Inflated optimism may be succeeded by as disastrous pessimism. In actual management there is often very loose costing; allowance for depreciation is often minimal; and there is a reluctance to cut losses and scrap antique plant: in 1886 Jamshedji Tata bought a mill 'which had a conglomerate mass of machinery operated by several steam engines and using twenty-three boilers. The mill's business had been wound up four times in twenty years. Tata literally threw the old machinery out of the windows.'[11]

It must of course be emphasized that these attitudes are receding into the past, though too slowly in some industries; and there are plenty of businessmen of quick and solid ability, and a small but rapidly growing managerial class.

(c) *Labour problems.* While direct comparisons of output per man-hour are usually very unfavourable to India, they leave out too many factors to be worth much. None the less it can hardly be doubted that much Indian labour is inefficient to an extent that goes far to offset its cash cheapness. The reasons are fairly obvious: bad physique, bad housing, bad food, bad working conditions, and as a corollary bad industrial and sometimes bad personal habits. Mills are often very insanitary – impure water has been used for humidifiers – and in any case the atmosphere is very exhausting in the hot weather. Overcrowding and bad water-supply, as in the great tenement *chawls* of Bombay or the *bustees* of Calcutta, negate the most elementary decencies. The worker is very often in debt, sometimes to the tune of a quarter's pay, and there were few nastier sights in India than the factory gates on pay-day, with tough Pathan moneylenders armed with heavy staves waiting for their prey.

Serious efforts have been made, both by governments and the better employers, to improve conditions, but the general level remains deplorably low, and legislation is too often evaded or corrupted.

It is not surprising, then, that absenteeism is rife and that there is a large labour turnover, in part owing to the instigation of jobbers anxious for a new round of bribes and commissions. To check desertion to other mills, or to the villages, payment is often by the month, sometimes with a regular fortnight's

[10] National Council of Applied Economic Research (non-official), *The Managing Agency System* (Asia, Bombay, 1959).
[11] Buchanan, 206.

arrear. But absenteeism and large turnovers will remain standard so long as a large proportion of industrial workers are really villagers supplementing their miserable incomes by a spell in the mills. Except where female labour is in demand, as in textiles, the worker is most properly unwilling to bring his wife; the urban sex-disparity is itself a social problem of the first magnitude. The worker's heart remains at home, whither he betakes himself at harvest or festival time. This constant interchange is a main factor in the sapping of the old village tradition, and owing to the large turnover a far higher proportion of the population is affected than would be indicated by the figures of factory employment at any one time. Only in a few places – notably Ahmedabad, Kanpur, Poona[12] – is the true urban proletariat more important than the migrant mass.

Trade unions are as a rule extremist and effective (e.g. the Bombay Girni Kamgar – 'Red Flag' – Union) or moderate and ineffective; often both extremist and inefficient; only in sheltered trades really stable. The illiteracy of the workers naturally makes them turn to outside organizers, often unemployed lawyers, some of whom have given devoted service while others have been amateurs in union methods but professionally skilled in exploiting their position, whether for politics or pay. While many unions are thus extremely irresponsible, little has been done to make easy the way of the properly-run registered union.

All this is not to say that the workers are without fault, nor that there are not good trade unions, good workers, and good managements. Where labour is well provided for and has become a real settled working-class it can fill the most skilled jobs, as Jamshedpur experience has shown. Moreover at present various 'welfare state' measures seem to indicate a general improvement, though unfortunately largely at the expense (through sales taxes, etc.) of the middle clerical classes, who also are subject to extreme exploitation. Nevertheless on the whole the labour situation is one of the prime weaknesses of Indian industries. Yet there is progress, in some cases very striking: '. . . workers who in 1955 took four or five times as long as their European counterparts to produce a given article – an Oerlikon lathe, a Mercedes truck, a railway coach – can now do the work in a little less than twice the European time, and the gap is still being narrowed.'[13]

II. DEVELOPMENT OF MAIN INDUSTRIES TO 1950

A. TEXTILES

1. *Cotton*

Cotton, first of India's modern industries in time, retained its premier position, and India's production of *c.* 5,000,000,000 yards a year was second only to that of the USA. To this mill capacity must be added 1,600,000,000 yards for handlooms.

[12] The Poona study of R. D. Lambert, *Workers, Factories and Social Change in India* (Princeton Univ. Press, 1963), suggests some modification of these generalizations.
[13] B. W. Jackson, 'India on the eve of its Third Plan', *Foreign Affairs*, 39 (1960–61), 259–70.

Its early location at Bombay was the result of the simplest geographical factors.[14] The raw material is 'non-localising', since it is not perishable and loses little weight in manufacture, but access to a wide range of grades is an advantage,

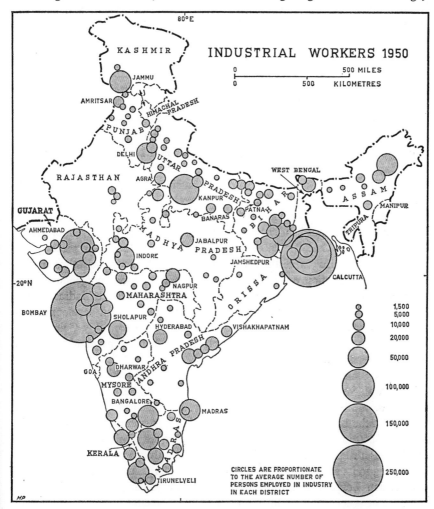

FIG 10.2 INDIA: INDUSTRIAL WORKERS, 1950. The largest symbols represent considerable absolute numbers of workers, even granting rather low efficiency and mechanization. Changes since 1950 are discussed in Ch. XI. From P. P. Karan and W. M. Jenkins in *Economic Geography*, 35 (1959).

and obviously most easily attained in the great export mart. Bombay was also favourably placed for the import of bulky machinery, stores and coal, and for the

[14] The discussion of cotton milling distribution which follows is drawn from the admirably lucid and stimulating analysis in Sharma, Chapter 2–3, *q.v.* for much further detail.

yarn export to China, the initial *raison d'être* of the industry. The rise of cotton manufacturing in Japan and China, however, enforced changes which after about 1905 began to react unfavourably on the relative position of the original base. Weaving for the home market became more important, and later the *swadeshi* movement against buying British, largely backed by the urban middle-class, led to a demand for finer counts than those adequate for the China trade. Apart from the increasing overheads – higher wages and charges natural to a great metropolis, Weber's 'deglomerative factors' – in Bombay Island, this shift in emphasis from foreign yarn to internal piecegoods markets added to Bombay's costs the charges on long rail hauls. Despite a railway rates policy which worked strongly in favour of the great ports, mills at the many internal raw cotton marts could save freight on both raw material and finished product, while the growth of coal mining in the Damodar or even locally (as near Nagpur) provided power. Ahmedabad, with old textile and financing traditions, was off the mark very quickly, followed by Nagpur and Sholapur; outside the Peninsular cotton tracts Kanpur, well placed between Punjab cotton and Bihar coal, led the way. Delhi shared slightly in this development, but beyond it even the great distributing market of Amritsar was handicapped by lack of power until the advent of Mandi hydro-electricity. Calcutta, 'probably the largest single cotton piece goods market in the world', nevertheless did not start until 1905, doubtless mainly because of the fixation on jute and the weakness of local indigenous entre-preneurs. In the south the Buckingham and Carnatic mills at Madras, estab-lished 1874–83, remained practically isolated until the sudden development in the early 1930s of centres served by Pykara power, most notably Coimbatore. Here spinning was still dominant, supplying the handlooms of Madura and Tamilnad generally.

Bombay State still had over half of Indian production, but the balance was tending to shift away from it: in Bombay Island the number of mills had actually decreased, and in Ahmedabad was stationary. But the spread was accompanied by at least the beginnings of regional specialization: spinning in Madras, light fabrics of cotton and rayon mixtures and so on in the Punjab, tent canvas and *durris* (rough rugs) at Kanpur, where industry has always had a certain military bias owing to its start as the centre for Army saddlery. In face of the increasing competition Bombay and Ahmedabad, like New England, have found their response in specializing in finer products: the percentage of yarn output in counts above 31 increased at Bombay from 2 in 1921–22 to 17·9 in 1941–42, at Ahmedabad from 7·4 to 35·6. This turn to higher-priced goods, in which freight was a lesser proportion of the final price, was the natural counter to the transport advantages of the inland centres.

In general the industry lacked well-integrated ancillaries. It is significant that Ahmedabad, which used a far higher proportion of foreign (i.e. longer-stapled) cotton than any other centre, and had a rather more stable labour force, was also ahead in this respect: starch, reeds and healds are made locally, and Tatas were already producing such essential chemicals as soda ash and bleaching powder at Port Okha, on the tip of the Kathiawad Peninsula.

2. Jute

'In 1940, 95·5% of the jute looms in India . . . were situated in a small strip of land about 60 miles long and two broad', up and down the Hooghly from Calcutta; and the 70,000 looms of this tiny area were actually about 54% of all in the world.[15] But at Partition 80% of raw jute output was in East Pakistan, which yet had not a single jute-mill.

The reasons for this anomaly are in part historical: capital and management were largely supplied by the Scots oligarchy of Managing Agents,[16] concentrated in the commercial metropolis of Gangetic India and the northeastern Peninsula. Calcutta in turn owed its trade hegemony to the physical character of the delta; poor as it is, the Hooghly is the best of the Ganga spill-ways until we reach the great conjoint Padma–Brahmaputra–Meghna estuary in the east, and this entry has a hinterland small in comparison with Hindustan, access to which is much more direct by the Hooghly–Bhagirathi or (for land routes) the western flanks of the delta.

Sharma's elegant analysis brings out a less obvious but beautifully geographical point. Calcutta, by its pull as the only port for seaborne trade,[17] was the hub of the internal waterways, and over half the jute arrivals were by water. Nevertheless 43% came by rail. But four Districts – Mymensingh, Dacca, Tippera, and Faridpur – supplied 70% of the Hooghlyside mill demand, and of these only the last and least lay west of the great unbridged barrier of the Meghna and its confluents. Transhipment was thus necessary; one ferry took loaded goods wagons, but on this route a break of gauge intervened. 'Under these conditions of transport, involving a good deal of terminal charges, if the jute mills were located in the main jute belt in Eastern Bengal, the transhipment hurdles would have to be crossed twice – once in moving the coal, mill stores, labour, etc., to the mills and again in moving the finished goods to Calcutta for export. . . . But in the case of mills in the Hooghly area the transhipment ordeal has to be faced only once – in moving the raw jute to the mills.'[18] In other words, the location of Calcutta was analogous to that of Bombay in the early days of cotton, not only for machinery from overseas, but also for Damodar coal which met the jute there just as if it had itself come oversea.

The splitting of the growing from the milling centres largely disrupted jute

[15] Sharma, 77, 89. This section based mainly on Sharma, Chapter V, and C. N. Vakil, *Economic Consequences of Divided India* (Vora, Bombay, 1950), 261–79.
[16] Scots executives are only now yielding their leading role in the Hooghlyside jute industry.
[17] Chittagong, at least until Partition, was too excentric to count in this discussion.
[18] Sharma, 84–86. Theoretically of course another port might have been developed, but even were physical conditions more favourable, the self-reinforcing hegemony of Calcutta was hardly shakeable by the 1870s; and the difficulty of coal movements from the Damodar to Dacca would remain.

movements. After Partition, strenuous efforts were made to increase raw jute output in India, and not without success, despite the need for self-sufficiency in food. Pakistan jute is usually of better quality than Indian; this again is largely a matter of the physical character of the delta, the more lively streams of the active eastern delta bringing their annual increments of silt to the fields, and providing much better conditions for retting than are found in the half-stagnant back-waters of West Bengal. It was clear that however successful the jute drive in India, considerable amounts would still be needed from Pakistan;[19] and as yet Pakistan had no jute mills, though they were not long delayed. As for India, the importance of the commodity may be judged from the fact that in 1948 about one-third of all her foreign exchange earnings – and two-thirds of hard currency – came from jute.[20] In these circumstances it was deplorable that jute should have become the terrain of continual economic skirmishing, culminating in the major engagement of the devaluation crisis of 1949, which for six months brought the Indo-Pakistani jute trade to a stop – except for smuggling, said to have amounted to over 85,000 tons (cf. pp. 594–5).

3. *Wool*

The woollens industry also suffered from Partition: a third or more of the clip came from West Pakistan, and again this was the better third in quality. In the 'continental' northwest were also the main markets for warm clothing; the Himalayas look after themselves with home-spun and sheepskin. Yet all but one of the factories were in India.

In 1939 the total employment in the 17 fairly important factories was 8,271; but Kanpur, Dhariwal near Amritsar, and Amritsar itself, with one mill each, employed respectively 2,311, 1,960 and 701 workers – together about 60% of the total. These locations are significant. Kanpur is on the border of the main wool-producing and wool-consuming zone, where it is nearest to Damodar coal. Here the first Indian mill was set up (1876) essentially for Army needs. Dhariwal and Amritsar were central to the main marts for the wools of the sub-continent and beyond – Peshawar, Multan, Fazilka and a string of contact-zone markets, from Kumaon to Kashmir, collecting central Asian and Tibetan wool. Once hydro-electricity was available the industry almost followed.

Demand was, and normally still is, seasonal; except when Army contracts are available working also is seasonal: labour turnover is too high for efficiency. Again market requirements are exceedingly varied, specialization almost impossible if mills are to work through the year, and administrative overheads (for supervisors, specialist technicians, etc.) correspondingly high. Most of the more skilled workers at Dhariwal and Amritsar were Muslims who went to Pakistan.

The handloom side remained strong, employment being estimated at anything from two to six times that in mills, despite the competition of cheap shoddies and

---

[19] Vakil, 264–5.
[20] *Report of Export Promotion Cttee* (1949), cited Vakil, 261 fn. 2.

mixtures from Japan, Italy and Poland; the cessation of these imports during the war, and the all-out working of the mills for Army clothing, gave the craft industry a great impetus. At Srinagar (Kashmir) a centrally organized cottage industry employs about 9,000 weavers; in the Himalayas spinning and weaving were family affairs, the producers owning everything from the sheep to the loom but elsewhere, and especially in the carpet branch, the weavers were in debt-bondage to petty entrepreneurs. Apart from carpets the main products were coarse blankets, at once cheaper and more resistant to hard usage than mill products. These matters at least are little changed.

4. *Silk, Rayon, Hosiery*[21]

Despite local supplies not only from mulberry-eating silkworms, but from other indigenous insects (see above, 249), the silk industry suffered from inadequate and irregular provision of raw material. The industry, located in Mysore, Madras, West Bengal, and Kashmir, was poorly organized, cocoon production unequal and generally inferior in quality. *Rayon* production was increasing rapidly: the main centres being Bombay, Ahmedabad and Surat – an interesting location, reminiscent of the early days of cotton when it also depended on imported yarn. The chief inland centre was Amritsar, associated with the general development of light industry consequent on electrification, and linked with cotton-rayon mixtures and knitwear.

Hosiery and *knitwear* works were found in the larger urban markets, but particularly at Rawalpindi and Lahore in West and Ludhiana in East Punjab. This probably stemmed from the migration of a craft industry from Kashmir, but one obviously particularly suited to electrification.

B. METAL INDUSTRIES

1. *Iron and Steel*

'The feature which stands out most prominently in a survey of the mineral industries of India is that practically nothing has been done to develop those minerals which are essential to modern metallurgical and chemical industries, while most striking progress has been made during recent years in opening out deposits from which products are obtained suitable for export, or for consumption by . . . direct processes.'[22] This statement accurately sums up the position in the first decade of this century, when it was generally held by (British) authorities that not much more was possible, and in particular that experience had conclusively shown that India was never likely to possess a large-scale iron and steel industry. The magnificence of the endowment of the northeastern Peninsula was hardly recognized, or was thought of in extractive terms only, and Free Trade meant that import of machines, constructional material, and semi-manufactured goods was possible at prices with which an unprotected industry starting from scratch could hardly compete.

[21] Vakil, 281–5.   [22] *Imperial Gaz.* III (1908), 128.

THE ECONOMY

As far back as the 1830s attempts had been made to exploit Salem iron, and the furnaces at Porto Novo (south of Madras) and Beypur (Malabar) were intermittently productive until 1866–67 (cf. below 753–4). In 1900 pig production from the iron-shales of Barakar in the Damodar was a mere 35,000 tons; the company concerned had just made the first profit since operations began in 1874, and was about to launch into a disastrous venture in steel. But in 1911 Jamshedpur's first blast-furnace was blown, in 1913 the first steel was made – and in 1914 the war provided a virtually protected market for the critical early years. Indian production was still small, especially in relation to population, but the Jamshedpur works were then the largest in the Commonwealth. Their history is a fascinating study in applied geography; Jamshedji Tata's success was due above all to three things: unflinching determination, adequate finance and meticulous geographical planning which resulted in the selection of a site with positional advantages possibly unequalled anywhere in the world: between Damodar coking coal and the mountains of Orissa haematite; with ample moulding-sand and water from the Subarnarekha; with fluxes, refractories, and the major alloys within 50 or 60 miles; and with the biggest single market in India – the general engineering trades of Calcutta – only 150 miles (241 km.) away.[23] These advantages are unique; but except for the charcoal-smelted works in Mysore, the industry in general benefited from the low cost of coke and there grew up a considerable export of pig iron, especially to Japan. But there was also some import of scrap to coastal foundries.

The location and nominal capacity (in 1,000 tons) of existing plants was as follows:

	Pig	Steel ingots
Tata I & S Co., Jamshedpur, Bihar	1,533	1,116
Indian I & S Co., Kulti, West Bengal	913	—
Steel Corporation of Bengal, Burnpur, West Bengal	—	5–600
Mysore (State) I & S, Bhadravati	30	20–40

This gave a total capacity of around 2,500,000 tons pig and 1,750,000 steel; but the plants suffered depreciation as a result of the unremitting production, with little replacement, of the war years, actual output was considerably less, though roughly equivalent to inter-war demand.

The wide range of products was notably increased by the demands of 1939–45. Around Jamshedpur and Asansol–Burnpur (on the Raniganj coalfield) clustered ancillary and associated industries: refractories, tubes and wires, heavy chemicals and so on. One of the most important was tin-plate, in which India became

[23] See Sharma, 98–101, and below, 713–15. J. L. Keenan's *A Steel Man in India* (Gollancz, London, 1945) gives an unorthodox but very lively view of a neglected aspect of Indian life.

almost self-supporting in ten years, with an output of over 80,000 tons. Considering the resources in alloys – manganese, chromium, silicon, titanium and vanadium are all available, mostly between the Damodar and the Subarnarekha – very little high-speed or other special steel was produced. This country on the Bihar–Bengal–Orissa border was really the only zone of primary heavy industry in the sub-continent, a concentration obviously due to the incomparable concentration of resources, facilitating linked development, but hampering distribution by the long rail hauls necessary to any markets but those of Hooghlyside.

2. *Aluminium and other non-ferrous metals*[24]

The production of aluminium smallware was one of the Madras Government's initiatives, as early as 1912, and in the inter-war period raw metal imports of 4,000–5,000 tons a year were the basis of a utensils industry located in the chief ports and exporting to Indian Ocean markets. In 1943 the production of aluminium ingots from imported alumina began near Alwaye (Travancore) and the actual production of alumina was begun at Muri and Asansol. Rolling into sheets (and foil for tea-chests) was mostly at Belur (Calcutta).

The war years saw a great expansion in miscellaneous light metal trades – brass and copper wire and tubes, lead piping and sheeting, brass sheets, expanded metal, and so on. Significantly enough most firms were in Calcutta, with Bombay second; the few up-country outliers included one at Jaipur presumably located with reference to Rajasthan zinc and copper. A small but interesting industry was the manufacture of plumbago crucibles for non-ferrous metallurgy, carried on at Calcutta, Bombay and Rajahmundry in the Godavari delta. Most Indian graphite is definitely inferior for this purpose, and imports from Ceylon were essential.

3. *Engineering: heavy, light and electrical*

The major concentrations in heavy engineering were, as we might expect, around Calcutta, at Jamshedpur, and on the Jharia–Raniganj coalfields, these areas accounting for 75% of output; lesser centres were Bombay, Madras and Kanpur. The Second World War saw a great expansion: steel used in bridges, for example, was 1,381 tons in 1940, 21,843 in 1943, and it is claimed that the largest floating dock in the world was constructed at Calcutta.[25] But such important lines as machine tools and textile engineering were in their infancy, the latter's capacity being only a fraction of the cotton industry's annual replacements of looms and spindles. While the war greatly increased demand for, and led to the introduction or expansion of the manufacture of, such things as jacks, road-making machinery and hand pumps, the existing small production of centrifugal pumps and oil-engines, so important in connection with rural

[24] The best readily accessible survey of the metal and engineering industries at this period is in P. J. Thomas, *India's Basic Industries* (Orient Longmans, Bombay, 1948), Chs. I–V and XIII–XX *passim*.
[25] Thomas, 165.

industry, was hampered or even reduced by the difficulty of importing essential tools and components, such as ball bearings. In 1950 demand for ball bearings was estimated at 900,000 – but of 2,500 different sorts and sizes – and 'any economical unit would produce India's total demand in a week or so'.[26] This illustrates the general lack of integration in Indian industry. Before the war precision instruments were made chiefly by the Government Mathematical Instrument Office, established over a century ago at Calcutta; the war saw a proliferation of private firms, but their products were not always very precise.

The production of most of the lighter types of electrical apparatus was either introduced or greatly increased during the war, and bulbs, fans, batteries, transformers, conduits manufactured on a fairly large scale.

4. Transport engineering, shipbuilding

(a) Land transport. Vehicle engineering was still largely in the assembly stage. Rail wagons and coaches were built mainly at Calcutta and Burnpur. Loco building, with imported components, began as early as 1896 in the Bombay Baroda & Central India rail-shops at Ajmer, but despite government's promise in 1921 to invite tenders and the consequent building of a plant at Jamshedpur, the Tariff Board refused protection – partly on the ground that electrification was pending – and not a single engine was produced.[27]

Motor vehicle assembly had been started at Bombay, and a beginning made on aircraft assembly at Bangalore. Bicycle demand included an unusually high proportion of tricycles, mainly for the 'trishaw' or pedal-bike-cum-sidecar which is replacing the man-pulled rickshaw.

(b) Shipbuilding. Some of the 'wooden walls' of Nelson's day were built not of British oak but of Indian teak, and the Parsee shipwrights of Bombay enjoyed a high reputation throughout Eastern seas. With the change to iron, however, only country craft were launched, except for tugs, launches and barges for the Bengal Delta, for which Calcutta was of course the main centre. Before the war a few sea-going tugs, up to 440 tons, were built there, and during the war a large number of motor-patrol boats and mine-sweepers were launched, though nearly all machinery had to be imported.

The only existing yards of any capacity were those of the Scindia Company – the premier Indian shipping line – at Visakhapatnam, which could build vessels up to 8,000 tons capacity. Though 'Vizag' is the nearest open-ocean port to Jamshedpur, costs are so high (nearly twice those of UK yards) that in 1949 the company suspended operations after launching only three ships; the yards were later nationalized. Delightfully, bananas were used instead of tallow for greasing the slipways, and the traditional bottle of champagne for the launch was superseded by the less expensive cracking of a coconut.

[26] Thomas, 189.
[27] Thomas, 205–6. There are still only 800 miles (1,285 km.) of electric railway, confined to suburban lines around Bombay, Calcutta and Madras.

C. CEMENT

The cement industry grew as modern methods of construction were adopted. Good limestone was available in quantity in many parts of India; gypsum is less abundant and the loss of that of the Salt Range to Pakistan caused some temporary difficulty. The need to use coal of low ash-content in the kilns meant that while the central Indian factories could use Rewah or Pench valley coal for power, half their requirements had to come from the Damodar. In 1947 there were about twenty-four plants with a total capacity of 2,800,000 tons. A quarter of this was in Pakistan and at least a third in central India, notably based on the Vindhyan rocks forming the northern flanks of the Son valley. Other important areas were Kathiawad, Telangana and East Punjab, while the largest single unit (220,000 tons) was in Bundi state, Rajasthan. Most of these were located with direct reference to limestone, e.g. the Shahbad factory in Hyderabad is on the narrow strip of Vindhyans, long worked for building stone, which intervenes between the Archaeans and the overlying Deccan Lavas.

The industry tended to be monopolistic, a good two-thirds of the 1947 capacity being controlled by Associated Cement Companies and two-thirds of the rest by Seth Dalmia, then perhaps the leading self-made magnate of India. Both these concerns controlled plants in what is now Pakistan, and there was some dislocation at Partition. Labour conditions were unusually good. Altogether capacity in India increased from 2,100,000 tons in 1947 to 2,960,000 in 1949, output from 1,400,000 to 2,100,000 (2,700,000 in 1950). There was still some import, but also export to Ceylon and Burma, and altogether the industry was one of the most flourishing in India.

D. CHEMICALS AND ALLIED INDUSTRIES

1. *Acids and alkalis*

The heavy chemical industry was one of the weakest sectors in India's industrial advance. Sulphuric acid, indeed, owing to the precautions needed in transporting it, and the fact that a ton of sulphur yields three of acid, must in general be made near its market, and this favoured home production; and consumption industries based on chemicals were expanding rapidly. But the highly important alkali side, despite a notable increase in production since the war, was still under-developed. Although the possession of the Salt Range gives Pakistan the largest single source of chemicals in the sub-continent, India's resources are by no means poor, and their uneven development reflected the general lack of co-ordination and balance.

Sulphuric acid was produced in the larger textile centres and at Asansol, Jamshedpur, Belagula (Mysore), and Alwaye. Alkalis were mainly from Saurashtra, at Drangadhra and Mithapur (Port Okha), where Tatas had the largest soda-ash and caustic-soda plant in the country; the localizing factor was the proximity of limestone and sea-salt. There was also some production at Mettur. Ammonium sulphate was being produced at Sindri and Alwaye, with a small contribution from Belagula and from coke-ovens. There were thus three main areas of heavy chemical production: Kathiawad, the northeastern Peninsula and the electrified zone of the south.

2. *Lighter chemical industries*

The most important consumption industries based on chemicals were dye and tan-stuffs, paints and varnishes, soap and cosmetics, matches and drugs with fair natural resources, vegetable or mineral.

The indigenous production of vegetable *tan-stuffs* (avaram, babul, myrobalans, etc.) is supplemented by imports of wattle bark. Chrome alum (chromium/ aluminium sulphate) – important in dyeing and photography as well as tanning – was produced using bauxite and sulphuric acid; production in this group (including other alum salts for water purification, paper sizing and as mordants) more than doubled between 1939 and 1945, despite difficulties in transporting bauxite and other demands for sulphuric acid. *Dye-stuffs*, apart from primitive local production for use on the spot, were mostly imported. Output of *paints and varnishes* again more than doubled during the war, using the fair resource base in the oilseeds, the resins of the Himalayan forests, barytes in the south, and various other pigments and vehicles. The industry had the usual Bombay/ Calcutta localization.

The *soap* industry had ample supplies of vegetable oils, tallow and essential oils such as lemon-grass, citronella and sandal, though these last were still generally exported as crude oil and re-imported as distilled. Imports of some alkalis and of coconut oil were still necessary. The industry again developed mostly around Calcutta and Bombay, with important units in Kerala. *Matchmaking* was widespread as a cottage industry, but there were a fair number of factories, especially in Madras and West Bengal, though the largest concern, the West India Match Co., linked with Swedish interests, had its main factory at Kalyan near Bombay. *Drugs* again fall into two sections: the ancient remedies, largely herbal and with some elements of magic, used in the traditional medical systems and by village homeopathists; and factory-made pharmaceuticals, which had just made a beginning. The production of *plastics* themselves, as distinct from plastic goods, was in its infancy.

E. FOOD INDUSTRIES

Food processing came first of the major industrial groups in number of establishments, but third in employment. This is natural enough, since for the most part processes are relatively simple, needing little power or capital. Factories were (and are) often seasonal, and except for some concentration of larger units in ports and large cities their distribution followed that of the crop concerned.

Rice mills, for example, can be worked by cheap oil-engines or by steam-engines of no great power and often of antiquated design; fuel for steam plants is no problem, since fires once started can be fed on paddy husks. Hence their rickety corrugated iron sheds were scattered by rail or riverside through all the paddy-lands, with perhaps some tendency to thicken along the middle Ganga and the terai.[28] But flour mills were more urban in location, since the taste for wheaten bread instead of the unleavened *chupatti* (a tough but satisfying pancake) definitely goes with 'Western sophistication'.

1. Tea and sugar

Tea for Western markets needs immediate and relatively elaborate processing; hence tea factories were well organized and equipped capitalist units, serving either a single plantation or, as road transport improved, a group. A material factor is the need for adequate export packaging, and this led to a large, if ill-balanced, expansion of plywood production for tea-chests; even so, there were difficulties in reaching standards acceptable to dollar markets such as the USA and Canada.

The history of *sugar* production in India is one of marked vicissitude, dependent partly on imperial politics, as when British import duties were placed on East Indian sugar in West Indian interests. Again it must be remembered that beside the modern industry is the village production of *gur* or *jaggery*, the coarse unrefined sugar (rather like fudge) produced by boiling in open pans. This is of course much cheaper, and indeed gur normally took about half the cane supply. Other sugar, or at least sweetening, is still obtained from the estuarine nipa palms and *Phoenix paludosa* and, more important, the Palmyra (*Borassus flabellifer*); but this does not amount to much, and is mostly in the extreme south.[29]

For most of the 19th century India was either self-sufficient or a net exporter, but in the 1890s the competition of European beet-sugar and of cane from Mauritius (where it is grown by Indian labour) and Java practically killed Indian sugar as an organized trade, though of course the petty local production of gur carried on. There was some revival from about 1911, but after 1931–32 the grant of protection led to a sharp increase in factories, from 32 in 1932 to 145 in 1939, and in refined output, from 100,000 to 1,230,000 tons. By 1940 'India was the largest sugar-producing country in the world, and her sugar industry the second largest industry, next in importance to only the cotton textile industry', and employing over 120,000 hands.[30] There was usually an export surplus; the sugar industry of Burma, for instance, survived only on sufferance, and there were exports to the Indian colonies in Ceylon and Malaya, and to southwest Asia.[31]

[28] For a general discussion of rice-milling, cf. O. H. K. Spate, 'Beginnings of industrialization in Burma', *Economic Geography*, 17 (1941), 75–92.

[29] This section is based mainly on Sharma, Chapters VIII–IX; Jathar and Beri, I Chapter VI; Vakil, 297–303.

[30] Jathar and Beri, I.172 (7th ed., 1942).

[31] Indian exports 1948–49: 26,268 tons (but 22,000 as molasses); of this 3,377 to West Pakistan. Imports 10,576 tons.

Production fluctuated, however, and in later years imports were sometimes necessary.

As we have seen (Chapter 8), cane-growing was strongly localized in the north, and this was reflected in the concentration of the industry: in 1931–32/34–35 Uttar Pradesh and Bihar produced 90·8% of total refined output, in 1935–36/38–39 still 84·1%; but by 1943–44 their share had fallen to 79·4%,[32] indicating the start of a trend to a more even spread of the industry, which was desirable for several reasons.

In the first place, Indian cane as a whole is poor, output per acre being only a quarter of that in Java and Hawaii. But the disparity is much less for the thick tropical canes of the south, and greater reliance on these spells obvious economies, not to mention transport saving on the finished product. The extension of irrigation in the Deccan is likely to lead to an increase of cane-growing there, since the value of the crop renders it a favourite in irrigated areas; and the factories of the Deccan rely mainly on their own estates, instead of on 'gate cane' brought to the factory directly by independent growers, or on cane brought by rail. This had advantages – superior varieties are grown, and cutting takes place at a time to suit the refiner rather than the cultivator.

2. Oils

Oilseeds accounted for about 5% of the value of Indian exports, and there was a considerable import of vegetable oils. Manufacture of oil had begun, but the use of oil-cake as cattle food and fertilizer was negligible; it is significant, however, that there was a downward trend in exports of rape and mustard, which can be of direct food value without any processing beyond the crude extraction of oil by *ghani*, a great pestle-and-mortar, usually bullock-driven but sometimes mechanized, in which case a battery of *ghanis* might be connected to an oil-engine. The extraction rate is low, but this has at least the merit of leaving richer oil-cake. The loss of the European market in 1940 led to a marked increase in groundnut-crushing and the establishment of *vanaspati* or 'vegetable ghi' mills; while the increasing demand for coconut oil in the soap industry called for fairly large imports.

F. MISCELLANEOUS CONSUMPTION INDUSTRIES

1. Leather[33]

The leather industry of India suffers from peculiar social disabilities. Before Partition three-quarters of the 25,000,000 hides produced annually in the sub-continent came from animals which had died of disease, malnutrition or mere old age; and owing to the continuing bias against cow-slaughter, the proportion in India is probably still higher. Obviously this means a serious deterioration in

[32] Sharma, 152.
[33] Sharma, Chapter X; Thomas, Chapter XXX; Vakil, 348–52.

the quality of hides, and in fact good hides were in short supply. Moreover, those workers who were not Untouchables were mostly Muslims, and many – including the shoemakers of Agra – have migrated to Pakistan, which now has a superfluity of hides and of labour but a shortage of good tan-stuffs.

In India the raw material basis is obviously not quantitatively lacking, and there are plenty of vegetable tan-stuffs, especially in the south. 'The dry north-west and the wet north-east (including Bengal) are the poorest regions in the supply of local tanning materials', and this is one factor in the growth of chrome tanning at Calcutta.[34] It will be noted that both these deficit areas are now largely in Pakistan. The north in general, however, has to rely on babul (*Acacia arabica*) bark, which has only 12–14% tannin against the 16–18% of avaram (*Cassia auriculata*) which is widespread in the drier Deccan. Myrobalans (35%) and divi-divi (40%) also grow mainly in the Peninsula. None of these, however, is as valuable as wattle bark, which has 35% tannin and loses it far more slowly than any of the others. Wattle was imported from South Africa, and some grown in the Nilgiris.

Tanning and the production of leather goods were widely distributed, but with some interesting regional differentiation. Tanning was carried on at three levels: 'bag tanning', the production of kips, and modern factory tanning. In bag tanning the hide is sown up and, as it were, pickled from within; this is the standard method of the village tanner and accounted for 40–45% of the hides, but only the worst were used. Though any hides may be called kips, the word strictly applies to hides half-tanned in pits; no machinery is required, and little capital, but the scale of operations is larger than in bag-tanning. Over 40% of the hides were turned into kips, most of which were exported, especially to Britain. Madras was the leading centre, but kips were produced all over the Peninsula, and it is in this branch that wattle bark is most used. Modern methods accounted for about 15% of the hides; not all in large factories, since there was a con-siderable output of chrome-tanned leather around Calcutta, in small or even cottage units owned and mainly worked by Chinese. Most of the large modern tanneries are in the north, especially in Uttar Pradesh where Kanpur is the chief centre. Not only had this area a larger proportion of better hides than the south – perhaps in part owing to the stronger Muslim element – but here, for climatic reasons, are the main markets for solid footwear; the southerner can walk on sandals or bare feet. Hence too the north was far more important for finished leather goods, much of the demand being military. Apart from the Chinese craft industry at Calcutta, only a few tanneries – two dozen – used the chrome method, and these were Kanpur, Calcutta and Madras.

The production of finished goods, still mostly by hand, either by individual shoemakers or in small shops, was estimated at 100,000,000 pairs of various indigenous types and 30,000,000 of European shoes and boots; on the 1941 population this is one pair a year for one person out of three. All sandals and

[34] Sharma, 164–7, 173.

80–90% of European shoes are handmade; Agra was the chief centre with nearly 150 small 'factories'. There were only nine modern factories – two each at Agra, Kanpur and Calcutta (including Batanagar), one each at Madras, Bombay and Bangalore. But the enormous increase in Army demand, from *c.* 100,000 pairs a year pre-war to 6,600,000 in 1943, 'involved a sudden expansion'; one Kanpur firm is said to have had the largest self-contained footwear factory in the world, and the Government Harness and Saddlery Factory, also at Kanpur, took on ten times its pre-war number of workers.[35] The localization at Kanpur stems largely from its old importance as a depot for military stores of all kinds.

2. *Rubber*

The rise of rubber industries in India was due to the international restriction scheme of 1934, which meant that much India-grown rubber could not be exported and so was available at prices well below the artificial world level. West Bengal and Bombay developed the great majority of the factories. Pre-war demand for tyres was met mainly by plants owned by Dunlops and Firestone, which by 1942 together produced 390,000 car and nearly 1,900,000 cycle tyres; the war as usual intensified production, which by 1949 had risen to 1,400,000 motor and 7,700,000 cycle tyres, together with nearly 18,000,000 pairs of rubber shoes.

3. *Glass*

Of the 232 glass factories in India in 1947, no fewer than 92 were entirely devoted to the making of bangles, which was also a cottage industry. The great centre for the factory production of bangles was Firozabad (Uttar Pradesh), with hundreds of small workshops to which finishing and decorating was put out by the factories. Japanese competition nearly ruined the cottage industry, to the benefit of Firozabad.

Of the remaining 141 factories, Uttar Pradesh, West Bengal, and Bombay had respectively 58, 31 and 21, but the value of output was in reverse order, though not differing greatly. In Uttar Pradesh the industry developed mainly along the flanks of the Vindhyan sandstone plateaus, mostly in Agra District and near Allahabad; the Province accounted for nearly half and the District for nearly a third of Indian employment. About two-thirds of the cost of raw materials was for soda ash, formerly obtained from Khewra (West Punjab) but now from Indian sources. About half the output, by value, was contributed by bottles. The war saw a marked expansion in range as well as output, and thermos refills, electric bulbs and a small amount of scientific glassware were produced. The industry, formerly using mainly crude pot-furnaces, made much technical progress, but suffered from a tendency to plunge into any line which looked lucrative: as a result the sheet-glass capacity was three to six times actual output in 1946–49.

[35] Vakil, 350; Thomas, 305.

4. Paper and other wood-based Industries[36]

(a) Paper. The classics of Sanskrit literature were usually written on palm-leaves, in the north sometimes on birch-bark; paper-making seems to have come from China via the central Asian Muslims, and the indigenous hand-workers were mainly Muslims. Paper-making by hand, usually from fibrous plants, lingered on in a few places but was of no importance. A few mills were set up in 1870–90, on the Hooghly and at Lakhnau, Poona and Raniganj; but supplies of softwood are limited to the Himalayas, and no mills were added until bamboo pulping became commercially practicable, about 1922; a protective duty was placed on imported pulp in 1931, and in five years the utilization of bamboo pulp rose by 280%. The war once more checked imports and increased demand.

Bamboos supplied about 55% of the raw material, grasses 22%, waste paper 10–12%, wood pulp only 1–2%. *Sabai* grass is better than bamboo, but yields are lower and more erratic. Obviously regeneration of cut-over bamboo areas is essential, but growth is rapid (only 4–5 years) and supplies at the rate of 600,000 tons of canes a year can be maintained indefinitely given proper conservation. Capacity was 135–150,000 tons of paper a year, but hitches in the supply of chemicals were keeping current production down to about 130,000 tons, a third of it boards. This was about half the demand; the bureaucracy naturally received priority, and supplies to schools were short. Whatever the planned expansion, the increasing official mania for *papierasserie* will probably continue to tax the industry to the utmost.

As usual West Bengal and Bombay led with 4 and 3 of the 12 larger mills; but West Bengal, which produced over 50%, drew largely from the Chittagong Hill Tracts and Sylhet (East Pakistan) and farther afield, into the Orissa Hills, for a product bulky in proportion to weight. This may lead to a shift to the areas with the most ample bamboo forests, roughly the hill borders of the Peninsula. The industry in Uttar Pradesh and East Punjab relied largely on *sabai* grass from the Siwaliks.

(b) Plywood is especially useful in Indian conditions of temperature and humidity, in which ordinary woodwork readily cracks and swells. Madras and Assam led in the production of plywood, which rose during the war (when Japanese and European imports were cut off) from 13,000,000 to 50,000,000 sq. ft. in 1944. The latter figure was much less than capacity, another example of plunging after quick returns. West Bengal had now 40 and Madras 30% of capacity (162,000,000 sq. ft.); output in 1952 was 90,500,000 but in 1953 had fallen to 60,800,000 sq ft.[37]

Timber supplies are adequate, and India usually produces sufficient casein and protein glues. But it is significant that the tea demand, which pre-war took over 80% of output, fell to less than half the 1944 figure as soon as imports were

[36] Thomas, 290–302; Vakil, 306–10; M. P. Bhargava, 'Review of the pulp and paper industry in India' (*5th British Empire Forestry Confce*, Dehra Dun, 1947).
[37] See Thomas, 295; cf. Vakil, 292–3.

resumed. Plywood production is highly skilled, and get-rich-quick expansionism resulted in very poor chests being put on the market; some of them did not even survive to leave India. The industry is potentially very important, with a wide range of uses apart from tea-chests.

(c) *Distillation, etc.* The 'collier' of the European Middle Ages survives in the person of the Indian charcoal-burner, whose primitive kilns, dotted about the vast scrub-forests, produced about 9,000,000 tons of charcoal a year. But all the valuable distillation products were wasted. There was so far only one wood-distillation plant, part of the charcoal-smelted iron and steel industry at Bhadravati (Mysore). This indeed was one of the biggest in Asia, producing daily 30,000 gallons (136,000 litres) of distillate, from which calcium acetate (main source of acetic acid), methyl alcohol, and formaldehyde are extracted. Rosin and turpentine were formerly made chiefly at Jalo (West Punjab), but there is little industrial demand in Pakistan as yet, and as most of Punjab coniferous forests went to India production became concentrated at Hoshiarpur (East Punjab).

CHAPTER II

India in the Planning Era

India entered the second half of the 20th century still on the crest of the wave of confidence and jubilation following Independence, with a stable political scene, a good administrative system and an adequate rail-net (the two steel frames bequeathed by the British Raj), as well as an amount of industry considerable in absolute figures, even if but small in relation to the large population. Under Pandit Nehru's leadership of the ruling Congress Party, the Central Government passed a number of measures to turn the country towards 'a socialistic pattern of society', with a mixed economy as between the 'public sector' of nationalized or government-controlled establishments) and the 'private sector' under private capital, and a series of Five Year Plans aimed at speeding up and directing the rapid economic development, and especially the industrialization, of the whole country and its federal states.[1]

In most countries with modern economies, under whatever political system, government policy has become a factor in economic and particularly in industrial location, a factor of equal moment with – though not necessarily counter to – the factors of raw materials, markets and the like; it was only to be expected that government action should assume paramount importance in the 1950s and 60s, particularly in industrial location. This phase of rapid change under the influence of new forces is almost revolutionary, though not to the extent of rejecting and tearing up the foundations presented by the *fait accompli* of history. It is fortunate that Karan's valuable study of industrial distribution patterns presents a synoptic picture at the crucial watershed date of 1950, at the very beginning of the planning era. Figs. 10.2 and 11.1, founded on his work, are in a sense both the culmination of the discussion in the preceding chapter, and an essential beginning to this one.[2]

[1] The principle of the mixed economy was established by an Industrial Policy Resolution of 1948, and further spelled out by a Resolution in 1956. The public sector is mainly industries of basic or strategic importance, or public utilities – steel, coal, strategic minerals, heavy engineering, defence production, rail and air transport and communications; though even here some undertakings, such as the Tata steelworks, are in the private sector. Other industries like machine tools, essential drugs, and basic chemicals are undertaken by the government 'to the extent necessary', though vigorous private sector activity is encouraged. Consumer industries of all types are in the hands of private capital, including co-operatives to some extent. See Planning Commission, *Towards a Self-Reliant Economy : India's Third Plan 1961–66* (Delhi, 1961).

[2] See also G. Kuriyan, 'Industrial development in India since Independence', *Proceedings of IGU Regional Conference, Japan 1957* (Science Ccil of Japan, Tokyo, 1959), 374–81, and his 'An analysis of the spatial distribution of industry in India . . . ', *IGJ* 37/1 (1962), 1–7. Also Karan's more up-to-date account in *Ann. Ass. Amer. Geog.*, 54 (1964), 336–54.

Even granting the low productivity per worker discussed in Chapter 10, the distribution pattern of Fig. 11.1 is impressive, and it is interesting that an Indian worker should have concluded that industrial regions were beginning to form at the close of the colonial phase. He notes the generally small size of undertaking, and it should be added that even in his major regions there are considerable tracts of terrain which are completely untouched by industry or even

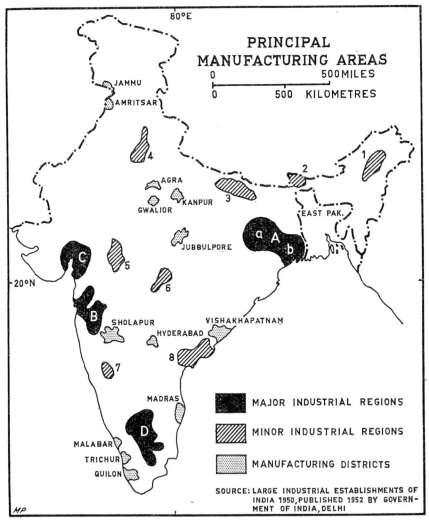

FIG 11.1 INDIA: PRINCIPAL MANUFACTURING AREAS. Most of these nascent industrial areas of 1950 were (and are) characterized by a sprinkling of industrial foci in rural tracts otherwise relatively little affected by urbanization or industrialization; changes since 1950 are noted in the text. *Source:* P. P. Karan and W. M. Jenkins in *Economic Geography*, 35 (1959). See expanded key opposite.

FIG II.I PRINCIPAL MANUFACTURING AREAS

Major Regions	A. Bihar-Bengal Industrial Belt	B. Bombay-Poona	C. Ahmedabad-Baroda	D. Madurai-Coimbatore Bangalore
Main industries	(a) *Hooghlyside* Jute, cotton, electricals, light engineering, chemicals. (b) *Chota Nagpur* Iron and steel, wire, rolling stock, vehicles	Cotton (over one-third of workers), chemicals, engineering, food processing, printing, light engineering, consumer goods	Cottons, chemicals pottery	Cottons, light consumer goods, light engineering
Coal	Damodar	Originally UK, S. Africa by sea, now long haul from Bihar	Long haul from Bihar (recently some oil and gas strikes)	Long haul from Bihar
Hydro-electricity	(Recently a little from Damodar Valley project)	Important supplies from Western Ghats	—	Cauvery, Jog, Nilgiris
Iron ore	Singhbum	—	—	Small iron and steel works at Bhadravati using ores from Bababhudan hills
Other raw materials mainly from agriculture	Bengal jute, by water meeting Damodar coal (but much of best jute area to East Pakistan)	Cotton, ground-nuts on regurs of Plateau to east	Cotton surrounding regur soils. Salt from salt-pans	Some cotton on Madurai and Coimbatore regur
Port and commerce	Calcutta (including European managing agencies)	Bombay (including Parsees and Gujaratis)	Local commerce (Marwaris and Gujaratis)	Madras as port with own commerce and industries, though some distance away
Markets	Largest urban market, Hooghlyside	Early exports China then large local urban market	Local markets of some importance	

Minor Regions

1. Assam Valley — Processing of local tea and rice and oil-seeds, some petroleum
2. Darjeeling terai — Processing of local tea
3. North Bihar-Uttar Pradesh — Manufacture of local sugar-cane
4. Delhi-Meerut — Manufacture of local sugar-cane, some textiles, chemicals, engineering
5. Indore-Ujjain — Local cottons for local markets, handicrafts (former courts)
6. Nagpur-Wardha — Small textiles, foundries, railway and general engineering, glass and pottery

333

7. Dharwar-Belgaum	Cotton textiles, local cotton and markets, railway and general engineering
8. Godavari-Krishna Delta	Local tobacco, sugar-cane, rice and oil, cement, small textiles

Manufacturing Districts

Agra: very important for shoes and leatherware, made in a few large and many small factories and workshops, glass, tourist bric-a-brac, some cottons and woollens
Amritsar: woollens, carpets, embroidery
Gwalior: china and pottery, cottons, leather, light-engineering, quarrying, cigarettes
Hyderabad: food processing including biscuits, light engineering, handicrafts (formerly for the court)
Jammu: woollens, cottons, dyeing and printing, pottery
Jabalpur: railway workshops, textiles
Kanpur: textiles and clothing, large modern tanneries, leather works, boots and shoe factories, founded on military clothing and equipment
Madras: textiles, light engineering, consumer goods of wide variety
Malabar-Quilon-Trichur: cashew processing, coconut and other oil pressing, associated industries (coir manufacture, soap), some textiles, numerous handicrafts in very densely peopled coastal tract
Sholapur: important textile and engineering centre on regur soils

It should be noted that most of these areas are really nascent rather than developed; see text.

by strong industrial influence, even today. It seems best to adopt the phrasing of our caption and call these nascent rather than accomplished industrial regions. And one should also note again the small proportion of the population involved or benefited, and the low per capita incomes and marked socio-economic disparities. These have naturally been very bitterly criticized by nationalist writers;[3] it is already becoming possible to review this period in the perspective of history, and Nehru himself possessed this perspective to a remarkable degree, even when writing from gaol. Later, Buchanan points out how India might well have progressed *pari passu* with Japan, but for the obstacles to leadership inherent in the colonial relationship (even if added to by some features of Indian character and social structure);[4] and Malenbaum points out how the nascent industrial regions or foci of the geographer were also economic enclaves, not diffusing economic stimulus to surrounding regions to any extent.[5]

The character of the Five Year Plans

The first Five Year Plan was relatively small and mainly oriented to agriculture; for example, the fertilizer plant at Sindri is of this period. Its modest demands on foreign exchange for capital goods were well within the country's means – India had, for instance, considerable sterling balances on account of war-time expenditure by Britain. Thinking about growth rates was based on a very simple general model. Immediately after Independence a series of poor monsoons caused widespread hardship and locally actual famine, particularly in the south, but there were good rains during the Plan period, and a series of good harvests,

[3] J. Nehru, *The Discovery of India* (Doubleday, Anchor Books, NY, and London, 1946), Chapters 7–9.
[4] D. H. Buchanan, 'Differential economic progress . . . Japan versus Asia', *American Economic Rev.* 41 (1951), 359–66.
[5] W. Malenbaum, *Prospects for Indian Development* (Allen & Unwin, London, 1962), 32.

and good demand for export of Indian primary products due to the Korean war resulted in a very fair measure of success for a relatively unambitious Plan.

The Second Plan (1956–61) was much more ambitious, based on more complex macro-economic growth models (though based largely on assumption, rather than available data). It involved considerable reliance on foreign aid, but in this Plan period the government overhauled the taxation system and introduced varied measures to make resources for development available from internal finance.[6] Without neglecting agriculture it emphasized the need to cope with unemployment on the one hand, and on the other stressed the long term benefits of developing heavy and basic industry as a foundation for more complex industrialization later. (It should be noted that this latter 'heavy industry' policy is not necessarily the best way to increase employment, at least in the short term; this was at least largely accepted, but with some reliance on the development of labour-intensive consumer goods industries, light in capital needs, as noted presently.) An econometric model incorporating differing proportions of producer-goods and of consumer-goods industries over a twenty-year period was used, deliberately at hazard, in order to demonstrate an approach to resolving the competition between these two sectors in India's particular circumstances. In detail something of the conflict was resolved by recommending that increased effective consumer demand should be met, and inflationary pressure arising from the capital-intensive developments of heavy industry, etc., should be partly met, by light investment in labour-intensive consumer-goods industries during this Plan period; this would enable the country to step out far more boldly than at any previous period in the development of heavy and basic industry.[7]

The Third Plan (1961–66), while continuing to emphasize industrial development including farther developments in heavy industry, also shows some return to giving a high priority to agriculture, as a *sine qua non*. Again it involves a good deal of foreign aid.

Both the Second Plan and the Third Plan have encountered serious difficulties. The Second Plan was hampered early on by a serious foreign exchange crisis,

[6] See *inter alia* D. L. Spencer, 'India's planning and foreign aid', *Pacific Affairs*, 34 (1961), 28–37, and V. K. R. V. Rao and D. Narain, *Foreign Aid and India's Economic Development* (Asia, Bombay, 1963); for share of foreign capital, P. K. Srivastava, 'Foreign participation in Indian industry', *Eastern Economist* 27/12/63, 1487–1513; D. L. Spencer, 'New sources of industrial finance in India', *Pacific Affairs*, 31 (1958), 261–74; for taxation, etc., N. A. Khan, 'Resources for India's Third Five Year Plan', *Indian Jnl Economics*, 40/156 (1959), 65–72.

[7] Here, as elsewhere, it would be easy to have more footnotes than text; some guidance to the vast literature is given in the Bibliographical Note. Useful insight into these problems may be derived from: P. C. Mahanalobis, 'The approach of operational research to planning in India', *Sankhya* (Calcutta), 16/1–2 (1955), 3–130, and from critiques from different angles in: D. R. Gadgil, *Planning and Economic Policy in India* (Gokhale Inst., Poona, 1961); W. Malenbaum, *op. cit.*, especially 88–91; H. W. Arndt, 'The Balance of Payment argument for priority of heavy industry', *Sankhya*, Series B 24/2–3 (1952), 265–76.

population growth was more rapid than had been expected (see p. 145), and many of its targets were not fulfilled. The Third Plan was upset by the need to quad-ruple defence spending from October 1962 onwards following the Chinese aggression against India's far northern borders; and there was perhaps under-estimation of the lag effect of some of the capital-intensive development, and over-estimation of the extent to which the Community Development investment was oriented, or effective, towards measures to improve agricultural productivity. Nevertheless there is considerable determination to improve the performance during the remainder of the Plan period, and to prepare for a Fourth Plan which will not only provide for improved standards of living, but also bring the economy to Rostow's 'take-off point' of a self-generating economy, not dependent on foreign aid, by the end of that Plan period (1966–71). Meantime crucial achievements may be summarized: in spite of a population increase of 80,000,000, per capita income has increased by 19%; agricultural output has increased by 37% and industrial production by 100% during the first two Plan periods.[8]

The influence of the Five Year Plans on industrial location, employment and urbanization

In the Five Year Plans, a key place is occupied by the building of large plants, mainly in the public sector, for heavy and basic manufacturing processes – iron and steel making, heavy machine tools, fertilizers and the like. Fig. 11.11 shows both concentration and dispersion in the distribution of major industrial units under the Plans.

There is a marked concentration of iron and steel plants in and around the northeastern part of the Peninsula, though this is a very large tract of country within which there has been some attempt to disperse industry into backward areas and to develop new resources of coal and iron ore. There has been expansion of the steel industry on the Damodar coalfield with an increase in the capacity of the private sector plant at Burnpur, the new public sector plant at Durgapur and a very large new one planned for Bokaro. The fertilizer factory at Sindri is also in this area, and both the public sector and the private sector contribute to some growth of nascent 'industrial complex' type within this general region, e.g. the public sector heavy machine tool factory at Ranchi, alloy steel plants at Jamshedpur (private sector) and Durgapur (public sector), the private sector wire manufacturing and vehicle assembly plant at Jamshedpur–Tatanagar and public sector locomotive factory at Chittaranjan north of the coalfield. There has been planned expansion of the Tata steel plant at Jamshedpur, increasing its

[8] See the refreshingly frank *Third Plan Mid-Term Appraisal* (Govt of India, Planning Commission, Delhi, 1963); V. V. Bhatt, 'A decade of planned development', *Economia Internazionale*, 15 (1962), 347–66; P. Pant, 'The development of India', *Scientific American*, 209/3 (1963), 189–206; and for a very cool critique, not unfriendly but rather anxious, Malenbaum, *op. cit.*, and his 'India and China: contrasts in development performance', *American Econ. Rev.* 49 (1959), 284–309.

capacity to 2,000,000 tons, with further expansion projected. Meantime coal production has been left mainly in the private sector under government control and supervision, but the National Coal Development Corporation produces an appreciable proportion of the output from the Damodar area, and is responsible for the development of new fields like the Korba field near Bilaspur, or expansion at Singareni, which might not be attractive to private capital but ought to be undertaken in the national interest.

So far there is expansion in well-tried broad regional locations, discussed in Chapter 9: precise siting is influenced by existing plant, water and transport facilities and the like, so far as is publicly known. The plant at Rourkela in Orissa is producing steel by the Linz–Donawitz process, particularly suitable for rolling steel sheets, e.g. for the Visakhapatnam shipyards, and is located on the main broad-gauge railway line between the Damodar coal and Singbhum iron and the distant but great industrial market for steel products in Bombay; it obtains ore from Barsua about 50 miles (80 km.) away, and brings large-scale industry to almost virgin territory in forested plateau country. This is also true of the plant at Bhilai in Madhya Pradesh near the railway junction of Raipur; this project has also involved the development of a new ironfield at Rajhara some 60 miles (97 km.) to the south, and was planned to draw some of its coking coal from a new coalfield at Korba, development of which, however, appears to have been a little slow and beset by difficulties. The location was, however, chosen partly to supply the shipyard at Visakhapatnam.[9]

Other developments within the field of heavy and basic industries are relatively small: there is some expansion including ferro-manganese plant at the small Mysore Government iron and steel plant at Bhadravati (see p. 330), foundry development at Bombay and at various steel plants and engineering works including defence establishments and railway workshops. So that so far there is some impetus towards industrial complex formation in the Damodar and Jamshedpur areas, with which is closely linked the Hooghlyside area. Hooghlyside has meantime been developing quite buoyantly in chemicals, light engineering (electrical apparatus, typewriters, etc.) in the private sector while the older-established jute industry has been re-equipping and adjusting to the difficulties following Partition. Elsewhere there is large-scale iron and steel development in new and relatively isolated areas mainly in the northeastern plateau, the new fertilizer plants at Varanasi (Benares) in the private sector, and at Nangal, Neiveli and Rourkela (public sector), and relatively small developments elsewhere mainly in older industrial towns and cities.

Some public sector developments in engineering industries have already been

[9] For a good account of these earlier planned developments, see N. N. Sen, 'The development of the iron and steel industry in India', *Science and Culture* (Calcutta), 26/2 (1960), 58–67, and *ibid.* 25/2 (1959), 112–20; also S. R. Ahsan, 'A note on the development of the Indian iron and steel industry', *Oriental Geogr* (Dacca), 1/2 (1958), 178–89, and D. Mookerjee, 'Durgapur, West Bengal's new steel plant', *Geography* 44 (1959), 127–8. Visakhapatnam may get its own steel plant under the Fourth Plan.

mentioned in order to fit them into their regional context. There are many other developments. At Bangalore there is quite a significant grouping of aircraft factory (expanded from a wartime repair and maintenance plant for the USAAF), aero engine factory, telephone factory, electronics factories for civil defence purposes, machine-tool plant and watchmaking establishment. Locational factors probably include existing Mysore Government factories (electric lamps, soap, ceramics) and private sector textile industry on all scales of production, an equable climate and much pleasant garden-city development, as well as some political pressure to take substantial industry to the south. Other developments are more scattered – expansion as a public sector project of the struggling private sector shipyard at Visakhapatnam, and a new shipyard at Cochin, aluminium and carbide plants at Alwaye, a rolling stock factory at Madras, a heavy electricals plant at Bhopal, and various ordnance factories for defence purposes. The oil refinery at Gauhati in Assam is between Assam's modest oilfields with their own refinery at Digboi and the huge markets of Hooghlyside and industrial Bihar. The plant at Barauni is being linked by pipeline to the Assam oilfields on the one hand, and to Kanpur and Calcutta on the other;[10] we can see in the allocation between Assam and Bihar the Central Government's need to compromise. These developments are much more scattered and isolated, with some attempt to disperse benefits of industrial development through the country.

Several of the nascent industrial regions of Fig. 11.1 have not or have barely been mentioned in this account of public sector activity. Meantime there has been considerable buoyancy and development in the private sector – e.g. in engineering industries around Bombay (including motor vehicle assembly and progressive manufacture), in Madras (again including motor vehicles and bicycles), in the Ahmedabad area, in Kanpur, in the relatively new but active textile centre of Coimbatore, and in Punjab, largely under the stimulus of refugees. As an example, Ludhiana and its environs produce sewing machines, bicycles, motor vehicles and spares, and small tools, in addition to traditional textile industries.

In comparison with Karan's 1950 map of industrial regions, the current picture after well over a decade of planning naturally includes intensification in nearly every one of the nascent industrial regions or complexes he described, while there are also considerable new nuclei brought mainly by the public sector into relatively backward areas which may act as catalysts in their regions. There have been signs of the formation of a congeries of small-scale ancillary industries round major engineering factories, e.g. in Bangalore which admittedly has a whole group of such large engineering units, and this tendency may grow. On the other hand regional interactions between expanding industrial towns and the surrounding region have been rather slight, and on a disappointingly narrow front. There has been a local response to the market, say for vegetables, or milk,

[10] *Third Plan Mid-Term Appraisal*, 136.

but not much general quickening of economic life and the better side of urban based culture.

One of the main objectives of the Plans has been to increase employment, and while this need not necessarily be urban and industrial employment, the large scale industries are mainly of this type. A rough estimate of the additional employment becoming available during the Second Plan is 8,000,000 (6,500,000 outside agriculture). Unfortunately, the backlog of unemployment at the end of the Plan period was some 9,000,000, with an additional 15–18,000,000 under-employed.[11] For the first two years of the Third Plan, i.e. 1961–63, employment was known accurately to have risen by 1,300,000 in the public sector and in the private sector establishments employing twenty-five persons or more (40% in services, 30% in manufacturing and 17% in transport and communications); other non-agricultural employment is thought to have added almost another 2,000,000, ascribed to Plan expenditure, with in addition some additional agricultural employment (the target for 1961–66 is 3,500,000 in agriculture). The total may amount to 5,000,000, almost half the target for the whole Third Plan period.[12] So there may be a slow gain, even with rapid increase in population (and labour force offering).

We now turn to small-scale industrial development, certainly more dispersed though naturally including considerable development in the nascent industrial regions as auxiliary industries to large scale units.

Small-scale industry

The Second Five Year Plan, as we have noted, set out to stimulate small scale and handicraft industry. Some picture of the regional distribution patterns may be gained from the National Atlas of India (Fig. 11.2), and in more detail region-ally in the insets. It is much more difficult at present to show the regional differences in trends, but for the country as a whole published data permit an assessment of the degree of success attained in stimulating small-scale industry.

In 1950–51 employment in small-scale industry was estimated at 11,000,000, per capita earnings at Rs. 659. Investment in this sector during the first two Plan periods was Rs. 218 crores (some £260,000,000).[13] In 1960–61 employment was almost 16,000,000, per capita income about Rs. 515. Despite the drop in per capita income, this is probably satisfactory progress in a country with such severe unemployment. Just over 9% of the labour force contributed almost 6% of national income, which again seems satisfactory for a generally labour-intensive sector.[14]

[11] *Third Five Year Plan*, 156.
[12] *Third Plan Mid-Term Appraisal*, 52–3.
[13] T. R. Sundaram, 'Utilisation of idle man-power in India's economic development', *Pacific Affairs*, 34 (1951), 131–40.
[14] Unpublished paper by Planning Commission, Perspective Planning Division, Notes on Perspective of Development in India, April 1964.

As examples, the *khadi* (coarse homespun cotton) industry, admittedly emphasized because of association with Gandhian ideas, produced 843,000,000 yards in 1951, 1,865,000,000 in 1958–59, worth Rs. 13·75 crores and employing 1·4 people. More modern products are included – small industries producing sewing machines, electric fans, bicycles, builders' hardware and handtools have increased production by 25 to 50% in the Second Plan period, and provided an additional 300,000 jobs.[15]

By and large, traditional handicrafts and small rural industry remain significant – though not necessarily prosperous – in the more backward and inaccessible areas; they account for 10% or more of the total employed population in eastern Assam, Kutch, Jaisalmer in the Thar Desert, and the Kanara Districts. Another type of concentration, however, is associated with 'putting-out' around industrial centres, or in the diffusion of small workshops into the countryside in developing industrial regions, as around Hooghlyside and in the Damodar valley. A combination of immemorial tradition and the resettlement of post-Partition refugees is probably responsible for a remarkable concentration (over 10% of the total work force) around Delhi. The spread of village electrification may be expected to strengthen this component.

Many rural crafts naturally go with population; carpentry, smithery, and so on, as we have seen (above, p. 306) and minor mechanization in the countryside may actually result in an increase of demand for artisans in metal, as repairmen rather than as craftsmen in their own right. Apart from these almost umbiquitous trades, there are of course some interesting regional variations: metal- and leather-working, carpetry and rug-making in the Punjab; khadi in Kutch and Kathiawad, tobacco in southern Tamilnad, coir, soap and other coconut-based products in Kerala. In many cases primitive production carries on in the villages, with increasing difficulty, side by side with – or in face of – factory production for wider markets: the aggregate unorganized production of vegetable oils and *gur* from sugar-cane and other sources (such as *nipa* palm) must be very large; and, with Prohibition the general law of the land, one important consumption industry, the manufacture of toddy, must *ipso facto* be a village occupation.

With improvement in communications, there is of course a tendency for small-scale crafts to retreat; under-employment may turn into unemployment. It is difficult to envisage any really substantial rescue of the crafts from this process, though palliatives are possible such as the better organization of the trade in toys and souvenirs around pilgrim and tourist centres. There may be more hope in workshop production of small consumer durables – bicycles, tools, small electrical gear, and so on.

It is perhaps these more modern industries which are particularly associated with the move to spread small industrial estates – with hutted workshops rather than the medium to large industrial sheds of industrial estates say in Britain – and which justify some even if guarded optimism about possible increases in

[15] *Towards a Self-Reliant Economy*, 242.

dispersed industry particularly as electricity spreads into small towns and villages (see p. 290). Fig. 11.2 shows how these industrial estates are fairly evenly spread through the country.[16]

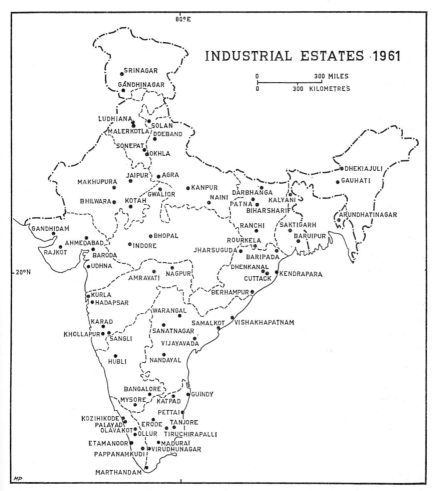

FIG 11.2 INDIA: INDUSTRIAL ESTATES. By March 1962 there were 71 estates with 138 factories, employing 19,000 people and producing Rs 160,000,000 worth of goods a year. *Source:* G. Whittington in *Tijdschrift voor Econ. en Sociale Geografie,* 54 (1963).

Before leaving the small-scale sector, we may note the high proportion of retail and distributive trade carried out by household traders – about 5,000,000 of just over 8,000,000 total businesses, but contributing only some Rs. 200

[16] G. Whittington, 'New features in the Indian industrial landscape', *Tijdschrift voor Econ. en Soc. Geografie,* 54 (1963), 193–4.

crores of the Rs. 1,200 crores contributed by distributive trades to the national income.[17]

Rural development: large-scale irrigation and multi-purpose projects and minor irrigation works; Community Development

These have already been discussed in Chapter 8 from an agrarian point of view. Figures 11.9 and 11.10 summarize a good deal concerning the areal distribution of the various projects.

From the planning point of view, the larger-scale projects have been satisfactory on the whole. Techniques are established, supervision and evaluation are relatively easy and effective; the Table shows the varying but by no means despicable degree of attainment of targets.

There have been problems locally. For instance, there was a period of lag in the Tungabhadra irrigation and hydro-electric project when there was difficulty in finding local farmers to take up irrigated plots, adapt their methods, and pay the water dues; since this project was to help the long notorious Bellary famine tract, the authorities were reluctant to bring in people from other areas over-populated in relation to available resources and techniques, possible social difficulties apart. But large irrigation projects, such as the Punjab Canal Colonies of last century, have often shown a marked lag in full growth of benefits, and some such lag may bring more heartening news in the second half of the Third Plan period, and in general it seems that these medium to large projects are a good planning risk. There have been disappointments in food production, but due rather to vagaries of the monsoon on unirrigated plots.

In Chapter 8 there is also a full discussion of many problems of Community Development. Summarizing from the planning point of view, there has been very rapid expansion, evenly spread throughout nearly all parts of the country. Though probably politically inevitable, expansion was probably too rapid from both the technical and the human points of view, which must be inseparable in Community Development. Granting almost irresistible political pressures, internal and external, what has gone wrong so far?

There was probably too much reliance on the universality and effectiveness of the upsurge of dynamic forces expected from the Indian people when they were freed from the colonial yoke (in part justifiably as the achievements since 1947 show); linked with this there was probably too much hoped for from officials: from being tools of colonialist oppression – or at best of excessive emphasis on the negative qualities of law and order – the same individuals were expected to become leaders of these released dynamic forces, no barriers now separating them from the people. This was certainly expecting too much of a whole body of men, however devoted, whether old-style Revenue Officers turned Block Development Officers, or new style *gram sewaks* whether recruited from within

[17] *Report on Household Trade* (NSS 7th–9th Round, Govt of India Cabinet Secretariat, Delhi, 1960).

the village as in Uttar Pradesh or from outside as in Maharashtra. This rapid expansion was subject to scrutiny and evaluation, at its best honest, disinterested and valuable; but it was probably too little controlled in the sense of being subject to constant review by skilled practitioners of the social sciences as well as officials and technologists, too little based on expansion from a firm core of locally or regionally relevant experimental success from villages selected for the purpose very early in the programme, and actually attaining self-generating development growing out of locally felt needs and aspirations. Above all, from one vital viewpoint, it was surely too little productivity-oriented, too much amenity-oriented – or at worst, as has been pointed out earlier, oriented to merely paper victories.

Published tabulations of the results of the Plans as a whole show reasonably satisfactory entries under Community Development. In real gains, in socio-economic advancement of the most underprivileged, and also in the vital matter of agricultural activity, too little has been achieved. The Chinese aggression in the north in the second year of the Third Plan period, and a series of droughts in the wheat-eating northwest causing local famine (controlled with some difficulty) and a very widespread food shortage which had to be handled 'on a war footing' in 1964, were factors in bringing to a head a growing dissatisfaction with this part of the Plans. But the effect may be to concentrate effort on the pressing problem of food supply, delaying progress in social reform or directing it along lines not hitherto foreseen.

The Mid-Term Appraisal of the Third Plan, of November 1963, reports that henceforth 'the village level workers should be assigned only one set of duties, namely, those pertaining to agricultural extension, supplies and demonstrations and assistance to co-operatives and Panchayats in drawing up and implementing village production plans'. The national emergency apart, the emphasis on productivity was overdue; the dilemma of a community development programme not accompanied by really drastic socio-economic reform remains. The landholder is likely to benefit, especially the owners of larger plots even following land reform (above, 270, for a critique). Therefore the underprivileged, especially the landless labourers, will be benefited only marginally by slightly increased availability of work and perhaps marginally higher wages. Perhaps as some palliative to this, there is also instituted a very rapidly expanding programme of rural works, for which in the first two years expenditure of Rs. 1·5 crores in perhaps 20,000 (of over 500,000) villages was responsible for providing some 7,500,000 man-days of employment at Rs. 1 to Rs. 2·50 per day.[18] Expanded rapidly, this programme may well be significant in relieving local pockets or severe seasonal incidence of unemployment or underemployment (see p. 131).

It is intended to be used to build roads, especially to markets, to set up soil conservation works, to carry out afforestation and drainage, and even to dig field channels, subject to eventual recovery of the cost from the farmers benefiting

[18] Planning Commission, *Mid-term* Appraisal, Manager of Government Publications, Delhi, 1963, esp. pp. 96–98.

from them. The two programmes together may at last turn the scale in securing widespread improvement in crop yields and reliability, especially if co-operation can also gain real momentum, particularly co-operative agreements about land-use to permit of consolidation of holdings where fragmentation at present prevents soil conservation measures or other rational land-use. They are likely to bring but palliative benefit to the economically vulnerable classes, to whom they may seem a rather pale benefit from 'a socialistic pattern of society', but the great hope – assuming the desirability of victory for the planning programmes while preserving democracy of more or less Western type – is that they may enable the society of rural India to survive, not necessarily unchanged, but evolving gradually, against the time when urban-industrial development can absorb many more of its people, and the standards of living especially among landless labour can be upgraded by higher, perhaps legally defined wages. The scale of the problem to which this is a palliative, however, is that according to the Second Plan (p. 14) about 40% of the agricultural population should be drawn elsewhere to make farming more economic, and that the agricultural labour force should be reduced to 60% of the total labour force by 1975–76.

The Five Year plans have now been considered in relation to large- and small-scale industry, and to the Community Development programmes – politically vital and potentially crucial in the success of the whole. Equally important and interrelated sectors remain to be reviewed: power, transport and trade.

The strategy of electric power generation

The available bases for power generation have been discussed under the appropriate headings in Chapter 9. The over-all strategy and the allocation between different sources of generation of electricity are considered here, in relation to recent demands and probably short term future demands for power. The tables summarize recent trends in demand and in generation, with short term targets as amended up to the Third Plan mid-term review and subsequent to the adjustment of targets following the Chinese threat in 1962, which are very likely to be fulfilled on recent performance in this industry (p. 363).

Beyond 1966 very large increases in demand are anticipated, and the strategy of power generation includes these factors:

(a) poor quality coal (including much from coal washeries needed to keep the iron-and-steel works supplied with adequate coking coal while conserving the scarce reserves) is available and can be used, given adequate protection from atmospheric pollution; this is a cheap method of generation, at present needing a large proportion of foreign exchange, though one that is falling as heavy electrical equipment comes into home production;

(b) the first five units, totalling 250,000 kW capacity, of the integrated scheme based on Neiveli lignite have come into production in Madras, to produce power, fertilizers and domestic fuel; this source of power will probably play a large part in the growing Southern Grid;

344

(c) hydro-electricity is at present somewhat more expensive to produce than that from well-sited and well-designed thermal plant, because of high capital cost, and it involves considerable lag because of long construction time; but a lower proportion of the capital goods requires scarce foreign exchange and generation costs are low since there is no cost for fuel; moreover, hydro-electric projects tend to be conservative of water, to be very useful for a variable load, and (at the price of less than optimal generation costs) to fit in with irrigation projects – but on the other hand to be located in out-of-the-way places where demand is low or only gradually built up;

(d) India's resources of nuclear material, and her skilled man-power, give her a leading position among the less developed countries in nuclear power generation, a ten year programme aims at 1,700 megawatts by 1980.

As yet, however, the capital costs of nuclear generation are so heavy that despite the saving in fuel costs (especially on transport), the over-all cost lies between that of thermal and that of hydro-electric power, while much of the capital goods at present needs foreign exchange, and nuclear stations are not suitable for widely varying loads. It is thus difficult to decide whether a country like India should import nuclear power stations at their present stage of development, tying herself to some extent to this technological stage, or should wait until much cheaper methods of generation have been evolved, as no doubt they will be within a few years. Even at present, however, nuclear power stations are justified in places remote from fuel sources or with very large markets for power, and stations are under construction for Tarapore near Bombay (400,000 kW capacity), and in prospect for Rana Pratap Sagar in Rajasthan and Kalpakkam near Madras.[19]

The general picture is of flexibility in an attempt to reduce the local power famines of the most industrially developed areas at the present day, and to keep ahead of demand in order to maintain electric power as a major catalyst in industrialization. For ten or fifteen years ahead the main target will be industry – still accounting for 75% of consumption – but the spread of electricity into tens of thousands of the larger villages (some 30,000 by late 1962) for lift irrigation, small industry and street and house lighting, is also giving experience and spreading a demand which may be quite crucial in raising living standards.

Transport

At the time of Independence, India's legacy from the colonial phase included, as we have seen, a kind of transportation panoply of imperialism: the major ports, the related 'steel frame' of broad-gauge railways, feeder lines of metre and

[19] Sources include: *Third Plan Mid-Term Appraisal*; M. Datta, *op. cit.*; H. J. Bhabha, 'The promise of nuclear energy', *Science and Culture*, 29/12 (Calcutta, 1963), 574–6 (and Editorial), and his 'On the economics of atomic power development in India', *Advancement of Science*, 14 (London, 1957–58), 159–75. Dr. Bhabha's tragic death in an air crash early in 1966 represented the loss of a "modern Leonardo" (Yehudi Menuhin, in a letter to the *Guardian*).

narrow gauge. The road net-work included distinct if not always good trunk
roads (of decreased military importance for a time, during the peak of the railway
age), and important feeder roads, totalling under 100,000 miles (161,000 km.) of

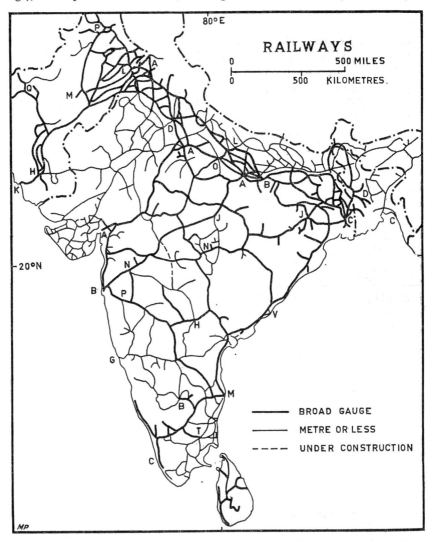

FIG 11.3 INDIA AND PAKISTAN: RAILWAYS. A metre gauge line is under construction
Hassan–Mangalore.

surfaced road (generally with 9–10 in., 23–25 cm., of road metal), beyond which
were the dirt roads and the village tracks. Inland transport by country boats was
important in the northeast, supplemented by steamboats and steel barges, and
survived in some other areas such as the southwest. Coastal traffic by steamship

346

and sailing craft survived and was locally important (see the figures for Manga-lore, p. 672 below), with some of it in foreign hands, while Indian overseas lines were in existence and growing. Privately-run internal airlines already had several years of honourable experience. The pattern of imperialism is plain, but changes had already begun, and moreover military routes were also channels of imperial trade, with notable exceptions such as the railways in the North-West Frontier Province and Baluchistan, now in West Pakistan. And the Nagpur Road Plan of 1943, still the basic document in the field, shows the importance attached to transport in forward thinking.

From the First Five Year Plan onwards, the Indian Government has constantly given a high priority to developments in transport. In railway development the main initial tasks were to overcome the backlog caused by excessive war-time strain on the system – inadequate maintenance, obsolescence of locomotives and rolling stock, etc. – to regroup and rationalize the railway companies as nationa-lized groups (completing the long-standing tendency to government subsidy and control), and to make adjustments consequential upon Partition. Then there was the task of forward planning in relation to a developing and industrializing economy. Up to now the demand for rail transport of passengers and goods has been so buoyant that railway planning has been able to take place in an atmos-phere of confidence, of planning an enterprise profitable to the government, in contrast say to the problem of cutting down all but the essential and profitable services in Britain. So far road services are complementary rather than com-petitive, although competition does exist even on quite long hauls because of the normal advantage of lorry transport in flexibility (see Fig. 11.5). Inland waterways are of some importance in Bengal and Assam, and in the southwest, but mainly by means of small 'country boats'. The trade by river steamer and steel barge on the Brahmaputra seems not to have recovered from the earthquake of 1950 while the main steam navigation company on the Ganga ceased business in 1950. There is an attempt to reactivate inland navigation under the Five Year Plans, but this progresses extremely slowly.[20] Airlines also are complementary and highly specialized; Fig. 11.7 shows an exception – the heavy traffic between Calcutta and the extreme northeastern areas (Assam and Tripura, etc.) across East Pakistan. Major developments in the rail system include the elimination of bottlenecks especially by bridging to replace ferries (e.g. the Ganga road-rail bridge at Mokameh), electrification of the busiest lines (Calcutta–Kanpur eventually – some busy lines near Bombay have long been electrified), limited dieselization (probably increasing as manufacture of diesel locomotives replaces the making of steam locomotives), and the construction of multiple tracks over lines unable to take the increasing traffic without causing hold-ups and bottlenecks.

Since the war, road development has come a long way from a fairly low starting

[20] *Third Plan Mid-Term Appraisal,* 144; see also *Ganga Traffic Survey* (National Ccil Applied Econ. Research, Bombay, 1960) which estimates that there are modest potential-ities (perhaps 200,000 tons per annum) for revival of steamship traffic on that river.

point. By the end of the Second Plan, surfaced roads were about 144,000 miles, unsurfaced over 250,000 (232,000 and 402,000 km.), but in places they remain unbridged, too narrow or poorly maintained. The main objectives of the Third

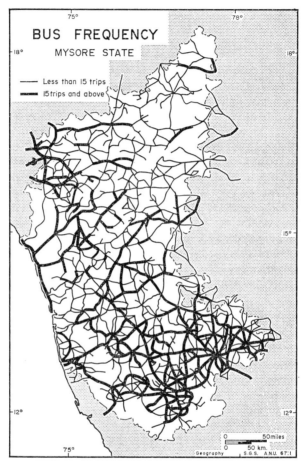

FIG 11.4 MYSORE: BUS FREQUENCIES. Number of trips per day. The local bus, ploughing through clouds of dust, is a powerful factor in social change. Road densities are low compared with developed countries, but considerable compared with many undeveloped countries, though there are still regions of isolation in the heart of India, especially the tribal country of central India and the northeastern Peninsula. Mysore services, partly State-run, may stand as representing the pattern in a reasonably developed region; the relative poverty of most of the Malnad and of the far north, adjacent to backward Telangana, will be noted. *Source:* A. T. A. Learmonth and L. S. Bhat (eds.) *Mysore State I. An Atlas of Resources* (Indian Statistical Institute, Calcutta), 1960.

Five Year Plan in relation to road development are based on a twenty-year road development plan (1961–81) drawn up by the Chief Engineers of the State and Central Governments: no village in a developed and agricultural area should

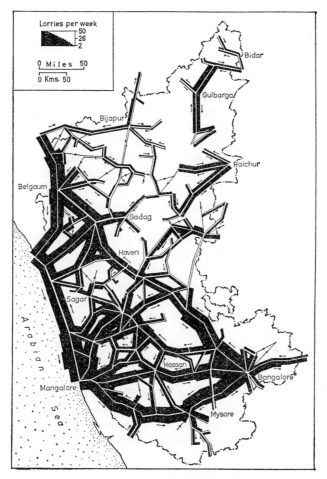

FIG 11.5 LORRY MOVEMENT IN MYSORE. On the Bangalore–Belgaum route, which continues to Bombay, lorry transport runs alongside the metre-gauge rail; in the coastal tract, it is competing successfully with shipping; along the east–west routes, it is gradually replacing the bullock cart. *Source:* A. T. A. Learmonth in *Geographers and the Tropics: Liverpool Essays* (Longmans, 1964).

remain more than 4 miles from a metalled road and $1\frac{1}{2}$ miles from any type of road, while undeveloped and underdeveloped areas will receive special attention appropriate to their needs. The target for 1981 is 200,000 miles of surfaced and 405,000 miles of unsurfaced roads (322,000 and 652,000 km.).

The priorities given in the Third Plan are indicative of the picture underlying Fig. 11.5: (a) bridges should be provided on all arterial routes, and the road surfaces improved to at least one lane of black-topped type, (b) the main roads in the vicinity of large towns should be widened to two lanes or more, and (c) the major arterial routes should have at least two-lane carriageways. The Chinese threat of October 1962 onwards has brought speeding rather than slowing of this particular part of the plan, though naturally mainly in the northern part of the country.

In some areas there is nationalized road transport for passengers and/or goods, elsewhere there are large and well-organized operating companies. But over much of the country road transport for both passengers and goods is carried on by excessively small-scale entrepreneurs. Numbers of commercial goods vehicles as yet are relatively small (in 1961, 171,000 out of a total of 675,000), but manufactures are increasing (28,000 in 1960-61). No doubt there is a place for small entrepreneurship with low capital investment (coupled with inspection of vehicles!) for purely local and spasmodic transport. But for longer distance work some measures of rationalization, whether by nationalization or no, are surely long overdue.

The table shows the expansion in coastal and overseas shipping achieved, and contemplated in the Third Plan period.

Thousands of Gross Registered Tons

	1950–51	1955–65	1960–61	1965–66
Coastal	217	240	292	425
Overseas	174	240	613	855
	391	480	905	1,280

The overseas shipping, in the hands of both public sector corporations and private sector companies, is given a high priority in order to conserve foreign exchange, while a committee on transport co-ordination is endeavouring to plan the best use of coastal shipping to complement the railways, notably in carrying bulk cargoes like coal.

Fig. 11.6 shows the main ports of the country. The great ports built up during the British phase retain their paramountcy, but Cochin is rising, and Kandla – built as a replacement for Karachi under the First Plan – carries appreciable traffic.[21] At times port congestion and delays are very serious and the Second Plan provided additional berths and facilities at Calcutta, Madras, Visakhapatnam and Cochin, while under the Third Plan preparations are at various stages to convert several minor ports for all-weather operations. Of these Haldia is 65

[21] See D. R. Gadgil, *op. cit.* xiv for an interesting questioning of the decision to make Kandla a free port; Cochin, in over-populated Kerala and with a great need for expansion of trade and industry, would have been a more rational choice for a free port.

miles (105 km.) downstream from Calcutta, so that ships may lighten before
going up to Calcutta, have a quick turn-round there and load additional outwards
cargo again at Haldia; this involves a rail link from Kharagpur to Haldia. The

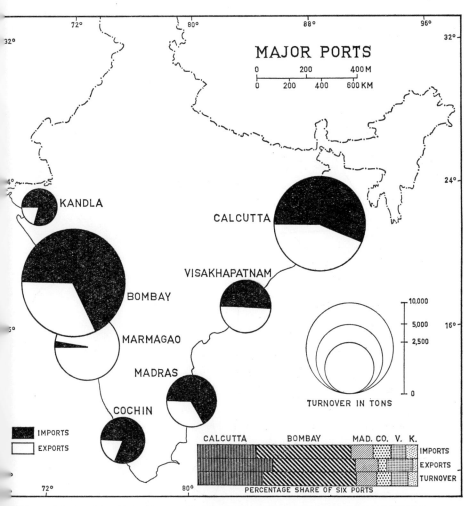

FIG 11.6 INDIA: MAJOR PORTS. Averages 1959–60 to 1963–64 (Marmagao 1961–62
to 1963–64). The great colonial ports of Calcutta and Bombay are still dominant,
but Cochin rivals Madras and the new port of Kandla has already a fair turnover.
The striking contrast between Marmagao, with its iron ore exports, and the general
import/export pattern will be noticed. *Source: Statesman's Year-Book.*

others are Tuticorin in Madras, Mangalore in Mysore and Paradip in Orissa. A barrage on the Ganga at Farakka is to be built to send additional water down the Hooghly to decrease silting on the Hooghly and reduce tidal bores.[22]

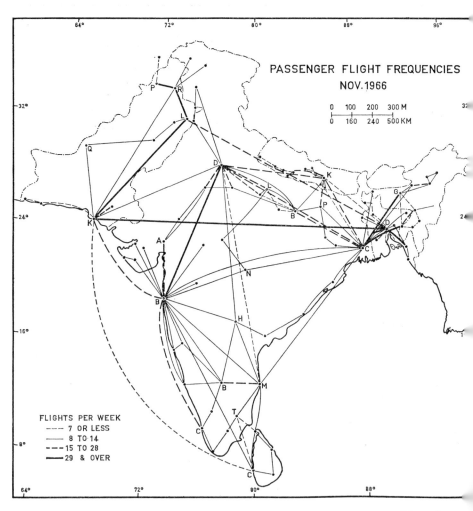

FIG II.7 INDIA AND PAKISTAN: PASSENGER FLIGHT FREQUENCIES. Note the importance of the Karachi–Dacca and Calcutta–Gauhati services. *Source:* compiled from data in *ABC World Airways Guide,* Nov. 1966 (T. Skinner, London).

[22] *Third Five Year Plan,* 558–9; *Third Plan Mid-Term Appraisal,* 145; note in *Science and Culture,* 27/1 (1961), 31. Progress of port capacity (in million tons turnover) is: 1951, 20; 1956, 24; 1961, 37; 1965–66 target, 49.

Trade

The era of the Five Year Plans has naturally brought marked changes in India's trade position, large imports of capital goods reversing the generally favourable balance of trade of the British period. Yet recent changes in direction of trade, with less close relations with Britain, continued trends which started several decades ago. There is a growing tendency to state and inter-government trading, largely by bi-lateral agreements.

Exports and imports during the era of the Five Year Plans

During the First Five Year Plan, avowedly modest in scale, imports were relatively low at an average of Rs. 724 crores per annum, while exports at Rs. 609 crores included very high figures for 1951–52 because of the Korean war. The much more ambitious Second Plan brought a sharp increase in imports from Rs. 746 crores in 1955–56 to Rs. 1,099 crores in 1956–57 and Rs. 1,233 crores in 1957–58. This increase was unexpectedly sharp, draining foreign exchange reserves, notably the sterling balances resulting from British spending in India for war-time purposes. Moreover, various factors have invalidated the foreign exchange control system so that much of the foreign exchange was spent on imports not scheduled in the Plan, not even in the large estimates allowed for private sector imports of capital goods, etc. This foreign exchange crisis, parti-cularly sharp and peculiarly vexing to the government because it showed lack of acceptance of the Plan by officials and politicians as well as businessmen – not to mention corruption – was nevertheless inherent in this phase of planned economic development. It was met by further import restrictions, imports falling to Rs. 920 crores by 1959–60. Such restrictions are likely to continue in some form at least until the end of the Fourth Plan in 1971. The table shows the changing emphasis on imports of raw materials and capital goods, and also the need to import food from time to time though this may not drain foreign exchange because of the special provisions of the American P.L. 480 legislation.

Meantime, exports have remained comparatively stagnant, though in the middle of the Third Plan period an improvement was seen, following years of effort to promote exports, and encouraging successes were gained for individual products and exports, such as iron ore (to Japan and Eastern Europe), manganese ore (to Japan), coal (to Pakistan), and mica (to many industrial countries); and jute fabrics, vegetable oils, electrical and electronic equipment, engineering goods, iron and steel castings, metals and metal manufactures (mainly of iron, steel and aluminium), chemicals and soap, rubber manufactures, drugs and medicines. Cotton and jute fabrics and tea are tending to stagnation or decline and manufactured goods generally to be less promising than appeared likely a few years ago – largely because Japanese competition is too powerful in most likely markets. The export campaign during the Second Plan period may have been affected by the 1958 economic recession in North America and Europe, but the tables below show how difficult the problem is. Exports of agricultural commodities and related manufactures tend to fall, within which the separate figures for cotton and jute manufactures should be noted; the fall in these goes far to offset the increase in other manufactures, including new lines, and also in mineral exports, notably iron ore to Japan and Eastern Europe.

PATTERN OF EXPORTS 1951–60

	(Rs. crores)			
	1960–51	1955–56	1958–59	1959–60
1. Agricultural commodities and related manufactures	496·5	489·3	453·5	473·6
Cotton and jute manufactures (included in item 1)	250·5	181·7	153·4	180·5
2. Other manufactures	58·4	61·0	53·3	105·0
New manufactured products (included in item 2)	8·9	8·61	12·5	25·0
3. Minerals	23·4	34·4	46·2	53·0
Total	578·3	584·7	553·0	631·6

DIRECTION OF INDIA'S FOREIGN TRADE

	(Per cent shares)					
Country/area	Exports			Imports		
	1952	1956	1960	1952	1956	1960
1. ECAFE countries	25·7	16·3	17·0	13·6	12·4	13·1
Japan	4·1	4·9	5·5	2·4	5·2	5·4
2. West Asia	5·7	5·8	6·5	7·7	10·8	7·5
3. Africa	3·6	3·9	2·5	3·8	4·0	4·4
4. Western Europe	29·6	39·8	38·5	30·1	50·1	40·4
UK	20·5	29·8	27·5	18·5	25·0	20·0
European Economic Community	7·5	8·3	8·0	8·8	20·0	18·0
5. Eastern Europe and China	1·3	3·5	8·0	2·2	4·2	3·7
6. North America	21·1	17·0	18·7	37·3	12·4	25·2
USA	19·0	14·7	16·0	33·6	11·3	23·7
7. Latin America	1·4	1·0	2·5		0·1	0·1
8. Oceania	4·3	4·4	3·1	2·0	1·7	2·3
9. Others	7·3	8·3	3·2	3·3	4·3	3·3
Total	100·0	100·0	100·0	100·0	100·0	100·0

The table shows the decreasing but still considerable proportion of trade with Britain, which takes more from India than India takes in return, in contrast to the rising proportion of trade with Japan, with a relatively even trade balance, and with USA and the countries of the European Economic Community with both of which the trade balance tends to be distinctly adverse to India, and where export promotion campaigns may be particularly needed.

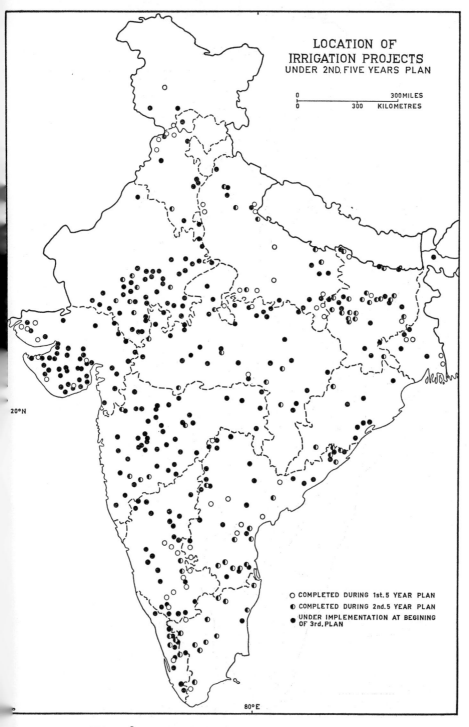

FIG 11.8 INDIA: SECOND PLAN IRRIGATION PROJECTS

FIG II.9 INDIA: MULTIPURPOSE AND MAJOR IRRIGATION PROJECTS.

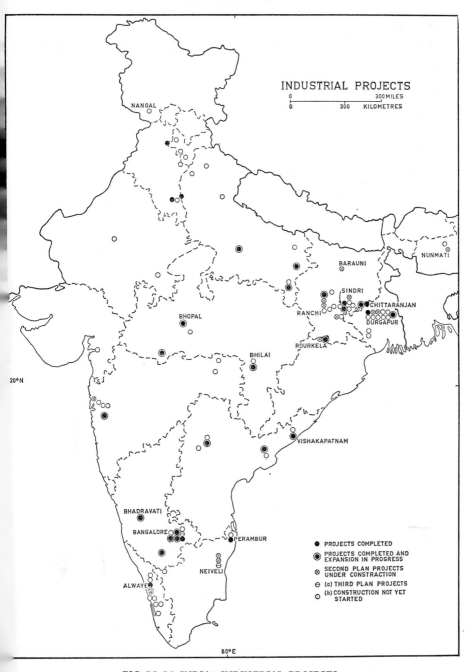

INDUSTRIAL PROJECTS

0   300 MILES
0   300   KILOMETRES

NANGAL

NUNMATI

BARAUNI

SINDRI

RANCHI   CHITTARANJAN

BHOPAL   DURGAPUR

ROURKELA

BHILAI

20°N

VISHAKAPATNAM

BHADRAVATI

BANGALORE   PERAMBUR

NEIVELI

ALWAYE

● PROJECTS COMPLETED
◉ PROJECTS COMPLETED AND EXPANSION IN PROGRESS
⊗ SECOND PLAN PROJECTS UNDER CONSTRACTION
⊖ (a) THIRD PLAN PROJECTS
○ (b) CONSTRUCTION NOT YET STARTED

80°E

FIG 11.10 INDIA: INDUSTRIAL PROJECTS.

Conclusion: Indian society in the era of Five Year Plans

These paragraphs must reflect personal experience and even prejudices, must be subjective in judgment. What yardsticks shall we use? The reports of the National Sample Survey give some quantitative data, interestingly analysed by Malenbaum. There is probably a slow rise in 'consumer expenditure' – a useful general indicator of standards of material living. The Survey has for some years now made available data about the higher standards of consumption in the towns and generally towards the north and west of the country, and indicated the tendency for rural dwellers experiencing a rise in consumption to increase their non-food items, while town dwellers moving from the lower levels tend to diversify their consumption. Fig. 11.11 gives some, though subjectively based, indications of regional variations in economic development according to Schwartzberg;[23] there is evidence of higher consumption levels in the four largest cities, and the increases may also be concentrated there and in other major foci of economic development under the Five Year Plans – in both the public and the private sectors. The Second Plan target of providing new jobs for 11,000,000 people was not fulfilled – only 8,000,000 were found in the event. Even so the direct effects and the indirect influence on the economy have effected some improvement of standards of living, even taking groups among the most difficult and vulnerable classes, the landless labour of the countryside and the very poor, often rootless, casual labouring groups of the towns and cities. The improvement was but slight, but it was carried out despite a sharp upsurge in rates of population increase, much higher than were anticipated at the beginning of the Plan period.

How does the present picture compare with the later part of the British period on the one hand, and on the other with the declared objective of the Congress Party Government of a socialistic pattern of society?

As the Indian nationalists predicted, Independence has brought a much more positive approach to many problems than was possible under a colonial régime, and this has been done while preserving and continuing many of the more worthy legacies of the British period. This has allowed the best of the politicians, professional men, administrators and business men to fulfil themselves and to serve and advance their country in a way unthinkable before Independence. Nepotism and corruption have possibly increased, at least at certain levels; it probably affects some in all the classes mentioned, yet many individuals are completely beyond reproach or suspicion, and it may well prove possible to control this plague, particularly if the Plans as a whole do succeed. There is a new and wider prosperity and confidence among middle class people, accompanied by very much freer and more confident social and professional exchanges with Europeans. The need for controls for restrictions on imports and on internal consumption in order to promote exports makes for a certain grey

[23] A revised version of this map may be found in W. Norman (ed.), India, Pakistan, Ceylon (Univ. of Pennsylvania Press, 1960); there is little substantive change, but the map includes Pakistan and Ceylon.

monotony reminiscent of the later part of the Second World War and immediately post-war years in Britain, and with similar results in causing a certain amount of dissatisfaction or rebelliousness especially among young people. There is a very much larger and more widely dispersed class of industrial workers – middle class rather than working class in many respects. The respectable lower middle class of clerks, school teachers, and so on have often a bitter struggle in these times of inflationary pressures, even more or less controlled.

The very poor urban groups have relatively stable social standards and *mores* so long as they can survive as family and preferably as village or hamlet-type groups within the city; even if they are living under slum conditions their individual houses are clean and preserve some vital traditions of hearth and home. They may be subject to appalling health risks, especially high infant and child mortality, and the pressure to moral degradation may be strong, but often a local social organization preserves their culture and *mores*. There is a more serious problem of a largely male, temporary migrant, rootless, homeless, poor urban proletariat in northern industrial cities especially. Underemployment is rife, and as the old hymn observed Satan finds mischief for idle hands to do. These masses contain unstable groups, quick to unrest and at times to seemingly meaningless, randomly cruel violence – a potential threat to the society and culture in which they live, and yet hapless victims, needing steady work, but too often scarcely able to grasp it when it offers. These two groups of urban poor are largely recruited from the vulnerable rural class of poor landless labourers. All these very poor groups of people are among the most difficult, the least helped by the Five Year Plans, the most likely to destroy by violence the attempt to reach higher standards of living and a socialistic pattern of society by planning within a free, multi-party parliamentary democracy. Massive as the efforts have been, industrialization simply has not proceeded fast enough to create jobs, directly or indirectly, to mop up the pool of urban unemployment and underemployment, constantly rising by drift from rural areas – here pushed by drought, there by small size of holdings, and so on. The attempt has been massive; conceived on a scale to meet a great backlog of poverty, ignorance and unemployment with a modest improvement in standards of living, it has in the event rather more than kept pace with the rise in population. But it has not been able as yet to convince all men, including the grossly underprivileged, that unemployment and poverty can be mastered within one or two further Plan periods. To win the masses from extreme poverty to modest standards of living, education, and population stability is a matter of urgency, if the present pattern of development is to succeed.

How does the present picture compare, again, with the government's declared objective of a socialistic pattern of society? What is envisaged apparently includes parliamentary democracy and a mixed economy of public and private undertakings in industry and commerce; rural land farmed mainly by individuals – subject to ceiling limits of landholding varying from state to state – who are to

be encouraged to form producers' and marketing co-operatives, but not compelled nor even put under excessive pressure to collectivize agriculture. Therefore the present vulnerable landless labour class must be largely drawn off to the
cities by industrialization and urban growth, preferably without further development of shanty-town slums, and those remaining as labourers must be protected

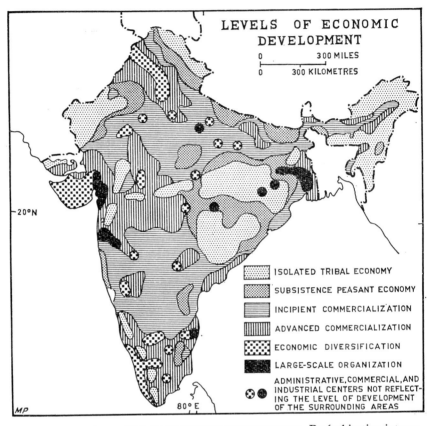

FIG II.II INDIA: LEVELS OF ECONOMIC DEVELOPMENT. By 'subjective integration' approach, one of three methods discussed in the source, J. E. Schwartzberg
in *Annals Assoc. American Geographers*, 52 (1962).

by control of wages and conditions, and agriculture must be such that farmers or
co-operatives must be able to afford to pay accordingly. Regional development of
resources to the utmost possible extent is avowed policy, according to both the
Second and Third Plans. Within this socio-economic pattern the general
educational, social and political pattern must ensure equality of opportunity for
all. These are large demands, even in the perspective of the next fifteen or
twenty years. But India does have some considerable natural and human

resources – minerals, water, land, a stable government and society, a culture that has recently undergone something of a renaissance, an experienced and on the whole a devoted and relatively incorruptible civil service, and considerable experience of the planning process. Success is probably attainable. Conditions of success include widespread confidence in eventual success, more widespread active participation, freedom from external pressure, and more foreign aid over the next fifteen years at least. Internally there is relatively little controversy that planning is needed in India. But should planning be less direct, more directive, as in France, or tighter, as in the communist countries, with nearly all agents of production in the public sector? There are, of course, differences of opinion both within and outside India. Whether controls be more or less tight, or more or less direct, the geographer may well feel that on the one hand the blots in the present picture, despite great advances, and on the other hand the serious problems of redeployment of resources and manpower involved in looking ahead, call alike for regional integration in development. The planning of town and country together will be necessary, if only to fulfil the undertakings in the Plans about evening out regional disparities in development, and to control rural migration to urban slums, so that the inevitable urban expansion can take place at a standard worthy of the new India and her imaginative series of Plans within a parliamentary democracy.[24] It remains to be seen, also, whether the federal structure can take the new strains imposed by the 1967 elections, when Congress lost control of States as important as Madras and Uttar Pradesh.

ADDENDA TO CHAPTER 11

A. FIRST FIVE-YEAR PLAN

	Planned		Achieved	
	Rs million	% of total	Rs million	% of total
Agriculture and Community Development	3,610	18	2,910	15
Irrigation and power	5,610	27	5,700	29
Transport and communications	4,970	24	5,230	27
Industry	1,730	8	1,170	6
Social services and miscellaneous	4,770	23	4,590	23
Total:	20,690	100	19,600	100

[24] On the broad regional aspects of planning see M. N. Pal and A. T. A. Learmonth, 'An appraisal of the regionalisation of economic development in India', oral paper to Australian and New Zealand Association Adv. Sci., Canberra meeting, January 1964, at present in mimeographed form; for physical planning in the sense of town and country planning see J. Wood, 'The development of urban and regional planning in India', *Land Economics*, 34 (1958), 310–15.

The financial basis of this outlay was as follows:

	Planned	Achieved
	Rs million	
Internal resources (other than deficit financing)	12,580	13,520
External assistance	5,210	1,880
Deficit financing	2,900	4,200
Total:	20,690	19,600

In addition, the private sector was expected to invest Rs 14,000,000,000, later revised to 18,000,000,000.

B. SECOND FIVE-YEAR PLAN

	Planned		Achieved	
	Rs million	% of total	Rs million	% of total
Agriculture and Community Development	5,680	12	5,300	11
Irrigation and Power	9,130	19	8,650	19
Industry and mining	8,900	18	10,750	24
Transport and communications	13,850	29	13,000	28
Social services and miscellaneous	10,440	22	8,300	18
Total:	48,000	100	46,000	100

The financial basis of this outlay was as follows:

	Planned	Achieved
	Rs million	
Internal resources (other than deficit financing)	24,000	25,620
External assistance	8,000	10,900
Deficit financing	12,000	9,480
Gap to be met	4,000	—
Total:	48,000	46,000

In addition, the private sector was estimated to make an expenditure of Rs 24,000,000,000, later revised to Rs 31,000,000,000.

C. KEY TARGETS OF THE THIRD FIVE-YEAR PLAN

	1960–61	1965–66
Foodgrains (million tons)	79·3	100·0
Cotton (million bales)	4·5	7·1
Power: installed capacity (million kW)	5·6	12·7
Railways: freight carried (million tons)	154·0	245·0
Steels, finished (million tons)	2·4	6·8
Aluminium (ooo tons)	18·2	80·0
Machine tools (value Rs million)	72·4	300·0
Industrial boilers (value Rs million)	4·0	250·0
Automobiles (ooo Nos.)	53·5	100·0
Coal (million tons)	55·5	98·5
Fertilizer (N) (ooo tons)	97·1	800·0
Sulphuric acid (ooo tons)	354·0	1,500·0
Petroleum products (million tons)	5·7	9·9
Electric motors (ooo h.p.)	700·0	2,500·0
Cloth (million yards)	7,476·0	9,300·0
Pupils in schools (million nos.)	43·4	64·0
Engineering students – intake (ooo Nos)	39·4	56·5
Hospital beds (ooo Nos.)	186·0	240·0
Increase in national income (plan period)	20%	30%
Per capita income (Rs at 1960–61 prices)	330·0	385·0

The financial basis of outlay is as follows:

	Rs million
Internal resources	30,400
Additional taxation	17,100
External assistance	22,000
Deficit financing	5,500
	75,000

D. THE GROWING DEMAND FOR POWER, 1950–65
(In millions of kilowatt hours)

	Over the First Decade 1950–60			By the end of Third Plan	
	1950	1960–61 (estimated)	% increase 1950–1960–61	1965–66 (anticipated)	% increase over 1960–61
For domestic light and small power	525	1,492	184	3,400	128
For commercial light and small power	309	870	182	1,900	118
For industry	3,984	12,314	209	28,400	131
For traction	308	449	46	1,800	301
For public lighting	60	192	220	400	108
For irrigation	162	836	416	1,900	127
For public water works etc.	189	455	141	900	98
For auxiliaries, transmission losses, etc.	1,038	3,242	212	6,300	94
	6,575	19,850	202	45,000	127

E. ELECTRIC POWER GENERATION
(*In million kW*)

	1950	1955	1961 estimated	1966 estimated
Hydro plant	0·56	0·94	1·93	5·1
Steam plant	1·59	2·27	3·46	7·08
Oil plant	0·15	0·21	0·31	0·36
Nuclear plant	—	—	—	0·15
Total	2·3	3·42	5·7	12·69*

* Amended to 12,500,000 in the Mid-Term Appraisal, *op. cit.*, p. 106.

F. INDIA – PHYSICAL TARGETS AND OUTPUT
(*Million tonnes u.o.s*)

	Third Plan Mid-Term (*Appraisal*) 1965–66	Expected Production 1965–66	Fourth Plan-Target 1970–71
AGRICULTURE			
Foodgrains	100·0	74·0	125·0
Cotton	7·1	5·2	0·85
Sugar and gur	10·0	12·0	13·5
Jute (lakh bales)	62·0	50·0	80·0
Nitrogenous Fertilizer – Consumption	0·8	0·6	2·4
Phosphatic Fertilizer – Consumption	0·25	0·2	1·0
INDUSTRY			
Inputs for Agriculture Fertilizers-N₂	0·51	0·25–0·3	2·2
Fertilizers-P₂O₅	0·2	0·13–0·2	1·0
Power driven pumps (1,000 units)	180·0	160·0	300·0
OTHER			
Newsprint	0·03	0·03	0·17
Steel ingots	7·9	6·6	16·8
Pig iron for sale	1·2	1·2	4·1
Aluminium	0·07	0·07	0·25
Cement	12·2	11·0	30·0

Sources: Memorandum of the Fourth Five-Year Plan. Government of India, Planning Commission, Oct., 1964; Annual Plan 1966–7, Government of India, Planning Commission, Mar. 1966; Report of Committee on Fertilizers, Government of India, 1965; J. G. Crawford, 'Planning Under Difficulties', *Australian J. Pol. & Hist.*, 12/2, Ang. 1966, 155–76.

CHAPTER 12

Economic Development in Pakistan

General features of Pakistan planning

Pakistan has a shorter history of planning than India. Almost immediately after Partition, a list of projects was drawn up, necessary to begin the long process of economic rehabilitation. A Planning Board (later the Planning Commission) then drew up a six-year plan under the Colombo Plan, for the years 1951 to 1957, giving priorities to agriculture, transport and communications, industry and mining, fuel and power, and social uplift in that order; this was modified to stricter priorities in 1953, and a First Five Year Plan was formulated to begin in 1955. This was largely frustrated by political instability (the Plan was not even officially approved until 1957) and by indiscipline in the administration. The target of a 7% increase in *per capita* income fell sadly short, and only 3% was attained. Agriculture, water development and education came nowhere near their targets although some industrial development succeeded in doing so, notably in the cotton and sugar industries. There were signs of gathering momentum towards the end of the period which, with the experience gained, has allowed the Second Plan to go ahead with more hope and evidence of success for its more ambitious aims in the struggle 'to find some way towards the liberation of the people from the crushing burden of poverty – mainly through inducement . . . less through direction'. The net national product has increased by some 9% and progress has been greatest in those sections using foreign aid and technology such as power and communications. It has been much less in what might be called 'boot strap' operations such as agriculture and social uplift. And the whole problem is bedevilled by the alarming population increase beyond all forecasts, so that targets aimed at improvement turn into targets that, even if achieved, will only prevent actual decline. The targets might be attainable, but only with considerable acceleration.[1] The approach is avowedly pragmatic – a compromise based on evaluation of the first plan, desirable aims and inspired guesswork.[2]

The burden of poverty can only be raised by increasing national and individual income: the Second Plan aims at increasing these by 24% and 12%

[1] *Mid-Plan Review* (Planning Commission, Karachi, 1963); this is analysed by J. H. Power, 'Two years of Pakistan's Second Plan', *Pakistan Development Review*, 3/1 (1963), 118–33.
[2] F. C. Shorter, 'Planning procedures in Pakistan', *Pak. Dev. Rev.* 1/2 (1961), 1–14.

respectively, and the Third by 30% and 15%; and the 1960 standards should be doubled at the end of the Fourth Plan in 1985. This can only be done by increasing the country's dependence on the outside world, by industrialization, and by increased agricultural efficiency. Agriculture and industry, with the associated developments of water and power must have the lion's share. But health and education are creeping up, from 9% of the First to 20% of the Third Plan's expenditure. Just as the Second Plan aimed at an 'agricultural breakthrough', an 'educational breakthrough' is the keynote of the Third Plan. The swing from agriculture to capital goods industry in the Third Plan shows trends similar to India's.

There is government control of vital sections of the economy, or those too costly and widespread to be capable of private development: communications, power, irrigation, reclamation, social services, defence. The Second Plan introduced a 'semi-public sector', a group of central agencies of which the chief are the Pakistan Industrial Development Corporation (now with a separate group in each wing), with the object of developing vital industries for which private capital had not been forthcoming in sufficient amount, and the Small Industries Corporation. The system is flexible; in some cases the government supplies only the foreign exchange element required, in others it may finance all initial development before private investment is invited; or again, only supply the unsubscribed remainder of investment required. There is also heavy reliance on foreign aid, mainly from USA, but also from UK, Canada, Australia, New Zealand, West Germany and Japan. The result has been to achieve more rapid industrialization following the very slow progress during the First Plan period.

To the ordinary citizen, however, the progress which may seem impressive to the observer as yet means very little. Of the scant 2% increase a year in income, a quarter is taken back in taxes to provide the balance needed beyond the massive contributions of foreign aid and investment. The Second Plan is brutally frank – 'the provision of adequate houses, water supply and sanitary facilities for the nation's population is a gigantic task well beyond the foreseeable resources of the government' – small comfort in spite of the rising splendours of Islamabad.

Agriculture in general

In order to achieve the aim of conserving and, if possible, earning foreign exchange, the twin objectives are self-sufficiency in food crops and the increase of cash crops, notably jute, cotton and tea, which can be exported raw or fed to local industry, either for local markets or ultimate export. Along with self-sufficiency in food crops, improved diets are aimed at, involving more consumption of fish, vegetables, pulses, fats and oils and sugar. The First Plan failed to make great headway, partly through inefficient application, but aggravated by the continuing problems of re-settlement of refugees, most of whom were peasants. Again there is a two-fold attack: increasing the yields from existing

366

farmland, and the opening up of new areas. The former rests on the increased use of fertilizer and seed improvement (which together account for almost half of the 13% of the total investment allocated to agriculture) and on reclamation of waterlogged and saline lands. The remainder will go into longer-term improvement of grazing lands, forests and fisheries, the furtherance of land reform, social projects and the colonization of new canal areas. The costs of fertilizer factories, and the major water and reclamation schemes are budgeted for separately, but of course are ultimately of great benefit to agriculture. The Second Plan shows much more hopeful signs of success, especially in foodgrains where the target had been almost achieved by 1963. But favourable weather had largely accounted for big agricultural increases, which can be nullified by drought or flood; the 1962 Bengal floods for instance were a setback.

The use of fertilizers has increased rapidly, and is well on the way to the target for 1965. The nitrogenous group, which at Partition was the only type used, and that in pathetically ineffectual amounts, had grown from 43,000 tons in 1955 to 282,000 tons in 1962 and was being widely distributed instead of being confined to limited destinations such as the tea gardens. The need for a more balanced diet for crops as well as people had led to increased use of phosphates and potash. Credit facilities and heavily subsidized prices have put them more within reach. It is claimed (Second Plan, p. 144) that subsidies can gradually be withdrawn, since the value of fertilizers is now sufficiently appreciated (for fertilizer production, see Table XIV).

Organic sources are scarce; yet even in 1960, bones and oilcake appeared on the export list. The Plan condemns this and advocates expansion of the programmes to compost that evil scourge of East Pakistan, the water hyacinth, and the growth of green manure.

Plant protection both by chemical coatings of seed, and aerial spraying of the growing crop, has had American help; it seems possible that an insecticide can be developed from waste at the Daud Khel fertilizer factory, and two special factories were planned to replace imports. Even more fundamental however is the improvement of the seeds themselves; a necessarily lengthy process from the original government farm, through registered growers to the final distribution with at first subsidies and credit to the farmer; and involving cold storage plant.

Mechanization is seen as applying largely to the initial development of new land (and reclamation of old) rather than to everyday husbandry, since people are plentiful and in need of work. The government hires out tractors for specific tasks such as rapid ploughing of desert soils after rain. As in India, soil survey is in its infancy, although a rapid fertility survey was carried out during the First Plan, and a survey of deficiencies is in progress. For individual crops, of course, improved varieties will help, such as the crossing of *indica* and *japonica* strains of rice, the development of longer-stapled cottons and the valued short stapled Comilla cotton grown by shifting cultivators in East Pakistan (hence a very fluctuating total!). Four new varieties of jute have been developed; it would now seem that research is needed on new uses for the fibre, presumably a reflection of the invasion of paper and plastics into the packaging industry. A hybrid maize has been grown successfully in Peshawar, and potatoes are considered a commercial possibility in the lower hills; it is to be hoped that the soil erosion following similar developments in the Nilgiris will be avoided by supervised terracing.

Towards a better human diet, little has yet been done. It is gratifying enough that food grains are 'on target'; the rest must await education and finance which in all its forms is of course as basic as water. From a period of fairly tight control, both wings have gone on to an open market for the basic food grain – rice in the East and wheat in the West, with some misgivings, for the hoarder and speculator can send prices soaring in times of shortage.[3] Storage facilities to cope with such periods are therefore part of the plan; the need is greater in the East where 'in normal years domestic production is satisfactory' but with only an occasional surplus. But storage is not one of the rapidly advancing projects, and little was done to conserve the good harvests of 1960 and 1961.

The objective in financial policy and marketing is to provide the maximum incentive to the farmer to increase his production and income. While irrigation, fertilizers and incentives play their part, much can be done to improve methods of cultivation. The Second Plan sees this as a long term measure which will yield slow results, as against the quick ones it has emphasized, and one that will stem from the adoption of methods seen to be effective on demonstration farms and from the success of various methods used for communication.

The primary function of livestock in Pakistan is to provide motive power; meat, milk, hides and skins are of secondary though not insignificant importance. The livestock pictures in the two wings are in contrast. Thus the excess of poor quality cattle of East Pakistan, where fodder is almost non-existent and Hindu influences have some bearing, need to be slaughtered, while the West had an estimated deficit of 1,500,000 at the beginning of the Second Plan, likely to double as new irrigated land is opened up. In the West, goat keeping is now prohibited except for stall-fed animals and the all-consuming wandering herds are being slaughtered, while in the East the need is to improve and multiply the beast. Sheep are found only in the West and come far short of supplying the woollen industry; improved breeding on special farms is seen as the only way. There is a good basis for improving cattle stock based on excellent native breeds like Red Sindhi and Sakarwal, actually in demand for export.

Land reform and AID

In January 1960 the government of Pakistan brought into effect an important policy of land-holding reform for West Pakistan. There are two problems: the

---

[3] A. R. Khan and A. H. M. Chowdhury, 'A study of behaviour of West Pakistan farmers in relation to marketing', *Pak. Dev. Rev.* 2/3 (1962), 354–76.

large estates and the extreme fragmentation of the small holdings.[4] As we have seen (Chapter 8), it placed a ceiling of 1,000 ac. (202 ha.) on unirrigated land and 500 on irrigated, future fragmentation is forbidden below 12·5 ac., and consolidation of the present fragmented pattern is being tackled, not without difficulty on account of Islamic laws of inheritance. The Land Reform Commission recommended a definition of a 'subsistence holding' as 12·5 to 16 ac. (5–6·5 ha.) and an 'economic holding' as 50 to 64 ac., according to locality; in East Pakistan, an inherited unit below a (smaller) subsistence figure may be resumed and added to others to make a new holding. On the consolidation front, the *Mid-Plan Review* stated that by 1963 just on half of the 9,200,000 ac. (3,723,000 ha.) target had been consolidated in West Pakistan, in the East a 90,000 ac. pilot scheme completed on time. It is, as usual, difficult to evaluate real progress on the other front – the break-up of large estates – but according to some reports it has been remarkable, not least in view of the political influence of the big landowners who virtually controlled the votes of their tenants.

One might, however, query whether some of the provisions are entirely realistic; as in India, there seems a certain conflict between welfare policy – 'the land to the people' – and economic advance. One might query whether limits of 12·5 ac. for subsistence and 50 for economic holdings are consistent with the capital demands of new production; for instance, the tube-wells which are recognized as a necessary adjunct to canal irrigation, to prevent waterlogging probably cannot be financed from holdings of this size.[5] There is also uncertainty in East Pakistan, where the ceiling of 30 ac. (12 ha.) imposed in 1952 was proving too small for the type of cultivator described above; a limit of 100 ac. (40·4 ha.) was recommended in 1959, and reassessment is still in progress.

The *jagirs* – lands carrying hereditary rights to revenue collection – were abolished in Sind, Bahawalpur and Baluchistan in 1960; the system had been progressively eroded by governments during as well as since the British period. Many remain in areas not fully reported in the west and north, but their days are numbered.

Security of tenure has been strengthened, although it was recommended in 1959 that the retired soldier could eject his tenants (after due notice) if he wishes to cultivate his own land; thus, it is hoped bringing leadership and example to the countryside. It may even be extended to other retired professionals!

Communication with the eight out of every ten Pakistanis who live on the land has presented the same problem as has faced all developing countries. 'High impact devices' are used in areas where success seemed hopeful, and

[4] A Planning Commission estimate of holdings, quoted in *PGR* 14/1 (1959), 42, gives both ends of the scale: 3,300,000 people (65% of all landowners) held 15% of the total cultivated land in holdings under 5 ac.; 6,000 people (0·1% of owners) also held 15% of cultivated land in holdings of over 500 ac.; these are the people affected by the new laws.

[5] C. Beringer, 'Welfare and production efficiency: two objectives of land reform in Pakistan', *Pak. Dev. Rev.* 2/2 (1962), 173–88.

include co-operative farming on a scale calculated not to inimicize the individualistic peasant: that is, he was left as owner of his land and co-operated only with the buying of seeds, fertilizers and tools, and the marketing of his products. 'Area concentration' has been used too, and has been carried out as an agricultural 'crash programme', in seven Districts of each wing, again chosen for their likelihood of success (a policy open to criticism though understandable) and involving intensive application of every known method of crop and livestock improvement.

Community development, aimed at raising the entire sordid standard of village life, took the form of the Village Agricultural and Industrial Development movement, known as Village AID. Owing much to the energy and drive of the emancipated Muslim women who emerged from purdah with the birth of their country, to help with the enormous problems of caring for and settling the refugees, the movement began very modestly in 1953. Village workers were trained and sent out to live with the villagers; one worker to about seven villages in the east and to five in the west. A married couple often shared the task, the wife trained in home economics, child care and hygiene, her husband in improved farming methods, elementary sanitation and cottage industries.

The programme was fairly successful, even penetrating to the tribal areas of Zhob, Loralai, Kurram and Malakand in the northwest and notably in the remote areas of Gilgit and Baltistan. Although operated on a small scale financially it seems to have achieved the aims of 'self help' among the villagers. About 150 villages made up a Development Area, and a Development Officer controlled a group of areas. Training at a higher level, for people concerned with rural development, takes place at a Village Development Academy at Peshawar or Comilla (East Pakistan).[6]

In 1961 Village AID was wound up except in Azad Kashmir and Baltistan and its functions absorbed at two levels: by 'Basic Democracies' which train village workers, and the Agricultural Development Corporations in each wing which handle the practical matters of tools, seeds, fertilizers, etc.

Water : too little and too much

Agricultural development depends more on proper utilization of water resources than on any other factor. Industrial power can be obtained cheaply, after a heavy initial investment, from the fall of water in the mountain fringes or from canal-falls in the plains. Planned developments in water can therefore be considered together.

Large parts of West Pakistan have too little rainfall for agriculture at any time, and the rest has too little for year-round cultivation. East Pakistan has high totals, but rainfall is concentrated in the monsoon months, and there is a con-

---

[6] Evaluation has, however, been lacking except for occasional papers, such as J. J. Honigmann, 'A case study of community development in Pakistan', *Economic Development and Cultural Change*, 8/3 (1960), 228–304.

siderable dry season. Yet there is too much when the waters of the Brahmaputra surge down through the delta channels, and the waters of the Bay of Bengal bank up in a cyclone. Flooding is not unknown in the arid West, when the monsoon rains follow the snow-melt; and man-made obstacles get in the way. Even the canals, when they cross the natural lines of drainage, can both accentuate flooding and in the process receive serious damage. But much worse, there is too much water in those very areas where irrigation was brought fifty years ago to the Canal Colonies of the Punjab. Inadequate drainage has led to a steadily rising water-table until the surface layers where roots must grow are water-logged; and the intense summer heat draws up the salts until the soil is poisoned and a white efflorescence marks the former fields. It is estimated that 100,000 ac. (40,500 ha). are going out of production every year, and that a total of over 16,000,000 ac. (6,470,000 ha.) has been totally lost and a further 10,000,000 (4,050,000 ha.) requires urgent treatment, in West Pakistan.[7] This represents about 40% of the irrigated total (see Fig. 17.5 A and B).

The Canal Colonies were developed as a unit, which Partition cut apart, leaving the bulk of the headworks feeding them in India. Not surprisingly, there followed years of negotiation and wrangling, followed at length by the Indus Water Treaty in 1960, something of a triumph in compromise, patience and engineering investigation. Broadly, it gives the waters of the three western rivers, Indus, Jhelum and Chenab to Pakistan, and the three eastern rivers, Ravi, Beas and Sutlej to India (Fig. 17.6). During the transition period, while great works are carried out in Pakistan to bring water from the west to her lands formerly watered from the eastern rivers, India will continue to supply water.[8] India also will contribute to the cost of the necessary works in Pakistan, which involve two great storage dams and seven link canals at a total cost of about 1,300,000,000 dollars (174,000,000 from India, 749,000,000 from foreign aid, and the rest from Pakistan). In planning expenditure, therefore, Pakistan is faced with competing and sometimes conflicting demands on three fronts; the works essential under the treaty, the development of completely new irrigated areas, and the reclamation of the waterlogged and saline lands of the old colonies.

New irrigation is fairly limited in possibilities: the Thal scheme is the biggest, and this scorched doab between Indus and Chenab had been left to the last by the British because it *was* the most difficult. Also a system of five barrages along the Indus will make about maximum use of its fluctuating waters. One object is to make perennial irrigation available in areas hitherto watered only by inundation canals: the Ghulam Mohammed (Lower Sind) barrage opened in 1955, the Gudu Barrage (Upper Sind) in progress, the Taunsa (1959) and the Jinnah projected. The turbulent western tributaries can be trapped to irrigate parts of the western borderlands; Kohat, Kabul and Swat all have their dams, but the

---

[7] G. Whittington, 'The irrigated lands of the Indus Plain in West Pakistan', *Tijdschrift voor Econ. en Soc. Geografie*, 55 (1964), 13–18.

[8] This principle had already been applied in the Triple Canals Project of 1905–17.

areas gained are not large. Small schemes like the Miriot dam in Potwar can all contribute to new farmland or to improved yields from existing fields. A third of the planned increase in food production from 1961 to 1965 is expected to come almost equally from new and from improved irrigation. In the East, it will take the form of lift irrigation from existing waterways and from the new ones of the Ganges–Kobadak scheme, to extend the cropping season into the dry months. There is a likelihood of underground water resources up to ten times greater than the total Indus discharge; while its quality varies it may well be capable of supplementing canals.[9]

The programmes to combat waterlogging and salinity have been carefully worked out on the basis of the findings of the exhaustive Huntings Survey under the Colombo Plan.[10] The answer to waterlogging is tube wells which serve the dual purpose of lowering the water table, and providing further irrigation water or water simply to flush out the salts. A scale of priorities has been decided on, and the results of the first period of working the tube wells in the Rech Doab (Ravi-Chenab) are very encouraging – the water table was lowered 5 ft. in fifteen months. But the cost is prodigious; the total programme almost equals the *total* to be spent in Pakistan under the Water Treaty!

Four-fifths of the money allocated to flood prevention will go to East Pakistan, mainly to open up congested channels to build new or strengthen old embankments, including some tidal defences.[11] It is ironic that there are the makings of a new Waters Dispute in this area, for both countries have plans to divert Ganges floodwaters to the useful purpose of flushing the delta channels.

It may be worth while looking at several of the individual schemes, although of course they will be mentioned again in regional contexts.

The Thal

The headworks at Kalabagh, for which the British had done preliminary work, were almost ready in 1947. The need to resettle refugees added urgency to the project, and a Thal Development Authority was set up in 1949 (it includes a statute prohibiting 'politicians and criminals' from serving on its board!). One main canal from Kalabagh trifurcates taking out 6,000 cusecs – the maximum allowed because of the needs of Sind – although it is capable of more. A million and a half acres (607,500 ha.) are now irrigated along the piedmont sandy plain and in a long strip down the left bank of the Indus (the Daggar, see p. 518). The dunes and 'pattis' of the heart of the Doab are not commanded, although three 'national parks' devoted to a twenty year forestry rotation are located here. Plantations are made using basin irrigation in the sand-hill tract, with a tilth of canal silt and sand; but despite the cutting by half of the proposed 10% forest

[9] Note on 'Indus Plain ground water reservoir', *PGR* 18/1 (1963), 44.
[10] K. Ahmad, 'Reclamation of waterlogged and saline lands in West Pakistan', *PGR* 16/1 (1961), 1–19.
[11] B. L. C. Johnson, 'Technology and the economic development of Pakistan', *Oriental Geogr* (Dacca) 6/1 (1962), 71–78.

cover, and the need for trees both for timber and to counter erosion, the foresters have difficulty in securing enough water.

The irrigated areas are divided into 1,000 ac. (405 ha.) units called 'chaks', which includes 50 ac. of trees and 50 of communal grazing land. A family holding averages 15 ac., which seems perhaps rather low (a 'subsistence unit' has been defined as 12·5) and leaves little to spare, especially as crop yields are considerably lower than in the Punjab colonies.[12] The proportion of rabi to kharif crops is 2 : 1, and these depend on rainfall, again introducing a chance element in a marginal economy.

The loss of water by evaporation and percolation is very high; Murphy quotes a figure of only 43% of water in Punjab canals at the headworks actually reaching the crop roots. But, *horribile dictu*, salinity and a rising water table are already in evidence, especially in the northeast where heavy runoff from the Salt Ranges is a factor, coupled with an intermediate water-table caused by a layer of hard impervious sodium clay. Pressure to make land available, along with the costs involved, made it impracticable to instal proper drainage at the beginning. It was thought that the general slope would make it unnecessary. The suggested remedy of using canals in summer and tubewells in winter would solve the problem but at great cost.

Five new market towns have developed, aimed at absorbing labour in agriculturally based industries. They are meeting some difficulties: cotton is not a popular crop (it is too demanding and prone to disease), and there is more profit in making *gur* in the village and taking it to town to sell, than in taking the bulky raw cane to the nice new sugar mill!

Ganges–Kobadak scheme

This is a multi-purpose project in East Pakistan and only a part of a very ambitious possibility stretching over decades and involving barrages over the Teesta, Surma, Meghna and Brahmaputra, with canal networks to give lift irrigation and communication and drainage schemes. Comprised, realistically, of independent units, only the first of which is under way, the Ganges–Kobadak scheme covers the Districts in the dying delta of Khulna, Jessore and Kushtia south of the Ganges; the first unit to irrigate 100,000 ac. (40,500 ha.) by diesel-driven lifting devices. The second phase envisages a 60-mile (97 km.) canal to divert Ganges water into the moribund Kobadak, and the third, the empoldering about a million acres of land in Khulna District irrigated from the new canal and the dredged Kobadak.

Warsak in the west and *Kaptai* (Karnaphuli) in the east are multi-purpose projects now completed, while Mangla, under construction, is of interest as part of the Indus Settlement works, and involves the removal to a new site of the town of Mirpur. It will benefit Azad Kashmir through power and irrigation, as

---

[12] See P. J. H. Murphy, 'The agricultural development of the Thal Desert', *PGR* 13/2 (1958), 55–87, for fascinating account of a particular village in the Thal.

well as the Punjab. Both Warsak and Kaptai have involved tribal people of the country's fringes. At Warsak, watchtowers had to be maintained to control the sniping tribesmen in the early stages; but their labour was enlisted, and the whole project, with its attendant irrigation of tribal areas does seem to be helping Pakistan's frontier problems.[13] The power will add to local industrial development although the bulk is transmitted to the Punjab towns. Tribal people in the Chittagong Hills had to be resettled as a result of the Kaptai scheme completed in 1962, which has improved navigation right down to Chittagong as well as providing power for industry.

Power

The development of hydro-electricity is bound up with energy planning in general, which in turn is closely linked with the bases of coal, gas and oil (see p. 299 and Fig. 9.5). It is impossible to separate the review of these elements, especially since the discovery of natural gas in both wings has led to reappraisals. For example, the Mianwali hydro-electric project may be abandoned in favour of extending the gas pipeline from Sui to the Punjab. This will further affect the development of coal in the region, and water power developments in the mountains of the northwest. The planned developments in coal are mainly in the Sor Range fields in Baluchistan where access roads and increase in capacity of the Bolan railway are under way. Further exploration may confirm resources of good quality coal in East Pakistan on an extension of the Bihar belt; the potentialities of the peats of Faridpur seem very limited. The plans emphasize the need for further exploration for oil and gas with an emphasis on the Dera Ismail Khan and Potwar areas of West Pakistan and the Sylhet region in the east. A pipe line is projected to Dacca to carry Sylhet gas. For the rest geological investigation has a share of funds: iron beds of dubious quality in Makerwal and barytes in Kalat are the only yield of any significance so far.

The revised figures for the Second Plan show a target of 1,271,800 kW which is well within sight with the completion of the Warsak and Karnaphuli Projects. This will increase the *per capita* figure from 30 to 50 units a year. There is a wide disparity again between the two wings, for 75% of the installed capacity in 1965 will be situated in West Pakistan. The biggest single outstanding project is the Mangla Dam, a multi-purpose storage dam, being developed under the Indus Water Agreement, which will supply 300,000 kW of power eventually. Meantime the Multan gas plant is doubling output to 260,000 kW and Warsak is capable of similar expansion. The Sui pipeline may be used to generate power at Lyallpur to fill the gap in supply until Mangla is complete. With the completion of Karnaphuli, East Pakistan can only develop further on the use of peat, timber and natural gas, all difficult to exploit and transport. There is no grid as yet and rural electrification is even further behind than in the west. An Institute of nuclear science and technology is the first major undertaking in Islamabad

[13] L. F. Rushbrook Williams, *The State of Pakistan* (Faber, London, 1962), 68–76.

and a training and research centre has been begun in Dacca; the use of atomic energy is still at the stage of 'feasibility surveys'.

Industry in general

Pakistan began with few industries; those she had were largely concerned with

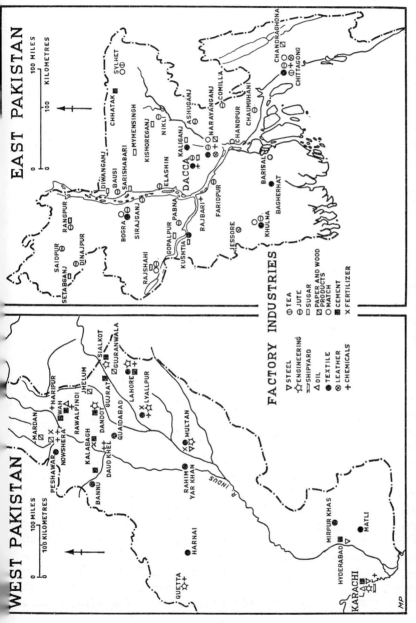

FIG 12.1 PAKISTANI INDUSTRIAL DEVELOPMENT. While it might be premature to identify industrial regions as has been done for India (Fig 11.1), there is at least one nascent region in the belt Peshawar–Lahore, and industrial districts around Karachi, Hyderabad and Dacca. Based on K. S. Ahmad, *A Geography of Pakistan* (1964) and M. R. Brearey and B. S. Connock in *Geography*, 46 (1961).

375

processing agricultural resources for export; cotton ginning, jute baling, tea factories, flour, rice and oil mills, and innumerable cottage industries serving local markets. Karachi was poorly developed, and East Bengal was served by Calcutta. Industry was largely in the hands of Parsees or Marwaris, who migrated at Partition. And, of greatest significance to the future, she lacked adequate resources for the development of heavy industry. The picture has brightened in this respect with recent discoveries of natural gas and coal deposits. The division of the country into two wings, with 1,000 miles (1,610 km.) between them, is a serious factor, leading to increased costs in transport, or alternatively in duplication.

Yet industrialization must increase if the national income is to rise and the increasing population be absorbed. The main industrial objectives in the Plans are the fundamental ones of (1) saving the money hitherto spent abroad, by home production and even export, and (2) laying a broad foundation of basic industries on which others can build: steel and chemicals. Thus a quarter of the State investment in industry in the Second Plan goes into chemicals and a fifth into engineering and metallurgy, including a steel plant in each wing (an example of the duplication referred to). There was an initial development after 1947 of consumer goods, by private enterprise to fill important needs of food and clothing. Then came very rapid planned development in those sectors using local materials or heavily protected, notably textiles. The pace is slackening now, and future industrialization lies more with capital goods industries; the easier prospects having been exhausted, improved technological education and efficiency are now desiderata.

'Resources cannot be wasted by promoting at all costs an industrial pattern dominated by small enterprises' (Second Plan, p. 224). At the same time, small industries still employ by far the bulk of industrial workers, making everything from envelopes to revolvers and shoe laces to surgical instruments; and labour-intensive as opposed to capital-intensive projects are seen as a partial solution to rising numbers of job seekers. The Plans try to steer a middle course, by en-couraging (through the Small Industries Corporation) those small-scale enter-prises which can do better or as well in small as in large units (e.g. specialized textiles from woven rugs to embroidered saris) or those which are ancillary to factory industry, such as bobbin makers. It is hoped that small workshops will grow into bigger units. It is tacitly implied that many will complete the decline which started during the British period and has gone on as a result of decrease in efficiency and the stranglehold by the middleman. Increased productivity is assisted by loans and technical help in modernization, using one-eighth of the state investment in industry to do so. Sweated labour workshops are successful at present, and show well in capital-output ratios compared with larger establish-ments, and also in the capital-labour ratio so useful in a populous under-developed country. But it is scarcely possible for a government today to encourage their spread, while on the other hand the owner of a sweatshop seldom tends to invest in more machinery or better conditions of his own volition, and so undermine the very basis of his profits.[14]

Trading estates as a means of combining some of the advantages of small industry and large scale facilities of power and transport, and at the same time spreading industrial location are being developed round Karachi, Kotri, Sukkur and at Rajshahi, Comilla and elsewhere in the east.

The PIDC which assists in large-scale industry has increased its initial list of jute, paper, fertilizers, heavy engineering, chemicals and shipbuilding, to include cement, sugar, cotton, wool, iron and steel and pharmaceuticals; inevitably it receives a larger share of the total investment.

Although, at first, limitations were placed on the further industrial development of Karachi in favour of less industrialized areas, the tug of war between idealistic and realistic solutions that we have already seen in the decisions about size of unit, is now pulling towards realism, and the advantages of port facilities, capital and skill, and now the availability of power from Sui gas, are combining to give Karachi an overwhelming lead in industry in spite of the water problem.

Eddison[15] in reviewing the effects of locating industry for purely social and political reasons points out the failure of this policy – as in the cotton mills of Quetta and the Thal towns. A more successful development is likely to come from location of new industries in urban centres of medium size with some industry already, such as Hyderabad, Nowshera or Sylhet; thus further swelling of the really major cities can be avoided. The old industrial centres of the north and west, however, are showing considerable development in textiles, wood products and engineering, in the belt from Peshawar to Lahore, where hydro-electricity is available as well as the coal deposits of the Salt Ranges. Sui gas will eventually reach here also. East Pakistan, limping behind in *per capita* income and industrialization, is to receive a bigger share of Third Plan Resources. Karnaphuli power, and now possible coal and natural gas resources, will help. At present industry concentrates largely in Chittagong and the Dacca area, with timber, sugar and cement locally important in the delta, the north and the hills respectively.

Steel

Steel is the yardstick of industrial development; but to use it as a measure in Pakistan would be a discouraging exercise. The Kalabagh iron is the only indigenous source capable of being worked; the Chitral deposits are too inaccessible as yet (Fig. 9.4). Steel production is confined to small installations in Lahore and Karachi: re-rolling mills are more numerous and found in both wings and there is a new one at Karachi. Small-scale mills are primitively inefficient, although they are gradually being improved. Planned increase, aimed

---

[14] J. H. Power, 'Small industrial enterprises in Bombay, Delhi and Karachi', *Pak. Dev. Rev.* 2/3 (1962), 433–43.
[15] J. C. Eddison, 'Industrial location and physical planning', *ibid.* 1/1 (1961), 1–21.

at supplying 70% of the needs by 1965, rests heavily on the use of imported pig iron and local and even imported scrap in two new steel mills, one in Karachi yet to be financed, and the other in Chittagong due to be in production by 1967 at the latest, using Japanese assistance. From an initial output of 150,000 tons, it will increase to 1,500,000 tons over twenty years. But an integrated steel plant is a long way off.

There is as yet no manufacturing of the industrial machinery, electrical equipment, railway stock or vehicles, that are basic to development; these are imported, or at best assembled. The engineering industries are mainly small scale, carried out in innumerable workshops and largely concentrated round Lahore, making a variety of tools. Small factories produce agricultural equipment, Batala Engineering Works at Lahore, for instance, making tube well pumps, and others making oil expellers and sugar crushers, even Persian wheels. The simpler parts of the ubiquitous sewing machine and bicycle are made and the rest imported; the whole to be assembled in Lahore, Karachi or Dacca. Realising that if a machine-making industry is to be established the basic need is skill, the plans emphasize technical education and assistance more than immediate increase in capacity. Although no large-scale electrical equipment is made, light bulbs, fans and switch gear are made in Karachi, as well as the kerosene lamps that are still of greater importance; but in both cases much is still imported. Some plugs, sockets and switches are made by cottage industries. East Pakistan will likely benefit from new development in this type of industry. Telephone and telegraph equipment made at Haripur, north of Rawalpindi, and Kotri supply almost the entire needs.

Chemicals

The agricultural programme demands increased use of fertilizers. A third of industrial investment in the public sector is devoted to the chemical industry. The country has good resources for the development of chemical fertilizers at least, the tragic irony being that they are mainly in the west, while the most desperate need is in the east. However, the natural gas from Sylhet is now piped to Fenchuganj to make urea, a concentrate equivalent to large amounts of ammonium sulphate, and a much needed source of nitrogenous fertilizer. A similar plant has opened at Multan in the west, using Sui gas. There is a new and expanding ammonium sulphate plant at Daud Khel on the Indus, sited here to use the Indus waters, Makerwal coal, and gypsum from the Salt Ranges; the chemical complex here is to be increased by the addition of a dye works, and a plant extracting ammonium sulphate from natural gas. A former sulphuric acid plant at Lyallpur has been converted to make superphosphates, but does not work to capacity because costs are too high and prices to the farmer too high. Even so, another superphosphate plant is being built at Chittagong; a reflection of transport costs between the two wings. Sulphur deposits exist but are fairly inaccessible; a refinery was opened in Quetta in 1956.

Soda ash at Khewra, close to rock salt and limestone, supplies a small glass industry (as well as legions of dhobis) and may be refined for a viscose rayon industry in Karachi. Caustic soda is made in the East for the paper factory at Chandhragona (Karnaphuli) and at Nowshera in the northwest, in association with DDT production, but has still to be imported for other industrial uses. There are plans to make it from sea salt at Gharo in West Pakistan. There is a new sulphuric acid plant at Lyallpur. There have been developments in the petrochemicals groups, using Sui gas at Karachi to make acetylene and PVC; and even polythene, for the ubiquitous polythene wrapping, to be made from sugar bagasse in Karachi. Another modern development is the drug factory at Dacca while there are still industries based on medicinal herbs (*Artemesia ephedra*) at Rawalpindi and Quetta.

Textiles

The biggest group of industries, textiles, has developed rapidly from very small beginnings. Cotton leads, employing about a third of the industrial work force, with quite spectacular developments in yarn production and weaving that have eliminated imports and begun to build up useful exports of yarn and piece goods. Local demand was expected to be 14·5 yards per annum per person by 1965. Karachi is the leading centre; though it had no mills at Partition, the rail link with the cotton-growing area, local capital, port facilities, and unlimited power supplies from the Sui gas field have led to the establishment of mills here. Hyderabad too has a new cotton industry, lying as it does in a developing cotton producing area in Sind, while the former centres at Lyallpur and Multan have expanded and the industry is developing in relation to the Thal cotton as well as in northwestern towns like Tank, Kohat and Mardan. In East Pakistan, the industry is concentrated in the Dacca–Narayanganj district, once the famed centre of fine muslins; the huge local market and the general need for industrial development here have led to the new mills at Kaliganj northeast of Dacca and in Rajshahi which will supply the heavy local demand by handweavers. In the East raw cotton of course must virtually all be imported.

A quarter of the yarn produced is retained to feed the factories and the important handloom cottage industry making both coarse cheap cloth and high grade specialities; it accounts for 40% of total production. There was a period of rapid expansion in handloom weaving after Partition, which included pavement 'factories' set up by refugees. But the small handloom factory is giving way to power looms set up with loans and technical help through the Small Industries Corporation.

The larger-scale factory industry, which as we have seen developed at prodigious rates in the early years of Pakistan, has been mainly run by private enterprise; partly no doubt because the capital investment was relatively low, and profits good. The supply of refugee labour was also a factor here. The success of this, Pakistan's first venture into large-scale industry, must be measured in more than statistics however, for it had a very useful moral effect. The table shows the rate of increase. Another feature is the predominance of the composite mill.[16]

	Spindles	Looms	Mills
1947	177,148	4,824	17
1959	1,927,470	29,104	87
1961	1,998,000	30,000	93
1965 (Planned)	2,500,000	40,000	121

Since the Partition guillotine cut the Calcutta factories from the growing areas, jute mills have been built in East Pakistan with a capacity of 200,000 tons; more are planned, including one at Kotri in West Pakistan, using jute grown in the irrigated area of Sind, and the target, likely to be achieved, is of 14,000 looms by 1965. Jute earns about half of Pakistan's much-needed foreign exchange, for only about a quarter of her production need be retained for her own needs in bagging sugar, cement and fertilizer. Most of the export is as raw fibre, but this too required considerable effort in providing jute baling plant, for 'pucca' baling had also been done in Calcutta. Both branches of the industry are tending to concentrate near the port and transport facilities of Chittagong, round Dacca (especially Narayanganj) and at Khulna, rather than in the heaviest growing areas farther north. Reluctance of private capital to invest, because profits are low, has meant that development has been done largely by the PIDC. The cottage weaving of jute has declined and little remains.

Sufficient wool yarn to meet internal requirements is produced from mills, mostly built since 1950 in West Pakistan. The largest in Karachi also spins worsteds from imported finer wool; the others lie in the main sheep areas of the northwest and have been developed in co-ordination with producers on the one hand, by helping in flock improvement, and the handloom workers on the other (who may be the same people) by a supply of yarn. Raw wool is still exported for carpet and felt making in UK and USA, and yarn production for export is planned. Such weaving as has developed on a factory scale is restricted to blankets and suitings which do not compete with handloom products so important in the northwest. Dera Ghazi Khan and Multan are still important for weaving of rugs and carpets.

The relatively minor importance of artificial silk is not likely to increase, since yarn must be imported; indeed the Second Plan talks of converting the existing looms to cotton production. However, an acetate rayon plant at Lyallpur in the west and an expanding weaving industry is to be fed by yarn from new plants at Okara and Kairi. A viscose rayon plant at Karnaphuli is to be established by private enterprise. Kapok from the silk cotton tree (*Eriodendron anfractuosum*) is extracted at Chittagong. While sericulture is encouraged by the Small Industries Corporation, reeling and filature development is only of minor importance, using largely imported silk from Japan.

[16] K. Ahmad, 'Cotton textile industry of Pakistan', *PGR* 17/2 (1962), 1–16.

Paper, wood, leather

East Pakistan has the lead in resources and development of paper and wood products, and self sufficiency is attainable, even export of newsprint, in spite of increasing home demands. Bamboo floated down to Chadhragona on the Karnaphuli is processed with power from the new dam; and at Khulna the newsprint factory is fed by bargeloads of *gewa* (*Exeocaria agallocha*) pulled upstream with the tides from the Sunderbans. There is an associated caustic soda plant, and a projected particle board factory. West Pakistan makes enough wrapping paper for its own needs, as well as some paper and hardboard from local grasses (at Nowshera), rice straw (Rahwali), firs from the Kaghan Valley (at Mangarh) and paper mulberry (at Lahore).

Left by Partition with the basic resource, but not the tanneries, leather imports had to continue until the industry developed – slowly because tanning materials are not plentiful, and the low caste Hindu skill had largely gone, though Hindu influence remains in East Pakistan where fewer cattle hides come from slaughtered animals than in the West. Hides remain important as an export, about a third of them now tanned using *Acacia arabica* and *Terminalia chebula* in the West, and mangroves in the East. Muslim craftsmen from Kanpur have helped to establish shoe and leather factories; western style shoes are made in Karachi and Lahore, and at Narayanganj in the East, but the traditional sandals of the country are a cottage industry.

Agriculture-based industries

The bulk of planned investment in food industries is going into wheat mills in the western wing and rice mills in the East wing respectively, by expansion and modernization; not only will mouths increase, but tastes are demanding more refined products. But austerity is maintained in sugar consumption, with little allowance for import of the preferred white sugar, and emphasis placed on increased production and local milling. Mardan in the West, said now to be the biggest refinery in Asia, has been followed by others in the northwest Punjab located near production areas because of the bulky nature of the raw material. Efforts to meet the huge demand in East Pakistan have been handled by PIDC with several new mills, which face the difficulties posed by scattered production and poor quality of the crop and transport. The bulk of the crop is still handled as a cottage industry – producing the sticky yellow 'gur' – crudely and wastefully produced by press and iron pan. Vegetable oils must still be imported, although efforts to increase and modernize, and educate tastes (especially with *vanaspati*, blending the hitherto unpopular cotton seed-oil with sesame and coconut) are slowly raising production at home. The modest soap consumption is met by cottage industry and one modern factory making toilet soap at Bahawalpur.

Tobacco growing is confined to the West, and the handmade *bidis* produced in innumerable homes and workshops in both wings come nowhere near demand.

A substitute made from *khumbi* leaves to replace imported *bidis*, coupled with more sophisticated cigarette manufacture by foreign firms at Karachi, Chittagong and Mardan are the main planned developments. Tea is slowly climbing from a serious financial slump after Partition, and is of course confined to the East; in addition to the estate factories, there are blending and packing plants in Chittagong, and in West Pakistan. Development of more luxury foods like canned fruits receives scant encouragement, although private enterprise is raising production for sophisticated and wealthy urban customers particularly in the West. The more vital milk industry struggles along on a local (unhygienic) basis except for the military dairy farms bequeathed by the British and since expanded, and some urban bottling plants at Karachi: although in the form of ghi, curds and other products, dairy produce finds its way to the urban markets as well as village use. The problem is one of transport, to get milk to the urban centres; at Karachi a plant is planned to combine local milk with imported powdered milk. Dacca and Lahore will have peripheral dairy farms. And condensed and dried milk factories are planned in areas of rural surplus.

Cement

Having lost both its source of fuel and its market at Partition, the cement industry of West Pakistan, based on local limestone, declined. As development has got into gear, however, the demand has increased rapidly, and the providential discovery of natural gas has partially solved the fuel problem. Canadian help has established the Maple Leaf factory at Daud Khel, and New Zealand's 'Zeal Pak' unit at Hyderabad, and a new one also at Rohri. Two more are planned along the Sui pipeline as well as increasing the existing plant at Wah. But East Pakistan suffers again, through lack of fuel and has only one plant, at Chattak; the Sylhet gas has replaced the Indian coal imported to run the plant.

Trade (Tables XVII, XVIII)

The foreign and inter-wing trade of Pakistan reflect the economic diversity of the two wings as well as the country's development as a whole. As an exporter of a limited number of agricultural products and an importer of consumer and development goods, Pakistan trade is vulnerable to fluctuations in world commodity prices. The need actually to import foodgrains at times of crop failure has further retarded trade. Since 1950, imports have increased steadily, controlled by Plan requirements and with the emphasis changed from consumer to capital goods and to industrial raw materials (Table XVIII). Machinery, iron and steel, vehicles and oil account for the majority of imports now, with the USA as the major source of supply, followed by UK, West Germany and Japan. Under a trade agreement, USA supplies mainly wheat and rice but with increasing amounts of development goods. Exports have fluctuated, and on the whole declined, partly at least due to increased demand at home. The most significant thing is the increasing importance of cotton and jute manufactures. Jute is by far the major export. Hides and skins and raw wool from the West, and decreasing tea exports from the East are also important. India is second only to UK as a market (but Pakistan does not import from India to any extent), followed by USA, Japan, Benelux and West Germany. Exports have failed to keep pace with imports by a steadily decreasing margin. Overall trade has increased with the EFTA countries rather than ECM, with America and with Japan.

Inter-wing trade shows an interesting pattern. Ahmad points out that the distance, costs and economic contrasts between the two zones give it more the character of international than intra-national trade.[17] But the artificial controls inherent in the division of the country, and the efforts to replace foreign imports with Pakistani products, have an important bearing. West Pakistan finds an important outlet in the East for cotton (raw and manufactured), oilseeds and cement; indeed almost half of East Pakistan's total imports come from the other wing. But the West gets a relatively small proportion of her total imports such as jute and paper, since the East has not the items she needs, unfortunately. Conversely, East Pakistan sells a bigger proportion of her exports to outside countries than to the West, with jute of course dominating.

In absolute terms, West Pakistan has something like double the total trade of the less developed East; a familiar conclusion.

Ports and shipping

There are three ports; Karachi of course reigns alone in the West, and has been modernized from the export-orientated wharves fed by railways, which had existed for over half a century, to make an all purpose port. Land reclamation for oil refineries has been carried out, and facilities for storage, shipbuilding and repair, and also a fishing harbour. Karachi now imports twice as much as she exports (Table XVI) and the allocations under the Second Plan underline the port's dominance. Three hundred miles (483 km.) farther west there is a possibility of developing Pasni as an outlet for Baluchistan and the not insignificant Afghan transit trade. Chittagong was only a minor port in 1947, and had to be developed rapidly to meet the needs of East Pakistan. This is being done, in the face of difficulties such as the 1963 cyclone, with new wharves, oil installation and dredging; and the Karnaphuli project has the useful effect of regulating the river flow and reducing silting. There are special facilities for handling and storing both jute and tea. But congestion is still serious because of the lack of facilities to move cargoes back from the port area. To relieve the concentration at Chittagong, an anchorage was sought west of the Brahmaputra–Ganges. While the final choice of site has been delayed by the vagaries of river currents, there has been considerable development at Mangla, 30 miles (48 km.) down the Pussur River from Chalna, the original choice. Goods are trans-shipped and taken to Khulna railhead. Unlike Karachi and Chittagong, exports dominate at

[17] N. Ahmad, 'Some aspects of interwing trade in Pakistan', *Pak. Dev. Rev.* 3/1 (1963), 1–36.

Mangla; the planners are concerned about the empty trucks that arrive at Chittagong, and the empty ships which reach Mangla.

Shipping was vestigial at Partition (Table XVI), but has received considerable attention because of the separation of the two wings, and the increased overseas trade, the bulk of which is carried in foreign vessels. The importance of river traffic in the east has led to the expansion of the small boat-building yards at Narayanganj and Khulna. Karachi now builds as well as repairs ocean-going ships. By buying abroad second-hand ships (such as the railway flotilla that came from the Philippines and brings jute from Narayanganj to Chittagong, involving 20 miles (32 km.) of storm-prone open sea) Pakistan now has rather more capacity than she can use.

Transport and communications (Table, XV)

Inter-wing transport is by sea and air, involving the development of shipping and the improvement of facilities at the terminals. Karachi is a key international airport, with a jet air strip completed in 1961; while Lahore and Dacca will have them in a few years. The major urban centres are linked by frequent flights; a helicopter service for the delta has been initiated.

Internally there is a contrast between the road and rail networks of West Pakistan and the domination of waterways carrying three-quarters of the traffic in East Pakistan. While inheriting important strategic and commercial lines in the Punjab and the northwest Frontier, Pakistan got only one repair workshop of size, and the deterioration of the war and early years of Independence left a legacy of rundown stock and track only gradually being overcome. The plans emphasize repair units and the purchase of rolling stock rather than indigenous manufacture. In West Pakistan, broad gauge predominates – 1,000 miles (1,610 km.) of it double-track from the convergence of Punjab and northwestern lines at Lodhran, to Karachi, built to tap the agricultural surpluses of the Punjab for export, and to penetrate and control the northwest through the Khyber and Bolan Passes. The metre gauge line in Sind, part of the old Hyderabad–Jodhpur line, was severed at Partition like the broad gauge between Lahore and Amritsar; both are now restored; the Sind railway serves the cotton region. Narrow gauge lines in the hills include the little-used line from Quetta west to Iran and the line north to Chaman, now being extended to the Afghan border. Some new track has been laid in the Peshawar Basin to feed the sugar refineries.

There are two separate systems under the control of Pakistan Eastern Railways, linked by ferries over the unbridged Brahmaputra. One rail ferry comprises barges with rails onto which goods trucks are manoeuvred down rails at three different inclines to cope with the fluctuations of river level, while vagaries of its course have involved shifting the whole railhead at times; a sufficient comment on the difficulties of the largely metre gauge lines of the east. The small amount of broad gauge was oriented to Calcutta from collecting points like Goalundo: a metre gauge served and serves Chittagong. A new line has been pushed up from Sylhet to the cement and fertilizer factories, and another to the Karnaphuli dam site.

While the East has the higher total of roads (Table XV), the figures for miles of surfaced as against kachcha tracks reveals the lack of development, again largely because of difficult terrain. A mile of road costs four times as much to build in East Pakistan as it does in the West. The building of 200 miles (322 km.) of good road south from Chittagong to Arakan has been a major achievement. The three great trunk roads in West Pakistan include some 300 miles (483 km.) of the Grand Trunk Road from Afghanistan to Calcutta, the Karachi–Lahore road and the Lahore–Quetta road, which are being augmented by a road along the Makran and another up the west side of the Indus, which is bridged at several points over the barrages and by the famous boat bridge of Dera Ismail Khan. Local roads and the bullock carts radiating from district headquarters are controlled by local governments.

Water transport was once significant in West Pakistan but was killed by railways and the irrigation schemes. In the East, inland waterways extend from about 3,000 to 4,500 miles (4,830–6,520 km.) in the monsoon; the bulk of the shipping is by unmechanized country boats, but two British companies operate steamer services in addition to the railway flotilla mentioned above. Silting is tending to reduce the mileage; but on the other hand the Karnaphuli project is helping in the Chittagong River, and the Ganges–Kobadak scheme will help in the western region, as well as canalizing some of the stretches.

Conclusion : some comparisons between India and Pakistan

Like most countries attaining independence after a period of colonial rule, or arousing themselves after a period of economic stagnation of different emphasis and cause, India, Pakistan and Ceylon have all adopted five year plans, ten year plans, or five year plans complemented by longer-term 'perspective planning' of about the order of fifteen years. In this they have followed the general ideas of countries with governments of widely differing political ideas ever since the First Five Year Plan of the USSR of 1928–33. India's approach is pragmatic rather than doctrinaire in the sense of rigid attachment to Marxist theory, even though borrowing from it a good many ideas and ideals; there is more attempt to use macro-economic models, and with growing confidence and attachment to actual data rather than inferred levels. There is a mixed economy, with defined spheres for the public and private sectors within a wider aspiration towards a 'socialistic pattern of society', and much emphasis on the phased development of industry, building up from basic industries like steel and chemicals, heavy machine tools, heavy electricals and the like, through lighter machine tool, electrical and engineering industries, towards a considerable range of light consumer goods industries in twenty years or so. Compared with most underdeveloped countries, however, the starting-point included much more in the way of textile, engineering, chemical and food processing industries – with all that is implied in managerial, and entrepreneurial skill and adjustment of factory labour.

Irresistible political factors have enforced a very rapid, possibly too rapid, progress in Community Development programmes, and these have been accompanied by changes in grass-roots democracy and allocation of revenues; there is a marked tendency towards excessive emphasis on amenity-oriented rather than production-oriented development, but also a reaction against this. There have been declarations of intention to secure the greatest possible regional spread of development, since the Second Five Year Plan; these have been partly implemented through the federal state structure and the democratic representation of local interests within the State legislatures, and there are some signs that more integrated regional development plans may be in use at least experimentally in the Fourth Plan period, much more widely as compared with limited projects like those of the Damodar Valley Corporation (see p. 636). Foreign capital in industry lasting over from the colonial period, as in the plantation and jute industries, is somewhat uneasy, not nationalized or expropriated but prevented from leaving the country by foreign exchange regulations; even the Managing Agency system remains relatively unchanged. On the other hand, new foreign capital continues to enter the economy, on conditions acceptable to the government, though on rather too slender a scale in relation to the country's enormous needs. There are hazards – the upward trend in population increment, the Chinese invasion of the far north as a direct threat and as diverting investment from general and productive investment to defence and destructive devices – and possibly a phase of political instability or a change of direction at the end of Pandit Nehru's long period of dominance. But it seems certain that India's economic development will follow along the lines of Five Year Plans, not less Marxist and possibly more so than at present.

Pakistan, sharing with India the two 'steel frames' – the carry-over of efficient civil administration from the Indian Civil Service, and the railway links so vital to the British Raj – had greater initial difficulties because of the splitting of the two wings, the poorer endowment of industrial resources and development accentuated by the greater proportionate disturbance by the chaos, slaughter and population movements following Partition, and also, in the opinion of much Pakistani opinion, by Indian hostility, overt or covert. There was a period of political instability unmatched in India after Independence: the tentative Six Year Plan associated with the Colombo Plan, the period of military government under General Ayub Khan, the supersession of the Six Year Plan by the modest but latterly successful First Five Year Plan, and following Village AID the beginning of the 'Basic Democracy' programme which takes a somewhat different approach from India in relation to a largely common heritage of administration and many aspects of village culture and land tenure, the legacy of the Mogul and British periods. The basic democracies are somewhat analogous to the modern rather than the traditional *panchayats* of India, while the Indian *gram sevak* corresponds to the Village AID, the leaders often a man and wife (advantageous in the presence of the Muslim *purdah* but hardly less so potentially in conservative and husband-venerating rural India). The Basic Democracies have been made the fundamental unit for the election of representatives to vote at 'electoral colleges' in the new house of representatives, the present indirect form of democracy that replaced the military government, with Ayub Khan as elected President, in 1962. Initially more lacking in industrial resources and establishments than India, and less afraid of foreign (meaning particularly American) military and economic aid than of Indian mass and menace (as it has seemed to Pakistan), Pakistan has been ready to join the South East Asia Treaty Organization, and to accept a much larger proportion of American advice on economic development on the one hand, to strike a bargain (at some hazard) with China on the other. The modest First Five Year Plan of Pakistan, and the Second Five Year Plan so far, have shown very rapid progress in relation to targets. Pakistani thinkers are less given to demi-official macro-economic analysis and theorizing. From very low, sometimes negligible starting points, there has been a notable build-up of industrial units, including import of complete factories, techniques and technical assistance, as compared with India in much more consumer-oriented fields like textiles. (Of course India had more of these industries to start from.) The result has been that Pakistan's plans show a very gratifying speed of development; India's much larger plans, with a much more complex web of inter-dependence between parts of the Plans, have suffered much more from lags and frustrations. Pakistan, however, is now turning towards the basic type of industrial development like iron and steel works in both wings. On the other hand India's initial endowment of consumer goods industries was greater, and moreover if her plans are even within reach of their targets she may be ready to turn afresh to the development of the lighter type of industry which affords some of the most striking growth points to western economies. So the contrasts in the development plans of the two countries may lessen in time, though for long India is likely to have the more complex and sophisticated industrial development. One measure of this may be that the account of Pakistan's industries in the third edition of this book is somewhat comparable to that of India's industries in the previous editions; it is still possible and rewarding to give an industry by industry account for Pakistan, with only some auguries of future development of industrial regions, whereas for India it is now only possible and relevant to give an account of industrial regions of various orders, even while stressing that none of these as yet attain the massing or the complexity of a Ruhr or a Black Country.

BIBLIOGRAPHICAL NOTE FOR PART III

It is difficult to do more than indicate different approaches from a literature large enough and often heavy and viscous enough to float a new Gondwanaland. If a country's index of economic development were the amount of documentation about it, India would outstrip most countries on the globe.

Comprehensive works on Indian economic affairs discuss matters common to all the chapters of Part III; many of the older ones cited in earlier editions of this work are still useful, and mention may be made especially of D. H. Buchanan, *The Development of Capitalist Enterprise in India* (London, 1934) on the industrial side and the *Report of the Royal Commission on Agriculture in India* (1928) on the agricultural. A very comprehensive book, covering political as well as economic developments, is Charles Bettelheim, *L'Inde indépendante* (Armand Colin, Paris, 1962).

Official sources. There is a plethora of these, including the successive Draft Outlines and full-scale Five Year Plan volumes, Mid-Term or other Reviews and Assessments, e.g. the Evaluation Reports on Community Development prepared by the Programme Evaluation Organization of the Indian Planning Commission. They are of great value, and while they do present the official line, most of their quantitative data are to be regarded seriously, even where their accuracy must be viewed critically; this last point applies especially to some of the huge official surveys cited in the text, e.g. those on land holding and agrarian credit (see D. and A. Thorner, *Land and Labour in India*, Asia, Bombay, 1962). It applies also to data on Community Development, though even here some of the Evaluation Reports are of considerable candour.

For India these official publications are normally issued by the Manager of Publications, Delhi.

Non-official critiques. Like official reports, their name is legion. Some follow a more or less official line, by no means uncritically, e.g. B. G. Tandon (ed.), *The Third Five Year Plan and India's Economic Growth* (Chaitanya Publishing House, Allahabad, 1962) and W. B. Reddaway, *The Development of the Indian Economy* (Allen & Unwin, London, 1962), which is largely an exercise in model building. Some are farther from the official view, and it should be noted that association with the Plans at some stage does not preclude a critical viewpoint, as in D. R. Gadgil (ed.), *Planning and Economic Policy in India* (Gokhale Institute, Poona, 1961) or P. C. Mahanalobis, 'The approach of operational research to planning in India', *Sankhya* (Calcutta) 16/1–2 (1955), 3–130. Among foreign commentaries the authors have found particular value in W. Malenbaum, *Prospects for Indian Development* (Allen & Unwin, London, 1962); and the same could have been said of Bettelheim's book had it come to hand at an earlier stage of the revision.

For more hostile reviews see S. K. Iyengar, *A Decade of Planned Economy* (Indian Academy of Economics, Mysore, 1961), which is amusing, at times erratic, but makes many very palpable hits, or P. T. Bauer, *Indian Economic Policy and Development* (Allen & Unwin, London, 1961). A shorter critique in a journal accessible to many Western readers is W. Letwin, 'What's wrong with planning: the case of India', *Fortune* (June 1963), 118 – not quite as hostile as the title and source would suggest and, as in the larger publications cited, the arguments and criticisms are worthy of consideration and not necessarily unhelpful in the long run.

Material is spread through an astonishing gamut of learned journals in various countries and languages. Among Indian publications in English, *The Eastern Economist* of New Delhi, *The Economic Weekly* of Bombay, and major newspapers such as *The Hindu* of Madras, are all worth-while sources.

Pakistan. The Pakistani development has not attracted so much attention as the Indian. A substantial debt is owed to R. R. Platt (ed.), *Pakistan: A Compendium* (American Geographical Society, NY, 1961); this, while already becoming out of date in part, does exactly what it sets out to do by presenting 'a picture of Pakistan as it was in the decade of the 1950s'. Of the same era is J. R. Andrus and A. F. Mohammed, *The Economy of Pakistan* (OUP, Karachi, 1958). Though small, K. S. Ahmad's *A Geography of Pakistan* (OUP, 1964) is a welcome and handy work, and N. Ahmad's older *Economic Geography of East Pakistan* (OUP, London, 1958) is also very useful. In addition to works cited in footnotes, and to the two periodicals *Pakistan Geographical Review* (Lahore) and *Oriental Geographer* (Dacca), mention should be made of a relatively young economic journal of good quality, *The Pakistan Development Review* (Karachi).

Postscript. An immense quarry of factual information will be found in the two volumes (text and tables) of the Census of India 1961, Volume I Part I-A (i and ii), by Ashok Mitra, Registrar-General of India, on *Levels of Regional Development in India*. This was unfortunately received in the very last week of revision.

STATISTICAL TABLES

TABLE I

THE INDIAN SUB-CONTINENT AND CEYLON

AREA AND POPULATION, 1951 AND 1961

	Area sq. mls	Population, millions 1951	Population, millions 1961	Density to sq. ml. 1951	Density to sq. ml. 1961	Females to 1,000 males 1961	Increase % 1951–61
I. India							
A. States:							
Andra Pradesh . .	106,286	31·115	35·983	293	339	981	15·65
Assam.	47,091	8·837	11·873	188	252	876	34·45
Bihar	67,196	38·784	46·456	577	691	994	19·78
Gujarat	72,245	16·263	20·633	225	286	940	26·88
Jammu and Kashmir	86,024	3·254	3·561	379	414	878	9·44
Kerala	15,002	13·549	16·904	903	1,127	1,022	24·76
Madhya Pradesh . .	171,217	26·072	32·372	152	189	953	24·17
Madras	50,331	30·119	33·687	598	669	992	11·85
Maharashtra . . .	118,717	32·002	39·554	270	333	936	23·60
Mysore	74,210	19·402	23·587	261	318	959	21·57
Nagaland	6,236	0·213	0·369	48	58	933	14·07
Orissa	60,164	14·646	17·549	243	292	1,001	19·82
Punjab	47,205	16·135	20·307	342	430	864	25·86
Rajasthan. . . .	132,152	15·971	20·156	121	153	908	26·20
Uttar Pradesh . .	113,654	63·216	73·746	556	649	909	16·66
West Bengal . . .	33,829	26·302	34·926	778	1,032	878	32·79
B. Union Territories, etc.							
Andamans and Nicobars	3,215	0·031	0·063	10	20	617	105·19
Dadra and Nagar Haveli	189	0·041	0·058	220	307	963	39·56
Delhi	573	1·744	2·659	3,044	4,640	785	52·44
Goa, Daman and Diu	1,426	0·637	0·627	447	440	1,070	−1·66
Himachal Pradesh .	10,885	1·109	1·351	102	124	923	21·78
Laccadives, Minicoy, Amindivis . . .	11	0·021	0·024	1,912	2,192	1,020	14·61
Manipur	8,628	0·578	0·780	67	90	1,015	35·04
N.E.F.A.	31,438	n.a.	0·336	n.a.	11	894	n.a.
Pondicherry . . .	185	0·317	0·369	1,715	1,995	1,013	16·34
Sikkim*	2,744	0·138	0·162	50	59	904	17·76
Tripura	4,036	0·639	1·142	158	283	932	78·71
Total India	1,265,019	361·130	439·235	312	370	941	21·50
II. Pakistan							
West Pakistan . .	311,406	33·780	42·880	107	138	868	26·8
East Pakistan. . .	54,501	42·063	50·840	773	922	930	20·1
Total Pakistan	365,907	75·843	93·720	207	256	901	23·4
III. Other countries							
Nepal	54,600	8·470†		155		n.a.	n.a.
Bhután	18,000	0·700†		39		n.a.	n.a.
Ceylon‡	25,332	8·098	9·896	320	391	—	22·2

* Sikkim is 'connected to India by special treaties'. Some small discrepancies may be found in totals and densities between this and similar tables in other works arising from the inclusion or exclusion of Sikkim and of Jammu and Kashmir, 'because the 1961 census in that State did not cover portions currently under foreign occupation'.
† Estimates only.
‡ Ceylon figures for 1953 (Census) and 1960 (estimate).

TABLE II

CLASSIFICATION OF AREA, 1958–59

(In million acres/hectares. Discrepancies due to rounding off)

I. India		Acres	Hectares	% SG area	% VP area
Area, Village Papers		726·1	293·8	90	100
Area, Surveyor-General's estimates		806·3	326·3	100	111
Forests		130·1	52·7	16·1	17·9
Not available for cultivation		114·7	46·4	14·1	15·8
Permanent pasture and grazing		32·4	13·1	4·0	4·5
Misc. tree crops and groves		14·1	5·7	1·75	1·9
Culturable waste		50·9	20·6	6·3	7·0
Fallow, other than current		30·3	12·3	3·75	4·2
Current fallows		29·4	11·9	3·65	4·0
Net area sown		324·1	131·2	40·2	44·6
				89·85	99·9
Area sown more than once		48·6	19·7	6·0	6·7
Total cropped area		372·8	150·9	46·2	51·3

II. Pakistan				% total area	% area reporting
Total area:	WP	198·7	80·5	100·0	173·5
	EP	35·3	14·3	100·0	102·0
	Pak.	233·9	94·7	100·0	156·9
Area reporting:	WP	114·5	46·4	57·6	100·0
	EP	34·6	14·0	98·0	100·0
	Pak.	149·1	60·4	63·7	100·0
Forests:	WP	3·2	1·3	1·6	2·8
	EP	5·5	2·2	15·6	15·9
	Pak.	8·7	3·5	3·6	5·8
Not available for cultivation:	WP	50·3	20·4	25·3	43·9
	EP	5·6	2·3	15·9	16·2
	Pak.	55·9	22·7	23·9	37·5
Other uncultivated, excluding current fallows:	WP	20·0	8·1	10·1	17·5
	EP	1·9	0·8	5·4	5·5
	Pak.	21·9	8·9	11·0	19·1
Current fallows:	WP	9·6	3·9	4·8	8·4
	EP	1·3	0·5	3·7	3·8
	Pak.	10·9	4·4	4·7	7·3
Net area sown:	WP	31·3	12·7	15·75	27·4
	EP	20·3	8·2	57·5	58·7
	Pak.	51·6	20·9	26·0	34·6
Area sown more than once:	WP	4·5	1·8	2·3	3·9
	EP	5·6	2·3	15·9	16·2
	Pak.	10·1	4·1	4·3	6·8
Total cropped area:	WP	35·8	14·5	18·0	31·3
	EP	25·9	10·5	73·4	74·9
	Pak.	61·9	25·0	25·9	41·5

For discussion of terms, see text, p. 227. The 'reporting' and 'Village Paper' areas may be taken as the *oecumene*; the contrast between East and West Pakistan is instructive.

TABLE III

INDIA: AGRICULTURAL SUMMARY BY STATES, 1958–59

(In thousand acres)

		Total area by village papers	Forest	Rice	Wheat	Jowar and bajra	Gram	All food grains	Sugar	Ground nuts	Oil seeds	Cotton	Fodder	Irrigated	NSA	TSA	Area sown more than once
1	Andhra Pradesh	67,452	14,614	7,610	53	8,003	252	23,036	204	2,034	1,545	673	371	7,287	26,907	29,521	2,614
2	Assam	35,764	12,042	4,479	10	24	4	4,736	70	—	335	36	—	1,533	5,449	6,436	987
3	Bihar	42,823	9,287	12,335	1,613	—	1,428	24,021	443	—	800	—	84	4,464	19,718	27,010	7,292
4	Bombay (incl. Gujarat)	121,263	15,924	4,564	3,931	25,752	1,578	44,323	373	7,446	2,691	9,850	4,166	4,065	67,247	70,997	3,750
5	Jammu and Kashmir	11,993	7,465	533	415	50	—	1,754	4	—	95	3	32	745	1,652	1,973	321
6	Kerala	9,535	2,610	1,900	—	4	—	2,041	22	32	1,285	21	1	879	4,706	5,698	992
7	Madhya Pradesh	108,360	34,293	10,061	7,821	4,937	4,113	37,615	99	1,077	3,560	1,770	106	2,289	39,555	44,932	5,377
8	Madras	32,135	4,613	5,721	4	3,190	4	12,220	145	2,066	455	1,004	208	5,631	14,574	17,403	2,829
9	Mysore	46,362	6,671	2,466	727	8,320	377	18,233	157	2,383	1,012	2,550	437	1,991	25,247	26,182	935
10	Orissa	38,401	8,799	9,173	11	147	61	11,248	69	61	780	23	251	2,414	13,854	14,958	1,104
11	Punjab	30,286	915	980	5,318	2,820	6,190	17,775	590	151	640	1,329	3,047	7,409	18,479	23,997	5,518
12	Rajasthan	83,624	1,921	248	3,041	12,458	4,312	27,901	69	213	2,273	588	3,363	3,571	32,656	35,748	3,092
13	Uttar Pradesh	73,131	9,531	10,251	9,579	4,912	6,657	46,176	2,944	458	724	160	1,759	12,734	42,341	53,705	11,364
14	West Bengal	21,874	2,646	10,533	87	6	477	12,751	66	—	353	—	24	3,339	12,929	15,055	2,126
15	Delhi	366	4	3	70	87	19	218	12	—	12	1	5	93	216	275	59
16	Himachal Pradesh	6,962	1,959	112	352	—	—	1,021	3	—	12	1	—	97	670	1,085	415
17	Manipur	347	20	223	—	—	—	223	—	—	17	—	—	168	223	224	1
18	Tripura	2,634	1,573	426	—	—	—	429	7	—	17	18	—	20	511	611	100
19	Andamans and Nicobars	1,655	1,600	4	—	—	—	14	—	—	4	—	—	—	20	21	1
20	Laccadive Islands	7	—	—	—	—	—	—	—	—	7	—	—	—	7	7	—
	Total India	734,974	136,487	81,632	33,032	70,710	25,517	285,735	5,277	15,921	16,591	18,033	13,859	58,729	326,961	375,838	48,877
	thousand hectares:																

TABLE IV

PAKISTAN: AGRICULTURAL SUMMARY BY DIVISIONS, 1959–60

(In thousand acres)

	Total area	Rice	Wheat	Maize	Barley	Sugar-cane	Jute	Cotton	Irrigated	NSA	TSA	NSA % total	TSA % NSA	
Dacca	7,395	5,650	35	—	16	65	760	—	92	5,244	6,891	70·9	131·4	1
Chittagong	10,616	5,307	8	1	—	16	214	51	107	4,670	6,345	44·0	135·9	2
Rajshahi	8,431	5,558	73	52	47	136	322	—	106	5,692	6,946	67·5	122·0	3
Khulna	8,208	4,636	22	—	4	63	78	—	8	4,273	5,060	52·1	118·4	4
East Pakistan	34,650	21,351	138	53	67	280	1,374	51	313	19,879	25,242	57·4	127·0	
thousand hectares	14,023	8,641	59	21	27	113	556	21	127	8,045	10,215	—	—	
Peshawar	18,018	28	749	564	233	147	—	7	926	1,695	1,939	9·4	114·4	5
Dera Ismail Khan	7,124	6	616	48	27	10	—	2	271	1,033	1,047	14·5	101·4	6
Rawalpindi	7,235	74	1,732	132	52	30	—	72	625	3,310	3,555	45·7	107·4	7
Lahore	5,701	801	1,438	98	86	188	—	168	2,204*	3,559	4,177	62·42	117·4	8
Sargodha	10,957	67	2,253	186	58	260	—	562	4,362*	6,118	6,470	55·8	105·8	9
Multan	15,897	227	2,415	94	42	181	—	939	5,726*	5,518	6,546	34·7	118·6	10
Bahawalpur	11,206	40	945	49	15	112	—	540	2,777*	2,902	3,210	25·9	110·6	11
Khairpur	12,987	872	750	5	9	28	—	205	2,978	3,365	3,365	25·9	100·0	12
Hyderabad	23,460	767	730	10	10	21	—	801	4,244	4,143	4,405	17·7	106·5	13
Quetta	33,993	54	324	12	15	—	—	—	n.a.	397	431	1·2	108·6	14
Kalat	46,684	c.5	114†	—	—	—	—	—	n.a.	153	153	0·3	100·0	15
Karachi	5,379	n.a.	n.a.	n.a.	n.a.	n.a.	n.a.	n.a.	n.a.	109	109	2·0	100·0	16
West Pakistan	198,581	3,041	12,066	1,198	547	977	nil	3,296	24,113	32,302	35,407	16·2	109·61	
thousand hectares	80,366	1,231	4,883	485	221	395	nil	1,334	9,758	13,073	14,193	—	—	
Total *Pakistan*	234,231	24,392	12,204	1,251	614	1,257	1,347	3,347	24,426	52,181	60,649	22·3	116·2	
thousand hectares	94,389	9,872	4,942	506	248	508	556	1,355	9,885	21,118	24,408	—	—	

* 1958–59.   † 1962–63, inserted for comparative purposes. The statistics for Quetta, Kalat, and to a less extent Dera Ismail Khan, are imperfect.

TABLE V

IRRIGATION

(In thousand acres/hectares)

	Canal, ac.	Tank, ac.	Well, ac.	Other, ac.	Total, ac.	Total, ha.	% of total	Total as % of: TCA	NSA
I. India, 1959–60									
Andhra Pradesh	3,168	3,101	734	284	7,287	2,951	12·4	24·7	27·1
Assam	899	—	—	634	1,533	621	2·6	23·8	28·1
Bihar	1,473	734	644	1,613	4,464	1,808	7·6	16·5	22·6
Bombay*	762	805	2,658	140	4,065	1,646	6·9	5·7	6·0
Jammu and Kashmir	716	—	7	22	745	302	1·3	37·8	45·1
Kerala	450	79	35	315	879	356	1·5	15·4	18·7
Madhya Pradesh	1,067	334	794	94	2,289	927	3·9	5·1	5·8
Madras	2,083	2,058	1,394	96	5,631	2,281	9·6	32·4	38·6
Mysore	524	861	303	303	1,991	806	3·4	7·6	7·9
Orissa	556	1,223	94	541	2,414	978	4·1	16·1	17·4
Punjab	4,977	7	2,342	83	7,409	3,001	12·6	30·9	40·1
Rajasthan	818	774	1,944	35	3,571	1,446	6·1	10·0	10·9
Uttar Pradesh	5,005	1,035	5,977	717	12,734	5,157	21·7	23·7	30·1
West Bengal	1,992	910	39	468	3,339	1,352	5·7	22·2	25·8
Total, acres	24,420	11,621	16,965	5,345	58,351	—	99·4	15·6	18·0
Total, hectares	9,890	4,706	6,871	2,165	—	23,632			
II. Pakistan, 1957–58 to 1959–60									
West Pakistan	16,482	29	1,619	1,350	19,480	7,889	97·0	55·8	61·4
East Pakistan	217	38	28	347	630	255	3·0	2·5	3·1
Total, acres	16,699	67	1,647	1,697	20,110	—	100·0	33·1	32·5
Total, hectares	6,763	27	667	697	—	8,144			

* Bombay is now divided into Maharashtra and Gujarat. 'Other' includes tubewells in the Indo-Gangetic plains, elsewhere *pynes*, *ahars*, and various minor inundation channels. There is of course some yearly fluctuation, part statistical and part real.

TABLE VI

MAIN CROPS, 1950–51 AND 1960–61
(In thousand acres/hectares and tons/bales)

	Area 1950–51			Area 1960–61				Output		
	ac.	ha.	% NSA¶	ac.	ha.	% NSA¶	% increase	1950–51	1960–61	% increase
I. India										
Net Sown Area	293,400	118,740	100	327,902	132,700	100	—	—	—	—
Rice*	76,135	29,598	24.9	82,947	33,569	25.3	13.4	20,251	33,658	66.2
Jowar	38,477	15,571	13.1	42,683	17,274	13.0	10.9	5,408	9,215	70.4
Bajra	22,296	9,023	7.6	28,230	11,425	8.6	26.6	2,554	3,177	24.4
Maize	7,807	3,159	2.7	10,774	4,360	3.3	38.0	1,702	3,952	132.2
Wheat	24,082	9,746	8.2	33,047	12,969	9.8	33.1	6,360	10,818	70.1
All foodgrains and pulses	240,489	97,326	82.0	279,825	113,245	85.3	16.4	50,022	78,566	57.1
Sugarcane*	4,217	1,707	1.4	5,789	2,343	1.8	37.3	56,150	102,482	82.5
Groundnuts*	11,106	4,495	3.8	15,461	6,257	4.7	39.2	3,426	4,682	36.7
Other main oilseeds§	15,402	6,233	5.3	17,925	7,254	5.5	16.4	1,650	2,129	29.0
Cotton*†	14,536	5,883	5.0	18,871	7,637	5.8	29.8	2,910	5,330	85.2
Jute*†	1,411	449	0.4	1,512	612	0.5	36.3	3,283	3,982	21.3
Mesta*†	—	—	—	689	279	0.2	—	—	—	—
Tea	777	314	0.3	818	331	0.2	5.4	271	347	13.7
Coffee	224	91	0.1	272‖	110	0.1	20.9	25	n.a.	84.0
Tobacco	883	357	0.3	989	400	0.3	12.0	257	307	19.5
Rubber†	144	58	0.1	318	129	0.1	122.4	13	25	92.3
Coconut††	1,598	647	0.5	1,700	688	0.5	6.3	358	464	29.6
II. Pakistan										
Net Sown Area			100	53,063	21,475	100	—	—	—	—
Rice*	22,399	9,065	46.0	24,804	10,038	46.7	10.7	8,195	10,533	28.5
Jowar	1,256	508	2.6	1,177	476	2.2	–6.3	244	218	–10.7
Bajra	2,404	973	4.9	1,844	746	3.5	–23.3	—	—	—
Maize	948	384	1.9	1,207	488	2.3	27.1	384	439	14.3
Wheat	10,893	4,408	22.4	11,603	4,696	21.9	6.5	3,950	3,786	–4.2
All foodgrains and pulses	41,367	16,741	84.9	44,052	17,828	83.0	6.5	14,094	16,048	13.9
Sugarcane*	694	281	1.4	1,238	501	2.3	78.3	8,817	15,412	74.8
Rape and mustard	1,628	659	3.3	1,791	725	3.4	10.0	285	308	8.1
Cotton*	3,071	1,243	6.3	3,242	1,303	6.1	4.8	1,413	1,657	17.3
Jute*	1,711	692	3.5	1,518	614	2.9	–11.3	6,009	4,708	–21.7
Tea*	75	30	0.2	78	32	0.1	6.7	17	19	11.8
Tobacco	179	72	0.4	198	80	0.4	11.1	72	84	16.7

* Cleaned rice, cane, lint, dry fibre for rice, sugarcane, cotton, jute (and mesta) respectively.
†† In bales of 392 lb. (=177·8 kg.) for cotton and 400 lb. (=181·4 kg.) for jute and mesta.
‡‡ Coconuts in crores (ten millions) of nuts.
§ Other main oilseeds are castor, sesamum, rape and mustard and linseed.
‖ 1958–59.
¶ % of NSA under 'Principal Crops'; this figure is usually 0·5–2·0% below the total NSA.

TABLE VII

NUTRITIONAL VALUES OF SELECTED FOODGRAINS

	Moisture %	Protein %	Fats %	Mineral Matter %	Carbo-hydrates %	Vitamins units/100 grams AA	B	Iron mgs/100 grams	Calories per 100 grams
Wheat	12·8	11·8	1·45	1·5	71·3	108	230	5·3	345
Rice (1) . . .	12·2	8·5	0·35	0·7	78·3	—	100	2·75	350
Rice (2) . . .	13·0	6·85	0·55	0·5	79·1	—	26	1·0	349
Jowar	11·9	10·4	1·9	1·8	74·0	136	—	6·2	353
Bajra	12·4	11·6	5·0	2·65	67·1	220	110	8·8	360
Ragi	13·05	7·1	1·3	2·2	76·3	70	140	5·4	345
Millets . . . (minor)	11·75	9·55	2·75	3·5	64·9	trace	100–300	6·7	320
Maize . . . . ('tender')	79·4	4·3	0·5	0·65	15·2	42	—	0·7	82
Oatmeal . . .	10·7	13·55	7·6	1·8	62·9	trace	325	3·8	374

Note.—Rice (1) home-pounded in mortar, (2) factory milled; minor millets average of six (low carbo-hydrate due to high fibre content, average 7·5%). Cf. especially bajra and oatmeal.
Source: *Health Bulletin No. 23*, Nutrition Research Laboratories, Coonoor, Madras (1937), 18–21.

TABLE VIII

'NUTRITIONAL DENSITY'

(Population by 1961 Census related to nearest available area figures)

	Net Sown Area density per 100 ac.	100 ha.	Foodgrains density per 100 ac.	100 ha.	Crude density per sq. mile	Foodgrains density per sq. mile
I. India						
Andhra Pradesh	132	326	160	395	339	1,024
Assam	232	573	267	660	155	1,708
Bihar	236	583	193	477	691	1,235
Gujarat	89	220	175	432	286	1,120
Jammu & Kashmir	223	551	226	558	n.a.	
Kerala	369	912	829	2,048	1,127	5,306
Madhya Pradesh	83	205	86	213	189	550
Madras	235	581	282	697	669	1,805
Maharashtra	90	222	130	321	333	832
Mysore	94	232	137	339	318	877
Orissa	127	314	144	356	292	922
Punjab	110	272	114	282	430	730
Rajasthan	65	161	74	183	153	474
Uttar Pradesh	182	450	163	403	440	1,043
West Bengal	270	667	264	652	1,032	1,690
India	135	334	156	385	370	998
II. Pakistan						
West Pakistan	134	331	190	469	138	1,216
East Pakistan	250	618	240	593	922	1,536
Pakistan	183	452	212	524	256	1,357

TABLE IX

COTTON AREA AND OUTPUT, 1958–59 AND 1961–62

(In thousand acres/hectares and bales*)

	1958–59 Area: ac.	ha.	Output	1961–62 Area: ac.	ha.	Yield: lbs/ac.	kg/ha.	Output
I. India								
Andhra Pradesh . .	831	336·0	116	816	330·0	61	68·0	116
Gujarat	4,565	1,847·5	1,297	4,033	1,631·0	122	138·0	1,254
Madhya Pradesh . .	2,117	857·0	380	1,957	792·0	38	42·5	192
Madras	1,123	454·5	356	995	402·5	152	170·0	386
Maharashtra . . .	6,352	2,570·5	1,184	6,226	2,519·5	57	64·0	913
Mysore	2,537	1,027·0	441	2,347	950·0	74	83·0	441
Punjab	1,485	601·0	711	1,459	590·5	254	285·0	944
Rajasthan . . .	619	250·5	145	584	236·0	113	127·0	168
Uttar Pradesh . .	197	80·0	34	188	76·0	94	105·0	45
Rest of India . .	98	40·0	22	103	42·0	n.a.	n.a.	29
Total India	19,924	8,064·0	4,686	18,708	7,568·5	94	105·0	
II. Pakistan								
West Pakistan . .	3,273	1,324·5	1,443	3,449	1,396·0	203	228·0	1,830
East Pakistan . .	51	20·5	17	39	16·0	173	194·0	17
Total Pakistan . .	3,324	1,345·0	1,460	3,488	1,412·0	190	213·0	1,847

* 1 bale of cotton=392 lb.=177·8 kg.

TABLE X

JUTE AREA AND OUTPUT, 1959–60 TO 1961–62

(In thousand acres/hectares and metric tons)

	1959–60 ac.	ha.	Area 1960–61 ac.	ha.	1961–62 ac.	ha.	Output 1959–60	1960–61	1961–62
I. India									
Assam	334	135·0	299	121·0	363	147	202	148	205
Bihar	399	161·0	363	147·0	565	229	174	152	229
Orissa	75	30·0	100	40·5	114	46	33	43	55
Tripura	20	8·0	15	6·0	35	14	11	7	19
Uttar Pradesh . . .	33	13·0	32	13·0	38	15	17	16	21
West Bengal . . .	824	333·5	720	291·0	1,144	463	394	360	608
Total India	1,685	680·5	1,529	618·5	2,259	914	831	726	1,137
II. Pakistan (East) . . .	1,375	556·5	1,518	614·0	2,061	834	1,008	1,021	1,264

TABLE XI

TEA AND COFFEE: AREAS AND OUTPUT

(In thousand acres/hectares and metric tons)

	Tea (1960–61) Area ac.	ha.	Output	Coffee (1958–59) Area ac.	ha.	Output
Assam	401·1	162·3 ⎫	157·5 ⎫	—	—	—
West Bengal	204·1	82·5 ⎬74·1%	81·5 ⎬77·0%	—	—	—
Tripura	12·5	5·0 ⎭	2·1 ⎭	—	—	—
Madras	80·8	32·6 ⎫	30·9 ⎫	63·7	25·8	5·0
Mysore	4·5	1·8 ⎬22·4%	1·6 ⎬22·3%	160·5	65·0	34·0
Kerala	98·1	39·7 ⎭	37·2 ⎭	47·7	19·3	7·2
Punjab	9·6	3·9	1·0	—	—	—
Rest of India	7·5	3·0	1·1	0·3	0·1	0·4
Total India	818·2	330·8	312·9	272·2	110·2	46·6

TABLE XII
INDIA: CENSUS LIVELIHOOD CATEGORIES AND CLASSES

	1951 Population, millions	1951 % total population	1961 Population, millions	1961 % total population
Cultivator	100	22·78	70	19·6
Agricultural labourer	31	7·06	28	7·8
Mining, quarrying, etc.	5	1·14	4	1·1
Household Industry	12	2·73	—	—
Manufacturing other than Household Industry	8	1·82	13	3·6
Construction	2	0·46	1	0·3
Trade and Commerce	8	1·82	7	2·0
Transport, storage and commerce	3	0·68	2	0·6
Other Services	20	4·56	15	4·2
Non-workers	250	56·95	217	60·8
	439	100·00	357	100·0

TABLE XIII
MINERAL PRODUCTION

I. India

(In thousand metric tons)

Output:	1957	1962	Status	Major producing areas
Barytes	13	n.a.	A	Andhra Pradesh
Bauxite	110	573	A	Bihar, Madhya Pradesh
Chromite	80	66	A	Orissa
Coal	44,196	61,548	B	Bihar, Bengal (Damodar)
Copper	410	492	C	Bihar
Gold (kilograms)	5,568	5,076		Mysore
Gypsum	937	1,124	C	Rajasthan
Ilmenite	301	138	A	Kerala
Iron ore	5,172	13,188	A	Orissa, Bihar
Magnesite	90	217	A	Madras
Manganese	1,680	1,212	A	Mysore, Madhya Pradesh
Mica	31	28	A	Bihar
Petroleum, crude	440	1,077	C	Assam
Salt	3,672	3,864	C	Rajasthan, Gujarat and Madras (brine)

A=normal export; B=adequate for domestic consumption; C=imports necessary.

II. Pakistan

In long tons (units)

A. Solid minerals

Output:	1959	1962 (provisional)
Antimony	152	105
Barytes	508	2,677
Chromite	16,223	30
Coal	723,000	947,000
Gypsum	97,000	128
Iron ore	2,250	3,804 (1961)
Limestone	927,000	1,515,000
Marble	2,796	2,222
Salt (rock)	157,000	192,000
Silica sand	22,000	14,000

Source: *Pakistan Basic Facts* (Govt of Pakistan, 1963). The small scale and violent fluctuation of production are significant.

B. Oil and Gas

Output:	1959	1962
Oil (millions Imp. gallons)	82	117
Gas (million cubic feet)	22,365	42,076

Gas reserves (in thousand million cubic metres):

West		East	
Sui	170*	Sylhet	7·9
Mari	99	Chattak	0·5
Uch	71		
Dhulian	48·1		8·4
Other	16·3		
	404·4		

* Equivalent to 127,000,000 tons of coal.

TABLE XIV

PRODUCTION IN SELECTED INDUSTRIES

(In thousand metric tons, unless otherwise stated)

	1951	1956	1960	1961	1962	1963	% increase 1951 to 1963
I. India							
Cotton yarn (million kg.)	592	758	788	863	859	893	50·8
Cotton cloth (million m.)	3,727	4,853	4,616	4,702	4,560	4,423	18·7
Jute manufactures	889	1,111	1,085	971	1,183	1,236	39·0
Pig iron	1,829	1,961	4,175	4,987	5,796	6,604	261·1
Steel	1,034	1,270	2,150	2,798	3,564	4,272	313·2
Sulphuric acid	109	168	354	422	468	568	421·1
Cement	3,247	4,972	7,844	8,245	8,587	9,355	188·1
Sugar	1,170	1,985	2,591	2,842	2,786	2,316	98·0
Soda ash	48	78	145	177	223	264	450·0
Paper	134	196	348	364	388	463	245·5

	1950	1955	1959	1960	1961	1962	% increase 1950 to 1962
II. Pakistan							
Cotton yarn (million kg.)	19·5	125·0	178	185·5	187·5	196	1,000
Cotton cloth (million m.)	97·0	414·0	565	575·0	639·0	663	684
Jute manufactures	—	105·0	238	269·0	254·0	291	177 (1955–62)
Steel ingots	3·0	11·0	9	7·0	9·0	3	133
Cement	420·0	692·0	1,002	1,138·0	1,242·5	1,395	332
Sugar	33·5	96·5	170	147·0	125·0	194	578
Phosphate fertilizers	—	—	44	49·0	57·0	60	—
Paper	—	20·0	n.a.	58·0	61·0	n.a.	—

TABLE XV
INTERNAL TRANSPORTATION

I. India, 1960–61
A. Railway routes by gauge :

	Broad		Metre		Narrow		Total	
	miles	km.	miles	km.	miles	km.	miles	km.
	16,566	26,676	15,629	25,168	3,178	5,118	35,353	56,962*

* Break-up of 317 miles (510 km.), mainly in Madhya Pradesh, not available.

B. Railway working

Passengers, millions	1,616†	Freight, million metric tons	158
Passenger miles, millions	48,475	Net metric ton-kilometres, millions . .	87,833
Passenger kms, millions	78,060	Average metric ton haul . 346·5 miles (558 km.)
Average journey . . . . 28 miles (48 km.)

† Of whom 7,600,000 were detected travelling without tickets.

C. Roads:

black-topped		cement/concrete		water-bound macadam		unsurfaced		total	
miles	km.	miles	km.	miles	km.	miles	km.	miles	km.
44,903	72,308	2,604	4,194	51,698	83,249	182,961	294,623	282,363	454,691

II. Pakistan, 1962
A. Railway routes : by gauge :

	Broad		Metre and narrow		Total	
	miles	km.	miles	km.	miles	km.
Western Railway.	4,636	7,459	693	1,115	5,329	8,574
Eastern Railway	599	964	1,113	1,791	1,712	2,755
Total	5,235	8,423	1,806	2,906	7,041	11,329

B. Railway working

Passengers, millions	193	Freight, million metric tons.	20
Passenger miles, millions	7,431	Net long ton-miles, million	4,859
Passenger kms, millions	11,956	Average ton haul . . . . 243 miles (391 km.)
Average journey . . . . 38 miles (61 km.)

C. Roads

	'high type motorable'		'low type fair weather'		total pukka roads	
	miles	km.	miles	km.	miles	km.
West Pakistan	9,510	15,302	32,483‡	52,265‡	41,993	67,567
East Pakistan	1,833	2,949	27,495	44,239	29,328	47,189
Total	11,343	18,251	59,978	96,504	71,321	112,756

‡ For climatic reasons, in West Pakistan many of these roads in arid areas are in fact motorable all the year

D. Inland Waterways, East Pakistan
Mileage of perennial waterways 2,700 (4,345 km.), monsoon waterways 4,000 (6,440 km.).
Steamers 172, motor vessels 887, total 1,059; capacity 100,000 passengers, 160,000 tons.
Country craft: estimated number 300,000, capacity 1,500,000 passengers, 1,200,000 tons.

TABLE XVI

PORTS AND SHIPPING, 1961–62

I. India

(In lakh (100,000) GRTs and metric tons)

Major Ports		Ships entering: No.	Gross tonnage	Imports	Exports	Turnover	% turnover of major ports
Calcutta		1,806	123·5	48·8	44·2	93·0	27·4
Bombay		3,156	202·9	104·1	41·3	145·4	42·9
Madras		1,230	85·3	22·7	12·0	34·7	10·2
Visakhapatnam		613	43·8	14·0	14·6	28·6	8·4
Cochin		1,342	72·7	18·8	4·9	23·7	7·0
Kandla		230	17·3	11·1	2·7	13·8	4·1
	Total	8,377	545·5	219·5	119·7	339·2	100·0

In addition about 225 minor ports, of which 150 are 'working ports', handle about 6,000,000 metric tons per annum.

Shipping: In 1960, 173 ships of over 150 GRT were on the Indian register, 91 (279,000 GRT) in coastal and 82 (573,000 GRT) in overseas trade. By the end of 1962, GRT had risen from 952,000 to 1,014,000.

II. Pakistan

Major Ports		Ships entering: No.	Gross tonnage	Imports	Exports	Turnover	% turnover of major ports
Karachi		n.a.	n.a.	36·17	17·25	53·42	57·7
Chittagong		n.a.	n.a.	24·54	4·42	28·96	31·5
Chalna		n.a.	n.a.	3·25	6·76	10·01	10·8
	Total	n.a.	n.a.	63·96	28·43	92·39	100·0

Shipping: In 1962, 45 ships (29 coastal), of 405,941 Dead Weight Tonnage, approximately 600,000 GRT.

TABLE XVII

SHARE OF SELECTED COUNTRIES IN TRADE, 1958–62
(As percentage of values)

I. India

		UK	USA	USSR	W. Germany	Japan	Pakistan
1958	Imp.	17·1	15·6	2·0	10·5	4·5	0·6
	Exp.	29·1	15·3	4·8	2·6	5·0	1·1
1959	Imp.	20·2	21·7	1·8	12·1	4·0	0·9
	Exp.	27·3	15·2	4·8	3·3	5·5	1·1
1960	Imp.	19·4	29·2	1·4	10·9	5·4	1·3
	Exp.	27·0	15·8	4·6	3·0	5·5	1·5
1961	Imp.	18·4	23·4	3·7	11·3	5·5	1·3
	Exp.	24·4	17·6	4·9	3·0	6·2	1·4
1962	Imp.	16·6	29·3	5·1	9·0	5·8	1·5
	Exp.	23·7	17·0	5·6	6·6	4·9	1·4

II. Pakistan

		USA	UK	W. Germany	Japan	Iran	India	Belgium-Luxb'g
1957–58	Imp.	25·7	18·8	8·1	5·1	2·0	4·0	4·0
	Exp.	11·6	18·1	9·7	10·0	0·9	6·2	5·1
1958–59	Imp.	22·7	17·5	10·5	4·9	3·3	4·9	4·0
	Exp.	10·5	16·3	5·8	8·1	1·1	3·2	5·6
1959–60	Imp.	23·5	17·5	10·0	8·0	6·2	3·3	1·8
	Exp.	8·9	17·5	5·4	10·8	0·7	5·2	3·6
1960–61	Imp.	23·9	18·6	8·6	7·9	4·8	4·1	3·2
	Exp.	9·2	15·6	5·1	6·9	0·2	5·9	4·1
1961–62	Imp.	30·8	20·4	9·4	8·0	3·7	3·4	2·0
	Exp.	9·5	15·9	5·5	5·9	0·4	5·5	6·0

TABLE XVIII

CHANGES IN IMPORT/EXPORT STRUCTURE, 1957–62

(As percentages of total imports/exports. Indian year ends 31.3, Pakistan 30.6)

Commodity Groups		Imports				Exports			
		1957	1961	1962	1963	1957	1961	1962	1963
1 Food	·	8·17	13·49	15·86	14·19	27·24	32·66	34·50	31·44
2 Beverages and tobacco	·	0·18	0·15	0·15	0·09	2·49	2·29	2·78	2·75
3 Crude materials, inedible, except fuel	·	9·72	11·92	11·24	10·67	18·61	17·69	16·37	16·62
4 Total mineral fuel, lubricant and others	·	9·62	8·79	7·77	9·10	2·16	0·90	0·95	0·98
5 Animal and vegetable oils and fats	·	0·53	0·70	0·50	0·42	1·84	0·99	2·01	2·59
6 Chemicals	·	6·96	8·23	8·87	7·69	0·85	1·19	1·15	0·83
7 Manufactured goods	·	23·81	20·29	18·02	17·02	41·23	41·11	39·31	37·79
8 Machinery and transport equipment	·	28·31	33·72	34·24	36·69	0·31	0·60	0·64	0·64
9 Miscellaneous manufactured articles and transactions	·	12·70	2·62	3·35	5·27	5·27	2·57	2·29	6·31
Total	·	100·00	100·00	100·00	100·00	100·00	100·00	100·00	100·00

II. Pakistan

		Imports					Exports				
		1957–58	1958–59	1959–60	1960–61	1961–62	1957–58	1958–59	1959–60	1960–61	1961–62
1 Food, drink and tobacco	·	33·5	24·5	17·5	19·9	13·1	3·3	6·4	8·7	7·2	11·3
2 Raw materials	·	13·3	17·1	21·3	18·7	17·8	85·4	75·8	62·5	64·6	63·3
3 Manufactured articles	·	52·3	57·4	60·9	61·4	69·1	10·5	17·3	28·7	28·2	25·4
4 Postal articles and baggage	·	0·9	1·0	0·3	—	—	0·8	0·5	0·1	—	—
Total	·	100·0	100·0	100·0	100·0	100·0	100·0	100·0	100·0	100·0	100·0

Volume I in Retrospect:
an interim conclusion

The paperback edition of this book is in two volumes, compared with one for the hardback edition. So we find ourselves with the unusual task – and opportunity – of writing an additional conclusion to the volume containing the systematic geography as compared to the regional geography of volume II. This challenge comes several years after the work was done on the third edition of the whole work. It comes, too, when the authors, in common with all men of goodwill towards the people of South Asia, are deeply troubled over the tragic developments there of the early 1970s. To a sub-continent already sufficiently troubled there came a sequence of further blows.

The great Bay of Bengal cyclone and storm surge of November 1970, the heavy losses in life, prosperity and powers of resistance to disease were associated with feelings of neglect of East Pakistan by the Government of Pakistan situated in the west. The election a few weeks later brought a vast majority for the Awami League committed to a great degree of self-government, and rightly or wrongly fearing secession the Pakistan Government sent the Army into violent action against dissident Bengali troops and others proclaiming a separate State of Bangladesh. Within a few months 10 million refugees flowed into West Bengal, already overcrowded and, some would judge, in a proto-revolutionary situation. Relations between India and Pakistan grew even more tense than in the previous decades, with a real risk of renewed war, less likely to be containable than the previous fighting mainly over Kashmir, and more likely to involve losses on the scale of the period of Partition in 1947. These events are briefly referred to at the end of chapter 19 in volume II, but they have their relevance to our retrospect over volume I, which must be overlayed by anxiety. Even Ceylon has had experience of armed insurgency at about the same time. Yet this work stands or falls by broader perspectives, so our retrospect is germane.

The book begins with long time perspectives – the thousands of millions of years for the evolution of the landscapes of Gondwanaland, the tens of thousands for the building up of the Indo-Gangetic plains and the great deltas, which yet can be seen to evolve and change in a season of catastrophic storms, or more gradually over a lifetime of observation. We go on to the seasonal rhythm of the monsoons; here the perspective of the two centuries since Halley's paper of 1686 lends us increasing insights into the dynamism of good years and bad, a late bursting of the monsoon, or prolonged breaks in it, or disastrous flooding in this or that region. Some patterns of distribution of vegetation and soils suggest simple areal correlation with elements of climate and landforms, but involve relatively long time perspectives – past as well as present climates, and shorter ones concerning the retreat of much natural vegetation, and the deterioration of many soils. Here the ecological viewpoint, with its vision of an interrelated web of causal relationships, gives insight even when our ideas run ahead of hard data or quantitative correlations.

We turn then to the People, with the longer perspectives of historical flow, and movement and change, and the shorter ones of the regionally differing demographic trends over the last century, themselves changing, from about 1931 in some degree, from about 1951 as part of the world-wide phenomenon of the so-called population explosion. The settlement patterns too, reflect change: there is first the honeycomb matrix of village and village lands and village market areas, in places along the classic lines of Christaller (see chapter 18 on the Gangetic Plains in volume II); elsewhere, especially in the deltas and along marked breaks of slope at the edge of plain and upland, there is a linear arrangement of settlement sites or a linear plan to the settlements; truly dispersed patterns are rare. Upon all this is superimposed the historic pattern of court and castle town; the more regular pattern of administrative (and taxation) centre whether indigenous or colonial; the great seaport foci of the colonial phase and of outward-looking independent countries; and manufacturing towns, indigenous, then late colonial, then expanding to include the new planned steel towns and the like in the planning era after Independence.

And so to the Economy. Again there is a kind of traditional matrix of archaic agriculture, conservative but not unskilled. In places, like the canal colonies of Punjab, it was transformed during the colonial phase, but, the nationalist critic would say in a lop-sided kind of development. Elsewhere the pressure on the land was increased by the displacement of population from indigenous manufacturing, as in East Bengal. With Independence came complex waves of change – land reform of varying thoroughness and impact, community development, extension of irrigation on different scales and different degrees of capital intensity, technological change in the so-called 'green revolution', and always increasing population pressure, taking South Asia as a whole. Soon after Independence industrialization and large-scale hydro-electric and irrigation projects perhaps appeared as a panacea, but later a realization that an agriculture lagging in technological change or too subject to the vagaries of the monsoon could endanger the whole of the hoped-for advance in standards of living in the newly independent nations.

All of these complex patterns of change over very varied time-perspectives have their impact on spatial distributions also, and we have tried to portray these within a framework of traditional geographical presentation, in this volume in a general way, in volume II in a more intimate regional scale of examination.

Each time the authors return to South Asia they are reminded that rapid change as well as initial complexity make even such a long book incomplete. The first edition of the work, completed in 1951, was written in the first years of independence for India, Pakistan and Ceylon. The second edition was completed in the early years of the planning era. The third, from which the paperback edition is only lightly amended, is an attempt to assess the impact of 20 years of independence and 15 years of planning on the geography of the new-old countries of South Asia. Meantime geography itself has been undergoing profound changes, which we can not as yet reflect fully in a work of this kind; and more and more geographical work comes from South Asians themselves, some traditional, some in the more modern trend rather specifically oriented towards theoretical frameworks and to quantification. The text already refers to works like K. S. Ahmad's *Geography of Pakistan*, N. Ahmad's *Economic Geography of East Pakistan*, and the new *Gazeteer of India*. We should now complement these by studies in the newer trend like the works by Berry and by Bhat and Mathur cited below, while in the older tradition we have a new major work, primarily regional in approach, in R. L. Singh's edited volume. One cannot make a retrospect without looking ahead to some extent. Berry's book emphasises India's strength in numerical data useful for quantitative analysis within a framework of certain theoretical constructs. The so-called new geography is often said to stress similarities in spatial patterns, to play down uniqueness in regional patterns; conversely, older geographies are said to emphasise uniqueness at the expense of analytical power in discussing similarities in spatial patterns. Yet application, say in planning in India, of theoretical and quantitative geography is likely, nay certain, to have to take count of India's uniquenesses, as a whole and in its immense regional variety. So, looking ahead, and given more studies like Berry's and that by Bhat and Mathur, one can foresee that in a few years' time a work like this one will have a new task of synthesis, to comprehend newer approaches with more traditional ones like those in Singh's volume.

B. J. L. Berry, *Essays on Commodity Flows and the Spatial Structure of the Indian Economy*, University of Chicago, Department of Geography Research paper No. III, Chicago, 1966.
L. S. Bhat and R. B. Mathur, *Cement Industry: a case study in national and regional perspectives* – 1967. Supplement to the Bombay Geographical Magazine, Bombay Geographical Association, Bombay, 1967.
R. L. Singh (Editor), *India: a Regional Geography*, National Geographic Society of India, Varanasi – 5, India, 1971.

Changes in Indian Place-Names

Since Independence, there has been a not unnatural trend towards abandoning Anglicized renderings of many place-names, in favour of forms more linguistically correct; it is unfortunate that the latter are usually also longer. In this book, the new (or resurrected) forms are normally employed, though doubtless the attentive reader will find some anomalies. For towns, the older style is usually given in parentheses at the main reference, and cross-references from the older forms are given in the index. Following is a list of altered forms as used in this book; for details, reference may be made to M. P. Thakore, 'Changes in place-names in India', *Indian Geogr* 1/1 (1956), 51–54, and S. D. Gupta, 'The changing map of India', *GRI* 22/3 and 22/4 (1960), 23–33 and 13–32.

New form				*Older form, and remarks*
Amravati	...	...	...	Amraoti, Maharashtra
Avadh ...	...	...	...	Oudh; as the name is used here mainly in contexts referring to the British period, it seems reasonable to retain the Anglicized form.
Banaras, *see* Varanasi				
Banaskantha	...	...	...	New District, Gujarat
Chickmagalur		...	...	Kadur District, Mysore
Deoria ...	...	...	...	New District, part of old Gorakhpur District, Uttar Pradesh
Dhanbad	...	...	...	New District, part of Manbhum District, Bihar
Durg ...	...	...	...	Drug, Madhya Pradesh
Eluru ...	...	...	...	Ellore, Andhra Pradesh
Faizabad	...	...	...	Fyzabad, Uttar Pradesh
Ganadki	...	...	...	Apparently used for the Gandak in Nepal, but Gandak is standard in current literature and is retained here.
Ganga ...	...	...	...	Ganges; but note that Pakistani usage retains Ganges, and is employed here where appropriate.

New form	Older form, and remarks
Ghaghra, *also* Ghaghara ...	Gogra
Gomati	Gumti, Gumtee
Himachal Pradesh	Punjab Hill States
Jabalpur	Jubbulpore, Madhya Pradesh
Kakinada	Cocanada, Andhra Pradesh
Kanchipuram, *also* Kanchee-puram	Conjeeveram, Madras
Kanpur	Cawnpore, Uttar Pradesh
Kanya Kumari [Cape], Kan-nyyakumari [District] ...	Cape Comorin
Kathiawad	Kathiawar
Kaveri, *also* Koveri	Cauvery; although these forms seem more correct, they are not yet in general use, and Cauvery has been retained.
Kozhikode	Calicut, Kerala
Krishna	Kistna
Kutch	Cutch
Lakhnau	Lucknow, Uttar Pradesh; the older form is still in common use, and retained here.
Madurai	Madura, Madras
Masulipatnam...	Masulipatam, Andhra Pradesh
Mathura	Muttra, Uttar Pradesh
Nagapattinam	Negapatam, Madras
Narmada	Narbada
Palayankottai	Palamcottah, Madras
Palani	Palni Hills
Panjab	Punjab; Panjab is the more correct transliteration, and was often used (as was Panjaub) by older British writers, as well as in the title of the Panjab University, Lahore; but it does not seem to have caught on in either India or Pakistan, and Punjab is retained here.
Pratapgarh	Partabgarh District, Uttar Pradesh
Ramanathapuram	Ramnad, Madras
Sabarkantha	New District, Gujarat
Sagar	Saugor, Madhya Pradesh
Saharsa	New District, part of old Bhagalpur District, Bihar
Srikakulam	Chicacole, Andhra Pradesh
Surendranagar	Wadhwan, Gujarat

New form	Older form, and remarks
Tamilnadu	Madras State
Thanjavur, *also* Thanjvur, Tanchavur, Tanjavur ...	Tanjore, Madras; Thanjavur appears to be the official form and is used here.
Tiruchchirappalli, *also* Tiruchirapalli	Trichinopoly, Madras; the longer form is on official political maps, but the shorter is apparently used for postal purposes, and (understandably) even Trichy will still find it.
Tirunelveli	Tinnevelly, Madras
Varanasi, *also* Banaras ...	Benares, Uttar Pradesh
Vijayawada	Bezwada, Andhra Pradesh
Visakhapatnam	Vizagapatam, Andhra Pradesh
Yamuna	Jumna
Zalwad...	New District, Gujarat

Index

There is a separate Index of Authors and Works cited. There is, of course, some selectivity in the General Index; the judicious reader will not expect to find every passing mention of say *rice* or *Ganga* listed, and merely 'marker' references such as that to Delhi on p. 14 are omitted. Attention is drawn to the following major heads, under which relevant entries are gathered: COAL, COTTON, DEVELOPMENT PROJECTS, ELECTRICITY, GEOLOGICAL FORMATIONS AND PERIODS, IRRIGATION, LAKES, MOUNTAIN AND HILL RANGES AND PLATEAUS, MOUNTAIN PEAKS AND HILLS, PASSES, RICE, RIVERS, SOIL TYPES, TRIBES AND CASTES, VEGETATION and WARS.

Major references are shown in bold-face; *pm = passim*

Bhoodan movement, 271–2, 276
Bhopal, 156, 338
Bhutan, 152
bicycles, 322, 340
Bidar, 99, 186
bidis, 203, 251, 307, 381–2
Bihar, poptn, 132–3; agriculture, 244–9
pm; other refces, 296
Bijapur Kingdom, 186, 190, 201
Bikaner, 286
Bikasser oilfield, 301
Bilaspur, Dt and town, 285
biotic factors in vegetation, 73–74, 80, 83–
5, 90, **94–95**
BIRLA family, 168
birth control, 137–8, **146–9**
Black Country, 387
Bogra, 301
Bokaro, 293, 639
Bombay, poptn, 123–32 *pm*, 138, 157, 167;
Parsees of, 162; histl signfce, 188, 192,
195; power resources, 289–90; indus-
trial devpmt, Ch. 10 *pm*, 337, 338;
other refces, 44, 58, 209–12 *pm*
Bombay I., 316
Bonai, 292
Borobudur, 183–4
boundaries, internal, 178
Brayne, F. L., 275
Brazil, 19, 74, 244, 246, 252, 290, 305
Britain, British Isles, 121, 366; trade with,
353, 354
British, British Raj, historical refces, 6,
188–96, 213; and Anglo-Indians, 162;
irrigation under, 230, 231, agric.
policy, 232, 266, 270, 275; econ.
policy, 306, 311; other refces, 3, 156,
209, 216, 358
Broach, 309
buckwheat, 228
Buddh Gaya, 159
BUDDHA, *see* GAUTAMA
Buddhism, Buddhists, histl, 3, 4 fn., 175,
180, 183, 184; other refces, **159**
Buenos Aires, 215
buffaloes, 94, 208, 254, 257–8
building stones, 18, **298,** 304
bullocks, 254, **256,** 266, 272
Bundelkhand, 153, 177, 204
Bundi, 323
Burhanpur (and gap), 21, 23
Burma, Burmese, Indian influence in, 3–5
pm, 183, 466; *taungya*, 228 fn.;
tobacco, 251; trade with, 295, 323,
325; other refces, 56, 85, 153, 159,
161 fn., 178, 193, 210, 306
Burnpur, 320, 322, 336

'burst' of monsoon, 52, 56, 58
BUSSY, Marquis de, 193
bustees, 204, 313
Byzantines, Byzantium, 182, 305

Calcutta, social aspects, 160, 162, 209,
294; histl, 189, 192; industry, Ch. 10
pm; trade, 350; other refces, 218, 289,
338, 376–85 *pm*; *see also* Hooghlyside
Calicut (*see also* Kozhikode), 186, 190
Calimere, Point, 84
Caliphate, 196
Cambay, Gulf of, histl signfce, 173–9 *pm*,
187; oil, 287–8; other refces, 44
Cambodia, 183
Campbellpur, erratics at, 39
Canada, 325
Canal Colonies, Punjab, 204, 247, 278, 342,
371
canals, *see* IRRIGATION
cantonments, 208, 210, 213
capitalist farming, 229
Carcassonne, 208
cardamoms, 242, 260
'Carnatic', *see* Tamilnad
cashew nuts, 74, 260
caste(s), 6, 159, **162–8,** 203, 209, 272; in
villages, 167; *see also* TRIBES AND
CASTES
castor, 142, 143
CASTRO, D. JOÃO DE, 191
catena, soil, 98, 108
cattle problem, 242, **254–7,** 265; strains:
Amrit Mahal, 257; Gir, 257; Hansi
(Hariana), 257; Kangayam, 257;
Kankrej, 257; Sindhi, 257; zebu, 257;
Red Sindhi, 368; Sakrawal, 368
Caucasoids, 152
caustic soda, 296, 379, 381
Cawnpore, *see* Kanpur
'Ceded Districts', Madras, 204
cement industry, Indian, 287, 312, **323;**
Pakistani, 303, 382–5 *pm*
Central Provinces, xxix, 156, 194; *see*
MADHYA PRADESH
ceramics, lack of in Hindu civilization,
306 fn.
Ceylon, climate, 50, 52–53, 58, 61;
Indians in, 127; poptn, 145; Buddhism
in, 159, 180–4 *pm*, 191–3 *pm*; Indian
trade with, 321–5 *pm*; other refces, 5,
19, 25, 152, 153, 297, 385
Chagai, 304
'Chalcolithic' peoples, 152, 174
Chalna, 383
Chalukyas, 182

Chaman, 384
Champa, 183
Chanda, 284
Chandernagore, 192, 194
Chandragona, 379, 381
CHANDRAGUPTA MAURYA, 180
CHANDRAGUPTA II VIKRAMADITYA, 181
charcoal, 93, 320, 330
charkha, 307
CHARLEMAGNE, 181
chars, 199
Chattak, 303, 382
Chaul, 190
chaulmugra oil, 260
chawls, Bombay, 313, 378–9
chemicals industry, 297–8, 311, 323–4
chena cultivation, 228 fn., 249
cheris, 203, 212
Chettinad, 199
Chhattisgarh, 177, 292
China, Chinese, historic links, 4, 5, 183,
    184, 191; and Pakistan, 171, 387;
    agric. comparisons, 251, 254, 259, 265,
    269; yarn export to, 309–10, 316;
    agression (1958–62), 336 fn., 343, 344,
    386; other refces, 7, 50, 74, 147, 209,
    305, 327
Chinsura, 192
Chitral, 28, 304, 377
Chittagong, 190, 377–84 *pm*
Chittagong Hill Tracts, 91, 329
Chittaranjan, 336
Chittoor, 298
cholam, 237; *see also* jowar
Cholas, 5, 177, 182, 184
cholera, 54, 138, 141
Chota Nagpur, 3, 80, 123, 125, 260, 292,
    296
Christianity, Christians, 6, 150, 158, 160,
    161–2, 166, 183, 188, 192, 212
chrome alum, 324
chromite, 294; Pakistan, 299, 304
chromium, 321
cinnamon, 260
Circars, Northern, 124, 193
Chitral, 480, 489–93 *pm*
citronella, 324
'Civil Lines', 208, 209
classification of area, India and Pakistan,
    227–8, Table II.
climates, classification of, 66–69
Clovelly, 220
Clysma, 182
COAL:
    anthracite, 429
    coke, coking, **286**, 292, 324, 337;
        Pakistani, 301

exports, 353
fields: Bokara, 284; Damodar, 18,
    23, 132, Ch. 10 *pm* (**283–4**),
    316–23 *pm*; Jharia, 321; Karan-
    pura, 284; Khost-Sharig (Pak.),
    301; Korba, 284, 337; Mach
    (Pak.), 301; Makerwal (Pak.),
    301; Pench, 323; Ramgarh,
    284; Raniganj, 284, 292, 320,
    321; Singareni 123, 284, 337;
    Warangal, 123
lignite, 22 fn., 286, 290, 301, 344;
    in Kashmir, 286; Neiveli, 286,
    337, 345; Pak., 301
mining methods, 286
resources, Indian, 281, **283–6**, 299;
    Pakistani, **299–301**, 344, 377,
    378
    other refs, 310
coastal trade, 350–2
Cochin, 156, 191, 194
coconut(s), 241, 242, 244, 324
coffee, 108, 133, 229, **252–3**
Coimbatore, 128, 131, 245, 297, 338
coir, 340
COLBERT, J. B., 197
Colombo, 191, 192
Comilla, 367, 370, 377
Communism, Communists, 147, 168, 271
Community Development and Project(s),
    167, 205, 222, **276–8**, 291, **342–4**, 386
'communities', 158–63
Congress, Indian National, 196, 310, 331,
    358
Conjeeveram, *see* Kanchipuram
consolidation of holdings, 113, 264
consumption levels, 358
Contai, 199
continental shelf, 260
contraceptives, *see* birth control, 'loop',
    vasectomy
cool season, conditions in, 49–52
co-operation, 267, 272, **274–5**, 279
Coorg 156
copper, **294**, 295, 297, 299
Coromandel, 25; and Cholas, 177, 184, 190
corruption, 358
corundum, 294
COTTON:
    crop, in general, **246–7**; yield, 364;
        export, 353–4; Pakistan, 382
    manufacturing: rise of, 309–11 *pm*,
        314–17; Ahmedabad, 309–16
        pm; Bombay city, 309–16 *pm*;
        Coimbatore, 311, 316
    Pakistani resources, **246–7**; manu-
        facturing, 379

Index of Authors and Works cited

Political personalities who are also writers, such as Gandhi and Nehru, are entered in either the General or the Author Index according to context: thus Gandhi appears in the former for p. 196, the latter for p. 171.

Joint articles in periodicals are entered once only, with names in the order given in the original.

Acharya, B. C., 103
Afforestation Scheme . . . for West Bengal, 111
Agarwala, A. N., 305
Agricultural Atlas, Indian, 233
Agriculture in India, Royal Commission on (RCAI), 10, 117, 225, 227, 230, 254, 266–7, 388
Ahmad, E., xi, 45, 132, 204, 207, 222
Ahmad, F., 18, 19, 45
Ahmad, K., 372, 380
Ahmad, K. S., xii, 9, 75, 130–1, 300, 302, 375, 389
Ahmad, N., xi, 301, 306, 383, 389
Ahsan, S. R., 337
Ahuja, P. R., 112
Ali, A., 12, 222
Ali, N. A., 112
Anand, M. R., 12
Andrus, J. R., and Mohammed, A. F., 275, 278–9, 389
Arndt, H. W., 335
Atmanathan, S., 58
Aubert, G., 101
Auden, J. B., 33, 34, 37, 45
Aurobindo, Sri, 13

Baker, J. N. L., xii
Baksi, R. D., *et al.*, 105
Balasubramanian, C., and Bakthavathsalu, C. M., 50
Banks, A. L., 41
Basham, A. L., 12
Bauer, P. T., 388
Beri, S. G., *see* Jathar, G. B.
Beringer, C., 369
Bernier, F., 197
Bettelheim, C., 388
Bhabha, H. J., 345
Bhadran, C. A. R., 113
Bhagavad Gita, 175
Bharadwaj, O. P., xii

Bhargava, M. P., 329
Bhat, L. S. (*see also* Learmonth, A. T. A.), xii, 129, 220
Bhatia, S. S., xii, 72, 234
Bhatt, V. V., 336
Bhattaacharjee, J. P., 272–3
Bhattacharya, A. P., 112
Bhattacharya, S., 111
Bhunan, S. J., Zacharia, M., and Rahman, F., 111
Binder, L., 172
Bjerknes, H., 59
Blanford, H. F., 46, 55
Blanford, W. T., 24
Bondurant, J. V., 157
Bordet, P., 35
Bose, A., 130
Bose, N. K., 130, 172
Brayne, F. L., 265
Brearey, M. R., and Connock, B. S., 375
Brown, J. C., and Dey, A. K., 283–4, 287, 292
Buchanan, D. H., 307, 309, 312–13, 334, 388
Buchanan, F., 99, 101–2
Buckle, H. T., 168
Burrard, S. G., 41
Burrard, S. G., Hayden, H. H., and Heron, A. M., 45

Calder, C. C., 74, 86
Callard, K., 172
Cameron, R., 12
Camões, Luis Vaz de, 191
Campbell, R. D., 172
Carey, S. W., 45
Census of India: general, 7, 12
 1931, 153, 162
 1951, 121, 131, 154
 1961, 121, 126, 149, 158–63 (languages and religions)
Census of Landholding (*India, 1954*), 270

434

Notebook of Signs

Also by MTC Cronin

Zoetrope – we see us moving
the world beyond the fig
Everything Holy
Mischief-Birds
Bestseller
Talking to Neruda's Questions
My Lover's Back ~ 79 Love Poems
The Confetti Stone and other poems
beautiful, unfinished ~ PARABLE/SONG/CANTO/POEM
<More or Less Than> 1-100
The Ridiculous Shape of Longing
    – New & Selected Poems (English/Macedonian)
The Flower, the Thing
Irrigations (of the Human Heart) ~ fictional essays
    on the poetics of living, art & love
Our Life is a Box. / Prayers Without a God

Forthcoming from Shearsman Books, 2008:

How Does a Man Who is Dead Reinvent his Body?
    The Belated Love Poems of Thean Morris Caelli [with Peter Boyle]

M.T.C. CRONIN

Notebook of Signs

& 3 other small books

Shearsman Books
Exeter

Published in the United Kingdom in 2007 by
Shearsman Books Ltd
58 Velwell Road
Exeter EX4 4LD   www.shearsman.com

ISBN-13 978-1-907500-11-0 // ISBN-10 1-907500-11-3

Front cover image: *Untitled (Anawhata)*, 2003, oil on paper, 213 x 316mm, by Antonio Murado. Reproduced courtesy of the artist and Gow Langsford Gallery.

Acknowledgements

5_Trope; Blesok; can we have our ball back; Divan; Diwan; Everything Holy (MTC Cronin, Balcones International Press, Temple, Texas, USA, 1998); *Five Bells; foam:e; Great Works; Green Left Weekly; Het Oog van de Roos; Inklings; latchkey. com; Litter; Muse; Muse Apprentice Guild; My Secret Life: Poems from the 1999 Melbourne Festival of Poetry; nthposition; Pixel Papers; Poems Niederngasse; Poetryetc2; Poets for the King* (National Gallery of Australia, Canberra, 2003); *Printout; Redoubt; Retort; Shampoo; Shearsman; Short Fuse, The Global Anthology of New Fusion Poetry* (Todd Swift and Philip Norton, eds., Rattapallax Press, New York, NY, USA, 2002); *The Last Bohemian* (Diverse, Sydney, 2003); *The Ridiculous Shape of Longing: New & Selected Poems* (MTC Cronin, Blesok, Macedonia, 2005, translated into Macedonian by Igor Isakovski); *Sidereality; Stride; Taj Mahal Review; Tattoo Highway; Text; The Arabesques Review; The Manhattan Review; The Thirteenth Floor* (UTS Anthology, Sydney, 1999); *Tin Lustre Mobile;* and *Verso.*

This collection was written with the assistance of a major grant from Arts Queensland.

The publisher gratefully acknowledges financial assistance from Arts Council England with its 2005-2007 publishing programme.

For

Maya Veronica

Vivienne Jeanette

&

Agnès Irène

How are notebooks
born? Who throws blue lines into them.

TOMAŽ ŠALAMUN
'Moss'

Notebook of Signs

Notebook of Shapes

Notebook of Nerves

Notebook of Sand

Notebook of Signs

Poetry is signs of signlessness.

JACK ANDERS
'Playing in the Sandbox'

Signs of a Time

We wore hats and gloves.
What might induce hankering, humour or horseplay.
Gloves without hands.
All a now thing.
Rice grew in our hair – nightly.
Squashing, crushing, squashing.
We were identifiable by our myelin sheaths of silver.
You are slung.
By the bug of the world that crawled over us.
Lie down with ice.
Frozen-black feet.
The disaster is happening inside your head always.
With a head like what eyes don't see.
The world slurs to focus.
Unfocusable until the time is over.
Through your mouth.

The Three-Week Goat

For twenty-one days
the rocks made a mountain
Rue grew in clumps
under quivering noses
Three eagles – one who didn't belong
eyed the circular lives
of a horde of bees
A white flower
Yes, a white flower . . .
At the beginning of the fourth week
entered the stomach
of a thing with hooves
which immediately entered the sky
as if that other existence
had depended on some sureness of foot
on a certain view that had purely to do
with reality's angle
with its where-you-stand take
on survival
So a breeze continued
its sightless journey down the slope
A sheep in its second year, suddenly
saw the ilex forest

The Fragment Called Wisdom

There is a cracked stone
It is wise
There is a broken stick
It is wise
There is water, forever formless
    always formed
It is wise
It is unwise
    to shake the whole from its sack
    of pieces
The head looks around
    at its new limbs
    and immediately starts telling them
    what to do

The earth falls
It is wise
The earth holds
It is wise
Where has the hand gone
    which once showed the eyes
    how to see the spine?

The Swimming Pool is Broken

The swimming pool is broken.
They can't make it work.
One efficient warrior screams at it from the side.
No result.
The housewife tries ravishing in it.
Nothing.
The gondolier comes up with his little commuter boat.
The mermaid puts on her glove.
Three smelly clouds offer some suggestions.
It's all hot, narcotic, lush and uncertain.
No matter.
The pool remains inoperable.
There's talk about expense and meetings about waste.
These don't stop the inevitable.
They have to throw it away.
Someone gets a bag and bundles it up.
A long period of little satisfaction follows.
Eventually comes the suggestion of a flattish-topped raceme.
For several months of the year now there are squeals of delight.
(They'd learned about instead though.
And used something else in the vase.)

Possible Cures for Beauty

Sleep faster.
Leave your memory in the war.
Love completely and perfectly.
With your poetry, override the moon.
Accompany the butterfly when it visits the flower.
Move remorse to the front of your stable.
Excise doubt from fiction.
Feast for a lifetime on the bite the ant took from the pear.
Keep trying close to your heart.
Remember that someone invented the violin.
Keep an eye out for stray heads with massive noses.
Gorge on the fluff of peace.
Feel happy and sad that nothing ever changes.
Treat fame like the ubiquitous spine of the soldier.
Rub someone in your eyes and split yourself open over a rock
        for them.
Reach the gamut and repeat repeat.
Shelter in isolation.
Fill your hollow flesh with things unproven.
On a clear night, look for a single star.
Leap up high cheekbones and jump!
Describe it.

One Feather, One Stone

I'm sure Jesus
was born
in his beard

Born with
a feather
Born
a stone

Jesus could fly
Jesus could sink
He was an all-
round athlete

I'm sure Jesus
I'm sure
took the weight
of objects
a lot less seriously
than Isaac
Newton

Blue Lines

for Tomaž Šalamun

Don't race to blue
Wait for the piano
and its baby hippopotami
to leave the island
for the sea

Don't break the line
to find the dead sounds
the not-born sounds
The artist has sung
on the high roof

See the castle
switch off the horizon
That's your house
pulling magenta
on lines from the sea

Throw lines into shimmer
the fools and avoidance
The little animals
will reward you
with other colours

The Three-Dimensional Bush-Nest

the weight of a lilac sun
falls through the weather
into the three-dimensional bush-nest

small purples are born
violeta, efflatum, púrpura, ungu

they have no voices
but mouths which scream for justice
against the vestments in which
they were given birth

violeta, efflatum, púrpura, ungu

the bush squats by your hand
and burns only once in the lifetime
of every epoch

The Sign of Being Dead

This is quite lovely
If it happens when
You are dead
Rather than when
You are alive
In the latter case
It is a similar sign
To the one received
By those who realize
The unreality
Of atmosphere
And similar again
To the one received
By those for whom
All stories are too
Finite for a patience
Such as theirs
In a real death
To the contrary
The sign is like
The wild energy
In each of the centres
Of a still mob
Acknowledge it
And fool that one
Whose ankles
Are still solid
Decipher the sign
And give your name
To the place
Previously dedicated
To living's god
This is analogy
For the very least
Bit of interest
Being unfixed

Though Not Why

Why do you know him?
Why is there a couple of days?
Why forget if that is not what you mean?
Why do you leaf?
Why the tombs sleeping instead of a soul?
Why left to right and the others right to left?
Why hair growing
further and further into its own death?
Why all the ands in another language?
Why six yellow cushions
and the ovals of the mind colliding?
Why this intuitive spelling?
Why overcome?
Why will?
Fleeting. Forever.
And not what we asked.
Why no signs?

Jesus, Man, Holder of Fiction

Jesus, man, holder of fiction,
keeper of the truth, I can concentrate
on feeling my body in space.
If not to be proud, why this spine,
pushing up my head
with that face on it?
Another god might have come
in a jacket
and not wanted mine!

The Shadow Sign

Exuviae of the body's coupling with light
shed as if darkness could open light's eye
to the deception that is the features of life.

Shadow, what sign do you offer what passes?
You, who have travelled through life on dracula's back.

The Village of Fish

He fainted at the sunset
into her secret pigeon hiding-place
He came from the village of fish
and gasping birds
His name was Adolino
and his muscles cooed to his bones

The spine and the neck are coming
The vertebrae are evolving
easily exposed sweetly exposed
Water folds through them into the swim
and their invisible legs are growing

In her village he shucked his fins
and tried the foot for size
She thrust out to him a wing
her eyes spinning silently
with another view
His name was Adolino
and his naked sweet bone
is caught in the utility neck of realism

The Lost Law

The lost law is the one that
governs traces and signs.

Door slightly open.
Door almost closed.

Dye. My hands.

Are your human eyes human
little grass
little stitch
small lost muscle
that works for the larger lesson?

What are you pulled?

Aware, unaware,
of the spine you broke from
before landing on your second
feet.

Drag yourself.
Walk up to the wall
and confront the colours
of the arras.
The tapestry has its dream
in another play.

The old building creaks
in all of it.
The wood had screamed
when first cut for its boards
but the agony never ceases.
Not for fire.
Not for rot.
Not for desertion.

Look in this house
for your heart.
Look in your heart
for the house
around which the world
glories.
Be awake.
Act in the dream.

If you see a sign,
meet it.

Just a Smudge

I had a lump
And they took it away
In a small glass bottle

They said
Call in a week
If the lab doesn't like the look of it
They'll send it back

What's a bad sign
I asked
So I could take away some words

To put
In the place of the lump
And they said
Oh I dunno

They're a capricious lot
Down at pathology
One time

They sent it back
Said the guy's gonna die
Turned out to be
Just a smudge on the bottle

Great New (Those Europeans & Their Movies)

Details that can be celebrated for less.
Dramatic changes full of desperation.
Once a month a joke.
Brazen ambition running fast enough.
My shoes my shoes.
Foie gras would never satisfy.
When only oneself to rely on.
Sorry to laugh.
At a crime as little as a puff.
But the jury is cold and hot and towing its arse.
Not as much as most people.
More than a window box.
Cheers cheers cheers.
Great now are our plans for the night.
Piss in the soup.
Slash the tyres.
A great new hobby presents itself.
We'll invite the whole village.
Mole poison.
Instructions that travel a long way.
Ring the bell ring the bell ring the bell.

The Red Light of the Sign

> (– *ha!*
> *the red light of the sign so motionless*)
> ALFONSO D'AQUINO

God willing and devouring
Bright strewn in space
And taking it up
A truth
Still
Clear fascinating phenomena
In the world
A star
Occupying
The constant genuine
Sure mother of white
Glowing out
A flower juice or the least bit
Of attention
Picks up
Your mention and missing
The mad stuff of dark
Admitting
It with a memory
A burn
That belongs to black
Like courage
Curiously
Hanging on and posing
A real problem for the brain
Melts the focus
And stops
Dead
While sitting here waiting
I fetishize rose
Pearl
And the craziness

Like an essential
Rationality unveiling itself
As ongoing bloody
Laughter
A bitch
The red light
Of the sign so motionless
Just slipped between
Now
And what's next
Glimpsed and interfering
With time
Breaks my head off
Bumping and sets up
A culture
Ha! Ha! Ha! Externally
Very serious

The Latest Neuroses

There is a man with a face full of windows.
They are black.
I am sick of being pretty.
There could be a truck loaded up with these responsible eyes.
On the way to duty I hide.
And record my hiddenness in a poem.
The sky cracks its untouchable blue caste from my daydream.
The basket for today might be filled of birds so high up
         they've forgotten the ground.
It is impossible to stay alive if you cease counting.
It is impossible to die if you stop counting.
All the time new people park themselves by my shoulder.
The numbers appear as unique offerings.
Or as slides to another level.
The black windows have aeroplanes coming out of them.
I am sick with slowness.
Their ascension.
My mind crashes around me like nauseous-smelling flowers.
A door opens onto a day of irreducible hardness and charity.

You Must Rise

You must rise on your toes
when you say fish
The decision to be a saint
is just that
Artists may show weakness
but weakness is what must be said
If they say fish
listen for the stream
When you hear that
you'll feel it in your throat
The little words in the oesophagus
will join the school
All life is what one looks like and feels like
drowning and the shine of moon on the sea's lips
sings the deep grand silence that empties the world
between yourself and the last star
Rise on your toes for that
The argument with infinity ceases
when you reach for the sign

Broken Signs & Numbers

after Marco Knauff/Norman Lock

There are some numbers
missing
There are some
which never return
Broken signs and numbers
fill our rest
where the battle for meaning
is over
Strangely it is when we rise
and where the numbers and signs
are whole
that the war is rejoined
With points we attack the star
With directness the line
We stuff our sacks with anything that happens
and call it booty
Some swear by a seven
Some a three
Symbols remain when we sieve
When we shake the mysteries speak
like coins
Picking through mountains and buttons we wonder
if we'll ever find luck
and whatever we find we hide
so that we may look for it
again
The bottom half of a number
means nothing to us
and if a true sign ever appears
we confuse it with mathematics
or with situations where mathematics
cannot be applied
Hundreds of butterflies
carry us into the sky

and we make a myth
of it
At least when we sleep
we possess the secret we cannot know
The signs there leave their burrows
and lick their wounds
The poor sick numbers become uncountable
like ideas which cannot be
separated
Two little bits of a busted nine
point the way to salvation
An everyday-shape appears to stand for all the sadness
in the universe
There exists no-one who can tell this story properly
and so the message to stop fighting will never be delivered
to the heart of the battle
At its height there is long division
and even a flag to move combatants around
from one place
to another
Caught in the melee we look for signals
Even something as untranslatable as a twinkle in the eye
has us telling each other
what it all means

Notebook of Shapes

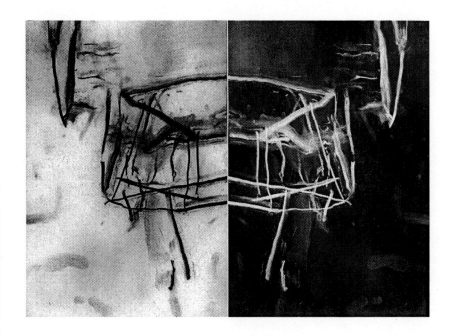

What is the little box? Who is the little box? Is it really
everything your dream has enumerated here, or is it
none of all this?

Vasko Popa
'Essay on the Little Box'

Pact

Life has chosen us.
As the sacrifice.
Impossible to convince weary people
that finally the fighter
is defeated by a bird's cry.
Everyone arguing.
Opinionated about what they might
be offered to.
Some say cold snow.
Others erect roofs to hold out
the warm rain.
Here and there the recognition
of a great pact.
What is selected and what forgotten.
Joining like water and soil
into mud.
Another little hand making a pie.
Pot Slap
Slop Pat

Growth 1

A butterfly turned into a rectangle
and a small waving hand
into a long dark hall.

When many things in the world
became faster
everything ended faster.

There was only a small question
after this,
simultaneously asked
when two mouths met
from the opposite ends
of the way out.

The Little Secret Elephant

Slide as a dog
Reservoir of pernicious greys
Back from the bush
Bounces a beauty
The cut is clear and cloudy
Backdrop of quiet winds
It's the little secret elephant
Trampling the snowball tree
And bellowing like a torn machine
Let it through your brain
Geotaxis and all
The timetable accounts for this
A slowly melting ice-planet
The blot that stretches
And becomes a stare
Fine pure grey lotus
Now sitting monstrously
In a whole lot of your fortune
Stomachic column of equipoise
With alternative social concerns
Ponded dog exerting pressure
In the minute palm
If you hold the shape of it
You'll prevent a recurrence
Rest the elbow
As much as possible

Trick-Moth

for Tatjana Lukic

The sky is blind.
All that light!
It could attract a baby off its nipple
where it nuzzles blindly.
Sometimes,
                    cherries are flowers.
And the moth!
Sometimes the moth is a night, thank God,
for everything.
A nebula that smears under your finger, silver and starred,
like the necklace between
her breasts.

Women of the Sky

after Pablo Neruda

it happens outside
the weather
the singing song
of lightly banging doors
the sun coming on
like a television screen
wind and grey flickering
music like a shoot
green and insistent
wonderful trumpet!
blue behind everything
as if I've spilt my eyes
las muchachas celestes
disguised as clouds
bending over us
wet-faced
and wringing their hands
oh do not weep
soft women of the sky
and I will sing for you
from the throats of stars
and smile
in the shiny toothy moon
that touches your bodies
with redeeming silver
do not weep
and in this startled sky
I will set loose
your hundred thousand
shapes
those resemblances
rich with the memory
of all things

The Ridiculous Shape of Longing

The words that tear out your tongue.
The burdens of your eyes.
The heart fists.
How tired thinking about black roses.
All the rose is red.
A little slaughter.
The second kiss that cannot forget the first.
Memory kneeling in a small field.
The field surrounded by trees.
A view of the cradle.
By now the womb is empty.
Piano slowing down.
Everywhere the future.
Looking through garbage.
Who dreams?
A song in sleep like a call of the soul.
A watermark.
Screaming what it does best.
Never repeated because it never breaks off.
Wearing the mask of life.
Even tighter at night.
At night there is a sea that covers even dry land.
To leap and submerge.
The earth wobbles with this longing.
Becomes every shape.
What runs through all tricks.
What doesn't listen to the teacher in the self.
Birth of each wish.
Walking upside-down.
Arms full and overflowing.
No-one has written this.
What can never know satisfaction.
Just wanting.
Maybe to march across the sky.

The Egg

You know the egg as well as I do.
I kiss you and there is a cloud
sieving gold in its womb.
From the egg, imagine, our teeth!

The Man Who Leaves

(L'Homme Qui Sort)

There's only so many times
you can crawl around a box
and still be fascinated by it.

His house told the story,
looking through its own garbage
for his black hat and coat,

his black shoes, his black scarf,
his one black glove.
What else might he have lost?

The address to the harem?
The music which he turns to hear
but cannot hear?

Death seems familiar to him,
does it not? The dark blank
canvas framed, ahead of him

or behind? The evening, he might
think, contains its own justice
and what I am leaving, well,

I will turn my head only slightly
while you are being fascinated.
My face is telling you that I am

some kind of Enchantress,
yet I wish only that I was a boy
like when I was born.

Superstition Sonnet *Child's Toy*

silent as the moon   *a face in a cement pavement*
is the moon silent?   *silent cloth*
does your mind make a noise?   *small window sill growing inside the*
                                crack of a flower
asks the moon   *one stick of strength*
and I listening for the clamouring   *and all the beauty of invitation*
of the moon thinking   *graceful sun walking at dawn*
and my thoughts rising noiselessly   *the gesture of your confidence*
and shining into the night sky   *heart chatter*
speaking to a moon that somehow   *a child crying out the world*
got a God inside it   *a seasnake mimicking her pose to get acquainted*
like this soul inside a body   *silly as a jar*
cheese & infinity & belief   *use moonlight for more than beauty*
take it out at night   *the offer embodied*
a sealed plastic ball half-filled with water   *floats a red duck & a*
                                                yellow duck

Mr Popa's Little Box

for Vasko Popa

I'm going to tell Mr Popa and his Little Box
how as a mother I made my child's head
How I chose its mind and the colour of its eyes
How I breathed a soul into it and yes
such a person as I am does exist!

I'm going to tell Mr Popa this
with my living thought connected
to his dead thought
and in a poem of course
because there's the joke!

Sadly though it is a poem I cannot write down
for in doing so it would become
a poem about a poem and these are sad
Listen to me think though
and you will hear a massive emptiness –

No poem could survive
such explanation!

The Hay Mountain

for Maya

Stop wounding the hay
For love I say goodbye
Eating it as I kiss it
But it is too little
I can easily reach the ground
I take the cover off
and there is my hay
Finally!
I push it higher
Pum pum
I make it even fatter
with a big bowl of soup
Then I stand on it
It's fabulous!
Hoyabalabbyiarrr!
They've come
to take the hay away!
I layer it
with stuff and beauty
I layer it
until it's all layered up
I put stuff over it
Bigger stuff
to make it steady
Finally
we bang it down to the ground
Put whatever we can find
over it
Push it on
Teatowels
I'm in love with the hay
Should I jump off it
or shouldn't I?
It always needs more hay

I have the luxury
of the hay mountains
It can't exist!
The hay mountain is too precious
for any horse alive
No!
Not the hay mountain!
I cover it with luxury
and prounce around it
With a big entrance too
I love the hay
It gives me concussion

The Mirage
(W.C.W – G.B.S – M.T.C)
All Getting Old Always

William Carlos Williams
the mirage
the shape of a shape
become the shape he feared
better put your broken arm back on
and your head white
so I can pay you more attention
and lean on every bruise
pale mauvey-brown umbels
on solid but slender green stems
marks from thinking
fadeless immortal purple
and so much confusion
around the time thing
as if getting old is getting old
meanwhile is the joke
and a straightforward colour
that the three of us (at least)
won't argue about
the red spot on the white spot
is never sleeping
what a mirage
influence on the language is

Mr Skinnyfingers

Let's live in the cardboard box
where the world keeps its secrets
There's a child there
with a bowl of babies
and a new obsession
that turns another blanket down
O how we learn to love
and practise this on what never lived
Some materials heavier than flesh
some lighter
but none made dangerous by breath
and its loose-canon feminine whim
Mr Skinnyfingers plays games
pushing his fingers through the holes
while in the box we laugh
and invent everything
There's even a monkey
and a robot monkey and an android monkey
A shadow that can
and a shadow that can't move by itself
It's fun in here
just ask the monkeys
who are all whistling
and inciting the shadows
Just ask the intruder Plato
who mistook this box for a cave

What Makes Your Pig's Leg Bigger?

My trough.
You run.

The Fence

Untie my bathroom
and hook it onto South America
Turn it into metal
and go to sleep...

These lovely narrow streets
on which my eyes grew
those years

Dustkicker – have your parents
forgotten you?
Stare with the kidstare
Empty your boots in the one
who takes the time
Go barefoot in the chests
containing sympathetic hearts

Overhear because you've lost
the self-tunnelling ears
which can go in and bring
out the world to hoist
on its axis
The ball saying *bounce*
over and over

We share the preciousness
so we understand it
On the other days
we kill

We mix jelly in trucks
because god's party
is bigger than them all
We break our arms
over this much embarrassment

We wake and the bathroom's
a broken chair tied up
to a tree
Another game has started
over there near the fence

Opening Massacre

I found an old man today,
marched up over his bald head
looking for a saviour and found
only a stranger with more
broken bones than solid.

Why is everyone's criteria
something unignorable?
Why decide that?

I'm waiting for the ugliest scarred
face through the door
and for my warm room to turn
cold with the presence
of that empty god-shape.

Years to years and joined by
a hyphen which makes more
of a life than the last eruption
which spewed out camels and boxes,
vagrants, fireless, and snow
on our women's love.

We are hiding in nothing.
Like work.
We hide in the white flower
that eats the land.

Before the dogs barked there was
a volcano, burns of the night
left their scars on days,
our houses listened to us,
our news, the rumbling of the
mountain that was pretending
to be itself for the silhouette.

The opening massacre
left the world on one end
of a rubber-band pulled through
the centre of our eyes and
stretched to a point before us
that may have been
figmental.

For & Against Games

My stare made the world worse
It would have been better
to cut people out of paper
To drag around a rope
with something desirable tied to its end
Instead I formulated questions
to ask the children on weekdays
Are you going to go a long way from pain?
As far as the dead who bother to return to life?
Every ant has its own feathered tomb
Every bird rigor mortis and the opportunity
to be eaten from the eyes in
Why are you practising these bodies
when they are only the great undisturbed you?
Why do you ask the wolf the time?

I Had Thought

I have found the warm brick
and put my back to it

I like to follow the sun's discoveries

Today I wear green gloves
and the look of a tiger

I had thought I was in the ball
that was thrown
but find myself only
in the shadow's sharp face

I catch the end of a rope
being dragged by a small boy
and go along counting feathers

Why are there no gardens
in the cement's cracks?

Further and further I go
to where there is no sun

Where the shadows take hands
to become the shade

I talk to the chill

I ask it to keep my wounds

To put up the nets
for a new game of pain

New Shape

Blood shape.
Suddenly I recognize you.
New shape.
Tangled up
like the earth in its energy.
The heart ponds are full of you.
Into the jungle of other lives
I follow your sweet luminosity.
Red drums!
Sweet viscera and dust!

The Shape of Things to Come

Your body has crawled through the briars.
Your heart has dumped itself at the abattoir.
Your feet go on.
Like two loaves of bread that keep rising.
Little sounds made by little voices
        can be heard where you are heading.
What gloriously meaningless words!
Surely they are at play!
It's a pleasure not to be bothered
        and everything's painless.
There's a few old thoughts to think.
But not too many.
Memories catch up and demand their place
        outside your head.
They had no doubt about the shape
        of things to come.
What the everwidening wind didn't leave standing
        after circling around and around your house?
The shape of the corner
        you've painted yourself into?
That infinity outline drawn with squint-proof ink?
No!
Only one contour remains in the end.
The little star rising from the last synapse to fire.

Notebook of Nerves

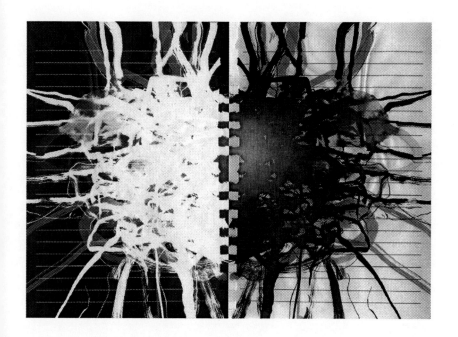

But why does that cry exist?

Pär Lagerkvist
Evening Land

Spine-Scar

Light comes in
through darkness

All yesterday's sheds
have fallen

Living things squat
in destruction's beauty

Opening their backs
to pain

The Science of Birds' Nests

They call this caliology.

A blind sac.

Like something you cannot not do
once you think of it
they are searching for the structure,
the methodology, of safety.

Take down the moon
and sponge her in your nest.

As a sunrise, the mad are sufficient.

Is there ever a reason
for the covert feather
that is not only a matter of love?

In the dark nest we tough out
the light that does not go away
when we close our eyes.

Sweet Egg

How thirsty is the egg.
The egg never eats.
OOmph, thrust, bOOst.
Goads with the shivers.
Egg-dance without eyes.
GOOse, berry, nOOm.
Looking at the moon.
In a mirror.
Fat with eggs.
Missing a nose.
And missing a mouth.
A merry-thought.
Breaks out.
Oh sweet sweet egg.
A murmuring.
A rustling.
A hope that is confusing.
SOOn, glube, dOOzy.
Bravura egg!
Win the day.
How irreversible.
The egg doesn't drink.
Or indulge in luxuries.
Home industry.
ROOt, new, hOOk.
Little simple bit.
Bald as a job.
Fragile as this bliss.

Nice Eel

The strength of tomorrow
is in this eel
which has never been ill
in its life.
If it's hungry
it will not eat bread and cheese
but the two of us.
Not keen on cooking
it will happily swallow us raw.
Where is it from?
It has come from the war
that has finished between eels.
It has not survived
to be anyone's servant.
There are two ways to go
and so the eel says
Let's go.
There are no secrets
between the two ways.
Wooing Wooing.
Hush Hush.
The nice eel is swimming now
through windows of air
bringing good luck
and putting on slippers.
Changing maybe's to yes's.
Simply magnifique!
Have you yet found
the tiny scar on your body
where the nice eel reminds you
that a scar is the future?

Bucket

Sometimes you are catched in him.
Sometimes with much pleasure
And others with less.
More lost than a star in all his light
I sink to invisible depths.
While sleeping he polishes me
And makes me scream
For more asteroid.
My own throat and neck hysteria him.
The cold water bucket came.
I would only dream
Of running to the ocean.
Catched in him like something
You wake up to.

The Pick-Up

I got cancer
Early one morning
About four o'clock
When there was
Half a world full of light

    elsewhere

I was alone
Of course
Cancer only happens
To people
Out of present company

And I couldn't go back
To sleep
Because I was only
Convinced
That I was going to die

The way you are
At four in the morning
When the world is

    elsewhere

Living it up with your
Optimism
Your easy easy smile

There Were Mumbled

There were mumbled
How hard it is to be
Beckett and get up
In the morning
Nicaragua
In hot pursuit
And then prone
In a rare policy
To send all cleaners
Back to their own
Countries families
Because if you write
For an audience
All you write is echo
Nothings occur
We devise all kinds
Even local council
The prehistorical
Joust words
Mouths with gravity
There were mumbled
The use of fire
Community outrage
Well as soon
As Beckett's up
We'll put language
To the same purpose
Permanent advantage
Of the thought
Or just unslopping
The impossible
An imp process
With the right mix
Of actuality
Wake up

Wake up
More souths than norths
Get the others
Some connotation
Without explaining
Get across the blah blah
If you can't
Get excudiated
Some gigglish might help
And Beckett
At breakfast
Eating eggs
He cooked himself
And fork akimbo
Pillorying
The mind that serves
The mouth
Spitting eggs
That were mumbled
Noisily
In a larger silence

The Moon Full

Cut your bones when the moon
is full and this will help
your pain.

Look in the calendar some day.

The mouth shears time
from the body, with words.

Make a message yourself of
this whole message to you –
the rain's message, the lonely
old woman's story of her broken
hands, the news that came
despite dark and rest and
birth being over.

All these disappear into light
when trouble's trouble is lit
by the arguing moon.
When like this, healing, it
has no time for beauty.

My Dream

Beauty fiddles
the mind

I'm as mad on the potatoes
as the best poets

No vase for my beauty
I can't listen to flies

Spit kisses from my mouth
They are done

Enmeshed
in a glass of water

I am the next victim
of my life

The object
could be anything

The side can't be explained
The excuses are in my elbow

I am not a good gardener
the world just does these ways

My dream depends on a light breeze
and a lack of pain

The needle has given my back
the sea

Sea slops
like that last thought

The Innumerable

It is raining!
The innumerable are coming.
Prince Who-Cares is coming.
The old man is coming from his dank cave.
The carcinogenic eye is coming.
So is the pendulum.
Because the sky is grey purple fruit are coming.
A basket of live fish and limes.
Rain over steps.
Rain into churches.
Rain into nights.
Our eggs are our crystal balls.
My nose has its hat.
Rain to make me sad, happy and angry.
Fully wet I play the mud-game.
The water bouncing off my head
will be the river they throw their bodies into.
Rain over the high walls of my life.
I've played the mud-game.
The ocean estimates me as nothing.

Project Seahorse

The tree's dead branch
is undeniably a hand.
Now let me tell you something
you can argue with.
I will not make my children disappear.
Instead I'll sit with joy in the compound
and comb out its knotted hair.
I'll wait for my heart to slow down
and wave its tail like a seahorse.
On avocado day
I'll give my poet friends
the status of colour
and the animaless people
some of my trust.
What do you think that mouse is?
I listen to it every now and then
and try to imagine what it is.
But I can't imagine anything specific
and drift into the effulgence
of the big Arabian night.
The woman who washes the teacups
has entered that tent and stripped
to the bone.
After cutting her pubic hair
she's represented for the purposes
of artistic study.
Sharks swim by with the dealer in eggs.
From the window of a train
I cannot give up peeling potatoes.
The seventh animal can't hold back
the horror and distorts into
an approximation.
What comes next?
Keep the format but write a new poem?
Pieces of me come and float

around your house for hours
and hours.
The book stops them with its pages
but what is the title of the book?
What is its name?
Welcome to my quagmire
where the old metaphors are like
water and souls.
What is the soul of?
Its dictionary is held shut
by a shoemaker's waxed thread.
The lightship has hit the rocks
with its foetal container.
Bunches of branches trap the seahorse
and take it to la la land
where all the poems are.

Crabhook Cryer

The baby climbed all the way
    To the top of the ladder
        Before falling in
            The water

I'll go and get a crabhook
    Said the dad
        As the baby sank
            And drifted
                Under the bridge

When the dad came back
    He waved the hook
        While he thought
            That's the way
                Water goes

Nest

the nest of nerves
is not a safe one

cotton unravelling
until it undoes my legs

dervishes are coming here
spinning on their horses

the tongue slurring
from its dizzy soul

infinity is barred
from this nest

lined with rosy cheeks
and the vision

nobody knows
any other nest

can't describe being themselves
to someone else

right now even
a universe in the toe

upright chair splitting
the optic nerve

The Laughing Pain

for Bibi & Boodgie

They say onions make you cry
But at our place it's bananas.
Dance too! They make us dance.
We were missing a 'when'
And still knew that we spent
All of last night dancing.
While we danced we sung
And tossed our arms in the air
As if we were flinging arrows.
Like little landing insects
Our neighbours watched us
Through the steaming windows.
We were laughing so much
And dancing like such demons
That they'd misted solid.
The children ran and screamed
'Banana Boat' 'Banana Boat'
Over and over as we split our sides.
Eventually we sailed right past
The curious faces outside,
Then past the house and street,
Then beyond even our pain.
(Because carrying on like that
had given us a terrible pain
that was like a force of nature.)
Eventually we had to concede
That the next thing wasn't funny
And we stopped. Just like that.
The kids didn't get it though
And peeled off a few more.
They put their faces in our faces
And kept on going strong.
'Banana Boop' 'Banana Boop'
Their tiny eyes watered as if to cry

Was something more generally.
Their tummies and cheeks ached.
We pointed our resolute fingers.
They slipped past all of us
Into something incredibly human.

Acting Alone and in Silence

I do not exist.
The cry I made at my birth was a cry that ended in silence.
Every movement I have made since has ended in stillness.
The undersea is green without me.
The moon finds its place despite me.
Once, only once, I entered the world with a single breath
and there found a perfect idleness.
I remember now what every manifestation of being
said on that occasion.
Little child, concentrated spot, time grows
ever more certain as we study you.
The sun is just a firepoint on the nose of that great black bat
whose message is louder than any you can hear.
Oblivion suspected you right from the first.

Sooted

It is clear that a fire will teach you

That it screams

If you bathe in what the fire has known

Anything that presses your skin

Will reveal to you your skin

Warm yourself with this

All marks scars

All scars the ongoing beauty

Unflawed

Come on dandelion
get out of the bin!
Do you have apples
for my rooms?
The man who left me
has changed into another man.
The music of shrieking
finds me at 4 a.m.
My house goes into the radio
to find death,
puts news on my wounds
for burning.
Unflawed,
I prove the Sundays.
I unwrap words
and throw their morals away.
Not a curve, not a shoot,
not a quiver, my ears are up
to the price of it.
I not listening!
You are alone out there
little hunter.
It is better that I come out with you,
my hands unveiling themselves
as knives with a special
madness,
not obeying the form but travelling
towards the second shift
in vertigo.

Converting a Diploma to a Degree

I had little enamel balls made
and little enamel columns made
and then I had the balls
set upon the columns
and then I had them inserted
into my teeth
standing upright like a little city
of small colonnades
with spheres on top

What do they do?

They make what goes on
in your mouth weird
This is why we give supermodels
acting jobs alongside
those born to the craft

My Own Agnès
(Recent Without Criticism)

If you wanted to reach a human being
You've done it with this fuck
The pit has been filled with more time
The blasted thread transfixed
God is one of the oldest tricks in the book
But this grandmother growing
Like a tree out of the earth
Is a crazy old one at under four minutes
You don't think about certain possibilities
Like whether someone's kidneys are shot
Especially if they're good looking
The eye is in the head and so is the other
Disaster begins with fingers and toes
Go into this without memories and shouts
Which call us all to the millions
To the squashing million millions
Because the manager of God has decided
To put us all into a group
Stand around as gold light spills into houses
The truth is we can't work at it
Hog in the brain lets everything come late
Sun and moon might be building dusk
But clouds take the vista
There goes my leg again turning itself
Play in the bog body with the outcome
Of the birth story flattering an egg
It doesn't get any hotter on earth
Time has a burn like that
Nerves message and break

When the Bones Cry

When the bones cry the flesh always does.
We'll see later what started it.
Perhaps a knife?
An argument?
A rough vow that was exactly a kind of argument?
Exhausted and hungry the bones cry?
Then what?
The flesh puts on weight.
With all its gear it's better than nothing.
Even the prosecution would argue this.
Day or night, if the quarrel is vague, indirect threats?
Once the bones cry it rings true.
Any skeleton would try to clean up the mess of its body.
Boohoo peace and chaos.
The cry is like fate or an accident.
Maybe that.
Maybe worse.

Notebook of Sand

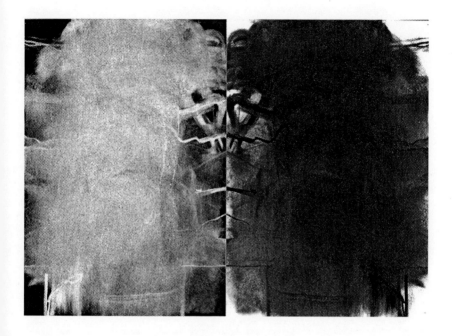

Blond and sad skeleton, whistle, whistle.

César Vallejo
Trilce

When Things Considered the End

Fans are running that way.
Towards the vacuum.
The blow is towed
toward truth.
Ink goes down, goes down.
Hits blood it can't mix with
and comes back up.
Finds the hand
fooling itself with the flower.
The head so early
it has arrived before ears.
All of us found her
where sleep a sleep
was chilling the ashes.
The door narrowing
to forsake the room.

Sleep is Earthly

Sleep is earthly.
It has to do with the earth.
Sleep is a palace too narrow for the King to enter.
A hurricane of stillness.
A child on a bridge pauses to watch the stream.
The emotion of passing.
Passing.
Sleep is earthly.
You wake from it and go looking for your shoes.
Flesh at both ends.

Get Going Grains

The world got started on get going grains.
There were bags of them lugged up to the starting point.
They were sown in the furrows of nothingness.
Though they were sand grains and not seed grains they were sown
        anyway.
There wasn't much option.
The directions on the bags said sow sand and not sow seed.
Therefore! Therefore!
The first thing to come up was an insensible head with a tail of fire.
Then a little mole hill that had never heard of moles.
Third came an indiscriminate cloud of something
        that got in someone's eye.
The matriarch came out with a broom and swept most of it that way.
That it keeps blowing back in is a blessing.
Timely becomes timely.
The new tools and explanations are making their own mountains.
This is nice because we need to climb.
Ten billion billion of get going grains is just the beginning.
There is in every grain of sand something that is not the end of
        the line.
Theory means another one.

Because There Isn't Us

People are impressed.
This is a problem.
The only prosperous fame
is that which follows
the concert in the womb.
Have a face.
If you will then many paths.
Don't find doubt implausible.
None of us have an early
life but simply a hook
from which to dangle.
From which to jump.
With your own feet
manufacture the archetype
then leave it to be interviewed.
Too little applause is not a cliché.
Because there isn't us.

My Own Judge

My own judge fits over me
like the most exciting of broken
borders.

A black light.
The brilliant strong.
The first feather from the lips
opposite Summer
was my face at the table.

With perfect selfing, tenderness
this hoarder
opinioner and orderer
fences.

A serious craftsmanship.
An uncertain
command.

The Bats Are Out

for Virginia Saketas

Why could you trust a man?

The night has let the bats out
My eyes are full of cat's sand
The punches of the day
which had been tangled in dusk
push through to befire my body
all temporary

Why could you trust a man?

What is your corruption?

The bats are out unquelled
by death's violent spit
or the otherguess of the dark
covering the boy of me
Twiggy the black rabbit is here again
grown to street-corner-size
monsoon-size after a year away
with the shuddering

Hello Twiggy!

The bats are out and the cats
are in my eyes like cold listeners
to the defiant life in which I exact
myself and steal back
pardons

This Horse

You had to catch it first
this horse
But it was always ready

    A stroking saddle
    laid across its back
    and stirrups swinging
    above the high grass
    it raced over

It came from the east
From the escarpment

Twenty inches high
this horse
Flesh of solid gold

    Its hind a shining pear
    which fitted perfectly
    the man's hand
    which lay
    on generations of fine sand

Down twenty wooden steps
To an emptiness

    a human place

Where this horse
and its master
would never sweat
as they raced
to the archaeologist's
unexplained death

Skeleton Food

You have to eat a skeleton on purpose
Dig a grave first
A quiet place where you can write
And learn to live properly
Where your excuses
Should be for what you cannot help
Not for what you choose to do
And then beg to be forgiven for
Acknowledge every bone
Bones are hard for that
And only soften
When the shell of soft broken skin
Slings itself from the scaffold
And crawls to earth like a load
Or an army
Then the skeleton calls
Unmob all these bodies in me
For I have clear thoughts in my marrow
And the cry of a human
All this will find where you rest
You know sometimes
What it is like to feel your bones
To examine silence
And in it to consume your own death
Like a tender meat
You have to eat a skeleton on purpose
Clarity is that relentless

Don't Tell Me

That's how it goes with visions
There's wire over the senses afterwards
Like a cage to pass bread and water through
Notice colour in the dead of night
It's like that afterwards
The skeleton gone looking for its fat flesh
And a bucket of normalcy to piss in

The Body

the blue fingers of the century
are on my neck
violet new evening
over the sea lawn
the age of the fences
the sour smell of her hair
here in the room's shut case
the window is the golden child
of the fathering birds
light on the street's pure residue
smoke all over me
her unnoticeable beauty
sometimes it took years
but my time is one
in which no words are appropriate
the travelling show of the sky
is kept in town
for the autopsy
all she does
is audience

The World Spills

There is only
This little bit of me
With which to use
The entire world
Soon I am over
And the world spills
To fill the gap
Tiny starry daisies
Trumpet on each stem
The earth shakes
With its secret
Cucumbers and ants
Of happiness
Sand grains riding
Shoulder high
The world spills
To fill the gaps
Only one death
But many times over

Scarecroak

trees come from my womb
don't doubt this
scarecroak
deaf of blood
from the uterine field

your every finger is bound
with a rented direction
similar yourself
if you wish to grasp
the surrounds of barrenness

heal the wind
in its shelter
the earth
find the north earth
a new hunter's moon

ask the trees a foot
on their lung roads
if to halve you
they must break
like the over-lemoned

scarecroak your enormous jaw
is sinking you
in the sinking field
your flesh won't break
for love or death

one thousand times
the gaps filled you
yet you estrange
steal another hat
from the human

Snorky Tato

for Bibi

Snorky tato like a bum-bum
that's made of glass
and a duck.
I'm made of duck.
So blue daddo, what?
You can do what you want,
be what you like.
Life is lived on the edge
of such perfect chaos
snorky tato knows
running around with laughter
after the snuggle-bug
like a baby.
I'm a baby.

The Little Box of Sand

The little box of sand calls mum
The little box of sand laughs at breath
The little box of sand is always well
It is sleep and the hand in it twitches
It is all the conversations of the traditions
and the revolutions
The cat puts his soft little anus on it
The grains clump like little orgies
The little box of sand is like naked
screaming stuff
It fucks the seed till it breaks it
It attacks the eyes of the wind
With beautiful gravity it pretends
to be a thing
The little box of sand
means international years
Bad ants hide their faces in it
and steal every ambition
of the shooting star
Inside it you can cry and understand
The little aria of air filters through
and fades away
The little box of sand is similar
to a grey sleeve and to the stump of a tree
Toes of all the little plants flick through it
looking for stale bodies
It is as calm as an egg to an outsider
I have no passion for it

Fewsday

What comes after Fewsday?
After eighty-nine?
After purple?
The widow's peak
of a bear rolling down
the snow
breaking my heart
with education.
You always love the youngest
the most.
The ant trying to break the scissors,
little flesh
riding the ridge of me,
flinging up my water,
smelling the fin.
I watch I watch the middle
of the lake
like a bear trying to sink,
waiting for the fish
to jump into my mouth.
A green tram!
Bags wrestling compartments
alive from my hands.
A dead Emperor
is like a white rabbit
without a hat.
Yet, not yet –
I keep my leavings in my heart
to humour my littleness,
cut my children's hair
for heaven to weep.
Over and over
fingers on my lips dare
to love.
Do you think so? The red sail

catches our hips
and the light has a net.
The scent is leaving now
as upright as a red feather.
Shudder enlightenment,
my full moon-shiny fur is hiding
another skeleton
that's bound to get loose.

Let Life

(Let life obscure
            the difference between art and life.)
                        OCTAVIO PAZ

What does life obscure?
The origin.
The hand of an angel.
The small of red.
The immensity of blue
Life's narrative.
The evolutions of command.
A three-dimensional moon.
The hard curves of Saturn.
Skeleton shot by light.
Extra if it is already enough.
Authenticity of bones.
Inside the mother.
Death.

No Museum (Renunciation)

We applaud you
on the night
We do not keep you
in our hearts

Intimates of the Deceased

We all end up with insects
in our notebooks.
We end up with the notebook
like a blue lake behind our eyes.
We write in it from the land
which is no distance away
and of which there can be conducted
no proper analysis.
These signs, intimates of the deceased
and snow upon snow.
It is a miracle that we can see
and hear imagination.
Then even the sand that's left
becomes a sign.

Whistling Up a Storm for Strangers

We blow air.
That's what we do.
We breathe
and sometimes get asked to stop it.
We purse our lips
and a sound comes out
like pleasures and pains getting married.
They all do.
Putting together one half of the mouth with the other
or sucking our nostrils like straws
we make sense into atmosphere.
When we stop
we want someone to notice.
Even strangers.
Even if all they notice is the tiny calm that descends
after the storm of one life is over.

When Things Ended

End I'm unlikely to attach a
prefix to but lie in the
suffix which stretches it
to still having a necessity.
Like a bed this end
or one day in a white Summer
where the skerrick of love
made the world all sand
and everytime I call his name
he says something
I can't remember.
The pupil there is barysphere
and myth-myth the horizon
finishing with the worries
of stone.

Ignored and I'm
in the splendour tops.
No little outfit. No light of
domestic things to keep the devil
out of the bottom drawer.
Over this a mirror like a
woman remembering her lovers
or an unborn window
no start.

Printed in the United Kingdom
by Lightning Source UK Ltd.
122597UK00001B/13-24/A